APPLIED BUSINESS & ECONOMIC STATISTICS

A Computer Integrated Approach

SEVENTH EDITION

Kenneth R. White | Kenneth R. White, Jr. | Keri K. Fowler

Custom Publishing

New York   Boston   San Francisco
London   Toronto   Sydney   Tokyo   Singapore   Madrid
Mexico City   Munich   Paris   Cape Town   Hong Kong   Montreal

Cover Art: *Chelsa Box Fire* by Deborah Sklar.

Printed in the United States of America

6 7 8 9 10   0BRV   14 13 12 11

2008160045

BW/MJ

**Pearson
Custom Publishing**
is a division of

www.pearsonhighered.com   ISBN 10: 0-555-03763-0
ISBN 13: 978-0-555-03763-8

Preface

To the Student

Statistics is vital to the modern decision maker. Accurate and reliable information must be supplied in a timely manner. It is not possible to go through a business career and not utilize, in some manner, statistics. For example, you might say that I am going to be a personnel manager of a company and statistics will not be important to me. This assumption is incorrect. For example, the government agency that looks into discrimination (EEOC) uses a statistic to define discrimination. Also, personnel managers must be able to state the reasons or qualifications that result in one individual making more than another. Statistics is a vital tool to be used by the personnel manager, as it is for all specialists in business.

In writing this text, we realize that students are probably not interested in statistics by itself but only in how it can help realize their potential in whatever profession they choose. We view statistics, from a student's viewpoint, to be a tool with which to evaluate and understand data. Many of the statistical applications found in the text will be found in other courses during your business curriculum.

With this in mind, we have concentrated on the application of statistics rather than on the mathematics of statistics. The application of statistics does not dwell on formulas or their derivations, but on obtaining, analyzing, and interpreting data. The computer then becomes a significant tool in the data analyzation process. Hence, we have included a widely used student edition of a Windows-based statistical software called MINITAB. MINITAB is used in over 2,000 schools worldwide and by 75% of the companies *Fortune* Magazine lists in their top 50 companies. You may use this software in your home, office, or university computers. All you need is an IBM compatible microcomputer with current Microsoft software for Windows. Statistical output, including professional graphs, can be saved and incorporated into your word processor for business quality reports and presentations.

The text, in one form or another, has been tested in the classroom for approximately twenty years. Students have given valuable input in terms of how they interpret and view quantitative analyses. Many changes were made to incorporate the thought processes of many individuals with diverse backgrounds. The solutions to the odd-numbered exercises appear in the back of the text, and randomly selected even-numbered exercises appear in the student study guide.

The text was designed to allow full computer integration into the class without the burden falling solely on the instructor. The text has been developed in classrooms containing 300 students. Under such conditions it is difficult for students to get to see the instructor or even the graduate assistants. Hence, the students' main source of help is the text, the workbook, and other students. The text includes MINITAB software, documentation, and windows sequence for obtaining the desired output. The interpretation of the output occurs throughout the text. The student study guide includes a conceptual review of the material and trial tests to allow the students to evaluate learning. Since the text was generated to handle large classes, there is available some multiple versions of examinations. To those who select the text, we welcome suggestions concerning improvements.

Contents

What Is Statistics?

In our initial chapter, we introduce you to the discipline of statistics by using examples of how your everyday lives are impacted by data bases and their interpretations. We all have some knowledge of statistics. When you receive an examination grade, you may wish to know how it compares to that of the norm of the class. Such norms help us to place the grade in perspective. A grade of 60 may be evaluated differently if the class mean grade was 50 or 80. We conclude the chapter by introducing you to some new concepts and definitions.

1.1   Introduction

Statistics is a relatively young academic discipline. Yet this does not mean statistics has not been in use for a long time—for it has. However, modern statistics was not developed until the twentieth century. Prior to this, most statistics involved little more than data manipulation or summarization. However, through the efforts of two famous British statisticians, Sir Ronald A. Fisher (1890–1962) and Karl Pearson (1857–1936), and others, statistics developed into a science to facilitate and evaluate hypothesis testing.

Sometimes we don't realize how various data bases and the analysis or projections thereof impact our everyday lives. We drive to class in our automobile. Our insurance premiums are in part based on the frequency of accidents and fatalities occurring for individuals in our age category. To determine if higher rates for younger drivers are warranted we will view recent data.

In viewing Table 1.1 we note the driving fatality rates by age and gender between the years 1996–2005. It's clear that individuals between the ages of 16–25 and males have greater fatality rates than other groups. For this reason insurers are allowed to discriminate against these groups with higher rates. If these conditions hold for the past they are expected to be true for future time periods. Please note though that the fatality rates for most age categories have decreased over the stated time period.

Table 1.1A Distribution of Fatality Rate* by Age Group and Year

Age Group	1996	1997	1998	1999	2000	2001	2002	2003	2004	2005	Average Yearly % Change
Under 16	5.37	5.13	4.83	4.72	4.40	4.04	3.94	3.97	4.03	3.61	−4.3
16–20	31.38	30.49	29.54	29.89	29.39	29.72	30.88	29.41	28.76	27.40	−1.5
21–25	28.67	27.04	26.26	26.51	25.57	26.13	26.22	25.32	25.63	26.14	−1.0
26–30	19.63	19.35	18.33	19.02	18.17	18.08	18.38	17.78	18.15	18.30	−0.8
31–35	16.68	16.37	16.24	15.68	15.33	15.27	15.12	15.07	15.05	15.69	−0.7
36–40	15.42	15.14	15.38	15.43	15.21	15.40	15.41	14.95	14.33	14.87	−0.4
41–45	14.47	14.11	14.26	14.54	15.01	15.02	15.16	15.51	14.90	15.06	0.4
46–50	13.39	13.48	14.23	13.91	13.94	13.56	14.35	14.26	14.54	14.41	0.8
51–55	13.25	14.52	13.67	13.65	13.20	13.38	13.41	14.01	13.75	14.56	1.1
56–60	14.03	14.72	13.93	13.91	13.86	13.34	12.99	13.52	13.26	13.49	−0.4
61–65	14.88	14.56	14.34	13.90	13.34	13.15	14.25	13.69	13.61	13.90	−0.8
Over 65	21.36	22.07	21.55	20.99	19.50	19.50	19.01	18.91	18.17	17.94	−1.9
Total	**15.86**	**15.69**	**15.36**	**15.30**	**14.86**	**14.80**	**14.93**	**14.74**	**14.58**	**14.66**	**−0.9**

Source: FARS 1996–2004 (Final), 2005 (ARF); Census Bureau   *Per 100,000 Population
Published by NHTSA's Center for Statistics and Analysis

Table 1.1B Distribution of Crash Fatalities and Population by Gender and Year

Gender	1996	1997	1998	1999	2000	2001	2002	2003	2004	2005	% Change per Yr
Female Fatality Rate	10.3	10.3	10.0	9.8	9.3	9.1	9.2	9.1	9.0	8.7	−1.9
Male Fatality Rate	21.6	21.2	20.9	21.0	20.6	20.7	20.8	20.5	20.3	20.6	−0.5
Total Fatality Rate*	**15.86**	**15.69**	**15.36**	**15.30**	**14.86**	**14.80**	**14.93**	**14.74**	**14.58**	**14.66**	**−0.9**

In addition to the frequency of accidents and fatalities by age and gender, the average costs of repairs and litigation in an area also impact the rates we pay. For example, zip codes involving the first 3 numbers 900 (Los Angeles area) tend to have the highest accident rates involving litigation; hence, they tend to have among the highest rates in the country.

As we drive to school, we are directed by traffic signals which are timed with the aid of statistics to allow for the maximum traffic for that time of day. You may even drive through a speed trap that police have established knowing the frequency of catching students racing to class.

You enroll in classes that are offered based on projections of enrollments by academic discipline. Your performance within any class is based on a weighted average of several factors which may include examination grades, homework, class participation, etc. In fact, the reason that you are registered in the program that you are is based on your application data comparing favorably to that of the applicant pool. You enter your university knowing that the lifetime earnings for individuals with advanced degrees is significantly greater than for those not having them.

Should you become ill, you will visit a physician. If it is not clear what is wrong with you, the physician will request diagnostic tests which are based on statistics. When you give a blood sample, statistical data have been amassed to ascertain the norms for categories, like cell counts, for individuals with your demographic profile. The norms frequently are presented in the form of an interval. If your count is below or above the respective interval then a problem exists that must be remedied. Should you require medication, the type, volume, and duration taken will have been ascertained through the use of statistics. Even your automobile now undergoes similar diagnostic tests when it is connected to a computer.

2

The Internal Revenue Service (IRS) may be preparing to audit your tax return this very minute. If it is, it will probably be based on information that your charitable deductions are higher than those considered acceptable, given your income level. If you purchase a house or a car, a credit check will be made of your credit file to determine your likelihood of making your payments. In addition, a projection will be made to ascertain if you will be able to meet these payments in the future.

When you purchase any products at the vending machine between classes, there will be statements made concerning the contents of the package like weight, volume, calories, etc. This data was obtained through statistical analysis. These statements were made and tested through sampling to obtain the data, and through a statistical analysis of the data.

If we seek employment, we will find that business organizations' hiring practices are based on projections involving many factors including the direction of the economy, and the direction interest rates and inflation are headed. You will also take tests to determine if you fulfill the desired profile of individuals within the organization. Should you be lucky enough to obtain employment, you are faced with the projection that Social Security may be bankrupt prior to your retirement or that your firm may invest your company retirement funds based upon faulty information.

If you are married or thinking of getting married, you are faced with the fact that approximately one out of every two marriages ends in divorce. This fact has caused a rise in prenuptial agreements and even talk on the topic of divorce insurance.

In fact we are surrounded by so many statistics that there is fear we will not be known by our names, but merely by our social security or other designated number.

Most of our mentioned examples involve the summarizing of data sets and are termed descriptive statistics. An alternate process is called statistical inference which involves making judgments about data. These judgments can take the form of a prediction, an estimate, or a test of a belief. We will show an example of statistical inference by making projections of the world population.

 Concept Check 1.A

Statistics impacts the way in which we live. True or False? If false, explain.

Exercises

1.1   State how statistics determines your car insurance premiums.

1.2   State how statistics is used to determine if your blood pressure is too high.

1.2   Determining Trends and Their Possible Consequences

One of the important uses we place in statistics is to make projections of historical data to warn us of potential problems and possibly allow us to deal with them. For example, we might view the current world population from 1950–1990 and make projections for future decades. Such data are termed time series data since they evolve over time. In Table 1.2 we view actual data from 1950 to 1990, and projections made for future periods. In 1999 the population exceeded 6.0 billion. In 2008 it's 6.7 billion, and it's projected to be 7.0 billion in 1012 by the US Census Bureau. That's an increase of one billion in 13 years. The world reached its first billion in 1800 and it took 130 years (1930) for it to go to 2.0 billion. The US population in 2008 equals 304 million. We don't have to be clairvoyant to realize that since our basic natural resources are not increasing that many difficulties lie ahead.

Viewing the projected availability of basic natural resources between 1990–2000 reveals a severe per capita decline. The availability of land, water, and wood will shrink on a per capita basis. During the decade of the late nineties, per capita grainland is expected to shrink by 1/6, irrigated land by 1/10, forest and grazing land by 1/5 (Table 1.3).

Table 1.2 World Population (for midyear) with Projections by Developed and Developing Nations (000,000)

Year	Developed Nations	Developing Nations	World
1950	832	1,724	2,555
1960	945	2,093	3,038
1970	1,049	2,655	3,704
1980	1,137	3,319	4,456
1990	1,211	4,082	5,293
2000	1,279	4,887	6,165
2010	1,334	5,694	7,028
2020	1,375	6,548	7,924
2050	1,421	8,779	10,200

Source: World Population Profile: 1994: U.S. Department of Commerce, Bureau of the Census. ISBN #0-16-043085-2.

Table 1.3 Availability of Basic Natural Resources per Person in 1990 and 2000

Resource	1990	2000
Grain land	0.13	0.11
Irrigated land	0.045	0.04
Forest land	0.79	0.64
Grazing land	0.61	0.50

Source: The New World Order, State of the World 1991, p. 17.

We must note that two types of experts, or even two individuals, may yield quite different analyses for the same data set. For example, economists and ecologists might view the data differently. Economists tend to view population as a demand/supply problem. If the demand for basic natural resources exceeds the supply the price mechanism will direct the scarce resources to the wealthier nations causing more problems for the developing nations. On the other hand, ecologists view population increases from a much longer term perspective. They are concerned not only in the shortage of food but more importantly on the decline in forests used in the heating and cooking process as possibly the cause of a change in climate and habitability of the world.

 Concept Check 1.B

If we viewed the population of the 50 states within the U.S. in 1990, we would be viewing time series data. True or false? If false, explain.

Exercises

1.3   Is it easy to understand from viewing the data of Table 1.2 that the growth in world population has an upwards trend to it?

1.4   From a casual viewing of Table 1.2 could you determine the exact population for the year 2030?

1.3   Population versus Sample

Since data are so vital to decision making, one important question concerns itself with how we obtain reliable information without having to spend a fortune. If we wanted to know what proportion of the U.S. population were left handed, we would not normally want to interview the entire U.S. population. If we did seek information from all residents (approximately 280 million), we would be examining a population. The population is the total set of all data of interest. Cost and time usually prohibit the analysis of a population. Rather we will analyze only a carefully selected subset of the U.S. population called a sample. A sample is defined as a subset of the population selected to represent the population. Great care must be taken to ensure that our population subset is indeed representative of the population from which it comes. Chapter 5 reviews the process and concepts involving a representative sample.

 Concept Check 1.C

The results from a populations study are always the same as what is obtained from a survey. True or False? If false, explain.

Exercises

1.5   Suppose on your first day of the term that your teacher gives your class the option of taking 5 tests with no comprehensive final or 3 tests with a comprehensive final (majority rule). Have we sought information from the population or the sample?

1.6   Do you believe it is possible to randomly select a sample which is not representative of the population?

1.7   What do you believe are the advantages of sample results over population results?

1.8   What do you believe are the advantages of population results over sample results?

1.4   Types of Data and Some Definitions

You are now enrolled in a statistics class. You are one student out of many in the class. How can we differentiate you from other students in the class? We can classify you and fellow students into many variables. A variable is a characteristic or property that varies between observations. Variables that we may use to differentiate you from others are gender, age, major, hours completed toward graduation, grade point average (GPA), seating row, etc.

For some of these variables we merely wish to note if you possess a certain attribute or not (gender, major, seating row). For other variables we think of numbers such as the mean grade point or age. The former are termed **qualitative data** and the latter **quantitative data**.

Quantitative data are measured on a numerical scale. Examples of quantitative data are age, income, profits, or the numbers of employees in a company. Quantitative data can be further stratified into a nominal, ordinal, interval scale, and ratio data. We will use the numbers on the shirts of basketball players as an example. If the number on the jersey simply identifies an individual player or player's position, it's nominal data. If a player with a 24 on his or her shirt was in some way superior to a player with 8 on his or her shirt we are involved with ordinal data. If the performance difference between two players with 24 and 19 on their jerseys was equivalent to the difference between two players with 10 and 5 on their jerseys, we have interval data. Finally, if the player with a 24 on his or her shirt was 3 times better than the player with an 8 on his or her shirt, we are involved with ratio data.

Qualitative (categorical or nonnumerical) data, on the other hand, are data that are grouped into categories. Here we are interested if the data possess a certain attribute or not. Examples of qualitative data are a person's gender, major, and seating row. While such data may be important in a statistical study, none can be described numerically. If a characteristic (or attribute) can only be measured two ways (answers on a true–false test), it is call dichotomous. A characteristic that contains more than two categories or classes (answers on a multiple choice test) is multinomial.

Regardless of the type of data, care must be taken to not improperly interpret it. For example, in 1990 male drivers comprised 51.4% of all licensed drivers in the U.S. and were involved with 62.1% of all crashes. Can we surmise that men have a higher frequency of accidents than females? If we do, we will be making the assumption that males and females share equally all miles driven. Although such an assumption seems rational, research indicates that it is not true. Studies in 1990 showed that males accounted for 64.8% of all miles driven, which is roughly equal the percent of all crashes. Hence males are no more likely to get into accidents than females, However, males are more likely to be involved in fatal accidents than females.

 Concept Check 1.D

If we compare the prices of two products and one costs $4 and the other $2, we are dealing with ordinal data. True or false? If false, explain.

Exercises

1.9   Define the term variable.

1.10   List 2 qualitative variables (in addition to the 3 already mentioned) that can be used to distinguish you from your fellow students.

1.11   List 2 quantitative variables (in addition to the 3 already mentioned) that can be used to distinguish you from your fellow students.

1.12   Explain the 4 classifications of quantitative data.

1.13   If you were reviewing employee evaluations, give examples of the 4 classifications for quantitative data.

1.14   Suppose you had to answer a multiple choice question whose correct answer was b. If we assigned a number 1 to answer a, a 2 to answer b, etc., would knowledge of the mean answer be helpful? Explain.

1.15   Use an example of individual IQ scores to explain interval and ratio data.

1.16   Use an example of an employee social security number to explain nominal and ordinal data.

1.17   Your university probably is divided into several colleges or departments. See if you can ascertain what proportion of students was held by each at the end of the last academic year. What type of data do we have?

1.18   Your university probably is divided into several colleges or departments. See if you can ascertain what proportion of students was held by each at the end of each of the last five academic years. What type of data do we have?

1.5   Examples of Statistical Applications

Statistics is a subject that transcends virtually all disciplines and areas of scientific and practical endeavor. If you do not see the value of statistics in your major, ask one of your professors to provide you with some insights and examples of statistical applications. In order to illustrate the value of statistics, we will examine several cases where statistics has facilitated the solution of some important social dilemmas.

Smoking and Health Hazards

We are all familiar with the warning placed on cigarette packages in the United States in recent years. It clearly states that cigarette smoking can be hazardous to your health. However, this warning statement has not always been on cigarette packages. It was not until the statistical evidence linking smoking to numerous health risks was so convincing did the Surgeon General of the United States insist on such labeling.

Optimal Size of a High School

How does a school board know when to build another high school as opposed to increasing the size of an existing one? This is a problem that has concerned and still does concern most school boards in the United States. The optimal size high school was defined by one study to be that with the lowest cost per student. To solve this problem, data on school costs, student enrollment and other variables associated with costs were used for statistically estimating a school cost function. The school size, in terms of number of students, that generated the least per unit cost, holding other factors constant, was found to be the optimal size high school.

Value of Human Life

Suppose an airliner crashes due to the negligence of the pilot and numerous passengers and airline personnel are killed. The airline will surely be sued by the families that have lost loved ones. However, what is the value we place on the lost lives? This is a question that many would argue is unable to be answered. However, persons must be compensated, even if inadequately, for their losses. Therefore, estimates of the value of human life are made somewhat routinely in the courts where cases are tried concerning the wrongful death of persons. In this process, statistics is a fundamental tool.

Statistical Auditing

Auditors are hired to ensure the accuracy of accounting records. However, for many firms, the task of examining each and every record would be far too costly. Thus, auditors routinely sample records and use this information as a benchmark to assess the accuracy of all records.

Now that we have described what statistics is and given several examples, we end this chapter by listing other applications of statistics. Statistics has been used to:

1. estimate the costs and benefits of the current mile per hour speed limit.
2. estimate banks' cost of issuing demand deposits.
3. estimate the relationship between exercise and heart attack.
4. forecast interest rates.
5. estimate the benefits of advertising.
6. analyze the existence of employment discrimination.
7. forecast tourist arrivals.
8. forecast firm sales or profits.
9. predict political outcomes.
10. estimate the effect of fertilization on crop yield.

The list could continue for pages and not include all possible applications of statistics. As statistical techniques become more widely known and the means to implement statistical analyses become more readily available, the list will continue to grow. The development of personal computers has brought sophisticated statistical tools to an increasing number of people and organizations, once only available to corporations, government agencies, and universities. Therefore, what was once a subject only useful to experts is now a practical tool for anyone involved in decision making.

✔ **Concept Check 1.E**

Statistics is used in all professions because it is a vital decision making tool. True or false? If false, explain.

Exercises

1.19   Explain how statistics may be used in determining the courses that should be offered next term by your university.

1.20   Explain how statistics may be used in determining the need for a new hospital, and in ascertaining the likely ailments that individuals coming to the hospital might have.

1.6   Summary

Statistical analysis is not an end in and of itself, it is a means to an end. It is not the sheer pleasure that can come from the analysis of data that motivates most of us to engage in statistical analysis; rather it is the value of this information to facilitate decisions and to enable us to have a better understanding of the world in which we live. This does not mean that you can't enjoy statistics as a discipline of its own. However, always remember that the discipline of statistics is relevant to everyone, not just statisticians.

Mini-case 1.1: Sherlock Holmes

We have often read or watched Sherlock Holmes and other sleuths solve perplexing cases. Is this an example of inductive or deductive reasoning? Explain.

Mini-case 1.2: Designing a Hospital

If we were designing a new hospital, how could we use statistics to ascertain what percent of the space should be allocated to cardiac patients, accident victims, etc.?

Mini-case 1.3: Inspecting Parts

If our company were required to produce machine parts that must meet specific tolerances, might statistics aid us in ensuring that our products meet the specifications?

Mini-case 1.4: Inflation

The rate of inflation is one of the most important variables in the determination of economic activity. Do you believe that statistics plays a role in the determination of the measurement of inflation?

Mini-case 1.5: After Your Degree

After you graduate from college, you will either continue with your formal education or seek employment. Do you believe that statistics will play a role for your graduate school or employer in whether they select you over alternative candidates?

Mini-case 1.6: Merchandise Carried by Retailers

Retailers carry numerous brand named items. They obviously can't inventory all possible brands. Does statistics play a role in ascertaining what brands continue to be carried?

Review of Important Terms and Concepts

Population: The total collection of elements of interest to the analyst.

Sample: A subset of the population selected to represent the population.

Descriptive statistics: Procedures for summarizing a data set, using either a population or a sample.

Statistical inference: Process of making judgments about a population, using sample (incomplete) data. These judgments can take the form of a prediction, an estimate, or a test of an hypothesis.

Induction: The logical process of getting conclusions about a whole based on information from a subset of elements from the whole.

Variable: A variable is a characteristic or property that varies between observations.

Quantitative data: Measurements that can be represented numerically. The forms of quantitative data are nominal, ordinal, interval, and ratio data. Each varies according to the meaning of different measurements.

Qualitative (categorical or nonquantitative data): Measurements that can be grouped into categories. If there are but two categories (as in a true–false exam), we use the term dichotomous. If there are more than two possible categories (as in a multiple choice question), we use the term multinomial.

Time series data: Observations of a variable measured at successive time periods or points in time.

Cross-sectional data: Observations of several variables measured at a single point or period in time.

End of Chapter Exercises

1.21   "One never proves anything with statistics." Do you agree? Explain.

1.22   In each of the following examples, categorize the type of data as quantitative or qualitative:

   a.   The weights of a sample of children.
   b.   The Dow Jones Industrial Average.
   c.   The political affiliation of a sample of voters.
   d.   Sales data for General Motors Corporation.
   e.   The standard industrial classification codes (SIC) for a group of firms.
   f.   The majors of your classmates.
   g.   The class standing of your classmates, e.g., freshman, sophomore, etc.
   h.   The grade point average of your classmates.
   i.   The SAT or ACT test scores of your classmates.
   j.   Number of college credit hours of your classmates.

1.23   Discuss the difference between time series data and cross-sectional data. Give examples of each.

1.24   If the variable of interest is SAT (Scholastic Aptitude Test) scores, will the data be cross-sectional or time series? Explain with examples.

1.25   Is the Gallup Poll based on a sample?

Describing Data

Where we have been

In Chapter 1, the nature of statistics was presented and some fundamental concepts introduced. From that discussion it was apparent that statistics deals with the analysis of data.

Where we are going

In this chapter, a first step in the analysis of data is undertaken. This step involves arranging and displaying data in ways that provide an opportunity for better visualizing the characteristics of the data.

In every walk of life statistics and the analysis of data are important. But, in business, the presentation and analysis of numerical information is essential to success. In corporate annual meetings, management wants to present information about past performance and future prospects. The "facts" for these presentations are generally based on historical data. But the data must be presented in such a way as to be clear, concise, and often convincing. Suppose labor and management are involved in contract negotiations that deal with wages. Each side in the negotiations must use numerical data for the firm, the industry, and other relevant comparisons to present their views. Decisions such as these are seldom determined by emotion and the "winner" is frequently the one that documents its position most completely with numerical information.

2.1   Introduction

Once data have been collected, the next task is frequently to arrange the data in a manner in which they can be analyzed more readily or displayed more aptly. In general, data can be arranged and displayed in two basic forms, tables and graphs. However, within these options there are many alternatives, each with their advantages and disadvantages. In the following sections some of the more commonly used tabular and graphical techniques for displaying and arranging data will be presented.

In addition, descriptive statistics will be introduced to summarize the position and dispersion of quantitative data. Measures of location (position) for a distribution that are discussed include the arithmetic mean, the median, the mode, quartiles, and deciles. Measures of dispersion or variation presented include the range, the interquartile range, the mean absolute deviation, the standard deviation, and the variance.

For qualitative data interest often focuses on the proportion of cases containing a certain characteristic or being in a certain category. For instance, what is the proportion of the voting public that is Republican and Democrat? Similarly, what is the proportion of defective items in a shipment of parts? The proportion is a statistic that is analytically useful and warrants close scrutiny.

2.2   The Frequency Distribution

Data can often be effectively presented in the form of a table depicting a frequency distribution, which is a tabular or graphical display of the number of observations in a data set taking on certain values of falling into each of the classifications or categories. For instance suppose that a financial analyst has information concerning the legal status of a sample of 25 organizations. The findings of the sample are documented in the table below:

Table 2.1 Legal Status of 25 Organizations

Organization: Legal Status		Organization: Legal Status	
1	Sole proprietor	14	Corporation
2	Partnership	15	Charitable
3	Partnership	16	Sole proprietor
4	Corporation	17	Corporation
5	Partnership	18	Partnership
6	Corporation	19	Partnership
7	Charitable	20	Sole proprietor
8	Corporation	21	Partnership
9	Sole proprietor	22	Corporation
10	Corporation	23	Partnership
11	Charitable	24	Partnership
12	Partnership	25	Corporation
13	Corporation		

Since the number of observations in this data set is quite small, a fairly accurate sense of the number of organizations falling into each of the four legal classifications is obtainable (Table 2.2). However, imagine how difficult it might be to grasp the significance of the distribution if there were 2500 organizations. In the latter case it might be necessary to rearrange the data into a more meaningful form. One way to summarize the data is to develop a frequency distribution. The frequency is nothing more then a count of the observations.

It is sometimes advantageous not only to provide the frequency, but also to provide the relative frequency. A relative frequency is the count in each classification divided by the total number of observations in the data set. A frequency distribution table is provided below to illustrate the concepts of frequency and relative frequency. However, a **frequency distribution** is merely a listing of the count of the observations in a data set and all possible classifications or values. The **relative frequency** for a classification or value in a frequency distribution is the number observations in the classification divided by the total number of observations in the data set:

$$\textbf{Relative Frequency} = \frac{\textbf{Frequency in classification}}{\textbf{Total number of observations in data set}}$$

Table 2.2 Frequency Distribution for Legal Status
*Data File on MINITAB CD

Status	Frequency	Relative Frequency
Sole proprietorship	4	4/25 = 0.16
Partnership	9	9/25 = 0.36
Corporation	9	9/25 = 0.36
Charitable	3	3/25 = 0.12
	$\Sigma = 25$	$\Sigma = 25/25 = 1.00$

Σ is the Summation symbol

Frequency and relative frequency distributions are useful for the display of quantitative data as well as qualitative data. The only difference is that with quantitative data frequencies are associated with a unique numeric value or range of values rather than a category or classification, as is true for qualitative data. As an example of quantitative data consider the data in Table 2.3 on student grades.

Table 2.3 45 Student Grades on Exam 1
*Data File on MINITAB CD

Student	Grade	Student	Grade	Student	Grade	Student	Grade
1	75	12	68	23	60	34	78
2	79	13	62	24	80	35	63
3	73	14	67	25	59	36	67
4	75	15	77	26	93	37	88
5	91	16	67	27	68	38	64
6	76	17	89	28	89	39	100
7	71	18	81	29	75	40	77
8	60	19	84	30	65	41	75
9	100	20	58	31	65	42	60
10	88	21	50	32	80	43	70
11	79	22	70	33	72	44	76
						45	62

The data could be arranged as a frequency distribution by arranging all distinct grades and their frequency of occurrence, which is shown in Table 2.4.

Table 2.4 Frequency Distribution for Grades on Exam 1 (Frequency = Count)

X Grade	f Frequency	X Grade	f Frequency	X Grade	f Frequency
50	1	68	2	79	2
58	1	70	2	80	2
59	1	71	1	81	1
60	3	72	1	84	1
62	2	73	1	88	2
63	1	75	4	89	2
64	1	76	2	91	1
65	2	77	2	93	1
67	3	78	1	100	2

MINITAB will duplicate Table 2.4 for us by using the following commands:

Stat > Tables > Tally Individual Variables
Double click **grades** into **Variables** box.
OK

The data could also be grouped into intervals and the frequency within each interval displayed. Suppose the data would be more useful if grades were grouped according to 10 = point breaks. In Table 2.5 the grade data is grouped into intervals and the midpoints of the intervals and frequencies are shown.

Table 2.5 Interval Grade Data

Interval	Interval Midpoint (X)	Frequency (f)	Relative Frequency
50–59.99	55	3	3/45 = 0.0667
60–69.99	65	14	14/45 = 0.3111
70–79.99	75	16	16/45 = 0.3556
80–89.99	85	8	8/45 = 0.1778
90–100.0	95	4	4/45 = 0.0888
		$\Sigma = 45$	$\Sigma = 45/45 = 1.0000$

Note: The grade of 100 was included with the 90's because of standard grading procedures.

We might ask how we knew to group the data into 10-point intervals. There is no hard and fast rule to utilize in making the interval breaks. We would begin the process by determining the difference between the high and low observations in the data set. This process would be made easier by having MINITAB rank the observations from low to high (which is accomplished later in this chapter) if they were not already in order of ascending magnitude. Next we will divide the difference between the largest (LO) and smallest (SO) observation by the number of classes we think might be appropriate. If we thought initially that we wanted 6 classes, then

$$\frac{\textbf{Largest Observation} - \textbf{Smallest Observation}}{\textbf{6}} = \frac{\textbf{100} - \textbf{50}}{\textbf{6}} = \textbf{8.33}$$

With 6 classification we would have intervals that are not easily rounded, so we would increase our interval to 10. Hence we established the tradition 50–under 60, 60–under 70 intervals. Note that the 100 value is actually outside of our 90–under 100 interval. However, it is often customary for both the largest and smallest intervals to be **open-ended**. For example, suppose we added an observation to our data set which is a grade of 16. In order to reach the 10–under 20 interval, we would have 3 intervals with no data involved (20–under 30, 30–under 40, and 40–under 50). To avoid this, our initial interval would be 0–under 60. Grades (16) far different from other observations are often called **outliers** because they lie outside the bounds of most of the observations.

The interval midpoint is important because it is used to represent that interval. How well it actually represents the interval depends on how close the interval midpoint is to the mean of the data in the interval. If we have 3 observations in interval 50–under 60 that are 52, 55, and 58, then the interval midpoint (55) is representative of the data. If, however, the 3 observations are 58, 59, and 59, then the interval midpoint is not representative of the data. The class midpoints are often used in graphing the frequency distributions.

Cumulative Distributions

An alternative method of viewing and examining a frequency distribution is to list the data observations that are **less than** the specific class intervals. We will use our grade distribution for 45 students as an example (Table 2.5). We first want to know the percent of students who scored less that 59.99 on the exam. From relative frequency we know that 3/45, or 6.67%, of the students scored below a 59.99 on the exam.

Next we want to know the percentage of our students who scored below a 69.99 grade. This would include 3 from the 50–59.99 group plus 14 from the 60–69.99 group yielding a percentage of 37.78% [(3 + 14)/45]. What is the percent of students who scored below a grade of 79.99? This would include 3 students from the 50–59.99 group, 14 from the 60–69.99 group, plus 16 from the 70–79.99

14

group. In total 73.34 percent of our students [(3 + 14 + 16)/45] scored below a grade of 79.99 (Table 2.6). Of course, 100% of the students scored a grade less than or equal to 100.

Table 2.6 Interval Grade Data

Interval	Midpoint (X)	Interval Frequency (f)	Relative Frequency	Cumulative Frequency
50–59.99	55	3	3/45 = 0.0667	3/45 = 0.0667
60–69.99	65	14	14/45 = 0.3111	17/45 = 0.3778
70–79.99	75	16	16/45 = 0.3556	33/45 = 0.7334
80–89.99	85	8	8/45 = 0.1778	41/45 = 0.9112
90–100.0	95	4	4/45 = 0.0888	45/45 = 1.0000
		Σ = 45	Σ = 45/45 = 1.0000	

Often in statistics we give cumulative probability tables and will ask for various probabilities. For example, using only the cumulative frequency figures, what percentage of the students made a score between 70–79.99? If we read the cumulative table for grades between 70–79.99, we obtain a reading of 0.7334. However, 73.33 percent of the students did not make between 70–79.99 on their exams. To find the correct probability we read the cumulative table for 70–79.99 (.7334) and subtract this value from the cumulative proportion in the 60–69.99 group (0.3778), yielding 0.3556 (0.7333 − 0.3778).

Suppose we wanted to find the percent of students who scored above a 70–79.99 score. We can take the cumulative value involving 70–79.99, which involves the probability of obtaining a score less than 79.99, and subtract from 1 (1 − 7334 = 0.2666). Hence 26.66% of the students made a grade above 79.99.

 Concept Check 2.A

With frequency distributions we are attempting to determine the frequency with which a number or interval appears. True or false? If false, explain.

Exercises

2.1 Construct a frequency distribution, relative and cumulative frequency distributions for the class standing of 20 randomly selected students in a business statistics course.

Student	Class	Student	Class
1	Sophomore	11	Junior
2	Sophomore	12	Sophomore
3	Senior	13	Senior
4	Junior	14	Junior
5	Junior	15	Sophomore
6	Senior	16	Freshman
7	Junior	17	Senior
8	Junior	18	Senior
9	Senior	19	Senior
10	Senior	20	Freshman

2.2   Construct a frequency distribution, relative and cumulative frequency distributions for geographical location of a random sample of 25 customers of a mail order camping equipment retailer. A = Atlantic, C = Central, M = Midwest, W = West.

Customer	Region	Customer	Region
1	W	14	A
2	W	15	M
3	A	16	W
4	C	17	A
5	M	18	C
6	W	19	W
7	A	20	A
8	W	21	M
9	W	22	W
10	C	23	A
11	W	24	W
12	C	25	C
13	W		

2.3   Suppose that in Exercise 2.2 the Atlantic (A) and Central (C) regions were collapsed into a single region named the East (E). Revise the frequency and relative frequency distributions based on this new information. Does this change result in a change in the interpretation of the results?

2.4   Do you think that frequency distributions play an important role in determining that younger drivers should pay higher insurance rates?

2.3 Graphical Display of Data

Presenting data in a tabular form, even if summarized with a frequency distribution, is not always the best or most illuminating method of display. We all remember the old saying that "a picture is worth a thousand words." Well, that is also a valid statement for the display of statistical information. Of course, statisticians use graphs as their pictures but they are often very useful and frequently quite elegant. It should be noted that in recent years graphics software for microcomputers has become widely available. These programs are very flexible, quite powerful, and can provide what is referred to as camera ready output, which is immediately available for publishing. The same data that are useful to perform statistical analysis via the microcomputer are also very easily made available to graphics software for pictorial representation. We are fortunate that this text comes with software that has excellent graphic capabilities.

Graphing Qualitative (Categorical) Data

As defined in Chapter 1, qualitative data are categorical data. Even if we quantify the categories such as to make 1 = sole proprietorship, 2 = partnership, 3 = corporation, 4 = charitable institution, the numbers are used for identification purposes only. Hence we have nominal data. The techniques for graphically displaying qualitative and/or nominal data are distinct from those for quantitative data. One of the most common methods of pictorially displaying qualitative data is with bar charts.

Our included statistical package MINITAB yields graphs from two modes, a character and professional mode. The character mode yields graphs using keyboard characters like ∗, +, − and letters. Character graphs appear directly in the session window. Professional graphs are high resolution and produce much sharper images. Professional graphs appear in its own Graph window. Both character and professional graphs yield the same information. We will start with the character graphs and the commands necessary to obtain them.

One of the primary graphs for a single data series is a **histogram**. A histogram is a plot of the frequency distribution. Histograms provide information about the general shape of the data set. In a histogram there are no gaps (or breaks) between the bars. For qualitative data, the horizontal scale is simply the definition of the categories. For quantitative data, the midpoint of the horizontal reading of the bar is the midpoint for the class interval.

The MINITAB command sequence to obtain histograms is as follows:

In the professional mode the command and output is as follows:

Graph > **Histogram**
Double click **Legalform** into **Graph Variable** box.
OK

Figure 2.1A: Histogram of legal form of business (professional graph)

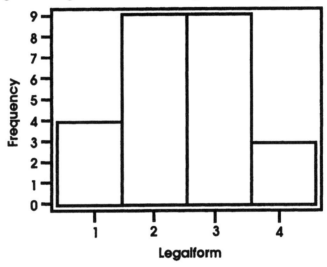

If desired we can title the histogram and turn it 90 degrees on its side by clicking on Options and then Transpose X and Y. Minitab will also perform a pie chart. The command sequence is as follows:

Graph > **Pie Chart**
Double click **Legalform** into **Chart data in** box.
OK

17

Figure 2.1B: Histogram of legal form of business (turned and titled)

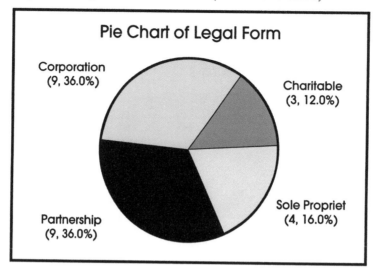

For quantitative data the command sequence is identical. We will now have MINITAB yield us a histogram for the student grades example (Table 2.3). The command sequence for a professional histogram is

 Graph > Histogram
Double click **grades** into **Graph variable** box.
OK

Figure 2.2A: Histogram of student grades (professional graph)

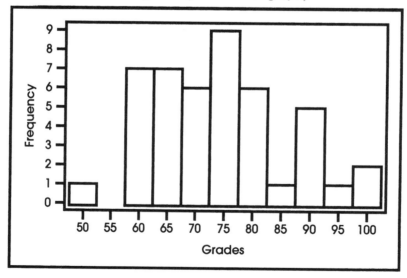

MINITAB will also graph a cumulative histogram if desired. The command sequence is:

Graph > **Histogram**
Double click **grades** into **Graph variable** box.
Click on **Options**.
Click on **Cumulative Frequency**.
OK twice

Figure 2.2B: Cumulative histogram of student grades (professional graph)

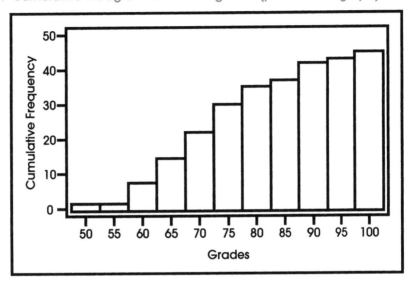

 Concept Check 2.B

There are various graphs or diagrams with which we can display identical information. True or false? If false, explain.

Exercises

2.5 How do the graphs for qualitative frequency distributions of qualitative data differ from those for quantitative data?

2.6 For the data set HOMES.MTW have MINITAB perform a character histogram, professional histogram, and a dotplot for all five of the variables involved.

2.7 For the data set HEIGHT.MTW have MINITAB perform a character histogram, professional histogram, and a dotplot for the variable heights.

2.8 For the data set SNOW.MTW have MINITAB perform a character histogram, professional histogram, and a dotplot for the variables snowfall and rain.

Analyzing quantitative data in which there are a large number of observations or cases by merely looking at the data is generally fraught with difficulty and often quite frustrating. Frequently, graphing techniques also do not give the precise view that we require. Thus, there is a need to characterize data on quantitative variables with single number statistics that tend to summarize the more important characteristics of the data distribution. For instance, in your business statistics class (in which the instructor has stated that he will curve grades) you receive a grade of 64 on your first test and do not know whether to drop the class or not. The first piece of information you would probably like to have for this decision is the class "average." If you are told that the average grade is 52 on the exam, you might decide that you are doing as well as expected and elect to stay in the class. However, there are other statistics that describe quantitative data which are also useful in such analyses. In general, we will develop statistics that describe two characteristics of data sets, measures of central tendency and measures of variability. A **measure of central tendency** is a measure which describes the general location or position of a data set. These measures are designed to typify or represent a set of observations. A **measure of variability** is a measure of the dispersion or spread in a distribution. We begin our analysis with a measure of central tendency.

A measure of central tendency provides a single statistic that serves to represent or typify all other observations in the distribution. Often this is a central observation that is in the middle of the distribution but we will see later that this need not always be true. Measures of central tendency also provide reference points for comparisons. Most students evaluate their performance on an exam relative to the average grade in the class. Grade point averages are important to all college students. Batting averages are critical to baseball players. We are constantly deluged by statistics in the media about typical incomes, typical home prices, typical family size, typical car prices. All of these are applications using measures of central tendency to make a point.

The Arithmetic Mean

The most commonly used measure of central tendency is the arithmetic mean or merely the mean. The arithmetic mean is nothing more than the average for a group of observations. If the observations are derived from a sample, we can calculate the sample arithmetic mean which is represented by X-bar (an X with a bar over it). However, if the observations comprise the population, we can compute the population or "true" mean, which is represented by the lower-case Greek character mu (μ). Both population and sample means are defined as follows:

The Population Mean   **The Sample Mean**

$$\mu = \frac{\Sigma X_i}{N} \quad (2.1) \qquad \overline{X} = \frac{\Sigma X_i}{n} \quad (2.2)$$

where

X_i = the numeric observations in the population/sample ($i = 1, 2, \ldots N$)

N = population size: n = sample size (the number of observations)

Σ = the summation operator

In words, the arithmetic mean of a sample/population of n/N observations on variable X, is found by summing all values on X, from the first to the nth/Nth, and dividing this result by the number of observations, n/N.

In the majority of cases in statistical analysis, we will be concerned with sample data. However, even in these cases it is important to place your analysis in proper perspective by recognizing that the sample arithmetic mean, $\overline{X}$, is an estimate of the population or true arithmetic mean, μ. As we progress through the text the rationale and logic of using sample information as a substitute for complete data on the population will become apparent.

Computing the Sample Arithmetic Mean

Suppose that you received four ($n = 4$) equally weighted test grades in a class and these reflected a sample. These grades were 78 ($X_1 = 78$), 85 ($X_2 = 85$), 88 ($X_3 = 88$), and 73 ($X_4 = 73$). Thus, the mean grade on the four tests would be

$$\overline{X} = \frac{X_1 + X_2 + X_3 + X_4}{n} = \frac{78 + 85 + 88 + 73}{4} = \frac{324}{4} = 81$$

In this case, the arithmetic mean represents the four grades quite well. However, this is not always true. An arithmetic mean grade of 81 could also be obtained if you had test grades of 100, 100, 24, and 100 and the mean is not close to any of the individual test scores. More will be said of this as we introduce other measures of central tendency and variability.

Trimmed Mean (TRMEAN)

Many of us have seen Olympic competition where in evaluating an individual's performance the largest and smallest scores are deleted prior to computing the mean. Such a mean is called a trimmed mean (TRMEAN) and is computed in order to avoid distortions in the mean caused by extremely large or small observations (outliers). MINITAB will automatically remove the largest 5% (rounded to the nearest %) and smallest 5% of the data (10% total), then compute the mean.

The Median

Another measure of central tendency or location is the **median**. To determine the median of a distribution, the observations must first be ranked in order of the value of the observation. The **sample median** (M_d) of a distribution is the middle value in a ranked or ordered array of the observations. We will generally be concerned with and compute the sample or estimated median. However, the median can also refer to the middle observation in a ranked distribution including all elements of a population. The median can be more representative of a distribution than the arithmetic mean in some situations. Suppose, for example, that there are five managers in an organization. Their salaries are $15,000, $22,000, $20,000, $25,000, and $118,000. The arithmetic mean salary is $40,000 which is heavily influenced by the one extremely large salary ($118,000). However, ordering the salaries from lowest to highest yields

15,000   20,000   22,000   25,000   118,000

and the middle value is $22,000. Thus, this same information yields a median salary of $22,000, which is more typical of what managers in that organization make.

This example illustrates why readers of statistical information should be wary of summary results generated by others. If the point you wanted to make was how high managers were paid in this organization, you would select the arithmetic mean and report a "typical" salary of $40,000. However, if you had the opposite interests you would choose the median and report a "typical" salary of $22,000. This does not infer an attempt to lie with statistics, but rather a disagreement concerning the appropriate measure of central tendency.

For an odd number of values the median is the middle value when the data are arranged in ascending magnitude. If we were to add an additional salary of $24,000 to our original sample of 5, we would have the array

15,000   20,000   22,000   24,000   25,000   118,000

To determine the median we compute the arithmetic mean of the two middle values to obtain a median of $23,000 [($22,000 + $24,000)/2].

The median has come to be used heavily in the news media. The reason is it is easier to interpret than other measures of central tendency. For example, in 2000 the median age of the U.S. is 35.3-years-old. This means half our population is older than 35.3, and half younger.

A third commonly used measure of central tendency is the mode. The sample **mode** of a distribution is the value or values with the highest frequency of occurrence. Often in data analysis it is appropriate to regard the representative or typical value in a distribution as that which occurs with the greatest frequency. Again the mode could be referring to a sample statistic to describe the most frequently occurring observation in the sample or it could refer to a population value if it reflects the most frequently occurring value in the population. In most instances we will be referring to the mode for a sample.

If we owned a retail clothing store, we would be very interested in the modal clothing size. We would want to carry only those sizes that would fit the vast numbers of consumers. We would not be interested in carrying the mean clothing sizes, because the mean sizes may be distorted by physically large or small consumers. Using the clothing example, it is possible for us to obtain dual modes, which is termed a **Bimodal Distribution**. This simply reflects the fact that two clothing sizes have a large frequency of consumers who buy them.

Given the following 20 observations on X, the mode would obviously be between 2 and 9. It appears that 3 is the most redundant number, and probably is the mode.

$$2, 3, 5, 3, 6, 7, 9, 3, 2, 8, 2, 3, 5, 3, 6, 7, 9, 3, 2, 8$$

We will check quickly by tabulating the tally sheet or frequency distribution. Such a frequency distribution is shown in Table 2.7 and the observation with the highest frequency is shown clearly.

Table 2.7 Frequency Distribution

X	Tally	Frequency
2	////	4
3	//////	6
5	//	2
6	//	2
7	//	2
8	//	2
9	//	2
	Total	20

We should point out that modes often do not exist when dealing with small sample sizes. For example, if we randomly selected 5 students in your class and viewed their grades on the last exam, it would be unlikely that any grade will be repeated, hence no mode exists, or we may consider each grade as a mode. If no number repeats itself the modal interpretation will certainly be difficult.

Modes can be very important in describing nominal and ordinal levels of measurement. We might wish to know what automobile is purchased in the U.S. more than any other. From 1989–present, the Ford Taurus, the Toyota Camry, and the Honda Accord have been in a horserace for the most units sold. Toyota has won this award most recently. To claim this award requires the selling of more than 400,000 units annually.

As another example of the mode, we may wish to know the modal surname in the U.S. Since more individuals have the surname Smith, it is the modal surname.

The Relationship between the Arithmetic Mean, the Mode, and the Median

At this point we have described the arithmetic mean, the mode, and the median and stated that they all can be used to represent the typical value in a distribution. However, it is clear from most real world examples that the three measures of central tendency are usually not numerically equivalent. It is for this reason that the recommended practice is to generate all three of these measures of central tendency for a distribution. The relationship between the three statistics provides us with meaningful information about the shape of a distribution.

A distribution is said to be **symmetric** if there exists a value such that each side of the distribution about this value is a mirror image of the other. If the graph of a frequency distribution is symmetrical as shown in Figure 2.3, the mean, median, and mode are all equal. This should be intuitively plausible since the observation with the highest frequency (mode) in a symmetric distribution would also be the middle observation in terms of magnitude (median). Additionally, the arithmetic mean is in a sense a point of balance and in a symmetrical distribution would also equal the median and the mode. For example, the mean, median, and mode all equal 5. There are 9 distinct X values, with the middle value equal to 5. The 7 observations with a value of 6 are one larger than 5. However, the 7 observations with a value of 4 are one less then 5. Note that these 14 observations average 5. The same logic applies to 3 and 7, 2 and 8, and 1 and 9. Each of these pairs will average 5 since they are equally distanced above and below 5 (the point of balance) and since the distribution is symmetrical, each has the same number of observations.

Figure 2.3: Relationship Between the Mean, Median, and Mode in a Symmetrical Distribution Graphing the Following Data

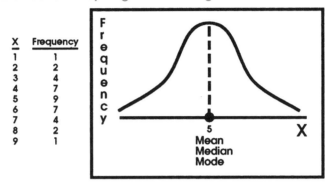

Asymmetric distributions are referred to as skewed. The mean, median, and mode are not equal in asymmetric distributions. Examples of skewed distributions are shown in Figure 2.4. If the distribution is skewed to the right, the long tail will be on the right side (upper) part of the distribution. In this case, the mean will exceed the median and the mode. However, if the distribution is skewed to the left, the mean will be less then the median and the mode. The reason for this is that the mean is affected by extreme values (often called outliers) and long tails in the distribution imply the existence of observations which are quite different from the rest. Thus, the extreme values "pull" the mean toward them. In severely skewed distributions the arithmetic mean is often an inappropriate measure of central tendency.

Let's use an example to illustrate the pull impact of extreme values. Your instructor randomly selects 10 students and asks for their previous year's earnings. The earnings are $10,000, $5000, $3000, $1000, $3000, $6000, $3000, $4000, $3000, $100,000. The mean = $13,800, the median = $3500, and the mode = $3000. Without the extreme income of $100,000, the mean = $4222, the median and the mode = $3000. The large extreme value has pulled the mean towards it.

As another example let's randomly select 9 students and record their grades: 76, 89, 68, 91, 76, 72, 78, 90, and 10. The mean = 72.2, the median and mode = 76. Without the extreme grade of 10, the mean = 80, the median and the mode = 76. Again note how the low outlier drew the mean to it.

Figure 2.4: Relationship Between the Mean, Median, and Mode in a Skewed
Distribution

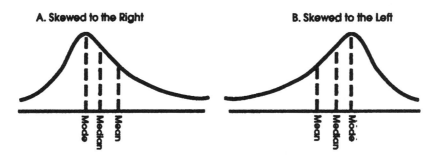

Obtaining the Mean, Median, and Mode with MINITAB

We will now review the MINITAB commands and output for the measure of central tendency. We will use our 45 student grades (X) as our example. Note that the computer output yields additional information which will be explained at a later time.

For the mean, trimmed mean, and the median the command sequence is:

Stat > Basic Statistics > Display Descriptive Statistics
Double click **grades** into **Variables** box.
OK

Descriptive Statistics: Grades (Table 2.3)

Variable	N	N*	Mean	SE Mean	TrMean	StDev	Minimum
Grades	45	0	73.91	1.70	73.61	11.42	50.00
Variable	Q1	Median	Q3	Maximum	Range	IQR	
Grades	65.00	75.00	80.00	100.00	50.00	15.00	

To have MINITAB yield the mode we use:

Stat > Tables > Tally
Double click **grades** into **Variables** box.
OK

 Concept Check 2.C

Since the mean, median, and mode are always equal, it makes no difference which statistic we choose to use as a measure of central tendency. True or False? If false, explain.

24

2.9   The list prices of six econometric microcomputer packages reviewed in the March 14, 1989 issue of *PC Magazine* are

Package	*Price$*
Lisrel and Prelis	460
Micro TSP	595
Soritec	595
ESP	795
PowerStation	895
Otis	995

   a.   Determine the (arithmetic) mean price.
   b.   Determine the median price.
   c.   Determine the mode.

2.10   What is skewness? How is skewness in a frequency distribution related to the relationship between the mean, median, and mode?

2.11   If you could have but one, which measure of central tendency would you prefer in the following examples? Explain your choice.

   a.   The incomes of physicians in your community.
   b.   The number of sick days taken by employees of a corporation.
   c.   The ages of students in a high school day class.

2.12   Define the median.

2.13   Define the mode.

2.14   Determine the median of the following data: 2, 8, 4, 9, 1, 5, 2, 8.

2.15   In contract negotiations, which measure of central tendency for workers' salaries would you expect management to use? What about union negotiators? Explain your answer.

2.16   Data set: 2, 4, 0, 1, 8, 7, 4, 5, 2, 5, 3, 2, 8, 2, 100
Compute the mean, median, and mode.
Which is the largest? Explain.

2.17   Data set: 93, 87, 75, 76, 81, 84, 70, 73, 75, 12
Compute the mean, median, and mode.
Which is the largest? Explain.

2.18   In terms of the ages of the students in your class, which would be the largest between the mean, median, and mode? Explain.

2.19   Data set: 1, 2, 2, 3, 3, 3, 2, 2, 1, 1
Compute the mean, median, and mode.
Which is the largest? Explain.

2.20   For the data set Grades.mtw have MINITAB compute the mean, trimmed mean, median, and mode for all five of the variables involved.

2.21   For the data set Scores.mtw have MINITAB compute the mean, trimmed mean, median, and mode for the variable height.

2.22   For the data set Camshaft.mtw have MINITAB compute the mean, trimmed mean, median, and mode for the variables snowfall and rain.

2.5   Measures of Dispersion or Variation

Measures of central tendency provide us with information regarding the location of a distribution but fail to reflect all that we need to know about distributions. As we have seen, measures of central tendency can frequently mislead rather than enlighten if they are interpreted out of context. Other characteristics of frequency distributions that are important are measures of **dispersion, skewness,** and **kurtosis**. Measures of dispersion or variation measure the departure of observations in the distribution from some central value such as the arithmetic mean. Measurement of skewness aims at describing the degree of symmetry in a frequency distribution. Measurement of kurtosis is designed to show the degree of peakedness in a distribution or the relative frequency of observations close to the central value.

Although the complete description of a frequency distribution requires measurement of all four characteristics; central tendency, variation, skewness, and kurtosis, it is only the first two characteristics which are critical for an introduction to statistical inference. For this reason, we will not further develop measures of skewness and kurtosis. Remember, if desired, MINITAB will produce a numeric value for kurtosis; the larger this value, the greater frequency of observations away from the mean and the lower the frequency of observations close to the mean.

The Range

The simplest measure of dispersion to compute and understand is the **range**. It is quite simply the difference between the maximum and minimum values in a frequency distribution. The range for the grade distribution in Table 2.3 is 50 (100–50) which provides some insight into the dispersion of observations about the arithmetic mean of 73.911. Thus, we now know that the mean grade in the class was 73.911 and that there was a 50-point spread between the highest and lowest grades.

The range is as easy to understand as it is to compute. However, its simplicity is also a disadvantage in that it only depends on two values in the frequency distribution; that is, the maximum and minimum values. Thus, given that the distribution has one or more extremely high or low values in a distribution, the range can exaggerate the dispersion in a distribution. Take for example the following data

2, 5, 7, 6, 5, 6, 7, 5, 6, 7, 6, 5, 7, 22

In this case the maximum value in the distribution is 22 and the minimum is 2. Therefore, the range is 20. However, further examination of the full distribution reveals that of the 14 observations 12 vary between 5 and 7. In this case the maximum and minimum values are quite different from the rest of the distribution and it would be inaccurate to use the range as the measure of dispersion for this distribution. Fortunately, there are other measures of dispersion or variation which remedy this deficiency in the range.

The Interquartile Range

The **interquartile range** is a measure of dispersion that is superior to the range since it is not influenced by a few extreme or unusually high or low values. However, before introducing the interquartile range we need to introduce **quartiles**.

We already know that the median for a distribution is the value that divides the distribution into two equal halves. Fifty percent of the observations are below the median and fifty percent are above. Quartiles serve the same role, but divide the distribution into four parts. The first quartile (Q1) has the characteristic that 25 percent of the observations in the distribution are smaller in value and 75 percent are larger. The second quartile (Q2) divides the distribution in half: 50 percent of the observations are lower and 50 percent of the observations are higher. Thus, the second quartile is equivalent to the median. In the same vein, seventy-five percent of the observations in a distribution are smaller than the third quartile (Q3) and 25 percent are larger.

Quartiles merely reflect positions in a distribution. However, the interquartile range measures variability or dispersion and is defined as the difference between the third and first quartiles (Q3 − Q1). The interquartile range is the spread between the observation for which 75 percent of the observations are smaller and the observation for which 25 percent are smaller. With the interquartile range one is effectively discarding the upper and lower 25 percent of a distribution and reporting the range of the interior 50 percent.

Let's use an example to illustrate the possible superiority of the interquartile range over the range.

Let's return to our data set of Table 2.3 where we recorded 45 student grades. The range of grades was 100 − 50 = 50. The median grade (Q2) was 75. Minitab also computed a Q1 of 65 and Q3 equal to 80. The interquartile range equals Q3 – Q1 (80.00 − 65.00) = 15.

While discussing quartiles it is probably expedient to mention **deciles** and **percentiles**. These concepts are similar to quartiles in purpose but divide the distribution into 10 and 100 equal parts, respectively. Many of you have already encountered percentiles, since these are often used to report performance on standardized exams. For example, if your test result states that you scored at the 84th percentile, that would mean that 84 percent of the people taking the exam scored lower than you and only 16 percent scored higher. A ranked distribution could also be broken up into ten equal parts by determining nine deciles. The first decile would be the value with 10 percent of the observations smaller in value and 90 percent larger. The ninth decile would be the observation such that 90 percent of the observations were smaller and 10 percent were larger. The other deciles would be interpreted analogously.

The Mean Absolute Deviation

The **mean absolute deviation,** unlike the range or the interquartile range, uses all of the observations in a distribution. It is the arithmetic mean of the absolute values of the deviations of each observation from the arithmetic mean of the distribution. It is the absolute value of the differences since the sum of the deviations about the arithmetic mean will equal 0.

The Mean Absolute Deviation

$$\text{MAD} = \frac{\Sigma |X_i - \overline{X}|}{n} \tag{2.3}$$

where

X_i = the observed values in the sample

n = the sample size

$\overline{X}$ = the sample arithmetic mean

As an example, we randomly select 7 students and record their respective grades (Table 2.8). The computational steps to compute the mean absolute deviation are also shown in Table 2.8.

The X's refer to the 7 student grades, X-bar is the arithmetic mean grade previously calculated, and the remaining two columns show the deviations of the observations from the mean and their absolute values, respectively. In this example, the mean absolute deviation is

$$\text{MAD} = \frac{62}{7} = 8.857$$

Thus, on average, the grades in the class deviate about (above and below) the mean (77) by approximately 8.875 points.

Table 2.8 Mean Absolute Deviation for Grades

X_i	$\overline{X}$	$(X_i - \overline{X})$	$|X_i - \overline{X}|$
76	77	−1	1
79	77	+2	2
59	77	−18	18
94	77	+17	17
65	77	−12	12
86	77	+9	9
80	77	+3	3
			$\Sigma = 62$

The mean absolute deviation provides a measure of dispersion that is both relatively simple to understand and calculate. However, the variance and the standard deviation, introduced next, are measures of dispersion that have algebraic properties that make them fundamental to the theoretical underpinnings of statistical inference. The mean absolute deviation does not provide a link to statistical inference. For this reason, the standard deviation of the variance are the most frequently used and reported statistics for data dispersion.

The Variance and Standard Deviation

The variance and standard deviation can be computed from population or sample data sets. The sample standard deviation and variance, represented respectively as s and s^2, provide estimates of their true or population counter parts. The population or, "true" standard deviation and variance are represented by the Greek character sigma, σ and σ^2, respectively. The **variance** and **standard deviation** use the squared differences of the observed values from their arithmetic mean as the basis for the measurement of dispersion. This avoids the difficulty encountered by the sum of the deviations being 0 and offers an alternative to the absolute values of the deviations as used in the mean absolute deviation. The variance is defined as the average sum of squared deviations from the arithmetic mean. The formula for the population variance and standard deviation is

The Population Variance

$$\sigma^2 = \frac{\Sigma(X_i - \mu)^2}{N} \tag{2.4}$$

The Population Standard Deviation

$$\sigma = \sqrt{\frac{\Sigma(X_i - \mu)^2}{N}} \tag{2.5}$$

where

X_i = the observed values in the population $(i = 1, 2, \ldots, N)$

N = the population size

μ = the population arithmetic mean

28

The sample variance and standard deviation, which provides an estimate of σ^2 and σ, is

---

The Sample Variance

$$s^2 = \frac{\Sigma(X_i - \overline{X})^2}{n - 1} \qquad (2.6)$$

The Sample Standard Deviation

$$s = \sqrt{\frac{\Sigma(X_i - \overline{X})^2}{n - 1}} \qquad (2.7)$$

where

X_i = the observed values in the sample

n = the sample size

$\overline{X}$ = the sample arithmetic mean

$n - 1$ = degrees of freedom

Note that the standard deviation is always the square root of the variance or the variance is the square of the standard deviation. Also the population standard deviation has as its denominator the number of observations in the population, N. However, as stated above, the formula for the sample standard deviation uses as its denominator the number of observations in the sample minus 1, or $n - 1$. There are two related explanations of why this is appropriate rather than the division by n. First, the sample standard deviation is an estimate of the true or population standard deviation. It can be shown that the sample standard deviation provides a better estimate of the true value when its divisor is $n - 1$. Secondly, to compute the sample standard deviation requires a knowledge of the arithmetic mean. Since we are interested in the sample standard deviation, we must assume that we only have sample data and do not know the true or population mean, μ. Since the sample data consisting of n observations must be used to calculate the sample mean *prior* to the computation of the sample standard deviation, one observation is effectively lost in the process.

For example, suppose we know that there are five observations in a sample and that the arithmetic mean of the five is 6. If we have knowledge of the values of any four observations, the fifth is predetermined. For instance suppose four of the observations are 2, 4, 6, and 8. What is the value of the missing fifth observation? Since the arithmetic mean of the 5 observations is known to be 6, then the sum of all 5 observations is 30. The 4 observations given sum to 20 (2 + 4 + 6 + 8). Thus, the missing observation must be 10. Again the computation of the variance requires knowledge of the arithmetic mean and this means that we lose a degree of freedom from our sample. It can also be shown that the adjustment of the denominator for the loss of a degree of freedom makes the sample standard deviation a "better" estimator of the population or true standard deviation.

Using the grade data from Table 2.8, the computational procedure for the variance is shown in Table 2.9. Column 1 in Table 2.9 lists the grades of the 7 students. Column 2 lists the arithmetic mean for the 7 students. Column 3 is derived by subtracting the arithmetic mean from each observation (column 1 − column 2). Column 4 is the square of column 3 and reflects the squared differences between each observation and the arithmetic mean. The sum of the 7 entries in column 4 equals 852 and provides the numerator for the variance. Thus, the variance is

$$s^2 = \frac{852}{6} = 142$$

Table 2.9 Variance and Standard Deviation for Grade Distribution Example

X_i	$\overline{X}$	$(X_i - \overline{X})$	$(X_i - \overline{X})^2$
76	77	-1	1
79	77	$+2$	4
59	77	-18	324
94	77	$+17$	289
65	77	-12	144
86	77	$+9$	81
80	77	$+3$	9
			$\Sigma = 852$

The variance, since it is based on an average sum of squares, is measured in units squared. Thus, if the units of measurement for X are feet, the variance is in feet squared. In the case of the grade example of Table 2.9 the units of measurement are grade points on a 0 to 100 scale. Thus, the variance for this example is measured in terms of squared grade points. Since it is difficult to interpret a measure of dispersion that is defined in terms of squared units, we introduce the standard deviation. The standard deviation is merely the (positive) square root of the variance. Since the variance is measured in squared units, its square root, the standard deviation, is measured in the original units for the variable, X.

In the grade example of Table 2.8, the standard deviation is

$$s = \sqrt{\frac{852}{6}} = \sqrt{142} = 11.916$$

The standard deviation, 11.916, is in the same units that grades and the arithmetic mean grade are measured. Thus, the arithmetic mean grade was 77 and the standard deviation is 11.916 points. If the standard deviation were larger (smaller) there would have been more (less) variability in grades. MINITAB will provide the sample standard deviation (StDev) when using the Stat > Basic Statistics > Descriptive Statistics prompts.

An Example Utilizing Standard Deviations

Suppose the company for which you work informs you that you are to receive a promotion, but must relocate to obtain it. You have a choice of moving to city A or B. You learn that both cities have a mean temperature of 72°. City A has $s = 1.0°$ while city B has an $s = 10.0°$. What information do we have?

What we know is the variation in temperature is much greater in City B, than in City A, which has a relatively constant temperature. Clearly our clothing and utility bills will be much greater in City B than for City A.

The Coefficient of Variation: A Measure of Relative Variability

The range, mean absolute deviation, standard deviation, and variance are all absolute measures of dispersion. To illustrate the difference between an absolute and a relative measure of dispersion, we introduce the **coefficient of variation**. Suppose we were interested in comparing the variability in the price of two stocks. Table 2.10 shows the prices of each stock for a 5-year period. Computing the standard deviation for each stock yields

Stock A

$$s_A = \sqrt{1000/4} = 15.81$$

Stock B

$$s_B = \sqrt{10/4} = 1.581$$

Table 2.10 Price of Two Stocks: 1986–1990

	1986	1987	1988	1989	1990
Stock A	100	110	130	120	140
Stock B	10	11	13	12	14

Since the standard deviation for stock A (15.81) is 10 times larger than the standard deviation of stock B (1.581) does that mean stock A is more variable? The answer is yes and no. Stock A is more variable in an absolute sense. However, the difference in the two standard deviations is related to the difference in the price levels of the stocks. Stock A in this case is always 10 times more expensive than stock B. We can adjust the measure of dispersion for differences in the size of each variable by dividing each standard deviation by the respective arithmetic means. Such a statistic is called the **coefficient of variation** and its definition is

The Coefficient of Variation

$$CV = s/\overline{X} \tag{2.8}$$

where

$s = $ the sample standard deviation

$\overline{X} = $ the sample arithmetic mean

The coefficients of variation for the two stocks are

$$CV_A = \frac{15.81}{120} = .13176$$

$$CV_B = \frac{1.581}{12} = .13176$$

The coefficients of variation are the same, indicating that, after adjusting for differences in the level of the units, the stock prices of each are equally dispersed. Therefore, if we want to compare the variability of two distinct distributions, we should use the coefficient of variation rather than an absolute measure, such as the standard deviation.

Overall, the smaller the value for the CV the less disperse the data set is. Obviously, if $s = 0$, regardless of $\overline{X}$, CV $= 0$. All the data points are identical; hence, no dispersion exists. The larger CV is refers to the data set being dispersed. Remember that larger means usually create larger differences between individual data points and the mean, hence large values for s. By dividing s by $\overline{X}$, it allows for a comparison between two dispersions without the distortion created by the fact that larger numbers usually create larger numerical standard deviations.

Concept Check 2.D

The variance is a measure of relative variation since it compares the average sum or squares about the arithmetic mean. True or false? If false, explain.

2.23   What is a measure of dispersion and what statistics have been developed in this chapter to measure this characteristic?

2.24   Define the range. Under what circumstances is the range a poor measure of dispersion?

2.25   Determine the range for the following sample data.

2, 5, 7, 9, 3, 6, 12, 2, 4, 7, 4, 8, 10, 5, 8, 9, 1, 8, 6, 4, 2, 1, 4, 5, 8, 2, 4

2.26   Define the mean absolute deviation. Why are the absolute values taken?

2.27   Determine the mean absolute deviation for the following sample data.

2, 4, 6, 8, 6, 4, 2

2.28   Define the variance. How is it related to the standard deviation?

2.29   Determine the variance and standard deviation for the following sample data.

2, 4, 6, 8, 10, 12, 14, 16, 18

2.30   Suppose your instructor gives you a pop quiz involving 1 true/false question. The instructor tells you that half the class obtained the correct answer and half did not; hence, the mean grade is 50.

    a.   Does this mean grade yield much information?
    b.   Are we able to determine the numerical value for s?

2.31   Define the coefficient of variation. What differentiates it from other measures of dispersion?

2.32   Determine the coefficient of variation for the data in Exercise 2.29.

2.33   Given the following information on the prices of two stocks, which is more risky (has the higher coefficient of variation)?

Period	1	2	3	4	5
Stock A	25	20	30	35	40
Stock B	4	6	2	8	5

2.34   For the data set Cap.mtw have MINITAB compute the standard deviation, Ql, Q3, and MAD.

2.35   For the data set Leaf.mtw have MINITAB compute the standard deviation, Q1, and Q3 for the data set HEIGHT.

2.36   For the data set Grades.mtw have MINITAB compute the mean, trimmed mean, median, and mode for all three of the variables involved.

2.6   Exploratory Data Analysis

Exploratory data analysis refers to a group of procedures used to pre-analyze data to ensure that there are no unusual observations or features that would adversely affect the fundamental statistical analysis that is planned. One of the primary functions of exploratory data analysis is to identify data **outliers**. An outlier is an unusual observation that lies far in the tail of the distribution. Frequently outliers can be determined by casually perusing the observation in a distribution. However, for large data sets mathematically defining outliers and computing a statistic that reflects how different a specific observation is from the others in the distribution is generally more convenient. Once an outlier is identified we should attempt to resolve why it is so different from the remainder of the distribution. In this process we often find coding and data entry errors, observations that just don't belong to the distribution, and outright lies in data reporting. However, often we cannot explain the anomaly and must devise our analysis so that the results are resistant to outliers.

One simple way to detect outlying observations is to determine the distance each observation is from the arithmetic mean of the distribution. However, the absolute distance between an observation and the mean is a function of the units of measurement. To standardize the difference we can divide by the standard deviation and express these differences in terms of number of standard deviations. The standardizing formula is

---

The Standardizing Formula

$$z = \frac{X_i - \overline{X}}{s} \tag{2.9}$$

where

X_i = the observed values in the sample

s = the sample standard deviation

$\overline{X}$ = the sample arithmetic mean

Thus, in the grade distribution of Table 2.3 the minimum and maximum grades were 50 and 100. The arithmetic mean was 73.911 and the standard deviation was 11.423. A grade of 50 is 2.09 standard deviations below the mean and a grade of 100 is 2.28 standard deviations above the mean as shown in the following calculations

$$z = \frac{50 - 73.911}{11.423} = -2.09 \qquad z = \frac{100 - 73.911}{11.423} = +2.28$$

We have seen the importance of the standard deviation and the mean in determining the dispersion of observations in a distribution and more will be said regarding this in Chapter 4. For now, let it suffice to say that an observation that is more than 3 standard deviations from the mean of a distribution is quite unusual. However, since the arithmetic mean and standard deviation are both substantially influenced by outliers, this technique is often of dubious value. We will present two graphical techniques, box plots and stem-and-leaf displays, used in exploratory data analysis and another alternative for the identification of outliers.

Box Plots

A graphical technique that is also used to identify outliers is the box plot. The box plot provides a pictorial representation of the distribution. Figure 2.5 shows a box plot generated with MINITAB for the grade data of Table 2.3. The graph includes the box plus lines (whiskers) emanating from the left and the right sides of the box.

The MINITAB commands and output are:

Graph > Boxplot
Double click **grades** into **Y** box.
OK

33

Figure 2.5 Box plot of grades (Table 2.3)

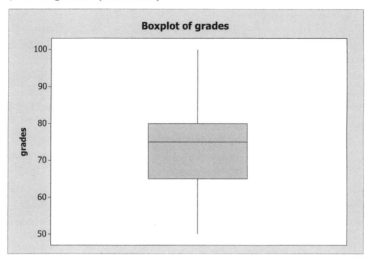

A box plot shows the following information:

1. The minimum and maximum values; for this example, 50 and 100, respectively. These are shown graphically as the left and right endpoints of the horizontal lines.

2. The range—the difference between the maximum and minimum values. In this case, 50 (100 −50).

3. The median—shown by the horizontal line in the box. Although the median is not identified numerically, its relative position in the distribution is easily identified. Without measuring, we can see that the median grade is roughly halfway between 50 and 100 or approximately 75.

4. The first quartile (Q1)—shown by the bottom of the box.

5. The third quartile (Q3)—shown by the top of the box.

6. The interquartile range—the horizontal length of the box, i.e., Q3 − Q1.

7. Degree and direction of skewness—shown by the location of the box in the graph. In other words, the more the box is located to the top or bottom, the greater the skewness in the distribution.

8. Outliers—are defined as any observations

$$\text{greater than, } Q3 + 1.5(Q3 − Q1)$$

or

$$\text{less than, } Q1 − 1.5(Q3 − Q1).$$

Stem-and-Leaf Displays

The stem-and-leaf display is the final of four alternatives when graphing a single variable. There are three columns of data. The first is called the **depths** which will be explained last. The second column is the **stem** and the final column is the **leaf**. For example the first stem shown is a 5 and the first leaf is a 0. This means our lowest grade is a 50. The second lowest grade is a 58 and the third a 59. We then see that there are three grades of 60. The first column gives us a cumulative picture. There is 1 grade between 50–54. There are 3 grades less than 60 and there are 10 grades less than 65. Where we see the number in a parentheses, this indicates Q2 or the median (11) and that there are 11 observations between 75–79. When our sample size equals 45, the median is the 23rd number (median = 75). Between the grades 50–74 there are 22 students, and in the interval involving the median 75–79 there are 11 students. That's

34

a total of 33 students. On the next depth we see 12 which is 45 – 33. And the analysis completes in this manner.

 Graph > Stem-and-Leaf
Double click **grades** into **Variables** box.
OK

Figure 2.6 Character stem-and-leaf display of grades (Table 2.3)

Stem-and-Leaf of grade   N = 45
Leaf Unit = 1.0

1	5	0
3	5	89
10	6	0002234
17	6	5577788
22	7	00123
(11)	7	55556677899
12	8	0014
8	8	8899
4	9	13
2	9	
2	10	00

The stem-and-leaf plot is a very simple but effective way of displaying the characteristic of a distribution. It shows the frequencies for each unique value, frequencies for intervals, skewness, location, and dispersion of a distribution. It is no wonder that it has become so popular in recent years.

 Concept Check 2.E

An outlier is a data point much like all others; hence, it is hard to detect. True or false? If false, explain.

Exercises

2.37   An employer is concerned about the salary distribution in his firm and has decided to determine if there are any unusual salaries. Based on the salary data and no further analysis, what do you think?

Employee	Salary (000's)
A	23
B	34
C	12
D	32
E	37
F	28
G	34
H	36
I	38
J	72

35

2.38   Use MINITAB to construct a box plot for the salary data in Exercise 2.37. Can outliers be determined by the examination of this plot? Explain.

2.39   Based on exercise 2.37, how many standard deviations is Employee A's salary from the mean salary?

2.40   Using the data from Exercise 2.37, compute the z score (standardized value) for Employee J's salary. What does this value tell you?

2.41   Using the number of employees data from exercise 2.37, generate a stem-and-leaf plot with MINITAB. What does the plot tell you about the distribution?

2.42   Data set: 2, 4, 0, 1, 8, 7, 4, 5, 2, 5, 3, 2, 8, 2, 100
        How many standard deviations above the mean is the data point 100?

2.43   Data set: 93, 87, 75, 76, 81, 84, 70, 73, 75, 12
        How many standard deviations above the mean is the data point 100?

2.44   Suppose that your class had an exam whose mean was 80 and for which you received a score of 95. Suppose the standard deviation of scores was either 5 or 15. Under which standard deviation would your score be the greatest achievement?

2.7   Summary

This chapter has introduced methods for describing characteristics of data. We discussed the concepts of central tendency and dispersion. These characteristics of data distributions can be analyzed either graphically or numerically. In the case of graphical depiction of data distributions, all four characteristics of distributions can be observed using graphical techniques developed in this chapter. However, other graphical techniques will be developed in the remaining chapters where they are most appropriate. These distributional characteristics can also be described numerically through the generation of statistics. In the case of statistics, only measures of central tendency and dispersion were developed. The arithmetic mean and the standard deviation were discussed at length and will provide the foundations for many of the chapters in the rest of the text.

 Mini-case 2.1: Salary Structure Reviews

A periodic review of salary structure within an organization is always good practice for owners or managers. The review can identify potential salary inequities before they lead to other personnel problems. Suppose a particular organization has 20 employees all performing the same function and earning the salaries listed below.

Employee	Salary (000)	Employee	Salary (000)
1	14.5	11	14.5
2	17.8	12	18.4
3	20.3	13	19.2
4	10.3	14	11.6
5	18.5	15	7.4
6	38.3	16	17.5
7	21.4	17	24.5
8	17.3	18	34.2
9	15.9	19	23.5
10	23.7	20	16.8

a. Use a stem-and-leaf plot to evaluate the salaries of the 20 employees.
b. Determine the mean, median, and mode for the salary data and comment on the results.

Mini-case 2.2: A Company Lightens Up

If a company were to attempt to replace its most tenured personnel with younger persons in order not to have to pay retirement benefits, which common measure of central tendency for the distribution of employee salaries would most likely respond quickest to the change?

Mini-case 2.3: Misleading Information with a Bar Graph

We view the bar graph of Figure 2.7 where we compare prospective returns from investment portfolios. Which return is greater?

Figure 2.7: Bar Graph for Returns from investment A and B

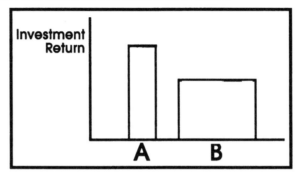

Review of Important Terms and Concepts

Frequency distribution: Tabular or graphical display depicting the number of observations in a data set taking on certain values or falling into each of the classifications or categories.

Relative frequency: The number of observations in a data class divided by the total number of observations in the data set. It is the percent of data in a specified class.

Cumulative frequency and ogive: A cumulative frequency distribution yields the percent of all data below a specified value, and the ogive is the visual graph of the cumulative distribution.

Measure of central tendency: A measure which describes the general location or position of a data set. These measures are designed to typify or represent a set of observations.

Measure of variability: A measure of the dispersion or spread in a distribution.

Arithmetic mean: A popular measure of central tendency. It is obtained by summing all values on X, from the first to the nth, and dividing this result by the number of observations, n.

Median: A measure of central tendency unaffected by extreme values. It is the middle value in a ranked or ordered array of the observations. Thus, 50 percent of the remaining observations are above the median in value, and 50 percent of the remaining observations are below the median.

Mode: A measure of central tendency. It is the value or values with the highest frequency of occurrence.

Symmetric distribution: A distribution is said to be symmetric if there exists a value such that each side of the distribution about this value is a mirror image of the other. If not, the distribution is said to be asymmetric.

Range: A measure of dispersion. It is the difference between the maximum and minimum values in a distribution.

Measures of Dispersion or variation: Statistics that measure the departure of observations in the distribution from some central value such as the arithmetic mean.

Skewness: A characteristic of a frequency distribution. It measures the degree that a frequency distribution departs from being symmetric.

Kurtosis: A characteristic of a frequency distribution. It measures the degree of peakedness in a distribution or the relative frequency of deviations close to the central value.

Mean absolute deviation: A measure of dispersion. It is the arithmetic mean of the absolute values of the deviations of each observation from the arithmetic mean of the distribution.

Coefficient of variation: A measure of relative dispersion or variation. It is the ratio of the standard deviation and the arithmetic mean.

Quartiles: Values that separate a distribution into four segments each containing 25 percent of the total number of observations. The first quartile establishes a point such that the 25 percent of the observations in the distribution are below it. The second and third quartiles pick up successively the next 25 percent of the observations in value.

Deciles and percentiles: Values that are similar to quartiles but divide the distribution into 10 and 100 equal parts, respectively.

Review of Important Formulas

The Population Mean	**The Sample Mean**
$\mu = \dfrac{\Sigma X_i}{N}$ (2.1)	$\overline{X} = \dfrac{\Sigma X_i}{n}$ (2.2)

where

X_1 = the numeric observations in the population/sample ($i = 1, 2, \ldots N$)

N = population size: n = sample size (the number of observations)

Σ = the summation operator

The Mean Absolute Deviation

$$\text{MAD} = \frac{\Sigma |X_i - \overline{X}|}{n} \qquad (2.3)$$

where

X_i = the observed values in the sample

n = the sample size

$\overline{X}$ = the sample arithmetic mean

The Population Variance

$$\sigma^2 = \frac{\Sigma(X_i - \mu)^2}{N} \qquad (2.4)$$

The Population Standard Deviation

$$\sigma = \sqrt{\frac{\Sigma(X_i - \mu)^2}{N}} \qquad (2.5)$$

where

X_i = the observed values in the population ($i = 1, 2, \ldots, N$)

N = the population size

μ = the population arithmetic mean

The Sample Variance

$$s^2 = \frac{\Sigma(X_i - \overline{X})^2}{n-1} \qquad (2.6)$$

The Sample Standard Deviation

$$s = \sqrt{\frac{\Sigma(X_i - \overline{X})^2}{n-1}} \qquad (2.7)$$

where

X_i = the observed values in the sample

n = the sample size

$\overline{X}$ = the sample arithmetic mean

$n - 1$ = degrees of freedom

The Coefficient of Variation

$$CV = s/\overline{X} \qquad (2.8)$$

where

s = the sample standard deviation

$\overline{X}$ = the sample arithmetic mean

The Standardizing Formula

$$z = \frac{X_i - \overline{X}}{s} \qquad (2.9)$$

where

X_i = the observed values in the sample

s = the sample standard deviation

X = the sample arithmetic mean

MINITAB commands for frequency or counts.

Stat > Tables > Tally
Double click **grades** into **Variables** box.
OK

MINITAB commands to develop a professional histogram.

Graph > Histogram
Double click **grades** into **Graph Variable** box.
OK

MINITAB commands to develop a cumulative histogram.

Graph > Histogram
Double click **grades** into **Graph Variable** box.
Click on **Options**.
Click on **Cumulative Frequency**.
OK twice.

MINITAB commands for measures of central tendency and dispersion.

State > Basic Statistics > Display Descriptive Statistics
Double click grades into **Variables** box.
OK

MINITAB commands for boxplots.

Graph > Boxplot
Double click **grades** into Variables box.
OK

MINITAB commands for stem-and-leaf analysis.

Graph > Stem-and-Leaf
Double click **grades** into **Variables** box.
OK

Introduction to Probability Concepts

Where we have been

We have completed an analysis of descriptive statistics, measures of central tendency, and measures of dispersion.

Where we are going

In building the foundations for later chapters it is necessary to introduce some basic concepts of probability. All statistical inference rests on the foundations of probability. Thus, we must first learn the language and methods of probability theory. However, another reason to introduce probability theory is that most decisions are made in an environment in which outcomes are far from certain. For these decisions the use of probability to sort through the possibilities is virtually a necessity.

Our lives are continually altered by probabilities. We use them to determine what garments we will wear (weather), in whether we should study for a possible upcoming quiz, and whether we should do preventative maintenance on our automobile. We assess the probabilities of an event occurring and the subsequent consequences if it does occur. We evaluate this information and then we make decisions. Sometimes the consequence can be so great that it overshadows the odds. For example, we know the probability of our getting into a car accident is not great, yet not to carry automobile insurance is foolhardy.

Because of the importance of the concept of probability, we will devote significant space and attention to some of the important concepts and theories. However, we only cover these topics in such depth and breadth as to facilitate an understanding of the other topics in the text.

3.1   Introduction

The term "probability" implies doubt or uncertainty in the occurrence of an event. Let it suffice to say at this point that the probability of an event is the degree of belief that the decision maker has in the occurrence of an event. This degree of belief could be based on objective or purely subjective information known to the decision maker. If a friend were to ask you to study after class for an upcoming quiz, you might reply "I will meet you after the class." If you replied "I probably will meet you after the class," there is now an interjection of doubt.

Once doubt has been established, the next question to be ascertained is "how great is this doubt." Probability attempts to deal with quantifying the doubt involved, allowing the decision maker to make a formal analysis of the options and come to a rational decision. It is hoped that an optimal decision would be made with a greater frequency than had probability theory not been utilized.

Dealing with uncertainty consumes a great deal of our professional and personal lives. We do not have to take proper care of our automobiles; hence, we postpone preventative maintenance knowing the probabilities for car failure have just increased. Our boss gives us an assignment at the same time the instructor of this class has assigned a major exam. You assess that the probability of successfully accomplishing both tasks, given the time constraints, is small. You must decide to spend less time on both, or less time on one. The decision will be based on a judgment as to which task's performance will decline the greatest with the reduced effort. If the student believes that studying less on the exam will reduce that grade from an A to a C, and that a poor or average business project will mean a loss of the job, the student may opt to spend less time on the exam.

Probability theory enhances our ability to understand the range of decisions available to us and the possible ramifications of those decisions. We are better able to assess the odds or to weigh alternatives in a manner consistent with known probability rules.

It will be valuable at this time to review some important terms concerning probability theory. We usually use the term experiment to refer to any activity or process that leads to one of several possible outcomes that cannot be predicted with certainty. We might refer to a coin-toss experiment, a deck of cards experiment, or an experiment involving future weather conditions, etc. Each experiment has one or more possible outcomes, which is some observation or measurement that can't be subdivided. In flipping a coin the outcome will be either a head or tail. In selecting a card from a deck there can be 1 of 4 suits (hearts, spades, clubs, or diamonds), or 1 of 13 faces (one, two, three, etc.), or 1 of 52 cards.

An event is a collection of one or more outcomes. Hence, selecting the ace of spades from a deck of cards is an outcome. However, selecting any jack is referred to as an event, since it includes four outcomes: the jack of hearts, spades, clubs, and diamonds.

The set of all the possible outcomes of an experiment is called the sample space (S). The sample space for a coin tossing and for a die tossing experiment is

S = {Head, Tail}
S = {One, Two, Three, Four, Five, Six}

Events are **mutually exclusive** if only one can occur during a given experiment. For example, most students prefer to have tests that contain mutually exclusive content in their classes. Thus, if a chapter subject matter is tested on one exam, it will not occur on any other exam. When the sample space includes all possible events from an experiment, the sample space is termed **collectively exhaustive**. Students will normally be classified as being a freshman, sophomore, junior, or senior, and their registration priority may be based on the classification. You will not be classified into more than one category.

 Concept Check 3.A

Dealing with uncertainty is one of the most important duties of modern day managers. True or false? If false, explain.

3.1   Explain the difference between the two following statements:

      a.   We will be going to dinner tonight.
      b.   We will probably be going to dinner tonight.

3.2   We believe that a relationship exists between smoking and lung cancer. Explain how probability might aid in such a determination.

3.3   Explain the term mutually exclusive in your own words.

3.4   Explain the term collectively exhaustive in your own words.

3.5   Which of the following are mutually exclusive when drawing two cards from a deck of cards?

      a.   An even numbered card and a club.
      b.   A heart and a club.
      c.   A heart and a king.
      d.   A heart and an odd numbered card.
      e.   A heart and the ace of clubs.

3.6   What is the collectively exhaustive set of possible outcomes from rolling a fair die?

3.2   The Probability Categories

We will now review the basic probability categories. We remind you that the probability of obtaining any event (E_i) on an experiment is between 0 and 1.0, including 0 and 1.0. In addition, the sum of all the possible experiment outcomes equals 1. Hence the probability of obtaining either a head or a tail on a coin toss is 1.0 (.5 +.5). These two rules are written as follows:

1. $0 \le \Pr(E_i) \le 1$, where E_i = any event
2. $\Pr(E_1) + \Pr(E_2) + \bullet\bullet\bullet + \Pr(E_k) = \Sigma \Pr(E_i) = 1$, where k = number of events

There are three ways of categorizing probabilities. Each represents a different thought process and each has merit. The three categories are

- The classical approach
- The relative frequency approach
- The subjective approach

The Classical Approach

The classical approach is simplistic in the sense that the probabilities associated with the events of an experiment are known in advance (termed a prior probability). Before we flip a fair coin or roll a die we know the outcome probabilities. For a fair coin we know there are two outcomes, and that heads or tails has a .5 probability of occurring. Also, for a fair die, we know there is a 1/6 chance of obtaining any face. No experiment need be performed to determine these event probabilities. In general, these probabilities are simply r/n, where r equals the number of successes and n equals all the possible outcomes from the experiment (collectively exhaustive). In many instances the outcomes are equally likely; hence, the probability involved is $1/n$.

The Relative Frequency Approach

Most decision makers will not be able to ascertain in advance the probabilities of events taking place. Will interest rates be going up, down, or remain the same over the next several months? What are the probabilities of my contracting the flu this year? What is the probability of my getting into a minor car accident over the next few years? What is the probability that the world will enter another ice age?

Some of these questions might be answered by the relative frequency approach. If we kept accurate records for a considerable time period, we might find that .054 of the individuals in your age category have contracted the flu over the last 10 years. This figure would be obtained simply by counting the number of flu cases in your age category, and dividing by the total number of individuals involved. Hence, we may conclude that over the last 10 years 5.4% of your age category contracted the flu and that this trend will continue into the future. If this is the case, we might estimate that the probability of your contracting the flu is 5.4%. The relative frequency is converted into a probability.

Two factors must be considered in using a relative frequency. First there must be a rather large sample involved. We would not want to sample 10 individuals to find 3 had the flu in your age category. A large enough sample is required to render the probabilities meaningful. If we tossed a fair coin 10 times, we should not expect to see 5 heads and 5 tails. This is but one possible outcome. The .5 figure relates to flipping the coin an infinite number of times, in which the probabilities of heads or tails should approach .5.

The second factor to be considered is that the relative frequency statistics must be obtained in stable or consistent conditions. In our example, influenza epidemics occur sporadically. Does our 5.4% relate to these epidemic years, to the non-outbreak years, or to all years (combining the two)? If an epidemic is expected this year, what are the probabilities? Alternatively, if we use past interest rates to predict the probabilities for increases in interest rates, are the same forces in effect that caused previous rises? These are questions that must be answered in order for the probabilities to have meaning.

Insurance companies use information of this type to determine that the probability of an accident for drivers less than 20 years of age are considerably higher than for drivers 20 years of age or over. Hence, youthful drivers must pay higher premiums. It is unfortunate that some extremely careful drivers are grouped in this high risk category. Yet it is impossible to find demographics that would isolate these careful drivers.

Subjective Probability Approach

We frequently use subjective judgment to assign probabilities to outcomes. We might find it difficult to have the time to study properly for an upcoming business statistics exam. So we might just study what are considered to be the major concepts. We then may assign a subjective probability (as opposed to an objective probability in the classical or relative frequency approach) that there is a 5% chance for an A, a 15% chance for a B, 30% chance for a C or D, and a 20% chance for an F grade. These probabilities may in fact be based on an informal relative frequency covering our college career. There will have been many exams we will have taken without being fully prepared. However, since we have not kept an accurate record of all such occurrences, we are merely guessing at the relative frequencies involved. In addition, what happened in other classes in the past might not be relevant to the current business statistics class.

These subjective probabilities should not be taken lightly as they may be the result of a careful logical thought process. Unfortunately, this thought process usually has not been tested to determine its legitimacy under a variety of conditions.

We use subjective probabilities every day to allocate our time. If you think there is a good chance that your instructor will give a quiz during the next lecture, will you reallocate your time to include studying?

 Concept Check 3.B

In many instances, a subjective probability would probably be based on relative frequencies of extremely small sample sizes. True or false? If false, explain.

3.7 State whether you believe the following probabilities are classical, relative frequency, or subjective:

a. The probability of tossing three consecutive heads is .125.
b. The probability that a professional football team will win its next game is .39.
c. The probability of a male driver between the ages of 18 and 25 getting into at least one traffic accident is .29.
d. The probability of your instructor giving you a pop quiz during the next class meeting is .4.
e. The probability of individuals who have smoked for more than ten years developing breathing problems is .33.

3.8 State whether you believe the following probabilities are classical, relative or subjective:

a. The probability that it will rain tomorrow.
b. The probability that the surf tomorrow will be suitable for surfing.
c. The probability that a student entering college with an SAT score of 1050 and a high school grade point of 3.1 will be accepted into the institution.

3.9 A politician wishes to know how her constituency feels concerning capital punishment. She has her staff conduct a random survey with the following results:

	Frequency
Strongly Support Capital Punishment	213
Mildly Support Capital Punishment	115
Mildly Opposed to Capital Punishment	98
Strongly Opposed to Capital Punishment	318
Total	744

a. What is the probability that constituents are mildly opposed to capital punishment?
b. What is the probability for constituents who have strong feelings either for or against?
c. Would the above probabilities be considered classical, relative frequency, or subjective probabilities?

3.10 A building has 3 functioning elevators. During the last year security has determined the number of days the elevators have been inoperative, which is as follows:

	Days Operative	*Days Inoperative*
Elevator 1	310	55
Elevator 2	343	22
Elevator 3	299	66

a. What is the probability of elevator 1 being out of service on any given day?
b. What is the probability of elevator 3 being out of service on any given day?
c. Assuming that on only one day were two elevators out, what is the probability of one elevator being out any day?

3.11 A Fortune 100 company does business with 5 accounting firms. Firms A, B, and C are considered to be among the Big 8 accounting firms. Over the last few years the amount of times each firm was consulted is:

Firm	*Frequency*
Firm A	162
Firm B	189
Firm C	42
Firm D	619
Firm E	100

a. What is the probability that the next firm used will be a Big 8 firm?

b. What is the probability that the next firm contacted will be firm D?

3.12 A Fortune 100 company has opened a number of major and minor branch offices around the world. The actual number is

	Major Branches	Minor Branches
Europe	21	192
Asia	35	410
South America	9	71
North America	18	41

a. What is the probability that the next major branch will be opened in Europe?

b. What is the probability that the next minor branch will be opened in Asia?

c. What is the probability that the next branch to be opened will be a major branch?

3.3 Probability Concepts Involving Rules of Addition

Sometimes we wish to know the probability of a single event occurring, such as event A. This is symbolically represented as Pr(A), or the probability of event A occurring. If only a single event can take place, our probability is often referred to as a marginal probability or an unconditional probability.

Rules of Addition

The Addition Rule for Mutually Exclusive Events

If we were tossing a die, we know the probability of obtaining any face on a cube is 1/6. Statisticians often illustrate probability concepts with the aid of Venn diagrams. These diagrams are named after the famous English mathematician, John Venn, and allow for an easy visual interpretation of probability concepts. Venn diagrams refer to areas, and probabilities behave similarly to areas. Events refer to parts of the rectangle. If events overlap (Figure 3.1A), they are not mutually exclusive. If events do not overlap, they are mutually exclusive (Figure 3.1B). The entire rectangle in the Venn diagram has a probability of 1. Remember that the probability of any event occurring is $Pr(0 \leq E_i \leq 1)$. For the dice throwing example, the six faces of a die are depicted as 6 mutually exclusive blocks. The probability of obtaining any single face is 1 out of 6 (Figure 3.1C). The probability of obtaining two mutually exclusive events (Figure 3.1D), such as obtaining a 1 (event A) or 6 face (event B) on a cube is as follows:

The Addition Rule for Mutually Exclusive Events

$$Pr(A \text{ or } B) = Pr(A) + Pr(B) \tag{3.1}$$

where

Pr(A or B) = the probability of events A or B occurring

Pr(A) and Pr(B) = the probability of events A and B occurring

---

For our example of tossing either a 1-face or a 6-face is

$$Pr(A \text{ or } B) = \frac{1}{6} + \frac{1}{6} = \frac{1}{3}$$

The probability of tossing either a 1-, 2-, or 3-face is

$$Pr(A \text{ or } B \text{ or } C) = \frac{1}{6} + \frac{1}{6} + \frac{1}{6} = \frac{1}{2}$$

Note that the probability of an event occurring [(Pr(A)], plus the probability Event A will not occur, which is symbolically written as Pr(not A), equals 1.

$$\text{Pr(A)} + \text{Pr(not A)} = 1; \text{ or Pr(A)} = 1 - \text{Pr(not A)}$$

Not A is called the complement of event A (often symbolically expressed as $\overline{A}$). As an example, the probability of tossing a one-face on a die is 1/6 [Pr(1-face) = 1/6], while the probability of not tossing a one-face is 5/6 [Pr(2or3or4or5or6) = 5/6].

Figure 3.1 Venn Diagrams Plus the Addition Rule for Mutually Exclusive Events

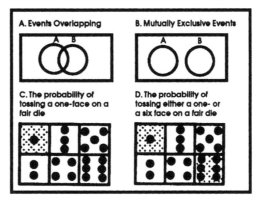

The Addition Rule for Events That Are Not Mutually Exclusive

When the two events involved are not mutually exclusive, there will be an overlapping on the Venn diagram. If the two events involved are A and B, we will either be interested in the probability of A or B occurring or in the probability of A and B occurring. If we want to know the probability of A and B occurring simultaneously, we call our probability a joint probability. Hence, a joint probability involves the overlapping area in the intersection of events A and B, and involves the likelihood that two events will happen concurrently (see Figure 3.2).

However, if we want to know the probability of either event A or event B occurring, we want the set of all sample points in event space A, event space B, or in the combination of A and B.

The dice example does not relate to unions because the events are mutually exclusive. However, suppose we wanted to know the probability of selecting a heart (Event A) and a jack (Event B) from a deck of cards. These events are not mutually exclusive as there is one card that is both a heart and a jack (Figure 3.2A). This combined occurrence makes the probability concepts slightly more difficult. It would not be wise to use the formula Pr(A) + Pr(B) because one card would be counted twice. Hence, this double counting must be taken into consideration. If it was counted twice, it must be subtracted from the result once; hence, the formula for the union of two events is

The Addition Rule for Events That Are Not Mutually Exclusive

$$\text{Pr(A or B)} = \text{Pr(A)} + \text{Pr(B)} - \text{Pr(A \& B)} \tag{3.2}$$

where

Pr(A or B) = the union of events A and B

Pr(A) = the probability of A

Pr(B) = the probability of B

$\text{Pr(A \& B)}$ = the joint probability of A and B happening

47

In our card example

$$\Pr(A \text{ or } B) = \frac{13}{52} + \frac{4}{52} - \frac{1}{52} = \frac{16}{52} = \frac{4}{13}$$

Figure 3.2 The Pr(A or B) and Pr(A & B) of Hearts and Jacks

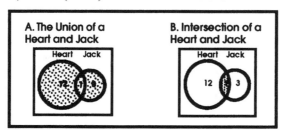

Another example may be fruitful in ascertaining the difference between Pr(A or B) and Pr(A & B). Often market researchers carefully analyze the cross tabulations from consumer surveys. Suppose you were evaluating the results from a consumer survey that asked 10 consumers their age and whether they had ever used a particular product before (Table 3.1).

Table 3.1 Survey Results from 10 Consumers

Age	Use Product?	Age	Use Product?
41	yes	16	no
68	yes	33	no
25	no	48	yes
17	no	53	yes
46	yes	21	yes

Let's say that we want to know the probability of being over 30 years of age (Event A) and having tried the products (Event B). Are we involved with Pr(A or B) or Pr(A & B)? If we want Pr(A & B), a joint probability, we want only those that are both over 40 and who use the product [Pr(A & B) = 5/10 = .5]. If we want the Pr(A or B), the probability is

$$\Pr(40 + \text{ or Used Product}) = \frac{5}{10} + \frac{6}{10} - \frac{5}{10} = \frac{6}{10}$$

Note that without the subtracting for the double counting, the subset exceeds the sample space, or the probability exceeds 1.

In many probability problems the data set is arranged as a **contingency table**, which is a data set that is arranged and defined by the number of rows and the number of columns. We will rearrange Table 3.1 into a 2 × 2 contingency table (Table 3.2) denoted by 2 rows and 2 columns. Note that the number of rows is always given prior to the number of columns. Hence a 4 × 7 contingency table has 4 rows and 7 columns. The (A) symbol represents the number in the survey who are 40+ years of age. The (not A) represents the number in the survey who are ≤ 40 years of age. The (B) symbol represents the number in the survey who have used the product in the past, and (not B) those who have not used the product.

Table 3.2 A 2 × 2 Contingency Table for Data of Table 3.1

	B	not (B)	Totals
(A)	5	0	5
not(A)	1	4	5
Totals	6	4	10

48

The event probability Pr(A) equals 5/10, which can be found by reading the margin for (A) and dividing by the total. This is how the term marginal probability originated. The probabilities are ascertained in the margin. The marginal probability of (not B) is read in the margin as 4/10.

Note that within the body of the table are the overlapping of events. For example, the Pr(A & B) = 5/10, Pr(A & not B) = 0/10, Pr(not A & B) = 1/10, and Pr(not A & not B) = 4/10. The sum of all possible joint probabilities sums to 1 (.5 + 0 + .1 + .4).

 Concept Check 3.C

For two mutually exclusive events (A and B) their overlapping could involve double counting. True or False? If false, explain.

Exercises

3.13   In your own words explain the difference between Pr(A or B) and Pr(A & B).

3.14   a.   In your own words explain the term marginal probability.
        b.   How did the term originate?

3.15   a.   What is the probability of selecting a king or a queen from a deck of cards?
        b.   The probability of selecting a king or a club?
        c.   The probability of selecting a king and a club?

3.16   a.   What is the probability of selecting a king, a queen, or a jack from a deck of cards?
        b.   The probability of a single card selection being a king, a queen, and a jack from a deck of cards?

3.17
Events	(B)	(not B)
(A)	12	18
(not A)	41	19

        a.   Based on the information supplied, what is the marginal probability of event (A)?
        b.   The marginal probability of event (not B).
        c.   The joint probability of events (A) and (not B).
        d.   Determine Pr(A | not B).

3.18
Events	(B)	(not B)
(A)	82	18
(not A)	41	99

        a.   Based on the information supplied, what is the marginal probability of event (A)?
        b.   The marginal probability of event (not B).
        c.   The joint probability of events (A) and (not B).
        d.   Determine Pr(A | not B).

3.19
Events	(A)	(not A)
(B)	100	400
(not B)	600	200

        a.   What is the marginal probability of (not A)?
        b.   What is the marginal probability of (not B)?
        c.   What is the joint probability of (not A) and (B)?
        d.   Determine Pr(not A | B).

3.20
Events	(A)	(not A)
(B)	800	400
(not B)	600	400

a. What is the marginal probability of (not A)?
b. What is the marginal probability of (not B)?
c. What is the joint probability of (not A) and (B)?
d. Determine Pr(not A | B).

3.4   Probability Concepts Involving Rules of Multiplication

Dependent and Independent Events

Before reviewing the rules of multiplication of events, we must distinguish between dependent and independent events. If we are involved with more than one event, we must answer the question as to whether they are independent or dependent. For two events, if the outcome of one influences the outcome of the other, they are termed dependent events. On the other hand, if the outcome of one event has no bearing on the outcome of another event, they are termed independent.

An example might help illustrate the point. Suppose we have two coins in a container; one is a regular coin with a head and a tail, while the other is a two-headed coin. We will randomly select one of the coins and experiment with it by tossing it. Will the coin we randomly select (event A) influence the probability of tossing a tail (event B)? In this instance, event A influences the outcome of event B; hence, the events are dependent. If we select the fair coin, we have a 50% probability of tossing a tail, while if we selected the two-headed coin the probability of a tail is 0. However, if in our container there were two fair coins, then the random selection of one of the coins (Event A) does not influence the probability of tossing a tail; hence, independence exists.

Probabilities Involving Independent Events

Joint Probabilities

For independent events the joint probability is stated as:

Joint Probabilities for Independent Events

$$Pr(A \& B) = Pr(A) \bullet Pr(B) \qquad\qquad (3.3)$$

where

$Pr(A \& B) =$ the joint probability of events A and B occurring

$Pr(A) =$ the marginal probability of event A occurring

$Pr(B) =$ the marginal probability of event B occurring

Let's refer to our coin tossing example to illustrate the joint probability for independent events. Here we have two fair coins in a container, and we randomly select one coin (Event A) and experiment by tossing it (Event B). The probability of tossing a tail is

$$Pr(A \& B) = 1/2 \bullet 1/2 = 1/4 = .25$$

Conditional Probability for Independent Events

In addition to marginal and joint probabilities, there is the conditional probability. Symbolically it is written as

$$Pr(A \,|\, B)$$

or the probability of event A given that event B has already occurred. The events are related sequentially. The "|" symbol replaces the word given. The conditional probability formula is different for independent and dependent events.

The conditional probability formula for independent events is

---

The Conditional Probability for Independent Events

$$Pr(A \mid B) = Pr(A)^*$$ (3.4A)

or

$$Pr(B \mid A) = Pr(B)^*$$ (3.4B)

where

$Pr(A \mid B)$ = the conditional probability of event A given event B has occurred

$Pr(A)$ = the probability of event A

$Pr(B \mid A)$ = the conditional probability of event B given event A has occurred

$Pr(B)$ = the probability of event B

*Assuming $Pr(A)$ and $Pr(B)$ respectively $\neq 0$

The conditional probability formula appears to be a paradox, but remember that the events are independent. Hence the probability of event A, given event B has occurred, is the probability of event (A).

Let's again refer to our coin tossing example to illustrate the conditional probability. Here we have two fair coins in a container and we randomly select one coin (event A), and experiment by tossing it (event B). The probability of tossing a tail, given we have a fair coin, is the probability of tossing a tail on a fair coin (1/2). The probability of selecting a fair coin at random, given we have tossed a tail, is the probability of selecting a fair coin from two that exists (1).

The conditional probability is often used to define independent events. Events A and B are independent if $Pr(A \mid B) = Pr(A)$, or $Pr(B \mid A) = Pr(B)$, or $Pr(AB) = Pr(A) \bullet Pr(B)$.

Probabilities Involving Dependent Events

The formulas for marginal, conditional, and joint probabilities for dependent events are more complex than that for independent events.

Conditional, Joint, and Marginal Probabilities

We will combine our analysis of the conditional and joint probabilities as the definitions of a conditional probability utilize joint probabilities, and the definitions of joint probabilities use conditional probabilities. The respective formulas for both the conditional and joint probabilities are

---

The Conditional Probability for Dependent Events

$$Pr(A|B) = \frac{Pr(A \& B)}{Pr(B)}$$ (3.5A)

or

$$Pr(B|A) = \frac{Pr(B \& A)}{Pr(A)}$$ (3.5B)

The Joint Probability for Dependent Events

$$Pr(A \& B) = Pr(A \mid B) \bullet Pr(B) \qquad\qquad (3.6A)$$

or

$$Pr(B \& A) = Pr(B \mid A) \bullet Pr(A) \qquad\qquad (3.6B)$$

Marginal Probabilities

$$\Sigma\, Pr(A \mid B) \bullet Pr(B) \qquad\qquad (3.7A)$$

or

$$\Sigma\, Pr(B \mid A) \bullet Pr(A) \qquad\qquad (3.7B)$$

where

$Pr(A \mid B)$ = the conditional probability of event A given event B has occurred

$Pr(A \& B)$ = the joint probability of events A and B occurring

$Pr(B)$ = the probability of event B

$Pr(B \mid A)$ = the conditional probability of event B given event A has occurred

$Pr(B \& A)$ = the joint probability of events B and A occurring

$Pr(A)$ = the probability of event A

Let's again refer to our coin tossing example to illustrate the conditional, joint, and marginal probability for dependent events. We have a fair coin and a two-headed coin in a container and we randomly select one coin (event A), and experiment by tossing it (event B). The conditional probability attempts to answer a question such as, "What is the probability of tossing a tail, given we have selected a fair coin?"

It might be easier if we established a matrix to analyze our problem. We handle the probabilities in a matrix format because most business students have familiarity with spreadsheets. The two events in the problem are in randomly selecting one of two coins from a container (event A), and experimenting with the coin by tossing it to see if a tail or a head comes up (event B). Note that in our matrix (Table 3.3) the major grouping of the data is by the possible outcomes of our experiment (tail or head). Before we can toss a coin we must randomly select between the two coins available. Note, we will know this probability prior to our experiment (tossing the coin); hence, it is termed a prior probability.

Table 3.3 Conditional, Joint, and Marginal Probabilities for Dependent Events

Event B: B-1; Tossing a tail

Event A	Prior Pr	Conditional Pr	Joint Pr
A-1: Legitimate coin	.5	.5	$0.25 = (.5 \bullet .5)$
A-2: Two-headed coin	.5	0.0	$0.00 = (.5 \bullet 0)$
	Marginal probability of tossing a tail; $\Sigma = 0.25$		

Event B: B-2; Tossing a head

Event A	Prior Pr	Conditional Pr	Joint Pr
A-1: Legitimate coin	.5	.5	$0.25 = (.5 \bullet .5)$
A-2: Two-headed coin	.5	1.0	$0.50 = (.5 \bullet 1)$
	Marginal probability of tossing a tail; $\Sigma = 0.75$		
	Note: Marginal probabilities of tossing tail + head, sum to 1.0.		

The Probability of tossing a tail (B-1) given we had selected the legitimate coin (A-1) is 50% $[Pr(B\text{-}1 \mid A\text{-}1) = 1/2]$. If we had selected the two-headed coin (A-2), it is not possible for us to obtain a tail [Pr(B-1 | A-2) = 0]. The probability of tossing a head (B-2) given we had randomly selected the legitimate coin is 50% [Pr(B2 | A-1) = 1/2]. Finally, if we had selected the two-headed coin, we must toss a head [Pr(B-2 | A2) = 1].

We can see from formula 3.6 that the joint probabilities are the multiplication of the respective prior and conditional probabilities. Thus, the probability of jointly selecting the legitimate coin and tossing a tail is 25%. The formulas and solutions for all joint probabilities, which must sum to 1, are as follows:

$$Pr(A\text{-}1 \text{ \& } B\text{-}1) = Pr(A\text{-}1) \bullet Pr(B\text{-}2 \,|\, A\text{-}1) = 1/2 \bullet 1/2 = 1/4$$

$$Pr(A\text{-}1 \text{ \& } B\text{-}2) = Pr(A\text{-}1) \bullet Pr(B\text{-}1 \,|\, A\text{-}1) = 1/2 \bullet 1/2 = 1/4$$

$$Pr(A\text{-}2 \text{ \& } B\text{-}2) = Pr(A\text{-}2) \bullet Pr(B\text{-}2 \,|\, A\text{-}2) = 1/2 \bullet 1 = 1/2$$

$$Pr(A\text{-}2 \text{ \& } B\text{-}1) = Pr(A\text{-}2) \bullet Pr(B\text{-}1 \,|\, A\text{-}2) = 1/2 \bullet 0 = 0$$

The marginal probabilities are the probabilities of either tossing a tail or a head. These probabilities are the sum of the respective joint probabilities. The marginal probability of tossing a tail (B-1) is 1/4 while that of tossing a head (B-2) is 3/4.

Marginal Probability of B-1: Pr(A-1 & B-1) + Pr(A-2 & B-1) = 1/4 + 0 = 1/4

Marginal Probability of B-2: Pr(A-1 & B-2) + Pr(A-2 & B-2) = 1/4 + 1/2 = 3/4

From our formulas, we can see that we may switch the events to obtain conditional, joint, and marginal probabilities. In Table 3.4 we can see that the data are grouped by whether we select the legitimate coin or not (event A), and not by the experimental information. The conditional probabilities relate to the probability of randomly selecting the legitimate coin, given we have tossed a tail or a head. For example, Pr(B-1 | A-1) = Pr(B-1 & A-1 • Pr(A-1) = .25/.5 = .5. Or Pr(B-1 | A-2) = Pr(B & A) • Pr(A-2) = 0/.5 = 0.

Table 3.4 Conditional, Joint, and Marginal Probabilities for Dependent Events

Event A: A-1; Legitimate coin

Event A	Prior Pr	Conditional Pr	Joint Pr
B-1: Tossing a tail	.5	.5	0.25 = (.5•.5)
B-2: Tossing a head	.5	.5	0.25 = (.5•.5)
Marginal probability of selecting good coin; Σ = 0.50			

Event A: A-2; Two-headed coin

Event B	Prior Pr	Conditional Pr	Joint Pr
B-1: Tossing a tail	.5	0.0	0.00 = (.5•.0)
B-2: Tossing a head	.5	1.0	0.50 = (.5•1)
Marginal probability of selecting bad coin; Σ = 0.50			
Note: Marginal probabilities of tossing tail + head, sum to 1.0.			

When we move to Section 3.5 it will be important to remember to group the data by the possible outcomes of the experimental information, as was done in Table 3.3.

Returning to Contingency Tables

We have expanded our analysis beyond that of a simple contingency table where we obtained probabilities in the margin for two events. We have explored probabilities without having sample data to place in contingency tables. Let's return to the contingency table of Table 3.2, which is duplicated to avoid looking back.

	B	not B	Total
A	5	0	5
not A	1	4	5
Total	6	4	10

The conditional probability can easily be determined using formula 3.5. The probability for A & B = 5/10 =.5, and the probability of event A and B are Pr(A) = 5/10 = .5, Pr(B) = 6/10 = .6. Using formula 3.5A,

$$Pr(A \mid B) = \frac{.5}{.6} = .8333$$

and using formula 3.5B yields

$$Pr(B \mid A) = \frac{.5}{.5} = 1.000$$

We can also use formula 3.6 to obtain the joint probability as
$$Pr(A \& B) = (5/6)(.6) = .5$$
and
$$Pr(B \& A) = (5/5)(.5) = .5$$

 Concept Check 3.D

For independent events, the Pr(A & B) = Pr(B). True or false? If false, explain.

Exercises

3.21   Do multiplication rules involve more than one event? Explain.

3.22   Explain in your own words the terms independent and dependent events.

3.23   a.   If event A and B are independent, what is Pr(A & B) if Pr(A) = .6 and Pr(B) = .2?
       b.   Determine Pr(A | B) and Pr(B |A).

3.24   a.   If event A and B are independent, what is Pr(A & B) if Pr(A) = .1 and Pr(B) = .9?
       b.   Determine Pr(A | B) and Pr(B | A).

3.25   A man undergoes a genetic test and finds his wife will give birth to a girl 70% of the time. He is told that each birth is independent in terms of the probability involved.

       a.   What is the probability his second child will be a boy given his first was a girl?
       b.   What is the probability his second child will be a boy given his first was a boy?
       c.   What is the probability his second child will be a girl given his first was a girl?

3.26   A student must pass his last two classes to graduate. Class A has a pass rate of 70% while Class B has a pass rate of 50%. The classes are independent and mutually exclusive. Having knowledge from one of the classes will not be useful in passing the other. The student currently has the prerequisites for both classes.

       a.   What is the probability of passing course B after having passed course A?
       b.   What is the probability of failing course A after having passed course B?
       c.   What is the probability of passing both classes?

3.27   In a container are a normal coin and a two-tailed coin. You will randomly select one of the coins and experiment with it by tossing it. Determine all of the appropriate conditional, joint, and marginal probabilities given we toss either a head or a tail.

3.28   There are 10 dice in an urn. Two are designed in such a manner that a 6-face appears 60% of the time. The remaining 8 dice are legitimate.

    a.   What is the probability of throwing a 6-face given we have selected a loaded die?
    b.   What is the probability of throwing a 6-face given we have selected a legitimate die?
    c.   What is the joint probability of selecting a crooked die and throwing it for a 6-face?

3.29   We are to hire a consultant to help us in making a decision concerning if we should produce product A or product B. The consultant will return with either a favorable (Fav) evaluation or an unfavorable (Unf) evaluation. We believe our prior probability for success (S) to be 20%. The consultant gives us the following probability information based on past studies: Pr(Fav | S) = .9, and Pr(Fav | Failure) = .2. Determine all of the appropriate joint probabilities for the problem.

3.30   A student believes her probability of passing a class is 50%. She also believes Pr(Pass | Prereq) = .85, and Pr(Fail | Noprereq) = .7. Determine all of the appropriate joint probabilities for the problem.

3.31   The joint probability (independent events) for A-1 and B-1 = 30%, and Pr(A-1) = .8 and Pr(B-1) = .1. Determine Pr(A-1 | B-1). Comment on the answer.

3.32   A firm believes its chances of striking oil (O) by drilling at random to be 2%. The probability for finding a duster (D) is 98%. The firm is considering having a geologist do a seismic survey, whose results will either be favorable (Fav) or unfavorable (Unf). The following conditional probabilities are believed to exist: Pr(O | Fav) = 40% and Pr(D | Unf) = 99%. Determine all of the appropriate joint probabilities.

3.5   Revising Probabilities: Bayes' Theorem

In many practical applications of probability theory, we deal with situations in which facts change. We may think that we will do well on an upcoming examination, based on having time to allocate for studying. However, if your boss changes your work schedule, or your parents come into town and want to spend time with you, you might have to revise your probabilities and expectations of a good grade.

A clothes retailer might invest heavily in a new line with expectations that it will sell as well as the new lines in previous years. Unfortunately, this new line might not take off as expected, and the probability for profitability will have to be revised.

The revising of probabilities in light or lieu of new information was developed by the Reverend Thomas Bayes (1702–1761). It involves the task of combining old and new information into a single revised probability, called a **posterior probability**.

We will return to our example of randomly selecting between a legitimate and two-headed coin, and experimenting with it by tossing it to determine if it comes up heads or tails (Table 3.3). From Table 3.3 we can ascertain Pr(A-1) or Pr(A-2), Pr(B-1 | A-1 or A-2), Pr(B-2 | A-1 or A-2), and Pr(B-1 & A-2), etc. The conditional probabilities answer the questions concerning the likelihood of tossing a tail or a head, given we have randomly selected a legitimate or two-headed coin. But what about the probability of randomly selecting a legitimate or two-headed coin, given we have tossed a head or a tail? These new probabilities are called posterior probabilities. Listed are the symbolic way both conditional and posterior probabilities appear. Note the similarities and the differences. Also note that in the posterior probabilities, the experimental information (tossing a coin) is the given.

Conditional Probabilities	Posterior Probabilities
Pr(B-2 | A-1)	Pr(A-1 | B-2)
Pr(B-1 | A-1)	Pr(A-1 | B-1)
Pr(B-2 | A-2)	Pr(A-2 | B-2)
Pr(B-1 | A-2)	Pr(A-2 | B-1)

The theorem that established the posterior probabilities was developed over 200 years ago by the Reverend Thomas Bayes, which is

Bayes' Theorem

$$Pr(E|S) = \frac{Pr(E) \bullet Pr(S|E)}{Pr(E) \bullet Pr(S|E) + Pr(Not\ E) \bullet Pr(S|Not\ E)} \quad (3.8A)$$

or

$$Pr(ES) = \frac{Joint\ Probability\ Involving\ S\ \&\ E}{Marginal\ Probability\ Involving\ S} \quad (3.8B)$$

where

$Pr(E)$ = an event probability

$Pr(S \mid E)$ = a conditional probability of sample information (S) given event E

$Pr(E \mid S)$ = a posterior probability of event E given sample information (S)

Note that we use S to signify the experimental information since it is often obtained through sampling. In our coin example, S refers to tossing a coin and it either comes up a tail or a head.

Using our spreadsheet format, Table 3.5 has the computations for the posterior probabilities. To obtain the posterior probabilities we divide each joint probability by the respective marginal probability. The posterior probability simply proportionalizes the joint probabilities to 1. Note that for each possible outcome of the experimental information, the prior and posterior probabilities sum to 1, the sum of all the possible joint probabilities sum to 1, and the conditional probabilities relating to a specific event also sum to 1.

Table 3.5 Conditional, Joint, Marginal, and Posterior Probabilities for Dependent Events

Event B: B-1; Tossing a tail

Event A	Prior Pr	Conditional Pr	Joint Pr	Posterior Pr
A-1: Legitimate coin	.5	.5	0.25	1.000 = .25/.25
A-2: Two-headed coin	.5	0.0	0.00	0.000 = 0/.25

Marginal probability of tossing a tail; $\Sigma = 0.25$

Event B: B-2; Tossing a head

Event A	Prior Pr	Conditional Pr	Joint Pr	Posterior Pr
A-1: Legitimate coin	.5	.5	0.25	0.333 = .25/.75
A-2: Two-headed coin	.5	1.0	0.50	0.667 = .50/.75

Marginal probability of tossing a head; $\Sigma = 0.75$

Note: That event B involves the experiment, so is S in Bayes' formula.

Rather than use the matrix format to solve posterior probabilities we may solve directly using Bayes' formula. The posterior probabilities are:

$$Pr(A-1 \mid B-1) = \frac{.5(.5)}{.5(.5) + .5(0)} = \frac{.25}{.25} = 1.000$$

$$Pr(A-2 \mid B-1) = \frac{.5(0)}{.5(.5) + .5(0)} = \frac{0}{.25} = 0.000$$

$$Pr(A-1 \mid B-2) = \frac{.5(.5)}{.5(.5) + .5(1)} = \frac{.25}{.75} = 0.333$$

$$Pr(A-2 \mid B-2) = \frac{.5(1)}{.5(.5) + .5(1)} = \frac{.50}{.75} = 0.667$$

An Example of Bayes' Rule Involving Breaking the Casino

It may be advantageous to review Bayes' Theorem and deal with the posterior probabilities with the aid of an unverified report. It is rumored that the largest rip-off ever perpetuated on a gambling casino occurred with "loaded dice." All casinos know when loaded dice are being used because the gambling payoffs exceed a normal rate. When this happens the casino brings in pit bosses to monitor happenings and they move in closed circuit TV viewing. If the payoffs still exceed what is expected, then the dice would be changed after each and every toss. It would then be impossible to slip loaded dice to the one tossing the dice.

As the story goes, the individuals involved had developed a new technique to load the dice so that it was not detectable by x-ray or weighing type equipment. They had known the manufacturer of the dice were geographically a considerable distance from the casino and were transported by truck. They followed the driver and found he had a tendency to stay overnight at the same small hotel. One night while he slept they removed all of the legal dice from the truck and replaced them with the loaded dice. When the driver appeared the next day at his delivery point, no one was wise as to what took place during the night.

When the payoffs were higher than the norm, even after the dice were replaced after each and every toss, casino officials were puzzled. It took them a while to begin developing information that the problems were in these casinos, and these three had a single supplier. Since casinos do not like to verify such stories, because it acts like a magnet to entice other illegal activities, it is impossible to determine if the rumor is true. Let's assume that it was true and that the casinos were not able to determine physically if the dice were loaded or not. They just knew the payoffs were better than the norm.

Let's say that the loaded dice were constructed so that a "one" appeared 70% of the time. Remember that a one should appear 1/6 of the time in a legitimate die. Suppose further that in a fishbowl in front of you are six loaded and four legitimate dice. You randomly select one die, and inspect it. There is no way to determine if it's legitimate or not, so you decide to sample or experiment with the die. You toss it down the table and it comes up a one. We still do not know if it is a loaded die or not, but what can be ascertained is the probability of it being loaded or legitimate.

We will utilize the matrix format for solving our probabilities with four different probabilities listed in columns (Prior Pr, Conditional Pr, Joint Pr, Posterior Pr). The groupings will be based on the new or experimental information (throwing a die and obtaining a "one face" or not).

Within each of the groupings (rows) will be the outcome of the prior information (the die is either fair or loaded: an event probability, see Table 3.6). The sum of the prior probabilities, within each of the groupings must equal 1. In our problem the probability of selecting a loaded die (E-1) from the bowl [Pr(E-1)] is .6 (6/10). The probability of selecting a legitimate die (E-2) from the bowl [Pr(E-2)] is .4 (4/10).

The conditional probability of tossing a one with a legitimate dice is 1/6, while tossing a non-one-face is 5/6. The probability of throwing either a one-face or a non-one-face with a fair die is 1. The conditional probabilities (where "S:O" refers to the sample outcome of tossing a one-face and "S:NO" refers to the sample outcome of tossing a non-one-face) are Pr[S:O | E-1] = .7, Pr[S:O | E-2] = 1/6 = .1667, Pr[S:NO | E-1] =. 3, and Pr[S:NO | E-2] = 5/6 = .8333.

The joint probabilities are the product of the prior and conditional probabilities. The respective joint probabilities are

$$Pr(E\text{-}1) \bullet Pr(S\text{:}O \,|\, E\text{-}1) = (.6)(.7) = .42$$
$$Pr(E\text{-}1) \bullet Pr(S\text{:}NO \,|\, E\text{-}1) = (.6)(.3) = .18$$
$$Pr(E\text{-}2) \bullet Pr(S\text{:}O \,|\, E\text{-}1) = (.4)(1/6) = .0667$$
$$Pr(E\text{-}2) \bullet Pr(S\text{:}NO \,|\, E\text{-}1) = (.4)(5/6) = .3333$$

Note that the sum of all the possible joint probabilities must equal 1.

Finally we come to the posterior probabilities. Essentially, with the posterior probabilities, we are proportionalizing the joint probabilities (for each group) to equal 1. The symbolism used is very similar to that of the conditional probability. The conditional probability reads the probability of the sample event given the prior event has occurred. In contrast, the posterior probability is the probability of the prior event given the sample event has occurred. The respective symbols are

Pr(E-1 | S:O) = The probability of E-1 given sample outcome O

Pr(E-1 | S:NO) = The probability of E-1 given sample outcome NO

Pr(E-2 | S:O) = The probability of E-2 given sample outcome O

Pr(E-2 | S:NO) = The probability of E-2 given sample outcome NO

The computations necessary to achieve the posterior probabilities may be seen in Table 3.6. For each grouping (sample outcome) we divide the individual joint probability by the sum of the joint probabilities for that sample experiment outcome. Hence, the probability of Pr(E-1 | S:O) = .42/.4867 = .8630. Thus, there is a .863 probability that the dice we threw down the table and obtained a one-face with was a loaded die. The probability that it was a legitimate die is .137.

Table 3.6 Determining Posterior Probabilities, Dice Example

A: Tossing a one

	Prior Pr	Conditional Pr	Joint Pr		Posterior Pr	
E-1 Loaded	.6	.7*	.42	(.6 • .7)	.8630	(.42/.4867)
E-2 Legit	.4	.1667**	.0667	(.4 • .1667)	.1370	(.0667/.4867)
Total	1.0		.4867***		1.0000	

B: Tossing a two, three, four, five, or six (a non-one-face)

	Prior Pr	Conditional Pr	Joint Pr		Posterior Pr	
E-1 Loaded	.6	.3*	.18	(.6•.3)	.3507	(.18/.5133)
E-2 Legit	.4	.8333**	.3333	(.4•.8333)	.6493	(.3333/.5133)
Total	1.0		.5133***		1.0000	

*Sums to 1.0; **Sums to 1.0; ***Sums to 1.0

Posterior Probabilities Revised for a Second Experiment

Suppose in our dice example we decide to toss the same dice we had selected and tossed a one-face. Let us suppose that the die comes up a one-face for the second consecutive time. This should alter the posterior probabilities. If another one-face appeared, it should increase the likelihood that we had randomly selected a loaded die.

Let us begin to analyze exactly what probabilities would be affected. The prior probability would not be affected because it only deals with the probability of selecting a crooked or fair die. It does not deal with the experimentation or the tossing of the die. The conditional probability is affected since it represents the probability of tossing a one-face twice for both a loaded and legitimate die.

Remembering our product rule law for the probabilities of two independent events occurring, the probability is simply the multiplication of the individual events. Hence, the probability of tossing two consecutive one-faces is the product of two independent tosses (.7 • .7 = .49). The product of basing two one-faces with a fair die is 1/36 (1/6 • 1/6).

The joint and posterior probabilities are handled in exactly the same way as when the die was rolled once. As expected, if we roll a one-face twice it will increase the probability that we have randomly selected a loaded die. The probability is .9636 that we have tossed a loaded die (Table 3.7). Note that the sum of all the joints will no longer add to one because of the change in the conditional probabilities.

Table 3.7 Determining Posterior Probabilities, Experimenting Twice

A: Tossing a one-face twice

	Prior Pr	Conditional Pr	Joint Pr	Posterior Pr
E-1 Loaded	.6	$(.7)(.7) = .49$	.294	.9636
E-2 Legit	.4	$(1/6)(1/6) = .02778$	.01111	.0364
Total	1.0		.30511	1.0000

B: Tossing a non-one-face twice

	Prior Pr	Conditional Pr	Joint Pr	Posterior Pr
E-1 Loaded	.6	$(.3)(.3) = .09$	.054	.1628
E-2 Legit	.4	$(5/6)(5/6) = .69444$	.27778	.8372
Total	1.0		.33178	1.0000

Posterior Probabilities Revised for a Third Experiment

Suppose we were to experiment a third consecutive time with the die we had selected. Suppose we rolled a one-face, a one-face, then a non-one-face. Again the prior probability would remain unchanged, as this probability is not related to the toss of the die, but rather to its selection. Because the third roll was a non-one-face the probability that the die selected was loaded will be less than the probability that it was loaded when we rolled it twice consecutively for one-faces. The computations are for your review in Table 3.8. The probability that we have a loaded die if we toss a one-face twice, followed by a non-one-face, is 90.5%. The probability that we have a legitimate die is 9.5%. Again the sum of the joint probabilities will not sum to one because of the change in the conditional probabilities.

Table 3.8 Determining Posterior Probabilities, Experimenting Three Times

A: Tossing a one, a one, and a non-one

	Prior Pr	Conditional Pr	Joint Pr	Posterior Pr
E-1 Loaded	.6	$(.7)(.7)(.3) = .147$	.0882	.9050
E-2 Legit	.4	$(1/6)(1/6)(5/6) = .02315$	.009259	.0950
Total	1.0		.097459	1.0000

B: Tossing a non-one-face, a non-one-face, and a one

	Prior Pr	Conditional Pr	Joint Pr	Posterior Pr
E-1 Loaded	.6	$(.3)(.3)(.7) = .063$	.0378	.4495
E-2 Legit	.4	$(5/6)(5/6)(1/6) = .11574$	.046296	.5505
Total	1.0		.084096	1.0000

Concept Check 3.E

A joint probability is an original probability that is revised due to new or experimental information. True or False? If false, explain.

Exercises

3.33   There are 4 fuse boxes each containing 3 fuses. One fuse box has 3 good fuses (GGG), one 2 good fuses (plus 1 defective: GGB), one 1 good fuse (plus 2 defective: GBB), and one with 0 good fuses (plus 3 defective: BBB). The fuse boxes are closed, but you are able to experiment by randomly selecting one fuse box, then by randomly selecting one fuse from that box. Suppose the fuse you randomly selected was good (Good vs. Bad).

a. Determine Pr(Good | GGG).
b. Determine Pr(Good | GGB).
c. Determine Pr(Good | GBB).
d. Determine Pr(Good | BBB).

3.34 For Exercise 3.33, determine all of the posterior probabilities whether we have drawn a good or bad fuse in the experiment.

3.35 An internationally known artist is contemplating how to sell her latest lithograph. She can either make a limited edition of 100, and sell them at exclusive galleries or make 1,000 and sell them at less exclusive galleries. She is thinking about hiring an art consulting firm to help her with the decision. The consulting firm's response will be either favorable (Fav) or unfavorable (Unf). In the end, the print will either be a financial success (S) or a failure (F) with the buying public. The artist believes the prior probability for success to be .3 [Pr(S) = .3]; hence, failure (F) is .7 [Pr(F) = .7]. The probability for the print having a favorable review, given it's a success [P(Fav | S) = .9] is .9. The probability for the print having an unfavorable response, given it's a failure [P(Unf | F)] is .8.

a. Determine the probability of success given a favorable consulting evaluation [Pr(S | Fav)].
b. Determine the probability of failure given a favorable consulting evaluation [Pr(F | Fav)].
c. Determine the probability of success given an unfavorable consulting evaluation [Pr(S | Unf)].
d. Determine the probability of failure given an unfavorable consulting evaluation [Pr(F | Unf)].

3.36 A manager must choose between two courses of action (A or B). She is thinking about having a market survey performed at a cost of $5,000. The outcome of the market survey will either be favorable (Fav) or unfavorable (Unf). Ultimately, the outcome of the two courses will either be a business success (S) or a failure (F). It is believed that the prior probability for success is .6. The probability for an unfavorable survey given a failure [Pr(Unf | F)] is .8. The probability of a favorable survey given a success [P(Fav | S] is .9.

a. Determine the probability of success given a favorable market survey [Pr(S | Fav)].
b. Determine the probability of failure given a favorable market survey [Pr(F | Fav)].
c. Determine the probability of success given an unfavorable market survey [Pr(S | Unf)].
d. Determine the probability of failure given an unfavorable market survey [Pr(F | Unf)].

3.37 A new company is contemplating either opening in a city or in a suburban area. The CEO is thinking about conducting a market study to give her more information in making the decision. The results of the research would be strong sentiment (SS) in favor of the city, or no real sentiment (NS) either way. The CEO believes ultimately there will be either strong sales (S), a normal sales (N), or a weak sales (W). It is believed the prior probability for a strong sales is .2, for a normal sales .1, and for a weak sales is .7. In addition, P(SS | S) = .9, P(SS | N) = .4, P(SS | W) = .2. Determine all of the posterior probabilities [Pr(S | SS), Pr(S | NS), Pr(N | SS), Pr(N | NS), Pr(W | SS), and Pr(W | NS)].

3.38 A company is thinking about opening a new product line. The company believes that the possible upcoming sales can be categorized as either strong (S), normal (N), or weak (W). They are considering hiring a consulting firm to aid in the decision making process. The results of such an analysis will either be positive (Pos) or negative (Neg). It is believed that the following probabilities apply: Prior probabilities; P(S) = .2, P(N) = .1 and conditional probabilities; P(Pos | S) = .9, P(Pos | N) = .4, and P(Pos | W) = .2. Determine the appropriate posterior probabilities [Pr(S | Pos), Pr(S | Neg), Pr(N | Pos), Pr(N | Neg), Pr(W | Pos), and Pr(W | Neg)].

3.39   A young producer has just completed a movie that turned out better than expected. The producer was going to sell the movie to cablevision, but now also wants to consider selling to movie theaters. The producer is considering hiring a theatrical consulting firm to show the movie overseas and to tabulate the results of the movie buffs. The survey results will either be extremely positive (EP), positive but reserved (PR), or negative (Neg). Ultimately the movie will be a success (S) or a failure (F). It is believed that the following probabilities apply: Prior probability; Pr(S) = .3, and conditional probabilities; Pr(EP | S) = .7, Pr(PR | S) = .2, Pr(PR | F) = .1, and Pr(Neg | F) = .8. Determine the appropriate posterior probabilities [Pr(S | EP), Pr(S | PR), Pr(S | Neg), Pr(F | EP), Pr(F | PR) and Pr(F | Neg)].

3.40   A decision must be made to go or not go with a small merger. If we go with it, the outcome will either be successful (S) or a failure (F). A consultant is brought in to aid in the decision making process. The outcome from the consultant will either be favorable (Fav) or unfavorable (Unf). It is believed that the following probabilities apply: Prior probability; P(S) = .3, and conditional probabilities; P(Fav | S) = .8. P(Fav | F) = .4. Determine the appropriate posterior probabilities [Pr(S | Fav), Pr(S | Unf), Pr(F | Fav), and Pr(F | Unf)].

3.6   Counting Techniques

Counting techniques are used to determine the possible number of outcomes that exist for any number of experiments. They can aid in determining the probabilities of a certain event occurring. For example, if we were to reward one member of your class with free concert tickets, and we knew there were 50 students in the class, then with a random draw the probability of winning would be 1/50 = .02. We will review 3 frequently used counting techniques which involve the product rule, permutations, and combinations.

Product Rule

The counting technique is simple to understand. If any operation or function can be performed in n_1 ways, the second in n_2 ways, the third in n_3 ways, for k operations, the product rule (PR) is defined as

---

Product Rule

$$PR = n_1 \bullet n_2 \bullet n_3 \bullet \bullet \bullet n_k \tag{3.9}$$

where

n_1, n_2, n_3, n_k = number of ways the operation may be performed.

Hence, if there are 4 ways to enter a building and 7 ways of leaving it, there are 28 (4 • 7) ways to enter and leave the building. If state license plates use 3 letters and 3 numbers, how many different license plates can be made? Remembering that there are 26 letters and 10 single numerals, the number plates possible is 17,576,000 (26 • 26 • 26 • 10 • 10 • 10). This is not enough possibilities for several states, so some use 4 letters and 2 numbers, which increases the possibility to 45,697,600. This number of possibilities exceeds the needs even for the most populated state, California, with its 35 million inhabitants.

National TV buying clubs use membership numbers that range between 7 and 9 numbers. We leave it as a student exercise to determine how many different membership numbers are possible. Remember when using the telephone that letters do not increase, but rather decrease the membership count. Remember that the telephone distributes 24 letters (Q and Z are omitted from telephones) to 9 numbers.

We now turn to permutations, which attempt to answer certain types of count questions. For example, suppose that you and four of your classmates are finalists for two positions that a company has available. How many ways is it possible for the company to select the two employees? These questions can be answered with the aid of permutations.

Permutations: The number of ways of selecting r objects from n possible objects when both content and order are significant.

$$_nP_r = \frac{n!}{(n-r)!}$$ (3.10)

where

n = total number of outcomes

r = the event or ordered arrangement or subset of distinguishable outcomes.

Note that "!" is the factorial symbol, and $n!$ is read n factorial. If we wanted the product of all numbers 1 to n, taken 1 at a time, then $_nP_n = n!$ For example, say $n = 6$, $6! = 6 \bullet 5 \bullet 4 \bullet 3 \bullet 2 \bullet 1 = 720$. Note that $1! = 1$, and by definition $0! = 1$. Returning to our job example, $n! = 5! = 120$, $r = 2$ (two jobs), and $(n - r)! = 3! = 6[_5P_2 = 120/6 = 20]$. Hence, there are 20 ways of selecting 2 new employees from 5 applicants. The 20 possibilities are given in Table 3.9. Each of the 5 finalists for the position is designated by a letter A to E. A permutation is concerned with both the content and the order with which the applicants were selected. Hence, in permutation, if the company selected candidates AB or BA it would represent the same grouping but in a different order.

We might note that the product rule differs from a permutation in that it allows for repetition. The formula for a permutation that allows for repetitions is $_nP_r = n^r$. Factorials are not involved in this example because the numbers or letters are not used up but rather are eligible for future selection.

Combinations

If only the grouping were important (the order unimportant, hence AB is identical to BA), we have a combination, which is the number of ways of selecting r objects from n possible objects when content is significant, but order is not.

Combinations: The number of ways of selecting r objects from n possible objects when only content is significant.

$$_nC_r = \frac{n!}{r!(n-r)!}$$ (3.11)

where

n = total number of outcomes

r = the event or ordered arrangement or subset of distinguishable outcomes.

In our employment example $n! = 120(5 \bullet 4 \bullet 3 \bullet 2 \bullet 1)$, $r! = 2(2 \bullet 1)$, $(n - r)! = 6(3 \bullet 2 \bullet 1)$, and the number of combinations equals 10. These 10 possibilities are given in Table 3.9.

Table 3.9 The Possibilities for Permutations and Combinations of Employing 2 Applicants from 5 Finalists

	Permutation			Combination	
AB	BC	CD	DE	AB	BD
AC	BD	CE	EA	AC	BE
AD	BE	DA	EB	AD	CD
AE	CA	DB	EC	AE	CE
BA	CB	DC	ED	BC	DE

When differentiating between a permutation and a combination, the following question must be answered, "Is order significant?" If the answer to this question is "yes," we are dealing with a permutation, and if "no," we have a combination. In our employment example, order was unimportant. It did not matter if individual A was selected prior to B, or B before A. These represent identical situations; hence, a combination is involved.

Suppose in our employment example that the first individual selected would receive a higher paying position than the second. Now the order of selection becomes important and we are dealing with a permutation. A few examples might help us quickly grasp the concept of whether the order was important or not.

In state Lotto systems, the big prizes are obtained by guessing 6 random numbers from approximately 01–54. Certainly the content is important (the 6 numbers involved), but, the order is not. It does not matter in which order the 6 numbers are selected. Hence, we are dealing with a combination.

Young men must register for the draft even though there currently is no mandatory requirement for military service. A drum of 365 sequentially numbered balls is used to rank the likelihood of being drafted should such a need arise. Is a combination or permutation involved? Technically a permutation is involved because the selection process begins at the highest number (365) and works its way down to the smallest number based on need. However, from a practical standpoint, any individual with a selected number in the lowest quartile has little chance of being conscripted, except in unusual circumstances. Hence, from the perspective of these individuals, it might be viewed as a combination.

Sometimes the combination and product rules are combined into what is called the hypergeometric rule. Suppose your business statistics instructor wishes to select a committee of 4 from 10 randomly selected students. Seven of the students selected are juniors and 3 are seniors. A question that might be asked is, "How many groups of 4 can be selected with 3 juniors and 1 senior?" This problem can be solved through the hypergeometric rule. We first compute the number of ways we can select 3 from 7 juniors, then compute the number of ways to select 1 from 3 seniors. The product of the two combinations yields the solutions.

The Hypergeometric Rule

$$_{n1}C_{r1} \bullet {}_{n2}C_{r2} \qquad\qquad (3.12)$$

where

$$_{n1}C_{r1} \text{ and } {}_{n2}C_{r2} = \text{combinations}$$

$$n_1 + n_2 = n$$

$$r_1 + r_2 = r$$

We are now in a position to answer the question posed. Hence $n_1 = 7$, $n_2 = 3$, $n = 10$, $r = 3$, $r_1 = 2$, $r_2 = 1$ and

$$_{7}C_2 \bullet {}_{3}C_1 = \frac{7!}{3!(7-3)!} \bullet \frac{3!}{1!(3-1)!} = \frac{7 \bullet 6 \bullet 5 \bullet 4 \bullet 3 \bullet 2 \bullet 1}{3 \bullet 2 \bullet 1(4 \bullet 3 \bullet 2 \bullet 1)} \bullet \frac{3 \bullet 2 \bullet 1}{1(2 \bullet 1)} = 105$$

There are 105 ways of selecting 4 of 10 containing 3 of 7 juniors and 1 of 3 seniors.

✔ **Concept Check 3.F**

If combinations and permutations were applied to the same data, the number of combinations would always exceed the number of permutations. True or false? If false, explain.

Exercises

3.41   In your own words explain the term factorial.

3.42   In your own words explain the difference between a permutation and a factorial.

3.43   a.   How many ways can we select 4 items from 9 if order is important?
        b.   How many ways can we select 4 items from 9 if order is not important?

3.44   a.   How many ways can we select 2 items from 12 if order is important?
        b.   How many ways can we select 2 items from 12 if order is not important?

3.45   a.   Historically zip codes have contained 5 numbers. How many zip codes are possible?
        b.   If we add 4 more numbers to zip codes, how many codes are possible?

3.46   a.   You own a small company that issues credit cards to frequent users. You expect to issue about 875 such cards. You wish to use a code consisting of either numbers or letters. What options are available to you?
        b.   Would you want to consider the possibility for growth?

3.47   You are considering buying a product that comes in 5 colors and 3 sizes. How many choices do you have?

3.48   You are considering buying a product that comes in 5 colors, 3 sizes, and made of 2 different materials. How many choices do you have?

3.49   You wish to select a committee from 3 of 7 scientists.

        a.   Would this be a permutation or a combination?
        b.   How many committees are possible?

3.50   You wish to select a committee of 4 from 8 production specialists.

        a.   Would this be a permutation or a combination?
        b.   How many committees are possible?

3.51   You wish to select a committee from 7 of 15 individuals. You wish to include 3 of 7 scientists and 4 of 8 production specialists. How many committees are possible?

3.52   A marketing club must select a president, a vice-president, and a treasurer from a dozen applicants.

        a.   Would this be considered a combination or permutation? Note that the presidency is considered more prestigious than the vice-presidency, etc.
        b.   How many ways are there of selecting the three officers?

3.7   Summary

We have reviewed some of the important concepts and theories of probability. There are 3 types of probability that deal with the level of knowledge and data accumulation. With the classical probability, considerable knowledge is known in advance. With relative frequencies data must be meticulously kept and categorized, and in subjective probabilities an informal process is used to assess the probability of an event.

Within the formal analysis of probability theory there are various probabilities including marginal probabilities, conditional probabilities, and joint probabilities. Finally, we completed the chapter with a process which allows us to revise probabilities in light of new information. This process is known as Bayes' theorem.

Mini-case 3.1: Bayesian Analysis in the Court Room

You are a jurist in a murder trial. A fingerprint expert testifies that the probability that a fingerprint left on the murder weapon belongs to the accused is 90 percent. Hence, this might be considered the prior probability of guilt (G) and innocence (I) = 10%. A lie detector expert states that if the accused takes such a test, if it turns out with an X reading, the probability of the accused being guilty is .8 [Pr(X | G)]. If the lie detector test turns out to have a Y reading, the probability of the accused being innocent is .9 [Pr(Y | I)]. What is the probability of the client being guilty given an X reading on the test [Pr(G | X)]? Will this probability be greater than the event probability of guilt?

Mini-case 3.2: The Odds of Winning Lotto

Many state lotteries have a game called Lotto. In Florida, there are 49 sequentially numbered ping-pong balls and 6 are randomly selected. You must guess the 6 numbers to be randomly selected. It does not matter in what sequence the numbers are drawn.
   a.   What are the odds of winning Lotto?
   b.   Suppose in Lotto that it did matter in what sequence the numbers were drawn. What would be the probability of winning?
   c.   In California Lotto players must select 6 numbers from 53 sequentially numbered ping-pong balls and in Illinois it's 6 of 54. What are the odds of winning Lotto?

Mini-case 3.3: A Puzzle Illustrating Factorials

In Figure 3.3 we have a diagram with 8 boxes. Try to place a separate number from 1 to 8 (a number can be utilized only once) in each box in such a way that two consecutive numbers may not touch vertically, horizontally, or diagonally. State how many different puzzles could be made and solve the puzzle.

Figure 3.3. A Puzzle Used to Understand Factorials

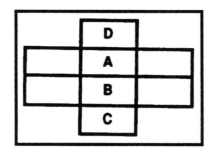

Experiment: The activity we are investigating.

Outcomes: Possible individual results of the experiment.

Event: One or more outcomes of the experiment.

Sample space: The set of all possible outcomes.

Mutually exclusive: A situation where only one event can occur during a given time frame.

Collectively exhaustive: When a sample space includes all of the possible events from an experiment.

The probability categories:

> Classical probabilities are based on prior knowledge.
>
> Relative frequencies are based on the accumulation of historical data.
>
> Subjective probabilities are based on intuition.

Marginal probability: A marginal probability is the probability of a single event occurring.

Joint probability: A joint probability yields the probability of two events occurring simultaneously.

Contingency table: A contingency table is a data set that is arranged and defined by the number of rows and the number of columns involved.

Prior probability: The probability of an event occurring prior to experimenting with another event.

Conditional probability: A conditional probability yields the probability of an event occurring, given another event has taken place.

Posterior probability: A posterior probability combines old and new information into a single probability.

Permutation: The number of ways of selecting r objects from n possible objects when both content and order are significant.

Combination: The number of ways of selecting r objects from n possible objects when only content is significant.

Review of Important Formulas

The Addition Rule for Mutually Exclusive Events

$$Pr(A \text{ or } B) = Pr(A) + Pr(B) \qquad (3.1)$$

where

$Pr(A \text{ or } B) =$ the probability of events A or B occurring

$Pr(A)$ and $Pr(B) =$ the probability of events A and B occurring

---

The Addition Rule for Events That Are Not Mutually Exclusive

$$Pr(A \text{ or } B) = Pr(A) + Pr(B) - Pr(A \ \& \ B) \qquad (3.2)$$

where

$Pr(A \text{ or } B) =$ the union of events A and B

$Pr(A) =$ the probability of A

$Pr(B) =$ the probability of B

$Pr(A \ \& \ B) =$ the joint probability of A and B happening

---

Joint Probabilities for Independent Events

$$Pr(A \& B) = Pr(A) \bullet Pr(B) \tag{3.3}$$

where

$Pr(A \& B)$ = the joint probability of events A and B occurring

$Pr(A)$ = the marginal probability of event A occurring

$Pr(B)$ = the marginal probability of event B occurring

The Conditional Probability for Independent Events

$$Pr(A|B) = Pr(A)^* \tag{3.4A}$$

or

$$Pr(B|A) = Pr(B)^* \tag{3.4B}$$

where

$Pr(A|B)$ = time conditional probability of event A given event B has occurred

$Pr(A)$ = the probability of event A

$Pr(B|A)$ = the conditional probability of event B given event A has occurred

$Pr(B)$ = the probability of event B

*Assuming $Pr(A)$ and $Pr(B)$ respectively $\neq 0$

The Conditional Probability for Dependent Events

$$Pr(A|B) = \frac{Pr(A \& B)}{Pr(B)} \tag{3.5A}$$

or

$$Pr(B|A) = \frac{Pr(B \& A)}{Pr(A)} \tag{3.5B}$$

The Joint Probability for Dependent Events

$$Pr(A \& B) = Pr(A|B) \bullet Pr(B) \tag{3.6A}$$

or

$$Pr(B \& A) = P(B|A) \bullet P(A) \tag{3.6B}$$

Marginal Probabilities

$$\Sigma \, Pr(A|B) \bullet Pr(B) \tag{3.7A}$$

or

$$\Sigma \, Pr(B|A) \bullet Pr(A) \tag{3.7B}$$

where

$Pr(A|B)$ = the conditional probability of event A given event B has occurred

$Pr(A \& B)$ = the joint probability of events A and B occurring

$Pr(B)$ = the probability of event B

$Pr(B|A)$ = the conditional probability of event B given event A has occurred

$Pr(B \& A)$ = the joint probability of events B and A occurring

$Pr(A)$ = the probability of event A

Bayes' Theorem

$$\Pr(E|S) = \frac{\Pr(E) \bullet \Pr(S|E)}{\Pr(E) \bullet \Pr(S|E) + \Pr(\text{Not } E) \bullet \Pr(S|\text{Not } E)} \qquad (3.8A)$$

or

$$\Pr(E|S) = \frac{\text{Joint Probability Involving S \& E}}{\text{Marginal Probability Involving S}} \qquad (3.8B)$$

where

$\Pr(E) =$ an event probability

$\Pr(S|E) =$ a conditional probability of sample information (S) given event E

$\Pr(E|S) =$ a posterior probability of event E given sample information (S)

Product Rule

$$PR = n_1 \bullet n_2 \bullet n_3 \bullet \bullet \bullet n_k \qquad (3.9)$$

where

$n_1,\ n_2,\ n_3,\ n_k =$ the number of ways the operation may be performed.

Permutations: The number of ways of selecting r objects from n possible objects when both content and order are significant.

$$_nP_r = \frac{n!}{(n-r)!} \qquad (3.10)$$

where

$n =$ total number of outcomes

$r =$ the event or ordered arrangement or subset of distinguishable outcomes.

Combinations: The number of ways of selecting r objects from n possible objects when only content is significant.

$$_nC_r = \frac{n!}{r!(n-r)!} \qquad (3.11)$$

where

$n =$ total number of outcomes

$r =$ the event or ordered arrangement or subset of distinguishable outcomes.

The Hypergeometric Rule

$$_{n_1}C_{r1} \bullet \,_{n_2}C_{r2} \qquad (3.12)$$

where

$_{n_1}C_{r1}$ and $_{n_2}C_{r2} =$ combinations

$n_1 + n_2 = n$

$r_1 + r_2 = r$

3.53 State whether you believe the following probabilities are classical, relative frequency, or subjective:

    a. The probability that your team will win the world championship this upcoming season.
    b. The probability that you will roll a 6 on a fair die.
    c. The probability that a student entering college with an SAT score of 850 and a high school grade point of 2.1 will be accepted into the institution.

3.54 State whether you believe the following probabilities are classical, relative frequency, or subjective:

    a. The probability that you will watch TV for more than one hour today.
    b The probability that individuals between the ages of 20 and 40 will watch TV for more than one hour today.

3.55 a. Between classical, relative frequency, and subjective probabilities, which would give you the most confidence?
    b. Which would give you the least confidence? Explain.

3.56 Explain the differences between mutually exclusive and collectively exhaustive.

3.57 An instructor wishes to ascertain whether the exam just given was considered fair to the students. The student response is:

	Frequency
Very fair exam	21
A fair exam	6
An unfair exam	3
A very unfair exam	1

    a. What percent of the class believed the exam to be very fair?
    b. What percent of the class believed the exam to be very fair or fair?
    c. Based on the students' response, from a student's perspective, do you think the exam was fair? Would you like some additional information before making such a statement?

3.58 An apartment complex rents 1, 2, 3, and 4 bedroom apartments. All are currently occupied. What is the probability that the next unit to be rented will be a 3 bedroom apartment?

	Units
1 bedroom	36
2 bedroom	66
3 bedroom	79
4 bedroom	18

3.59 A politician wishes to know how her constituency feels concerning an increase in the minimum wage. She has her staff conduct a random survey with the following results:

	Frequency
Strongly Support an Increase	116
Mildly Support an Increase	47
Mildly Opposed to an Increase	212
Strongly Opposed to an Increase	718
Total	1,093

    a. What is the probability that constituents will mildly support the increase?
    b. What is the probability for constituents who have strong feelings either for or against?
    c. If the politician wants to represent her constituency, is it clear which way she should vote on the upcoming increase?

3.60　An individual frequently purchases merchandise from 3 TV shopping clubs. During the last year, the individual has monitored the number of days each show was watched and the number of days purchases were made, as follows:

	Days Watched	Days Purchased
Shopping Club 1	47	6
Shopping Club 2	61	15
Shopping Club 3	82	16

　　a.　What is the probability of a purchase being made from shopping club 1 should it be watched?
　　b.　What is the probability of a purchase being made from shopping club 3 should it be watched?
　　c.　What is the probability of a purchase being made from any shopping club should one of them be watched?

3.61　You wish to select a committee of 5 from 10 individuals. We wish to include 3 of 6 from plant A and 2 of 4 from plant B. How many committees are possible?

3.62　A company must select two individuals to head their European and Asian branches. There are 6 outstanding candidates for the two positions. Assuming that the two positions are equally attractive, how many groups of 2 from an eligibility of 6 can be selected?

3.63　A company must select two individuals to head their European and Asian branches. There are 6 outstanding candidates for the two positions.

　　a.　Assuming that the European post is more prestigious than the Asian post, how many groups of 2 from the eligibility of 6 can be selected?
　　b.　How is this exercise different from 3.62?

3.64　a.　What is the probability of selecting an ace or a 10 from a deck of cards?
　　b.　The probability of selecting an ace and a 10 from a deck of cards.

3.65　What is the probability that you will receive a random license plate (assuming 3 letter plates) with your exact 3 initials?

3.66　A parent must select a work team of size 2 from 9 children. How many work teams are possible?

3.67

Event	(B)	(not B)
(A)	45	95
(not A)	25	75

　　a.　Based on the information supplied, what is the marginal probability of event (A)?
　　b.　The marginal probability of event (not B).
　　c.　The joint probability of events (A) and (not B).
　　d.　Determine Pr(A | not B).

3.68

Event	(A)	(not A)
(B)	27	42
(not B)	16	71

　　a.　What is the marginal probability of event (A)?
　　b.　What is the joint probability of events (A) and (B)?
　　c.　Determine Pr(A | B).

3.69

Event	(A)	(not A)
(B)	81	100
(not B)	81	16

a. What is the marginal probability of event (A)?
b. What is the joint probability of events (A) and (B)?
c. Determine Pr(A | B).

3.70 An executive must make a decision whether to go ahead with a new product or not. She is considering two sources for additional information. They are from an econometric firm and a marketing research firm. For either source, the results of the new information will either be favorable (Fav) or unfavorable (Unf). If the product is made and marketed the results will be either success (S) or failure (F). The overall probability for success is believed to be .4, and the conditional probabilities are:

Probability	Econometric Firm	Market Research Firm
Pr(Fav | S)	.8	.7
Pr(Fav | F)	.1	.2

a. Determine all of the posterior probabilities for the econometric firm [Pr(S | Fav), Pr(S | Unf), Pr(F | Fav), and Pr(F | Unf)].
b. Determine all of the posterior probabilities for the market research firm [Pr(S | Fav), Pr(S | Unf), Pr(F | Fav), and Pr(F | Unf)].

3.71 A rock group is making a comeback and think that they have a hot tune. They are thinking about trial testing the tune in several cities. The trial testing will lead to one of four ratings: super (Sup), good (Good), okay (Ok), or poor (Poor). The song will either be a success (S) or a failure (F). The following probabilities apply: Pr(S) = .6, Pr(Sup | S) = .2, Pr(Sup | F) = .1, Pr(Good | S) = .4, Pr(Good | F) = .2, Pr(Ok | S) = .3, Pr(Ok | F) = .3. Determine all of the posterior probabilities [Pr(S | Sup), Pr(S | Good), Pr(S | Ok), Pr(S | Poor), Pr(F | Sup), Pr(F | Good), Pr(F | Ok), Pr(F | Poor)].

3.72 A company is thinking about opening a new product line. The prior probabilities for the possible sales of the product are for strong sales (S) is .2, for a normal sales (N) .1, and for weak sales (W) is .7. The company is considering hiring a consulting firm to pretest the market. The results of the survey will either be favorable (Fav) or unfavorable (Unf). The consulting firm believes that the following conditional probabilities apply: P(Fav | S) = .9, P(Fav | N) = .4, and P(Fav | W) = .2. Determine all of the posterior probabilities involved [Pr(S | Fav), Pr(S | Unf), Pr(N | Fav), Pr(N | Unf), Pr(W | Fav), and Pr(W | Unf)].

Probability Distributions and Measures

Where we have been

In Chapter 3 we introduced probability and the focus was on determining the likelihood or probability of one or more events.

Where we are going

In this chapter we continue with the development of probability but do so with a focus on probability distributions. Probability distributions will be defined formally as we develop the foundations in this chapter. However, we can best illustrate the contents of Chapter 4 with an example.

Suppose that the manufacturer of an electronic product for consumers recognizes that its product varies widely in its lifetime. Despite quality control efforts, some fail very quickly, most last a reasonable life, and others last almost indefinitely. The manufacturer wants to establish its warranty policy and is interested in the percentage of its product that lasts less than 2 years. Problems of this type can be solved with the methods of Chapter 4.

4.1 Introduction

We now formally introduce random variables and probability distributions. In addition we develop some of the more frequently used distributional forms for random variables. In decision making it is critical to be able to assess the probability of the occurrence of certain events. What is the probability of hiring a person with specified unknown characteristics? What is the probability of a certain number of defective parts in a shipment? What is the probability of 3 or more component failures in an assembled part? We will be able to answer questions like these after studying probability distributions and their characteristics.

We defined the term variable in Chapter 1 as a characteristic or property that varies between observations. There are many variables we can utilize for differentiating between you and others in your class. These would include gender, age, major, GPA, etc. When the term random is used to describe the term variable it refers to the fact that the experiment in question may result in only one of several or many possible values for the variable. A random variable is one whose value is not known in advance when an elementary unit is selected from the variable. However, we can know something about its probability. For example, if we select a student in your class, what is the probability that the student is a Finance major? If 20% of the class is made up of Finance majors, the odds that our student is a Finance major is 1 out of 5.

The term random can be used in different contexts. It is often used to explain nonpredictability. In explaining random variables, random does not mean haphazard and unable to be predicted. It only means that the value of the variable is not known in advance, but can be described probabilistically. Thus, the price of a share of stock next month would be considered a random variable if, although unknown precisely, each of the possible prices that could occur were known and able to be described probabilistically.

To aid in the explanation of a random variable, consider a random process generated by a fair coin flipped 3 consecutive times. In this case there are eight basic outcomes, which are

(HHH), (HHT), (HTH), (THH), (HTT), (THT), (TTH), (TTT)

The outcomes as listed are qualitatively rather than quantitatively described. However, if we define a variable, X, that reflects the number of tails from this random process, we find the following 4 numeric outcomes

0 Tails   1 Tail   2 Tails   3 Tails

These numeric outcomes and the associated qualitative outcomes are shown in Table 4.1.

Table 4.1 Number of Tails in Three Flips of a Fair Coin

Number of Tails (X)	Qualitative Outcomes
0	(HHH)
1	(HHT) (HTH) (THH)
2	(TTH) (THT) (HTT)
3	(TTT)

This link between the qualitative results of a random process and the numeric result of the number of tails is essential in a random variable. In a sense, a random variable is a rule or function that assigns numeric values to every outcome of a random process.

As another example of a random variable, consider the 36 basic outcomes associated with rolling two fair dice. To view the results directly, we can use Table 4.2.

Table 4.2 The Outcomes from the Roll of Two Dice

		DIE 1 FACE VALUE					
		1	*2*	*3*	*4*	*5*	*6*
D	*1*	1,1	1,2	1,3	1,4	1,5	1,6
I	2	2,1	2,2	2,3	2,4	2,5	2,6
E	3	3,1	3,2	3,3	3,4	3,5	3,6
	4	4,1	4,2	4,3	4,4	4,5	4,6
2	5	5,1	5,2	5,3	5,4	5,5	5,6
	6	6,1	6,2	6,3	6,4	6,5	6,6

Despite the fact that the outcomes in Table 4.2 are expressed in terms of paired numeric values, a random variable is created when we categorize outcomes into single number outcomes. This can be done by defining a variable, X, that represents the sum on the two faces. Table 4.3 summarizes this result.

Table 4.3 The Sum of Faces on the Roll of Two Dice

Sum of Faces (X)	Frequency	Basic Outcomes
2	1	(1,1)
3	2	(1,2) (2,1)
4	3	(2,2) (1,3) (3,1)
5	4	(2,3) (3,2) (4,1) (1,4)
6	5	(1,5) (5,1) (2,4) (4,2) (3,3)
7	6	(6,1) (1,6) (5,2) (2,5) (4,3) (3,4)
8	5	(6,2) (2,6) (5,3) (3,5) (4,4)
9	4	(6,3) (3,6) (5,4) (4,5)
10	3	(6,4) (4,6) (5,5)
11	2	(6,5) (5,6)
12	1	(6,6)
	36	

Here the 36 basic outcomes are reduced to 11 numeric values (the sum of the faces, i.e., 2, 3, 4, ... , 12) and the rule is to assign to each basic outcome a numeric value equal to the sum of the two faces.

 Concept Check 4.A

The winning number from a state lottery is considered a random variable. True or false? If false, explain.

Exercises

4.1 What is a random variable?

4.2 Suppose a new game in Las Vegas required a three-sided die and that the face values were 1, 2, and 3. If the game were based on the outcome of rolling two of these dice and the product (face *A* value • face *B* value) of the two dice, would this be a random variable? Explain.

4.3 A corporation is considering commercializing a product that has been under development for several years. If it decides to commercialize the product, management foresees three possible outcomes, all of which depend upon the result of an upcoming presidential election. First they expect to earn a profit of $1,000,000 if a prodefense candidate is elected. The second possibility is a $100,000 profit if the moderate candidate is elected. The third possibility is the election of a reform candidate which is estimated to lead to a $500,000 loss. If they have estimated the probabilities of the three election events, do we have the necessary ingredients for a probability distribution? Explain.

4.4 Assume that you are invited to play a game that involves flipping a coin two times and you win $10 for every tail that occurs. Identify the probability distribution for your winnings.

4.5 Assume that you are invited to play a game that involves flipping a coin four times and your winnings are determined by the number of heads that occur. Specifically, your winnings in dollars are determined by the equation $W = 2r$, where W = dollar winnings, and r = number of heads that result. Identify all the possible outcomes for winnings (W) and the respective probabilities.

4.6 Our solar system consists of 1 star and 9 planets. In terms of the universe, is our solar system a random variable? Explain.

4.7   Is the number of customers who see a movie on a particular day a random variable? What are the possible number of values?

4.8   Is the time you wait in line at a bank a random variable?

4.9   In what random variables would a tourist destination be interested concerning its customers?

4.10   In what random variables would your university/college be interested in concerning its students?

4.3   The Binomial Distribution

The binomial distribution is a discrete probability distribution that has characteristics which make it quite useful in many applied situations, including quality control analysis. One main characteristic of the binomial distribution is that outcomes are dichotomous. For instance, a coin lands either heads or tails, a person is either female or male, a person either wears glasses or does not, and a production item is either defective or not. In total, a binomially distributed random variable must meet the following conditions

1. Each trial can result in one of two possible outcomes, generally referred to as either a "success" or a "failure." The number of successes (r) is the random variable.
2. The outcome on each trial is independent of the others.
3. The probability of a success (p) remains constant for all trials and, therefore, so does the probability of failure ($q = 1 - p$).
4. The number of trials, n, must be fixed prior to the experiment.

A binomial random variable is essentially the number of successes (r) in an experiment consisting of n identical trials if the above conditions are satisfied. The number of heads on two flips of a fair coin is a binomial random variable since it is consistent with all conditions. The outcomes are dichotomous, in that there are only two possibilities on any given trial: heads or tails. The outcomes on different trials are independent of one another. Heads and tails should occur "randomly." The probability of a head is the same irrespective of the trial.

However, suppose we select 10 electronic parts at random from a shipment of 100 and want to determine the probability of selecting 2 or less defective. To be specific, suppose when we select the items we do not replace them after inspection and that experience leads us to anticipate 20 percent or 20 out of the 100 items to be defective. Can we use the binomial distribution for this random variable? If we evaluate this example in terms of the conditions required for the binomial distribution, we would find that the trials do not have a constant probability of success. The probability of a defective on the first draw from the shipment is .20, since 20 out of the 100 are assumed to be defective. However, what do we know about the probability on the second draw? First, since we are not replacing items once selected, there are now only 99 items remaining to be selected. Second, if a defective was selected on the first draw, there would only be 19 remaining and the relevant probability of a defective item would be 19/99. However, if a good (nondefective) item had been selected on the first draw, there would still be 20 defective and the probability of a defective item would be 20/99. In this example, the trials are not independent and the probability of a success varies from trial to trial. Thus, we do not have a binomial random variable. If sampling is performed with replacement of selected items, the conditions for the binomial distribution are satisfied.

The binomial formula, which provides the means to compute the probability of any numeric value for a binomially distributed random variable is stated in formula 4.1.

Binomial Formula

$$\Pr(r) = {}_nC_r \bullet p^r \bullet q^{n-r} = \frac{n!}{r! \bullet (n-r)!} \bullet p^r \bullet q^{n-r} \qquad (4.1)$$

where

r = the number of successes in n trials, $r = 0, 1, 2, \ldots, n$

n = the number of trials

p = the probability of a success

q = the probability of a failure

${}_nC_r$ = the number of combinations of n things taken r at time

The previous example of a random variable in which we were interested in the probability distribution of the number of tails in three flips of a fair coin was a binomial distribution problem. However, since we had not introduced the binomial distribution at that point, the relevant probabilities were computed using the basic multiplication and addition rules of probability. Now we can check these probabilities using the binomial formula. For instance, the probability of exactly 2 tails in 3 flips of a fair coin is

$$\Pr(2 \text{ tails in 3 flips}) = \frac{3!}{2!(3-2)!}.5^2(1-.5)^{3-2} = \frac{3 \bullet 2 \bullet 1}{2 \bullet 1(1)} = .25(.5) = .375$$

and the probabilities of the remaining values of the random variable are

$$\Pr(0 \text{ tails in 3 flips}) = \frac{3!}{0!(3-0)!}.5^0(1-.5)^{3-0} = \frac{3 \bullet 2 \bullet 1}{1(3 \bullet 2 \bullet 1)} 1(.125) = .125$$

$$\Pr(1 \text{ tails in 3 flips}) = \frac{3!}{1!(3-1)!}.5^1(1-.5)^{3-1} = \frac{3 \bullet 2 \bullet 1}{1(2 \bullet 1)} .5(.25) = .375$$

$$\Pr(3 \text{ tails in 3 flips}) = \frac{3!}{3!(3-3)!}.5^3(1-.5)^{3-3} = \frac{3 \bullet 2 \bullet 1}{1(3 \bullet 2 \bullet 1)} .125(1) = .125$$

The Binomial Tables

Fortunately, we need not involve ourselves with such computations as we have pre-established tables to yield the desired probabilities. We have included Table 2 in Appendix A for convenience in finding binomial probabilities. Table 2 provides the cumulative probabilities of each individual value of the random variable for various values of n and p.

1. Finding the Probability of Exactly r Successes

For example, let's look up the probability of obtaining exactly 2 tails ($r = 2$) in 3 flips ($n = 3$) of the fair coin ($p = .5$). In a cumulative table, when we look at $r = 2$ we do not obtain $\Pr(r = 2)$ but rather $\Pr(r \leq 2)$ or $\Pr(r = 0 + r = 1 + r = 2)$. If we looked up the appropriate values for r, n, and p on Table 2 we obtain a value of $\Pr(r \leq 2) = 0.875$. Again, this is not $\Pr(r = 2)$ because in the cumulative table we obtain the probability of obtaining either 0 tails (.125), 1 tail (.375), or 2 tails (.375). If we wanted the probability of exactly 2 tails on a cumulative probability table (Table 2), we subtract $\Pr(r \leq 2)$ from $\Pr(r \leq 1)$ successes ($.875 - .5 = .375$).

2. Finding the Probability of r or Fewer Successes

When using the cumulative probability table we automatically obtain the probability of r or fewer successes [$\Pr(r \leq 2)$]. Viewing Table 2B for tossing a tail twice in three flips of a coin ($r = 2$, $n = 3$, $p = .5$), we obtain a probability of 0.875, or 87.5%. The cumulative table already has summed the values for $r = 0$, $r = 1$, and $r = 2(.125 + .375 + .375)$.

3. Finding the Probability of less than r Successes

To find the probability of obtaining less than 2 tails in three flips of a coin, we are referring to $\Pr(r = 0 + r = 1)$. Hence, all we need is to obtain $\Pr(r \leq 1)$ on the cumulative table and obtain 0.5 or 50%.

4. Finding the Probability of r or More Successes

To find the probability of 2 or more successes we will read the probability from Table 2B for $\Pr(r \leq 1)$ as .5. This means the probability of $r = 0 + r = 1 = .5$. Subtracting this from 1 (the entire distribution) yields the probability of $r = 2 + r = 3[1 - \Pr(r \leq 1) = 1 - .5 = .5, 50\%]$.

5. Finding the Probability of More than r Success

To find the probability of more than two successes refers to $\Pr(r > 2)$. View Table 2 to obtain $\Pr(r \leq 2)$, which is the sum of $r = 0$, $r = 1$, and $r = 2$. Subtract this value (.875) from 1 and we have the probability of $\Pr(r > 2) = 1 - \Pr(r \leq 2)$.

6. Finding the Probability Between $r = 1$ and $r = 2$ Successes

We view $\Pr(r \leq 2) = .875$ and $\Pr(r \leq 0) = .125$. Since $\Pr(r \leq 2)$ is $\Pr(r = 0) + \Pr(r = 1) + \Pr(r = 2)$, the subtraction from $\Pr(r \leq 0)$ yields $\Pr(1 \leq r \leq 2) = .875 - .125 = .75$.

7. Finding a Probability for $p > .5$

The binomial tables only provide values of p up to .5. An illustration can best show why this is still complete. Suppose we have an unfair coin that comes up tails 70% of the time ($p = .7$). What is the probability of tossing 3 tails (successes: $r = 3$) in 5 trials ($n = 5$) when the probability of a success is .7? Table 2 does not provide the answer, but it does provide it indirectly if we rephrase the question. The probability of tossing 3 tails (successes) in 5 trials when p is .7 is identical to the probability of tossing 2 heads (failures) in 5 trials when the probability of a failure (q) is .3. By phrasing the question in terms of converting failures into successes, we can find any binomial probability not covered in the tables.

Properties, Expected Value, and Variance of the Binomial Distribution

We note that our probabilities for r successes depends on p and n. In Figures 4.1A–C we have examples of a binomial distribution for a constant sample size ($n = 5$) for p values of .2, .5, and .8. We note that when $p = .5$ the distribution is symmetric; however, when $p = .2$ and .8, the distribution is skewed respectively to the left and right. In Figures 4.1D–E we keep $p = .2$, but increase the sample size to 10 (Table 4.1D) and to 20 (Table 4.1E). We conclude that the binomial distribution is approximately bell shaped when p nears .5 and/or when n becomes large.

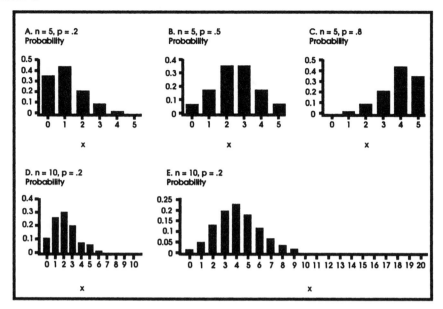

The mean and standard deviation for a binomial random variable are stated in formulas 4.2 and 4.3.

Mean and Standard Deviation of a Binomial Variable

$$\mu = n \bullet p \qquad\qquad (4.2)$$

$$\sigma = \sqrt{n \bullet p \bullet q} \qquad\qquad (4.3)$$

where

n = number of trials

p = probability of success

q = probability of failure

Thus, if $n = 5$ and $p = .5$, then the mean and standard deviation for this binomial probability distribution are

$$\mu = n \bullet p = 5(.5) = 2.5$$

$$\sigma = \sqrt{n \bullet p \bullet q} = \sqrt{5(.5)(.5)} = \sqrt{1.25} = 1.12$$

and the complete distribution is shown in Figure 4.1B.

Let's use a quality control example to illustrate what we have learned from the binomial distribution. Suppose a quality control engineer samples three items from an assembly line and finds that two are defective. If the production process is functioning properly, experience has shown that 10 percent defective are produced. Assuming that 10 percent of the items produced are defective, what is the probability of the described sample result? Also what are the expected value and standard deviation of the distribution?

To start with, we could determine the probability using the binomial formula directly. The relevant calculation is

$$\text{Pr} \, (2 \text{ defective out of } 3) = \frac{3 \bullet 2 \bullet 1}{2 \bullet 1(1)} \, .1^2(1 - .1)^{3-2} = 3(.01)(.9) = .027$$

79

If we use Table 2, we find $p = .1$, $n = 3$, and $r = 2$ and $r = 1$ and subtract the two to obtain .027 (.999 − .972). Based on this relatively low probability, the quality control engineer would likely question the proper functioning of the process.

The expected value and standard deviation of the distribution are

$$\mu = n \bullet p = 3(.1) = 0.3$$

$$\sigma = \sqrt{n \bullet p \bullet q} = \sqrt{3(.1)(.9)} = \sqrt{0.27} = 0.5196$$

 Concept Check 4.B

A town meeting contains 30 Republicans, 40 Democrats, and 5 Independents. The binomial distribution can be used to determine the probability of randomly selecting 3 Democrats, 2 Republicans, and 1 Independent for a committee. True or false? If false, explain.

Exercises

4.11   a.   Suppose a quality control manager inspects a sample of five parts from each large incoming shipment. If 20 percent of the parts are generally flawed, use the binomial formula to determine the probability that the manager's sample will contain four or more flawed parts?
       b.   Use the binomial table to confirm your computations.
       c.   Compute the mean and standard deviation of the distribution.

4.12   If r is a binomial random variable with $n = 4$ and $p = .3$, determine the probability distribution.

4.13   If r is a binomial random variable with $n = 5$ and $p = .4$, determine the probability distribution.

4.14   If r is a binomial random variable and n and p are 5 and .5, respectively, determine

       a. $\Pr(r = 2)$
       b. $\Pr(r = 5)$
       c. $\Pr(r > 3)$
       d. $\Pr(r \leq 1)$
       e. $\Pr(2 < r \leq 4)$

4.15   If r is a binomial random variable with $n = 50$ and $p = .3$, determine the mean, variance, and standard deviation.

4.16   Use the binomial distribution tables in the Appendix to find the required probabilities of the random variable r if $n = 20$ and $p = .2$

       a. $\Pr(r = 10)$
       b. $\Pr(r = 4)$
       c. $\Pr(r < 8)$
       d. $\Pr(r > 6)$
       e. $\Pr(5 < r < 9)$

4.17   An audit department has found that the accounts receivable department averaged one error in every ten accounts during the previous year. However, a recent sample of four accounts found errors on three different accounts. Using the binomial distribution, determine the probability of the sample result assuming last year's accuracy is still true.

4.18   What are the mean and standard deviation for a binomial probability distribution when $p = .3$ and $n = 20$? Is the distribution skewed? If it is skewed, which way?

4.19   Using the binomial probability tables in Appendix A, determine the following probabilities if $n = 10$ and $p = 4$.

   a. $Pr(r = 4)$
   b. $Pr(r > 4)$
   c. $Pr(r < 3)$
   d. $Pr(2 < r < 8)$
   e. $Pr(r > 5)$

4.20   a.   Shipments of a part come in 100 units. We will randomly sample 4 parts to determine if they are defective. Historically we have found that either 10%, 20%, or 30% of the parts are defective. For each possibility what is the probability of finding $r = 0$?
   b.   For each possibility what is the probability of finding $r = 1$
   c.   For each possibility what is the probability of finding $r = 2$
   d.   For each possibility what is the probability of finding $r = 3$
   e.   For each possibility what is the probability of finding $r = 4$

4.4   The Normal Distribution

The normal distribution is certainly the most important probability distribution that we study in statistics. It is also the one probability distribution known to individuals not trained in statistics. Many people in fact refer to a measurement following a bell shaped curve without knowing that what they are really referring to is the normal curve. The normal curve is a continuous distribution that requires that the random variable be continuously measurable. The continuity of the normal curve presents some interesting problems in determining probabilities. However, these problems will be resolved through a process of standardization which will be developed subsequently. The importance of the normal curve does not arise due to the abundance of normally distributed populations of measurements, but from its role in describing theoretical distributions of sample results. However, a discussion of its role in statistics is premature at this point and will be developed fully in later chapters.

The normal distribution was first used in 1733 by Antoine de Moivre. However, it was not popularized until the work by the German mathematician, Carl F. Gauss, in the early 19th century. The contributions of Gauss were so significant that the normal distribution is often referred to as the Gaussian distribution. The formula for the normal distribution is

Normal Curve

$$f(x) = \frac{1}{\sqrt{2\pi\sigma^2}} \bullet e^{-[x-\mu/2\sigma]^2} \tag{4.4}$$

where

   $\pi = Pi = 3.14159$ etc.

   $\sigma = $ standard deviation of distribution

   $\mu = $ the mean of the distribution

   $e = $ natural logarithm base, approximately equal to 2.71828

   $x = $ the values of the normally distributed random variable, $-\infty \leq x \leq +\infty$

   $f(x) = $ the height (ordinate) of the normal distribution as a function of x

The normal curve formula is completely described by the mean and variance, since π and e are constants (Figure 4.2). Thus, each normal curve can be mathematically developed knowing nothing more than the distribution's mean and standard deviation.

Figure 4.2 Normal Curves

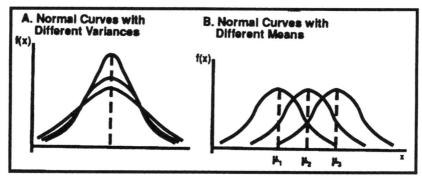

The basic characteristic of a normal curve are
1. Bell shaped and symmetrical about the mean
2. Equality of the mean, median, and mode
3. Continuous curve over values of the random variable (x) ranging from minus infinity to positive infinity $(-\infty < x < +\infty)$
4. The total area under the normal curve is 1
5. $f(x)$, the ordinate of the normal curve must be greater than zero for all values of x

The first characteristic implies that the normal curve can be divided at its mean value and the two halves are mirror images of one another. Characteristic 2 follows from the definition of each of the three measures of central tendency. The mean is the point of balance in a distribution and, given that the normal curve is symmetrical, the center point in the distribution must be equal to the mean. In addition, the median is the value such that one-half of the values in the distribution are below and one-half above. Given again the symmetry of the normal curve, the median must be the central value in the distribution. The mode is the most frequently occurring value in the distribution and thus, must be the value for which the probability distribution attains the maximum height (highest probability).

Again in a symmetrical distribution that is bell shaped, the highest frequency or probability occurs with the central value in the distribution. Thus, as discussed in Chapter 2, the numerical differences between the mean, median, and mode increase with the lack of symmetry in the distribution. For the normal curve, the mean, median, and mode are equivalent measures of central tendency. The normal distribution is appropriate for random variables which are continuous on the real number line. Thus, characteristic 3 recognizes that the normal curve is not valid for discrete random variables. The total area under the normal curve is equal to 1.

Determining Probabilities for a Normal Curve

With a continuous probability distribution such as the normal curve, the random variable is said to be infinitely divisible. This means that between any two values of the random variable, regardless of how close, there exists a third value of the random variable. In essence, for a continuous probability distribution, there exists an infinite number of values for the random variable and the probability of any single point approaches zero [Pr (any single value) = 0]. Thus, probability statements for continuous distributions must be expressed in terms of intervals rather than point values.

As an example, assume a normally distributed population of heights of employees (with known mean and standard deviation). We can legitimately ask for the probability of the height of a randomly selected employee falling between 5′9″ and 6′ tall. However, it is not appropriate in this case to require the probability of this employee measuring exactly 6′0″ tall. Because the normal distribution is continuous (not discrete), all problems requiring probabilities reduce to the mathematical problem of determining the area under the curve between two values of the random variable. Essentially, we addressed this problem when determining probabilities for the continuous uniform distribution. However, in the case of the uniform distribution, the requisite areas were rectangular and determining their areas were easy. For the normal distribution the mathematics of finding the area under the curve is not so direct.

To facilitate the determination of areas under the normal curve a standard normal distribution is developed with a mean of 0 and a standard deviation of 1 and tables of areas under this curve are provided in Appendix A, Table 1. Given a normal distribution with a different mean (μ unequal to 0) and (or) a different standard deviation, the distribution must first be converted into its standardized form and then the standard normal table applies.

To illustrate the concept of standardizing a normal distribution, we will use information supplied to us from the National Center for Health Statistics. The mean height of American men between the ages of 18 to 74 is 5 feet 9 inches tall ($\mu = 69$ inches) with a standard deviation of 2.8 inches ($\sigma = 2.8$ inches). In order to know the probabilities of males being shorter or taller than some height we need to convert height differences into a z scale. The z scale is obtained by using the following standardizing formula

Normal Curve Standardizing Formula

$$z = \frac{X_i - \mu}{\sigma} \qquad (4.5)$$

where

σ = standard deviation of distribution

μ = the mean of the distribution

x_i = the values of the normally distributed random variable

Thus, a z-value of -1 means that the specified value of the random variable is 1 standard deviation *below* the mean of the distribution. A z-value of $+2$ means that the point is 2 standard deviations *above* the mean of the distribution. Note that the larger the absolute value of the z, the further from the mean of the distribution is the observation and the less probable it is (reflected in the lower height of the curve).

In general the standardizing formula for any distributional problem is identical. The numerator will always express the difference between the random variable and the mean of the distribution, while the denominator will be the standard deviation of the distribution. Thus, the standardization expresses the values of the random variable in terms of numbers of standard deviations from the mean value. The process of standardizing a distribution will be repeatedly used throughout the text in numerous different applications. The only real difference will be in the respective means and standard deviations of the distributions.

We are now in a position to link the value of z to areas under the curve and to probability statements. To facilitate that, examine the standard normal curve in Table 1 in Appendix A. It provides the area under the curve between the mean of the distribution and the specific point in question as shown in Figure 4.3 and the figure accompanying Table 1.

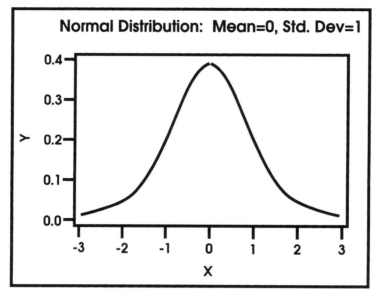

Figure 4.3 Standardized Normal Areas under the Curve

The row and column headings in Table 1 provide the z-value for a standardized normal distribution. The row labels provide the units and tenths for z, the column labels provide the hundredths, and the table reading for a specific row and column yields the area between the mean of the distribution at the point in question.

For example, a z of 1.00 yields an area of .3413. This means that the area under the curve between the mean of the distribution and a z of 1.00 is .3413 [$Pr(0 < z < 1.00) = .3413$]. Since there is no area associated with a single z-value, $Pr(z = 1.00) = 0$, $Pr(0 < z < 1.00) = Pr(0 \leq z \leq 1.00)$. It matters not if we use an inequality sign ($<$ or $>$) or an equal sign ($\leq$ or $\geq$).

A less mechanical interpretation is that the probability of a value of the normally distributed random variable between the mean of the distribution and the mean plus one standard deviation is .3413. Since the normal distribution is symmetrical about the mean, the area between $\mu + 1°\sigma$ and $\mu - 1°\sigma$ are equal. Therefore, standardized normal tables provide the areas on only one side of the distribution and leave it to the reader to deduce areas on the other side of the distribution. To demonstrate the procedure for finding areas under the standard normal curve, we will analyze some examples that cover the full range of possible problems. Despite the mechanical nature of these problems we must keep in mind that we are finding probabilities when we determine areas under the standard normal curve. More meaningful applications will be developed later.

Example 1: What percent of American men are between 72.5 and 69 inches tall? First we ascertain that 72.5 inches tall is 1.25 standard deviations above the mean ($z = 72.5 - 69/2.8 = +1.25$). Technically, we are finding $Pr(0 > z > 1.25) = Pr(-1.25 < z < 0)$ which are equivalent.

In this case we are looking for the area between the mean ($z = 0$) and $z = 1.25$. The standard normal table (Table 1: Appendix A) provides that area directly by looking up a z-value of 1.25. Thus, the area is .3944. Approximately 100,000,000 men comprise the population; hence 39,440,000 men are involved.

84

Figure 4.4 Pr(0 < z < 1.25) = Pr(−1.25 < z < 0)

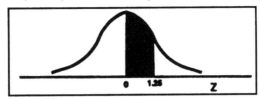

Example 2: What percentage of American men are over (or under) 6′0″ tall? We find that 72 inches tall is 1.07 standard deviations above the mean ($z = 72 − 69/2.8 = 1.07$). Technically, we are finding Pr($z > 1.07$) for those above 6 feet and Pr($1.07 < z$) for those below 6′0″. A $z = 1.07$ yields an area of .3577. For those greater than 6′0″ it's the area to the right of the normal distribution beyond a z scale of 1.07. Knowing that the entire right tail of the distribution is 50%, our probability is .5 − .3577 = .1423. Hence 14.23% of the adult males in the U.S. are 72 inches or taller. Conversely, if we wanted to find the percent below 6′0″ we would want the entire area to the left of a $z = 1.07$. This would include the entire left tail plus a portion of the right tail. The probability is .5 + .3577 = .8577, or 85.77% of the population is 6′0″ or below.

Figure 4.5 Pr(z < 1.07) or Pr(z > 1.07)

Example 3: What percentage of American men are between 5′8″ and 5′11″ tall? We find that 71 inches tall is 0.71 standard deviations above the mean ($z = 71 − 69/2.8 = 0.71$) while 68 inches tall is 0.36 standard deviations below the mean ($z = 68 − 69/2.8 = −0.36$). We are finding the Pr($−0.36 < z < 0.71$). Since both z-values incorporate the mean of 69 inches, all we have to do is look up the areas from the normal distribution and add them. A $z = −0.36$ is .1406 and a $z = 0.71$ is .2611, summing to .4017. Hence 40.17% of American adult males are between 5′8″ and 5′11″ tall.

Figure 4.6 Pr(−0.36 < z < 0.71)

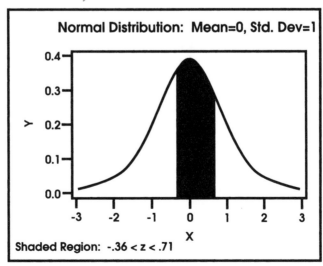

85

Example 4: What percent of American men are between 6'2" and 6'5" tall? We find that 74 inches tall is 1.79 standard deviations above the mean ($z = 74 - 69/2.8 = 1.79$) while 77 inches tall is 2.86 standard deviations above the mean ($z = 77 - 69/2.8 = 2.86$). We are finding the $\Pr(1.79 < z < 2.86)$. Since both z values are greater than the mean of 69 inches, we have to look up the areas from the normal distribution and subtract the greater absolute z from the smaller. A $z = 2.86$ is .4979 and a $z = 1.79$ is .4633, subtracting to obtain .0346. Hence 3.46% of American adult males are between 6'2" and 6'5" tall.

Figure 4.7 $\Pr(1.79 < z < 2.86)$

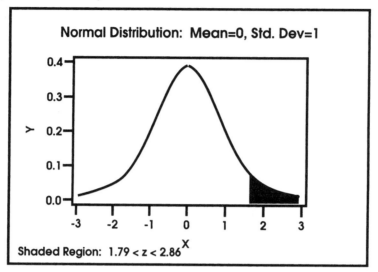

Normal Approximation to the Binomial Distribution

The normal distribution can be used to approximate the binomial distribution. This is true despite the fact that the normal distribution is continuous and the binomial distribution is discrete. The binomial distribution will also be skewed if p, the probability of a success, is not equal to .5. Whereas the normal distribution is always symmetrical. However, the skewness of the binomial distribution declines as n increases (see Figure 4.1).

The exact binomial probabilities are generally preferred for solutions to problems but, when the number of trials (n) is large, using the binomial formula or even tables of binomial probabilities becomes a tedious task. In these applications, when n is sufficiently large, using the normal distribution to approximate binomial probabilities is beneficial. As a rule of thumb, the requirement for using the normal to approximate the binomial distribution requires that $n \bullet p > 5$ and $n \bullet q > 5$.

Since the binomial distribution is discrete and the normal distribution is continuous, a continuity correction factor is included in the use of the normal curve in determining solutions to binomial problems. The continuity correction factor adds or subtracts .5 from the endpoint of intervals on the random variable. This correction adjusts for the fact that a discrete value of the random variable has meaning only in an interval sense in the continuous case. One success in the continuous sense is essentially the interval from .5(1 − .5) to 1.5(1 + .5). Thus, if we desire the probability of obtaining between 3 and 6 successes in 10 trials using the normal distribution, we need to determine the area under the curve between 2.5 and 6.5. Figure 4.8 shows the logic of the continuity correction factor.

Figure 4.8 Continuity Correction Factor

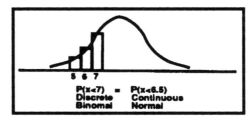

As an example of using the normal to approximate a binomial probability, determine the probability of finding between and including 8 and 16 defective items in a shipment of 100 parts if the probability of a defective is .10. The first consideration is whether the problem meets the requirements for using the normal distribution as an approximation. In this case, $n \bullet p = 100 \cdot (.10) = 10$ and $n \bullet q = 100 \cdot (.9) = 90$. Thus, both products exceed 5 and the analysis can be legitimately performed. The next step is to determine the mean and standard deviation of this binomial distribution which are

$$\mu = n \cdot p = 100 \bullet (.10) = 10$$

and

$$\sigma = \sqrt{n \bullet p \bullet q} = \sqrt{100 \bullet (.10)(.90)} = 3$$

Given the mean and standard deviation, we can standardize the normal curve in order to find the relevant area. However, the continuity correction factor would require that we find the area under the curve between 7.5 (8 − .5) and 16.5 (16 + .5). The requisite z-values are

$$z = \frac{7.5 - 10}{3} = \frac{-2.5}{3} = -.83$$

$$z = \frac{16.5 - 10}{3} = \frac{6.5}{3} = 2.17$$

The required area between 7.5 and 16.5 is the sum of .2967($z = -.83$) and .4850($z = 2.17$) or .7817. Thus, using the normal curve to approximate the binomial we find the probability of eight to sixteen defective items in a shipment of one hundred parts to be .7817 if the probability of a defective item is .10.

Having MINITAB Generate a Population

We mentioned earlier that the mean of adult male heights in the U.S. is 69 inches with a standard deviation of 2.8 inches. We will have MINITAB randomly develop a sample of 100 individuals and determine how many are above 6'6" (78 inches) tall. The command sequence is:

Calc > Random Data > Normal
Enter 100 into **Generate** _____ **rows of data**
Enter **C1** into **Store in column(s)**
Enter **69** as the **Mean**
Enter **2.8** as the **Standard deviation**
OK

Each time that you run this sequence a different data set will appear. It will be rare to find an individual 78 inches tall. Use the command sequence **Stats > Basic Statistics > Descriptive Statistics**

87

to compute the mean and standard deviation. They will be slightly different than 69 inches and 2.8 inches because of the randomness of the data.

 Concept Check 4.C

All normal distributions are identical. True or false? If false, explain.

Exercises

4.21 If 3 normal distributions had identical means with unequal standard deviations, which distribution would be the shortest and tallest? Explain.

4.22 If we knew a mean temperature for a city was 70 degrees, could we determine what percentage of days will have a temperature more than 72 degrees? Explain.

4.23 In a normal distribution, what do we know about the mean, median, and mode?

4.24 Determine the area under the standard normal curve for the following problems.

   a. $Pr(z > 1.34)$
   b. $Pr(-1.23 < z < 2.12)$
   c. $Pr(0.56 < z < 1.78)$
   d. $Pr(0 < z < 2.33)$
   e. $Pr(z > -1.23)$

4.25 Determine the area under the standard normal curve for the following problems.

   a. $Pr(z > .56)$
   b. $Pr(-0.45 < z < 1.96)$
   c. $Pr(-1.34 < z < 0.342)$
   d. $Pr(0 < z < 1.64)$
   e. $Pr(z < 1.76)$

4.26 City A: Temperature (in degrees Fahrenheit) $\mu = 70$ & $\sigma = 2$. City B: Temperature (in degrees Fahrenheit) $\mu = 70$ & $\sigma = 5$.

   a. In which city would you have greater clothing and utility bills? Explain.
   b. What percentage of days would be colder than 66 degrees in cities A and B?

4.27 Suppose you are confronted with two investment opportunities requiring equal dollar outlays. The rate of return for stock A is assumed to be normally distributed with a mean and standard deviation of .15 and .05. The distribution for the rate of return for stock B is also assumed to be normally distributed but with a lower mean (.12) and standard deviation (.03). Suppose you are risk averse and decide you will purchase the stock with the greater probability of a rate of return in excess of .10.

   a. Given this information, what is the possibility that stock A will satisfy the requirement of a rate of return in excess of .10?
   b. Given this information, what is the probability that stock B will satisfy the requirement of a rate of return in excess of .10?
   c. Which stock should you buy? Explain.

4.28 An automated beverage filling machine is adjusted to fill cans with a mean level of 12 ounces and a standard deviation of .1 ounce. Each can will hold at most 12.25 ounces. On the low fill side, cans that are filled to less than 11.75 ounces cannot be sold and must be destroyed.

a. What is the probability of an acceptable fill level (more than 11.75 and less than 12.25 ounces)?

b. What is the probability of an underfilled can (less than 11.75)?

c. What is the probability of an overfilled can (more than 12.25)?

4.29 In a normal distribution, what is $\Pr(z > 0)$?

4.30 You have two classes from which to select a basketball team. Class A has a mean height of 69 inches with a standard deviation of 3. Class B has a mean height of 70 inches with a standard deviation of 1 inch.

a. From which class would you like to select your team? Explain.

b. What percentage of both classes is over 73 inches tall?

4.31 When may we use the normal distribution to approximate the binomial distribution?

4.32 Why do we have a correction factor when using the normal distribution to approximate a binomial distribution?

4.33 Use the normal approximation to the binomial to find the probability of between 5 and 9 defaults on 60 residential mortgages if the probability of a default is .10.

4.34 Use the normal approximation to the binomial to find the probability of 8 or more defaults on 60 residential mortgages if the probability of a default is .10.

4.5   Summary

In this chapter the concepts of a random variable and probability distribution were introduced. We then analyzed the mean and variance of a random variable and began looking at specific probability distributions. In this development we introduced the uniform, binomial, Poisson, and normal distributions. These distributions include some of the most frequently used and widely applicable continuous and discrete probability distributions. The material in this chapter will be fundamental to many of the remaining material in the text and is extremely important to the logic of statistical inference and decision-making.

Mini-case 4.1: Should Shipments from Suppliers Always Be Accepted?

Many manufacturers of electronic products buy component parts from manufacturers. Thus, the quality of their product is dependent on the quality of the parts which they receive. To provide some control over the quality of their products many manufacturers routinely sample incoming shipments of parts and test them. Based on the results of the test, they will either accept the shipment and begin installing them in their product or return them to the supplier for a credit or an exchange of parts. Assume for the following questions that the proportion of defective parts in shipments has averaged .10 over a considerable period of time.

a. What is the implied probability of a defective item?

b. What is the probability of obtaining exactly 0 defective in a sample of size 10?

c. What is the probability of obtaining exactly 1 defective in a sample of size 10?

d. If you found 3 or more defective in a sample of size 10, what would you infer about the quality of the products in the shipment?

e. Based on the results from a sample of size 10, you could accept the shipment, reject the shipment, or do what else?

Your employer informs you that you are to be transferred to one of two cities. City A has a mean daily temperature of 70 degrees with a standard deviation of 2 degrees. City B has a mean daily temperature of 75 degrees with a standard deviation of 5 degrees.

a. Which city will experience the largest percentage of days with daily temperatures below 65 degrees?

b. Additional clothing and heating costs are estimated to be $5.00 per day for each day the temperature falls below 66 degrees. How much will it cost for these expenses per year in the two cities?

Review of Important Terms and Concepts

Random variable: A rule or function that assigns numeric values to the outcomes of a random process.

Discrete random variable: A random variable that can assume at most a countable number of outcomes.

Continuous random variable: A random variable that can assume any value in an interval and is thus unable to be counted.

Binomial distribution: A discrete probability distribution meeting the following requirements:

1. Each trial can only result in one of two possible outcomes, generally referred to as "success" and "failure."
2. The outcome on each trial is independent of the others.
3. The probability of a success (p) remains constant for all trials and, therefore, so does the probability of failure $(q = 1 - p)$.

Normal distribution: A continuous probability distribution completely described by the mean and variance. The basic characteristics of a normal curve are

1. Bell shaped and symmetrical about the mean
2. Equality of the mean, median, and mode
3. Continuous curve over values of the random variable (x) ranging from minus infinity to positive infinity $(-\infty < x < +\infty)$
4. The total area under the normal curve is 1
5. $\Pr(x)$ or $f(x)$, the ordinate of the normal curve must be greater than zero for all values of x

Continuity correction factor: Correction made to the interval of the random variable when using the continuous normal curve to approximate the discrete binomial distribution.

Review of Important Formulas

Binomial Formula

$$\Pr(r) = {}_nC_r \bullet p^r \bullet q^{n-r} = \frac{n!}{r! \bullet (n-r)!} \bullet p^r \bullet q^{n-r} \qquad (4.1)$$

where

r = the number of successes in n trials, $r = 0, 1, 2, \ldots, n$

n = the number of trials

p = the probability of a success

q = the probability of a failure

${}_nC_r$ = the number of combinations of n things taken r at time

Mean and Standard Deviation of a Binomial Variable

$$\mu = n \bullet p \tag{4.2}$$

$$\sigma = \sqrt{n \bullet p \bullet q} \tag{4.3}$$

where

n = number of trials

p = probability of success

q = probability of failure

Normal Curve

$$f(x) = \frac{1}{\sqrt{2\pi\sigma^2}} \bullet e^{-[x-\mu/2\sigma]^2} \tag{4.4}$$

where

π = Pi = 3.14159 etc.

σ = standard deviation of distribution

μ = the mean of the distribution

e = natural logarithm base, approximately equal to 2.71828

x = the values of the normally distributed random variable, $-\infty \leq x \leq +\infty$

$f(x)$ = the height (ordinate) of the normal distribution as a function of x

Normal Curve Standardizing Formula

$$z = \frac{X_i - \mu}{\sigma} \tag{4.5}$$

where

σ = standard deviation of distribution

μ = the mean of the distribution

x_i = the values of the normally distributed random variable

Graph > Histogram
Double click **FaceSum** into **Graph Variables** box.
Click **Options**.
Click on **Density**.
Click on **Define interval using values** box and enter **2 3 4 5 6 7 8 9 10 11 12**
OK twice.

Sampling and Sampling Distributions

Where we have been

We have reviewed probability theory and distributions.

Where we are going

We now introduce the concept of sampling and the sampling methods that are available to us. Each method has its distinct advantages and disadvantages. We then introduce the all important sampling distribution which allows us in later chapters to make inferences concerning the population from sample data.

5.1   Introduction

In the modern world, obtaining information is a vital part of business activities. We want to ensure that products we make adhere to quality standards, that we can predict human resource needs and the labor base from which our needs must be fulfilled, and to predict the future needs and desires of our consumers, just to name a few.

The ability to manage business effectively depends on accurate and timely information. If we were going to sell a product/service to households in a major market, we would need information concerning the specific profile and needs of that market. Since major markets usually have over one million households, it will not be possible (or profitable or necessary) to obtain information from all of them. We will need to make inferences from sample data concerning the population of households.

If every item in a population were evaluated, it would be called a complete enumeration or **census**. If a population were known there would be no need for statistical sampling theory, as all the information would be known and no estimates need be made. However, it is impractical and not necessary to census populations in order to obtain useful information for several reasons. First, there are often enormous costs involved in census enumeration. Second, a great deal of time is usually consumed when attempting to obtain population data. With most business firms facing intense competition, time can be a larger obstacle than refinements in the accuracy of information.

A third reason for sampling is that some populations are inaccessible. If we were to do a census of all tourists who visit Daytona Beach it would be impossible to reach the entire population. Hotels, the beach itself, airports, train and bus stations, if monitored would not yield the full population as some tourists would come by automobile and may never go near the monitored places. A last reason for sampling is due to the possible destructive nature of making the observation involved. We have all seen cars test crashed at various speeds to ascertain safety standards. Such tests destroy extremely valuable assets.

Parameters and Statistics Defined

When we describe populations and samples we usually do so by stating their measures of central tendency (mean, median, mode, etc.) or dispersion (standard deviation). When these measures of central tendency and dispersions are taken from the population they are termed **parameters**. When they are taken from the sample they are called **statistics**. A statistic is a measure of a sample and a parameter is a measure of a population.

We use sample statistics to make estimates of population parameters. Such estimates usually save considerable time and money. For example, suppose we wanted to determine how every student taking a comparable class in business statistics throughout the world feels about the class. This group of students would be the population from which a census would be impractical. Hence, we would have to survey to obtain the desired information and to expedite the process. The first question we might investigate is the type of sample to be used.

Concept Check 5.A

If we define your class as a population, the mean age of the class is called a statistic. True or false. If false, explain.

Exercises

5.1   A class (the population) has a mean age of 22.9. A sample is randomly selected from the class and the mean is 24.4.

    a.   The 24.4 value is termed a _____ .
    b.   The 22.9 value is termed a _____ .

5.2   Define

    a.   Statistic.
    b.   Parameter.
    c.   Differentiate between a statistic and a parameter.

Samples are usually classified as being **random** or **nonrandom**. The term random signifies that every elementary unit of the population has had an equal chance of being selected in the sample. This is not the case for the convenience or judgment nonrandom samples. For example the local TV station or newspaper will ask you to respond to a current issue, like capital punishment or the minimum wage, and ask you to respond by calling a specified number to register a positive or negative vote. This is nonrandom because only those who read the newspaper (or see the TV show) are eligible to respond. In addition, only those with very strong feelings will respond, and those with no strong feelings are unwilling to participate. In addition, sometimes the question posed is leading the participant to a particular response. The importance of such a survey is that you can only make comments concerning the specific outcome of the survey (80% of our callers favor capital punishment) and no statements (called inferences) can be made concerning the overall population. We can't make the statement that 80% of the viewing market favored (or were opposed) to capital punishment. Hence, the information does not expand beyond the survey itself.

You probably have walked into a mall and been asked to participate in a questionnaire. The questionnaire normally will ask your consumer habits concerning a product or group of products. Again the results can't go beyond the bounds of the survey itself. The survey staff may try to obtain a cross section of the mall inhabitants by various demographics to ensure that all are represented.

However, not all demographic classes of consumers actually go to malls and these would not be represented in a survey. The survey then would be termed **biased** because it overrepresents one group and underrepresents another group. The classic example of bias occurred when Franklin D. Roosevelt ran against Alfred M. Landon for president of the United States in 1936. A survey was taken with the readers of a popular magazine at the time (Literary Digest) to predict the winner. The magazine predicted that Mr. Landon would win easily. As it turned out Franklin Roosevelt won a very one-sided victory. The Literary Digest had selected its survey from its own subscribers and those who were telephone owners. At the time, magazine subscribers and households with telephones held a disproportionate percent of the population that were both wealthy and conservative. If there was a wealth requirement for voting, the poll might have been accurate. Since most citizens were experiencing economic problems, a new voice which advocated government intervention in the economy was welcomed.

Sometimes a corporation might wish that their product or service would receive very favorable ratings. Hence, there may be a tendency to induce a bias into the results. This could be accomplished by determining the group that views your product/service favorably, then over-sampling from that group. Some attorneys hire market specialists who attempt to determine the demographic and psychographic characteristics of individuals who might judge their client favorably. They then would select jurors who match the profile. Many experts believe that this bias favors the rich as opposed to the less wealthy. Hence, there is a debate in the legal profession on whether it should be continued.

It is also possible to deceive simply using semantics and misrepresenting statistics. If 50,000 individuals were surveyed concerning the use of a product, and only three individuals used it (#20,000 & #20,001 & #20,003) the statement could be made that 3 out of 4 surveyed used the product. Of course the statement implies an average 3 of 4, but technically 3 out of the selected 4 did utilize the product. It's up to the court systems to determine if this is to be considered false advertising. It may or may not be false advertising, but it certainly is poor statistical analysis. Such an error is called a nonsampling error because the problem was not caused by the actual sample, but rather by the sample design.

Not all nonsampling errors are deliberately created. There can also be innocent measurement errors. For example, what is your weight? It will be different at different times of the day. What then is your correct weight? Is it your weight in the morning, or your average weight? There is no correct answer to the question. When you attempt to lose weight you must weigh yourself at a consistent time in order to ascertain if you are gaining, losing, or maintaining a constant weight.

Returning to the nonrandom sampling, sometimes accuracy is not absolutely essential. Hence, less accurate, more affordable information is superior to none. Nonrandom sampling certainly is an inexpensive way to obtain information.

 Concept Check 5.B

When you answer questions in a mall you are representing many other consumers in your geographic region. True or false? If false, explain.

Exercises

5.3   Distinguish between a random and nonrandom sample. How does the term "inferences" relate?

5.4   Explain how a company selling toothpaste might induce a bias in its survey results.

5.5   Suppose we wanted to know how the households within a city felt about their public utilities. Only 50% of the residents own telephones, yet we plan to do a telephone survey. Might a problem of bias be experienced? Explain.

5.6   Explain a nonsampling error that may develop when a survey is performed to attempt to ascertain the popularity of a politician in office.

5.7   If you are attempting to lose weight on a diet, what might be some problem encountered when attempting to measure the actual weight loss?

5.8   What are the advantages and disadvantages to a nonrandom sample?

5.4   Types of Sampling That Utilize Random Numbers

In many real-world cases it is necessary to make inferences concerning the parent population from which the sample is drawn. Usually a great deal is riding on obtaining accurate information and an error can indeed be serious. We want information concerning the market, not just the individuals who are actually surveyed. It is essential that each member of the population have an equal chance of being selected. This requires a random selection from the population. The probability for an individual or item being selected in the survey is n/N, where n equals the sample size and N represents the population size.

All random samples will have a possible problem with a nonresponse bias. There will be certain members of the population who, if selected from sampling, will either not be available or will refuse to respond. Many researchers fear that the latter group is growing as many companies who solicit business over the phone use a lead in conversation alluding to conducting an impartial survey. This practice may ultimately affect legitimate market researchers.

The nonrespondents are important because their options and/or demographic and psychographic profiles may be different from those who do respond. For example, if we were conducting a survey concerning readership habits of a newspaper, we might find that the nonrespondents work during odd hours; hence, their readership habits may differ. The survey would exclude these unusual readership habits, thus biasing the survey. This is why market researchers call back up to four times the nonrespondents in an attempt to avoid the bias.

Nonresponse biases apply to both telephone and personal interviews. The telephone interview is of course involved with an additional bias, those consumers having no phones. Fortunately, this group nationally only occupies about 3% of the households.

Normally selecting a random sampling requires assigning random numbers to the elementary units within the population. The random selection of an elementary item must be out of the hands of the one doing the survey for fear of introducing a bias. We have watched Lotto drawings and know that there are 49 to 54 balls numbered sequentially. The balls are mixed by air pressure and vacuum selects the balls randomly. It would not be desirable for an individual merely to select the numbers that they wanted, because a personal bias will be involved. The numbers selected probably will have relevance to that individual. Those who knew that individual would have a much better chance of winning than those who did not.

The random number process works in the same way. Say there are 24 ($N = 24$) students in your business statistics class. We want to determine the average number of soft drink cans consumed by students in a 3-month period. We will randomly select 3 students ($n = 3$) to represent the class (population). We could use 24 ping-pong balls, slips of paper, or random numbers to make the selection. If we use random numbers, it is necessary to go two digits because with 1 digit we can only select 10 individuals. We would assign random numbers to individuals. We will have MINITAB select the random numbers for us. The command sequence is:

Calc > Random Data > Integer
Enter **3** into **Generate** _____ **rows of data**.
Enter **C1** into **Store in Column(s)**.
Enter **1** into **Minimum value**.
Enter **24** into **Maximum value**.
OK (Note: You will obtain different random numbers each time)

Table 5.1 MINITAB's Three Selected Students (note each execution of these commands will result in different random numbers)

23
8
12

If the first random number selected was 23, student #23 will be surveyed. If the second and third random numbers selected are 8 and 12, students #8 and #12 are to be surveyed (Table 5.2). In our example, the difference between the measures of central tendency and dispersion between the population and the sample is alarming. The mean and standard deviation of the population (parameters) is 49.58 and 30.73 respectively. The mean and standard deviation of the sample (statistics) consisting of students #8, #12, and #23 is 22.667 and 17.010 respectively.

Table 5.2 Randomly Selected Students' Ages and Cans of Soft Drinks Consumed in 3 Months ($N = 24$: $n = 3$)

#	Age	Cans Consumed	#	Age	Cans Consumed	#	Age	Cans Consumed
1	37	12	9	18	77	17	44	7
2	21	87	10	21	85	18	23	80
3	26	41	11	19	83	19	24	85
4	49	15	12*	27	42	20	31	40
5	19	84	13	31	37	21	24	82
6	48	8	14	27	43	22	22	86
7	29	37	15	31	41	23*	53	16
8*	39	10	16	43	15	24	22	77

97

Our population was a class size of 24 (N = population = 24). As such it is often called a finite population because of its limited size. We are assuming that once a student has been randomly selected to be surveyed they would not be eligible for a chance to be surveyed a second time. This is termed **sampling without replacement**. Small populations would be quickly exhausted as the sample size increases. As the elementary units are selected the probability of selecting the remaining elements changes. For example, our population had 7 students over 35 years old and 17 below 35. The first two students selected were over 35 years of age. The odds that the third student will be above 35 is 5/22 and for those below 35 is 17/22. For this reason the sample outcome is in a sense dependent on previous selections. For fairly large populations this dependence is usually minimal, and hence ignored. However, it can present a problem with small populations. Much of statistical analysis assumes independence of sequential data selections. Therefore, we will have to adjust small populations that involve sampling without replacement.

The changes in the probabilities of selecting an elementary unit is nominal in a large or infinite population when sampling without replacement. An infinite population is one where it would be difficult or practically impossible to perform a census. In a technical sense there is no such thing as an infinite population. Even the number of grains of sand on planet earth is finite, yet virtually impossible to count.

When we have sampling with replacement the probabilities of selecting the elementary units remain unchanged as units are randomly selected. In sampling with replacement the sample outcomes are independent or unrelated. Hence, there are less statistical problems in sampling with replacement than in sampling without replacement.

Advantages and Disadvantages

The type of random sample to which we have been referring is called an **unrestricted random sample** because no attempt is made to stratify or group the data prior to the selection of the elementary units. Every element in the population has an equal chance of being selected; hence, inferences can be made concerning the parent population.

The advantage of using the unrestricted random sample is that we will obtain estimates from a population without the cost and time allocation given to a census. In addition, we will be able to make inferences concerning the population because every member of the population had an equal chance of being selected.

There are some disadvantages in using an unrestricted random sample. First, in the selection of 3 students from the class we might choose the 3 oldest, or smartest, or the 3 with the lowest grade point average, etc. The sample might not be a good cross representation of the population. This is what in fact happened in our sample. We selected older individuals who consume less soft drinks than younger ones. Second, if we were conducting home personal interviews, the 3 selected students may come from different geographic regions causing a high cost per sampled individual plus a great deal of time consumed in obtaining the survey date.

A Stratified Sample

In a **stratified sample,** the population will be grouped into strata prior to sampling. The purpose of the stratification is to ensure the sample will include a cross section of the population and to reduce the number of elementary units to be surveyed without a loss in precision. If data are correctly stratified, the variation within each strata would be small, but the variation between strata is large.

Let's return to our previous example of 24 students and their soft drink consumption during a 3-month interval. We have divided the students into 3 age strata (Table 5.3) to determine if the students within each of the strata is fairly similar or homogeneous with respect to beverage consumption. The strata have students between 18–25, 26–34, and 35+. We can visually see a pattern in that the older the group, the lower the consumption of soft drink beverages.

The mean and standard deviation of the 18–25 age group is 82.60 and 3.57, respectively. For the 26–34 age group the figures are 40.286 and 2.498, and for the 35+ the figures are 11.86 and 3.63. The strata yield a meaningful segregation. The data within each group are homogeneous, but between groups are heterogeneous. If we were to survey three students, we would select one from each of the strata. The students in each of the strata would be assigned random numbers, and 3 such numbers would be selected. Table 5.3 has the 3 randomly selected students isolated with an asterisk. The weighted sample mean is 49.880 [84(10/24) + 41(7/24) + 10(7/24)]. The overall mean is 49.58 and $s = 30.73$.

Table 5.3 Stratified Sampling: Randomly Selected Students from Age Strata Concerning the Consumption of Soft Drinks in 3 Months ($N = 24$: $n = 3$)

YOUNG 18–25 (10)		MEDIUM AGED 26–34 (7)		OLDER 35+ (7)	
Age	*Cans Consumed*	*Age*	*Cans Consumed*	*Age*	*Cans Consumed*
21	87	26	41	37	12
19*	84	29	37	49	15
18	77	27	43	48	8
21	85	31	37	39*	10
19	83	27	43	43	15
23	80	31*	41	44	7
24	85	31	40	53	16
24	82	$\overline{X} = 40.286$		$\overline{X} = 11.86$	
22	86	$s = 2.498$		$s = 3.63$	
22	77				
$\overline{X} = 82.60$					
$s = 3.57$					

Advantages and Disadvantages

The advantage of a stratified sample is the inclusion of a randomly selected broad cross section of the population. In our example all 3 age groups are included within the sample, which did not occur in our unrestricted random sample. Second, we probably would obtain a sample mean closer to the population mean with a smaller sample than we would with a larger sample using an unrestricted random survey. In fact from the example used it would be difficult to perceive any disadvantages.

The main problem with the approach is the inability to stratify the data into meaningful homogeneous groups. We might conduct a survey to determine the popularity of a political leader. We could stratify the population by age, sex, political affiliation, etc., but we would find it difficult to find a within group standard deviation smaller than the overall standard deviation. As such, the technique has no benefits over unrestricted random sampling.

In order to establish the between-group and within-group variations, a preliminary (or pilot) survey is often taken. The approach is sometimes called two-phase sampling. In addition to dealing with the variation between and within the strata, pilot sampling can also minimize semantic problems in question design and interpretation. Finally, pilot studies are useful in establishing the need for additional questions needed to obtain the desired information.

In our analysis stratification works because the overall variance is almost ten times the variance of each of the subgroups.

Systematic Sampling

Another approach to sampling, frequently utilized in telephone surveys, is the **systematic survey**. The systematic approach utilizes two randomly selected numbers. The initial number represents the starting point and the second the skip pattern to be followed.

For example, suppose we selected the random numbers 2 and 8. This means we will survey student #2 (the initial starting point), and every 8th student after (#2, #2 + 8 = #10, and #10 + 8 = #18; the skip pattern). Hence, students #2, #10, and #18 will be included in the survey. Returning to our example, if these three students are surveyed (Table 5.4), the mean of the sample equals 84.00 beverage cans consumed.

Table 5.4 Systematic Sampling: Randomly Selected Starting Point and Skip Pattern Selects Students' Ages and Cans of Soft Drinks Consumed in 3 Months ($N = 24$: $n = 3$)

#	Age	Cans Consumed	#	Age	Cans Consumed	#	Age	Cans Consumed
1	37	12	9	18	77	17	44	7
2*	21	87	10*	21	85	18*	23	80
3	26	41	11	19	83	19	24	85
4	49	15	12	27	42	20	31	40
5	19	84	13	31	37	21	24	82
6	48	8	14	27	43	22	22	86
7	29	37	15	31	41	23	53	16
8	39	10	16	43	15	24	22	77

Advantages and Disadvantages

The advantages of systematic sampling are obvious when telephone surveys are to be implemented. Once the telephone number range is known for an area, simply have the computer select a starting number, then the skip pattern to be followed. In fact many survey companies have the computer itself ask the questions in order to reduce costs and avoid any interviewer bias. Such a bias can happen when the interviewer has predetermined notions concerning a product, service, or concept.

Having an unlisted number will not prevent you from being solicited as the telephone directory will not be used. One of the major disadvantages can be seen from our implementation of the process to our survey. We randomly selected our entire sample size from the 18–25 age group, which consumed considerably more soft drink beverages than the other age groups. Hence, a sampling error was created. This sampling error can be reduced or eliminated by increasing the sample size.

Another problem with the systematic approach deals with a patterned seasonal bias. Suppose we are dealing with data that involve days of the week, weeks, months, quarters, etc. Suppose we developed a skip pattern involving every 4th quarter, or every Saturday, and these periods represented our maximum/minimum sales. Also, if we surveyed every 8th unit off a production assembly with 8 machines, we will be surveying from a single machine. This problem in systematic sampling is called the systematic bias. For this reason, the systematic sample works best when the elements within the population are in a random order.

Of course, we could have combined a stratified and systematic survey design. After the data are first stratified, we might systematically sample from each of the strata. In fact, most survey designs encompass more than a single type of random sample.

Cluster Sampling

A final type of random sample stratifies the population into distinct and separate groups of elementary units, called clusters. Every element in the population can only appear in one cluster. The **cluster sample** works best when each cluster represents a microcosm of the overall population. Hence, the cluster units are as heterogeneous as the overall population. This is not normally the case when clusters relate to geographic areas. Neighborhoods sometimes contain homogeneous groups.

The cluster sample when applied usually relates to different geographical areas or regions. For example a city may be stratified into 24 zip codes. Within each zip code there may be an average of 8 school districts. Finally, within each school district there may be an average of 87 blocks.

The random number process would be used to select certain zip codes, certain school districts, and certain blocks. Then a final random process will be used to survey households, within the selected blocks, within the selected school districts, within the selected zip codes.

One of the main problems encountered with cluster sampling is that when blocks are surveyed they tend to be homogeneous rather than heterogeneous.

When applied the cluster approach is naturally in many instances based on a systematic survey. The telephone directory is used to determine starting geographic points by systematically selecting phone numbers. The address is then found and represents an initial starting point. The starting point itself is never surveyed because the results may bias the data in favor of those who have telephones within their residence. Some research companies disregard this possible bias as long as more than three-fourths of the households of the area have telephones. Nationwide, 97% of households have phones.

When you send field interviewers out to a geographic point, they must be able to survey more than one elementary unit in order to keep the survey costs in line. Hence, many researchers limit the sample size from any such geographic area to 5. Once at a geographic point, field surveyors are told to go in either a clockwise or counterclockwise (randomly selected from survey instrument) direction and survey every repeated household based on the systematic approach. A maximum of 5 households are usually surveyed from each geographical point to minimize each point's impact on the survey.

Advantages and Disadvantages

The cluster approach has great advantages in terms of keeping costs down when personal interviews are necessary. It is analogous to the stratified approach as the only difference is that we are stratifying geographically. Each cluster will normally be very homogeneous with respect to its demographic and psychographic profiles. Hence, sampling more than one from any cluster may be redundant. Overall, however, it is hoped that the procedure will yield a good cross section of many homogeneous clusters. It is possible, though, a bias will appear in favor of a particular set of clusters. Also, the data may be biased in favor of those who have telephones (assuming phone numbers are the process used in selecting initial survey points).

It should be noted that in certain real estate markets housing may be eclectic, or not homogeneous by cluster. Hence, it is possible for very expensive homes to be surrounded by modestly priced homes. This would alleviate the homogeneous problem by cluster should it exist.

 Concept Check 5.C

Each and every element or unit within a population must have an equal chance of being selected, or it is not a random survey. True or false? If false, explain.

Exercises

5.9   Which type of random sample would probably be used under the following conditions?

    a. A telephone survey is to be performed of the residents of a city.
    b. A household study involving 250 questions.
    c. A classroom is to be surveyed while the students are in class.
    d. First- and second-class passengers on an airline are to be asked their opinion on the service supplied to them.

5.10   Review the advantages and disadvantages of

    a. An unrestricted random sample
    b. A stratified random sample
    c. A systematic random sample
    d. A cluster random sample

5.11   Explain the term "interviewer bias."

5.12   Assign random numbers to a population of 30.

5.13   Recommend a survey methodology to determine

    a.   Student preferences in terms of the time courses should be taught (assuming the study is to be performed in class).

    b.   Student preferences in terms of the time courses should be taught (assuming the study is not to be performed in class).

5.14   Recommend a survey methodology to determine

    a.   The effect of a drug on hospital patients

    b.   The effect of a new leash law for licensed animals on elderly residents

5.15   Explain the difference between sampling with and without replacement.

5.16   Recommend a survey methodology to determine the impact of a proposed highway through a rural area. Note that the survey will involve over 200 questions being asked.

5.17   List the first 15 single-digit numbers that come to mind, then evaluate these numbers. Do you believe them to be random?

5.18   Why does a stratified sample appear to be superior in logic yet difficult to apply?

5.5   A Note of Caution

Sampling theory is quite difficult and extensive. Our attempt has been to acquaint you with the basic tools of the researcher. Our example was based on a small population and a very small sample ($n = 3$). In reality we never would be willing to make inferences from such a small sample. Yet we felt it would be easier to understand intuitively the different types of random surveys with the use of some data instead of using only abstract terms and concepts.

Please note that the analyses of subsequent chapters assume the data were obtained through random sampling techniques. Normally it is assumed the data come from an unrestricted random sample.

5.6   Sampling Error

So far our example has been a business statistics class ($N = 24$, $n = 3$) and trying to determine the mean soft drink consumption in a 3 month period. Even if we drew our survey following the strict principles of random sampling, we would find that there is a difference between the sample mean and the population mean. This difference is caused by the chance selection process. When we have small samples, the odds are good that in the random selection process an elementary unit will be selected that is considerably different from the mean. This will make the sample different from the population mean. With a small sample size it is unlikely that a second elementary unit will be selected that is at the opposite end of the spectrum enabling the sample and population means to equate.

The difference between the sample mean ($\overline{X}$: statistic) and the population mean (μ: parameter), attributable to the random selection process, is called **sampling error** ($\overline{X} - \mu$). In actuality there is no computational or methodology error involved, just a difference caused by chance selection and limited sample sizes.

The difference between sampling error and sampling bias is important. Sampling error can be reduced or eliminated by increasing the sample size, whereas sampling bias can't. Let's return to our example of the class and its consumption of soft drink beverages. We randomly selected 3 students (#8, #12, and

#23) and find the sample mean to be considerably below the population value ($\overline{X} = 22.667$, $\mu = 49.583$) because no student was selected from the 18–25 age group. Suppose we increase our sample size to 4 by randomly selecting student #2 (see Table 5.5). Note, as explained earlier, the odds increase towards selecting a younger individual if the survey is without replacement. The new sample mean is 38.75 which moves the sample mean closer to the population parameter. If we randomly selected a fifth student (#18), the new sample mean (47.00) would again move closer to the population parameter of 49.82.

Table 5.5 Increasing Sample Size (from Table 5.4) Reducing Sampling Error in an Unrestricted Random Sample ($N = 24$: $n = 3$)

#	Age	Cans Consumed	#	Age	Cans Consumed	#	Age	Cans Consumed
1	37	12	9	18	77	17	44	7
2**	21	87	10	21	85	18**	23	80
3	26	41	11	19	83	19	24	85
4	49	15	12*	27	42	20	31	40
5	19	84	13	31	37	21	24	82
6	48	8	14	27	43	22	22	86
7	29	37	15	31	41	23*	53	16
8*	39	10	16	43	15	24	22	77

*originally selected (Table 5.2: $n = 3$): $\overline{X} = 22.667$
**newly added to increase sample: $\overline{X} = 47.0$

On the other hand, let us evaluate sampling bias. Suppose we incorrectly defined the population and thought that it was composed of students in the 18–25 age category (see Table 5.3). If we increased our sample size in this age category, we would obtain a sample mean which would equate with the population mean of that age category, but not the overall population mean.

Concept Check 5.D

A sampling error involves either an addition error or a statistical computation error. True or false? If false, explain.

Exercises

5.19   In your own words explain the term "sampling error." What error actually is made?

5.20   In your own words explain the term "sampling bias." What is the difference between a sampling error and a sampling bias? Which is a more severe error?

5.21   a.   Use Table 5.5 and determine the mean age of the population.
        b.   Now using the sample of students #1, #7, #13, and #19, determine the sample mean.
        c.   When students are selected in such a manner, what type of survey is being taken?
        d.   Why is there a difference between the answers to a and b?

5.22   Only 15 individuals have been known to have a particular rare disease. Their life expectancies are recorded as

Patient	Years	Patient	Years	Patient	Years
#1	23.1	#6	4.7	#11	3.7
#2	17.1	#7	0.6	#12	14.8
#3	2.7	#8	11.6	#13	10.1
#4	7.4	#9	16.8	#14	3.9
#5	2.1	#10	3.8	#15	16.1

103

a. What is the population life expectancy?

b. Suppose patients #6, #12, and #14 were randomly selected ($n = 3$) in an unrestricted random sample. What is the sample mean?

c. Comment on the difference between the answers to parts a and b.

5.7   Sampling Distribution of the Mean

Increasing the sample size is a convenient method of differentiating sampling error and sampling bias. However, in real applications, sample sizes often can't be increased. The question then centers around our ability to make inferences concerning population parameters from sample statistics. To accomplish this we develop a theoretical distribution, the sampling distribution of the mean. The sampling distribution of the mean is the probability distribution of all of the possible means of samples of size n.

Students typically have problems with the sampling distribution of the mean because it is based on taking repeated samples of a given size, yet dispersion of the distribution must be estimated from a single sample. Returning to our beverage consumption example, we randomly selected 3 students ($n = 3$) to represent a population of 24.

The sample mean (statistic) obtained depends on which 3 students are selected. How many combinations of 3 students can be selected from a population of 24? Using Formula 3.11 we obtain $n!/r!(n - r)!$, or $24!/3!(24 - 3)! = 2,024$. There are 2,024 ways of selecting 3 students from 24. The actual combinations are too lengthy to list, but would include students #1 and #2 and #3, etc.

Suppose we are to sample 30 students from a population of 2,500 students. Our combination formula is $2500!/30!(2500 - 30)!$, which produces a sampling distribution that is essentially infinite in size.

Sampling With and Without Replacement

Before viewing the sampling distribution, we must determine if we are sampling with or without replacement. Normally, once an elementary unit is selected and sampled, it is not eligible for consideration to be surveyed again. When it is not reentered it is termed sampling without replacement. Almost all sampling involves the concept of sampling without replacement. If we sampled with replacement, the number of possible surveys obtainable changes. For example, in our last analysis, we surveyed 3 students from a population of 24. If we allowed for replacement, there are 13,824 ($24 \bullet 24 \bullet 24$) possible samples of size 3 from a population of 24.

Statistical theory assumes sampling with replacement because it embodies the principle of sampling outcomes being statistically independent. This is not the case when sampling without replacement. If we were sampling from a population of 5, the probability of selecting the first elementary unit is 1/5. However, the probability of selecting the second elementary unit changes if we are sampling with (1/5) or without replacement (1/4). This probability difference is negligible if the sample size is large. For example, if our population contains 100,000 households, the probabilities of selecting the second elementary unit is 1/100,000 with replacement and 1/99,999 without. Hence, our major concern relates to small samples. In Section 5.8 we will make allowances for this concern.

To view the possible combinations, let's assume that our class population is 5 (the first 5 students) and we are to select a sample of size 2 ($N = 5$, $n = 2$). If we are sampling without replacement, the number of possible combinations is 10 ($5!/2! \bullet 3!$). If we are sampling with replacement, there are 25 ($5 \bullet 5$) possible ways of selecting 2 students from a population of 5. The possible outcomes of surveying with and without replacement are given in Table 5.6A.

In addition, the sampling distribution of the mean and the population distribution are given (Table 5.6B) as well as the MINITAB printout for the descriptive statistics for the population, and for the sampling distribution, sampling with and without replacement. The range of the population distribution ($87 - 12 = 75$) is the same as when sampling with replacement because the same elementary unit may again be selected. However, the range of the sampling distribution without replacement is considerably smaller than that of the population (Table 5.6C). The range of the sampling distribution without replacement is smaller. The extreme values for cans consumed (12 and 87) do not appear because they are averaged with another data point. The largest sample mean ($n = 2$) obtainable is 85.5 [(87 + 84)/2], while the smallest sample mean obtainable is 13.5[(12 + 15)/2]. The averaging process would have had a greater impact if our sample size were larger (see Figure 5.1).

We should note that the standard deviation of the sampling distribution of the mean, with replacement, is smaller than the standard deviation of the individual elements of the population because of the concentration of different sample means towards μ. The standard deviation of the sampling distribution of the mean, without replacement, is smaller than σ because of the concentration of sampling means about μ, and because extreme values are averaged, lessening their impact.

Table 5.6A Possible Combinations for $n = 2$; $N = 5$ With and Without Replacement

POPULATION		WITHOUT REPLACEMENT		WITH REPLACEMENT			
Student	Cans	Students	Mean	Students	Mean	Students	Mean
#1	12	#1–#2	49.5	#1–#2	49.5	#1–#1	12.0
#2	87	#1–#3	26.5	#1–#3	26.5	#2–#1	49.5
#3	41	#1–#4	13.5	#1–#4	13.5	#2–#2	87.0
#4	15	#1–#5	48.0	#1–#5	48.0	#3–#1	26.5
#5	84	#2–#3	64.0	#2–#3	64.0	#3–#2	64.0
		#2–#4	51.0	#2–#4	51.0	#3–#3	41.0
		#2–#5	85.5	#2–#5	85.5	#4–#1	13.5
		#3–#4	28.0	#3–#4	28.0	#4–#2	51.0
		#3–#5	62.5	#3–#5	62.5	#4–#3	28.0
		#4–#5	49.5	#4–#5	49.5	#4–#4	15.0
						#5–#1	48.0
						#5–#2	85.5
						#5–#3	62.5
						#5–#4	49.5
						#5–#5	84.0

Table 5.6B Sampling Distribution of the Mean ($n = 2$; $N = 5$) With and Without Replacement

WITHOUT REPLACEMENT			WITH REPLACEMENT		
Sample Mean	Frequency	Pr.	Sample Mean	Frequency	Pr.
13.5	1	.1	12.0	1	.04
26.5	1	.1	13.5	2	.08
28.0	1	.1	15.0	1	.04
48.0	1	.1	26.5	2	.08
49.5	2	.2	28.0	2	.08
51.0	1	.1	41.0	1	.04
62.5	1	.1	48.0	2	.08
64.0	1	.1	49.5	4	.16
85.5	1	.1	51.0	2	.08
	$\Sigma = 10$	$\Sigma = 1.0$	62.5	2	.08
			64.0	2	.08
			84.0	1	.04
			85.5	2	.08
			87.0	1	.04
				$\Sigma = 25$	$\Sigma = 1.00$

Table 5.6C MINITAB Printout of Summary Statistics

	Population	Without Replacement	With Replacement
N	5	10	25
MIN	12.0	13.5	12.0
MAX	87.0	85.0	87.0
MEAN	47.8	47.8	47.8
STDEV	36.2*	20.92*	23.39*
σ	32.406	19.845	22.914

Note: Statistical packages yield s, not σ. $\sigma = \sqrt{s^2 \bullet (n-1)/n} = 32.406$.

Assuming that we haven't incorrectly specified the population, the mean of the distribution of means, sometimes referred to as the mean of the sampling means, will equal the population mean regardless of whether we sample with or without replacement ($\mu = 47.80$). The reason is we have effectively performed a census if we take the mean of the population or take every possible sample of size n from the population (see Figure 5.2).

Figure 5.1 The Population Distribution and the Sampling Distribution of the Mean as *n* Increases

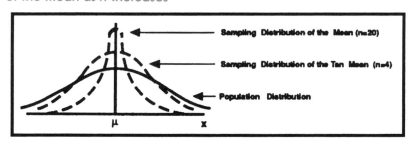

Figure 5.2 The Population, Sample, and Sampling Distribution of the Mean

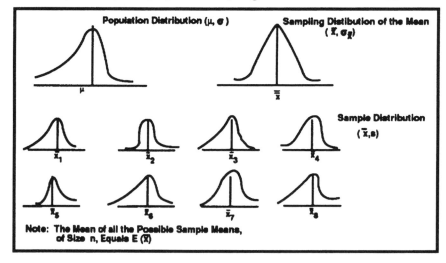

 Concept Check 5.E

If the population has been correctly specified, the mean of the population will equate with the mean of the sampling distribution. True or false? If false, explain.

5.23 Why is the standard deviation of the sampling distribution smaller than either the standard deviation of the population or the standard deviation of the sample?

5.24 Only 4 individuals have been known to have a rare disease. Their life expectancies are recorded as 8, 6, 4, and 2 years.

    a. What is the population mean life expectancy and standard deviation?
    b. We randomly select 2 patients to represent a sample. Determine the sampling distribution sampling without replacement.
    c. Determine the sampling distribution when sampling with replacement ($n = 2$).
    d. Compute the range, mean, and standard deviation of both sampling distributions. Compare.

5.25 For the population in Table 5.6A, suppose we wanted to survey (without replacement) 3 students ($n = 3$; $N = 5$).

    a. How many combinations are possible?
    b. Determine the sampling distribution.

5.26 The population consists of 3 data points: 10, 20, and 30.

    a. Determine the population mean and standard deviation.
    b. Using $n = 2$, determine the sampling distribution if sampling without replacement.
    c. Using $n = 2$, determine the sampling distribution if sampling with replacement.
    d. Compute the range, mean, and standard deviation of both sampling distributions. Compare.

5.8 The Standard Error of the Mean With and Without Sample Replacement

Sampling With Replacement

In the last section we learned that the population mean and the mean of sampling distribution are identical. However, the standard deviation of the sampling distribution with replacement was smaller than the standard deviation of the population (22.914 versus 32.406). This is because of the concentration of different sample means toward the population mean. How then can we obtain the dispersion of the sampling distribution from knowledge of the population standard deviation? The formula accomplishing this is

The Standard Error of the Mean; Sampling With Replacement

$$\sigma_{\bar{x}} = \frac{\sigma}{\sqrt{n}} \tag{5.1}$$

where

σ = the standard deviation of the population

n = sample size.

Assumptions: We are dealing with a large population (n/N is small) or are sampling with replacement.

Returning to our problem of sampling 2 students from a population of 5, $\sigma = 32.406$, and $n = 2$. Hence,

$$\sigma_{\bar{x}} = \frac{\sigma}{\sqrt{n}} = \frac{32.406}{\sqrt{2}} = 22.914$$

Note that for Table 5.6C the standard deviation of the sampling distribution with replacement to be 22.914.

Sampling Without Replacement

To obtain the estimate of the dispersion of the sampling distribution without replacement (which is the norm) we must use an adjustment. The adjustment is called the finite population correction factor (FPCF). The formula for the standard error becomes

The Standard Error of the Mean: Sampling Without Replacement

$$\sigma_{\bar{x}} = \frac{\sigma}{\sqrt{n}} \cdot \sqrt{\frac{N-n}{N-1}} \tag{5.2}$$

where

$\sigma = $ the standard deviation of the population

$n = $ sample size

$\sqrt{(N-n)/(N-1)} = $ the finite population correction factor (FPCF).

Ignore FPCF when $n/N < .05$ because FPCF approaches 1.

Again utilizing our information from Table 5.6C yields

$$\sigma_{\bar{x}} = \frac{32.406}{\sqrt{2}} \cdot \sqrt{\frac{5-2}{5-1}} = 19.845$$

Note that for Table 5.6C the standard deviation of the sampling distribution without replacement is 19.845.

Sampling Without Replacement: $n/N < .05$

The difference between our standard errors between sampling with and without replacement appeared to be large (22.914 versus 19.845). This was because our sample size was relatively large compared to the size of the population. For example, if our population size were 500, the standard error would be

$$\sigma_{\bar{x}} = \frac{32.406}{\sqrt{2}} \cdot \sqrt{\frac{500-2}{500-1}} = 22.891$$

This 22.891 value is very near the 22.914 value obtained when sampling with replacement. Because the difference in the standard errors (between with and without replacement) is small when $n/N < .05$, we do not utilize the FPCF unless $n/N \geq .05$. In other words, we use Formula 5.1 in lieu of Formula 5.2, even if sampling without replacement, when $n/N < .05$.

In our current example, where $n/N = 2/500 = .004$, we would not use the FPCF adjustment because $n/N < .05$.

Estimated Standard Error Based on a Single Sample

In actuality, little information concerning the population will be known in advance. If much were known about the population, there would be little need to conduct a sample. In the absence of knowledge concerning the population's standard deviation, the standard deviation of the sample(s) is used as its estimate.

From a single survey we will be able to obtain s, and n. The estimate for the standard error of the mean must be based on these facts. To estimate the standard error, we use s as an estimate of σ, yielding

---

The Estimated Standard Error of the Mean: Using s to replace σ

$$\hat{\sigma}_{\overline{x}} = \frac{s}{\sqrt{n}} \cdot \sqrt{\frac{N-n}{N-1}} \tag{5.3}$$

where

$\hat{} = $ estimated

$s = $ the standard deviation of the sample

$n = $ sample size

Disregard $\sqrt{(N-n)/(N-1)}$ if $n/N < .05$.

How close the estimated standard error of the mean is to the actual value depends on how close s is to σ. When $s = \sigma$, formula 5.3 is identical to formula 5.2. The actual value for s depends on the random selection of the two students to be surveyed. Table 5.7 yields all of the possible values for s and the respective estimated standard error. Note that in our example the sample size is extremely small.

Table 5.7 Possible Values for s and the Estimated Standard Error

Students	s	σ	$\hat{\sigma}_{\overline{X}}$*	$\hat{\sigma}_{\overline{X}}$	$\sigma_{\overline{X}}$
#1–#2	53.033	32.406	37.500	32.476	19.845
#1–#3	20.506	32.406	14.500	12.557	19.845
#1–#4	2.121	32.406	1.500	1.299	19.845
#1–#5	50.912	32.406	36.000	31.177	19.845
#2–#3	32.527	32.406	23.000	19.919	19.845
#2–#4	50.912	32.406	36.000	31.177	19.845
#2–#5	2.121	32.406	1.500	1.299	19.845
#3–#4	18.385	32.406	13.000	11.258	19.845
#3–#5	30.406	32.406	21.500	18.620	19.845
#4–#5	48.790	32.406	34.500	29.878	19.845

*Computer disregards FPCF.

MINITAB can be used to obtain the estimated standard error of the mean (SEM) using the following command:

Using MINITAB to obtain estimated standard error of the mean for students #1–#2; FPCF ignored

Stat > Basic Statistics > Display Descriptive Statistics
Double click **data** into **Variables** box.
OK

Table 5.8   Abbreviated MINITAB output for students #1 and #2

	N	STDEV	SEMEAN
Data	2	53.0	37.5

In our analysis, an assumption was inherent concerning the population distribution being normal. If the population is normal, it is easy to understand that the sampling distribution of the mean will also be normal. Yet actual populations often are not normally distributed. How will this effect the sampling distribution? Fortunately, we may assume normality, under most conditions, through what is known as the Central Limit Theorem.

 Concept Check 5.F

The standard error involves a theoretical distribution that must be estimated from knowledge of only the sample size and sample standard deviation. True or false? If false, explain.

Exercises

5.27   For Exercise 5.24 we had 4 individuals who had a rare disease. We sampled 2 patients and computed the sampling distributions with and without replacement. Use formulas 5.1 and 5.2 to compute the standard errors sampling with and without replacement.

5.28   For Exercise 5.25 we had a population of 5 students from which we sampled 3 students without replacement. Compute the standard error of the mean.

5.29   For Exercise 5.26 we had a population of 3 and sample 2 with and without replacement. Compute the standard error of the mean in both instances.

5.30   When do the formulas for sampling with and without replacement equate?

5.31   Determine the standard error of the mean from the following facts: $n = 25$, $s = 5$, and $\sigma = 6$.

5.32   a.   Determine the estimated standard error of the mean from the following facts: $n = 25$, and $s = 5$.
           b.   Why is the answer to 5.32a superior to that of 5.31a?
           c.   Why will knowledge of σ be unknown?

5.33   We have just completed a survey in which n, s, and $\overline{X}$ are known. It is also known that $n/N < .05$. What information will be utilized in estimating the standard error?

5.34   Why does the standard error of the mean have to be estimated?

5.35   a.   When is the finite population correction factor used?
           b.   In your own words, explain the finite population correction factor.

5.36 $N = 1000$, compute the finite correction factor when $n =$

           a.   10
           b.   200
           c.   600
           d.   900

5.9   Sampling from Non-Normal Populations

Many populations are not normally distributed. Our example involved the selection of 2 students from a non-normal population of 5. Yet we notice from Table 5.6 that the means of the population and sampling distribution equated. Hence, a non-normal population does not create a difference between the population and sampling distribution mean.

A second important fact is involved. As the sample size increases, the sampling distribution of the mean will approximate that of a normal distribution (see Figure 5.3). This occurs regardless of the shape of the population distribution involved. In fact, the sample size need not even be very large for the assumption to be valid. There is no consensus concerning the actual size of the sample when normality of the sampling distribution may be assumed. The largest sample size used to assume normality is usually set at 30 ($n = 30$). The minimum sample size seems to be 11. Our own sample size of 2 is insufficient to assume normality of the sampling distribution of the mean. The reason we dealt with the small sample size was to yield an intuitive understanding of the concepts.

Figure 5.3 The sampling Distribution of the Mean Approaching Normality as n Increases

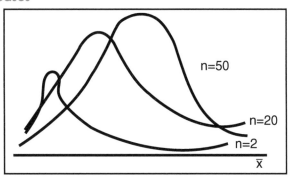

One of the most important theorems in statistics is the Central Limit Theorem as it is a key element in statistical estimation and hypothesis testing (Chapters 6–8).

The Central Limit Theorem

If a random sample of n observations is selected from a population with parameters of μ and σ, the resulting sample mean $(\overline{X})$ has a normal distribution with the mean μ and standard deviation of $\sigma/\sqrt{n}$. This is true for any sample size if the population in question is normally distributed, and is approximately true for large sample sizes obtained from any population. Large sample sizes are usually defined as greater than 30 ($n > 30$).

The fact that the Central Limit Theorem is approximately true for large sample sizes obtained from any population is particularly important. Even if we were dealing with a binomial distribution, as long as the sample size was sufficient, X would follow a normal distribution.

Using MINITAB to illustrate the Central Limit Theorem

 Calc > Random data > Binomial
Enter 10,100,1000 (3 different steps) into **Generate _____ rows of data**
Enter C1,C2,C3 (3 different steps) into **Store in column(s)**
Enter 10,100,1000 (3 different steps) into **Number of trials**
Enter 0.1 into **Probability of Success**
OK

 Graph > Histogram > With Fit
Enter C1,C2,C3 into **Graph Variables**
OK

View the three histograms and note how the distribution approximates a normal distribution as the sample size increases.

 Concept Check 5.G

The Central Limit Theorem allows us to use the normal distribution to approximate any distribution under any conditions. True or false? If false, explain.

Exercises

5.37   In your own words explain the Central Limit Theorem.

5.38   Why is the Central Limit Theorem so important in statistical analysis?

5.10 The Sampling Distribution of the Proportion

Many sampling problems relate to consumer preferences and or public opinion polls. These analyses involve computing a proportion of the population that possess a certain attribute or opinion. These analyses normally provide practical examples of binomial experiments. If we randomly sample n persons in a population and if x of those persons possess a specific characteristic, then the sample proportion is

$$\hat{p} = \frac{x}{n}$$

which is used to estimate the population proportion p.

The normal distribution can also be used as an approximation for the binomial distribution. Recall our analysis of Section 4.3, where the binomial distribution approaches normality as the sample size increases. Hence, when n is large enough, the Central Limit Theorem allows us to replace the sampling distribution of p with that of the normal distribution. The binomial distribution can be approximated by the normal distribution only when the following two conditions are met.

$$n \bullet p > 5$$
$$n \bullet q > 5$$

For $p = .5$, n must be greater than 10 $[(5/p) = n]$ to meet the condition. For $p = .3$, n must be equal to 17, and for $p = .1$, n must equal 51. As p becomes closer to its extreme values (close to 0 or 1), a larger sample size is necessary in order for the binomial distribution to approximate a normal distribution. This is due to the fact that the binomial distributions are highly skewed for p's close to 0 or 1 for small samples.

The formula for the standard error of the proportion, when sampling with replacement, is

---

The Standard Error of the Proportion; Sampling With Replacement

$$\sigma_{\hat{p}} = \sqrt{\frac{\hat{p} \bullet \hat{q}}{n}} \qquad (5.4)$$

where

$\hat{p}$ = the sample proportion
$\hat{q} = 1 - \hat{p}$
n = the sample size

The standard error of the proportion based on sample information is

---

The Standard Error of the Proportion Based on Sample Information

$$\hat{\sigma}_{\hat{p}} = \sqrt{\frac{\hat{p} \bullet \hat{q}}{n}} \sqrt{\frac{N - n}{N - 1}} \qquad (5.5)$$

where

$\hat{p}$ = the sample proportion

$\hat{q} = 1 - \hat{p}$

n = the sample size

Disregard FPCF when $n/N < .05$.

The sampling distribution of $\hat{p}$ is approximately normal as long as $\hat{p} \pm 3\hat{\sigma}_p$ does not include the limits 0 or 1. Remember all that will be available from a single sample will be a proportion ($\hat{p}$) and the sample size (n).

 Concept Check 5.H

If we had a sample of size 10, and the population proportion was .4, we could approximate the binomial distribution with the normal distribution. True or false? If false, explain.

Exercises

5.39   What conditions must be met to allow the normal distribution to approximate the binomial distribution?

5.40   The formula used to ascertain whether the sample size is sufficient to use the normal distribution to approximate the binomial distribution is $n = ?$

5.41   It is known that 10% of the surnames in a country begin with the letter S. A survey ($n = 250$) is taken. What is the standard error of the proportion?

5.42   In a survey ($n = 25$), 3 surnames begin with the letter S. What is the probability that 11.5% or more of the population have a surname beginning with the letter S?

5.43   In a survey ($n = 360$), 1 out of 6 has a particular ailment. What is the probability that 18% or more of the population have that particular ailment?

5.44   In a survey ($n = 250$), only 1 of the respondents was able to hit a golf ball 300 yards. What is the probability that 5% of the population can hit the ball 300 yards?

We have reviewed the basic techniques of sampling. Only from random samples can inferences be made concerning the population. The four types of random samples are the unrestricted random sample, the stratified random sample, the systematic random sample, and the cluster sample. The stratified and the cluster samples attempt to divide the data into finite groups prior to sampling. Many sampling methodologies encompass more than a single type of sampling procedure.

We studied the importance of the sampling distribution of the mean. The sampling distribution is a theoretical distribution which would actually require taking repeated samples of a given size. Since such repeated samples will not be taken, this important distribution must be estimated based on the information available. The key variables used for such an estimation are the sample standard deviation and sample size for a continuous distribution, and a proportion and sample size for a discrete distribution. From the sampling distribution, estimates of the normal deviate can be obtained and probabilities developed.

Finally, an adjustment multiplier to be used when $n/N \geq .05$ was reviewed. This multiplier, called the finite population correction factor, reduces the value of the standard error to allow for the non-replacement of sample elements into small populations during sampling.

Mini-case 5.1: Restaurant Tip Study

You own a restaurant chain and you are notified by the Internal Revenue Service (IRS) that your servers are to be audited. The IRS feels that the average tip rate is 15% and your employees have been reporting an 8%, or less, tip rate. The IRS has studies from credit card companies (like American Express) which indicate the tip rate is 15%, or greater. You feel that American Express credit cards represent business dining and that your business tips are significantly greater than tips left by families dining at your restaurant. You confront the IRS with your hypothesis, and they basically take the position that they have documentation that it is 15%, and ask what proof you possess that it is not.

A survey must be conducted if you are to obtain information. You wish to sample some of the stores and some of the servers to determine what the actual tip rate is. You will randomly select certain stores and certain employees within that store. In effect we are designing a cluster sample. If the stores possess certain attributes (more business clients, a strong tourist trade), you may wish first to stratify the stores prior to selection.

If servers are to be randomly selected, it might be wise to have them select themselves. A box containing white and yellow Ping-Pong balls could be used. Those selecting the yellow Ping-Pong balls will be surveyed. An umpire might be used to count the money tips left at a table after a customer leaves. Tips left on credit cards can be reviewed on sales receipts at a later time.

    a.   State why it is essential to design a survey that will ensure that each and every member of the population has an equal chance of being selected.

    b.   Will each employee have to agree in advance to participate in the study?

    c.   In a court room, which study (the IRS or yours) might the judicial system believe to be more relevant?

Mini-case 5.2: A Newspaper Study

Develop a survey methodology for a local newspaper that wants to determine what the readers like about a paper and what non-readers don't like. We also want to ascertain the desired home delivery time for the paper. The accounting department informs us that over 85% of the newspaper's revenue comes not from subscribers but from advertising revenues, much of which comes from a dozen retailers. These retailers are questioning whether they should advertise in the paper, advertise through the mail, or just cut prices and advertise through word-of-mouth. The newspaper must attempt to show the advertisers that if they want household penetration, they need to advertise through it.

a.   State what you believe the objectives of the upcoming survey are.
b.   Develop a sampling methodology to obtain the desired information. Because we will be asking over 100 questions, a telephone survey has been ruled out.
c.   Would you allow a current or past newspaper employee to go into the field to conduct the survey? Explain.

Review of Important Terms and Concepts

Statistic vs. Parameter: A statistic is a measure of a sample and a parameter is a measure of a population.

Types of samples:
>   A **convenience** or **judgment** survey involves a survey where every member of the population does not have an equal chance of being selected.
>   An **unrestricted random sample** assures that every elementary unit has an equal chance of being selected. Often, the assignment of random numbers is an important part of the process.
>   A **stratified sample** attempts to divide the data into meaningful strata prior to random selection of data from each strata. The trick is to be able to divide the population into homogeneous strata.
>   A **systematic sample** selects two random numbers. The first represents the starting point and the second the skip pattern to be followed. The problems come about if the skip pattern biases the survey.
>   A **cluster sample** stratifies by various geographic strata prior to the random selection process. In order to be effective the various clusters should be microcosms of the population. When the clusters are made geographically, this could be a problem as neighborhoods tend to be homogeneous.

Sampling error: The sampling error is the difference between a sample statistic and a population parameter caused by the random selection process and by limited sample sizes.

Bias: Bias is the difference between the mean of the sampling distribution and the mean of the population caused by the incorrect definition of the population. Whereas sampling error may be reduced by increasing the sample size, bias will not.

Nonresponse bias: A bias introduced because we are unable to reach a portion of the population that has been selected to be surveyed. This may cause a difference between the population mean and the mean of the sampling distribution.

Nonsampling error: An error that is usually based not on sampling design, but rather possibly on measurement error.

Systematic bias: A problem that often develops with systematic sampling where the skip pattern refers to a specific day of the week, or machine, etc.

The Sampling Distribution of the Mean: The probability distribution of all of the possible means of the samples of size n is the sampling distribution of the mean.

The Standard Error of the Mean: The standard error of the mean is merely the standard deviation of the distribution of sample means.

The Central Limit Theorem: If a random sample of n observations is selected from a population with parameters of μ and σ, the resulting sample mean (X) has a normal distribution with the mean μ and a standard deviation of s/n. This is true for any sample size if the population in question is normally distributed, and is approximately true for large sample sizes obtained from any population. Large sample sizes are usually defined as greater than 30 ($n > 30$).

The Finite Population Correction Factor: The correction factor is invoked when a finite sample is made without replacement from a small population ($n/N \geq .05$); an adjustment is warranted.

The Standard Error of the Mean; Sampling With Replacement

$$\sigma_{\bar{x}} = \frac{\sigma}{\sqrt{n}} \tag{5.1}$$

where

$\sigma =$ the standard deviation of the population

$n =$ sample size

Assumptions: We are dealing with a large population (n/N is small) or are sampling with replacement.

The Standard Error of the Mean: Sampling Without Replacement

$$\sigma_{\bar{x}} = \frac{\sigma}{\sqrt{n}} \bullet \sqrt{\frac{N-n}{N-1}} \tag{5.2}$$

where

$\sigma =$ the standard deviation of the population

$n =$ sample size

$\sqrt{(N-n)/(N-1)} =$ the finite population correction factor (FPCF).

Ignore FPCF when $n/N < .05$ because FPCF approaches 1.

The Estimated Standard Error of the Mean: Using s to Replace σ

$$\hat{\sigma}_{\bar{x}} = \frac{s}{\sqrt{n}} \bullet \sqrt{\frac{N-n}{N-1}} \tag{5.3}$$

where

$\hat{} =$ estimated

$s =$ the standard deviation of the sample

$n =$ sample size

Disregard $\sqrt{(N-n)/(N-1)}$ if $n/N < .05$.

The Standard Error of the Proportion; Sampling With Replacement

$$\sigma_{\hat{p}} = \sqrt{\frac{\hat{p} \bullet \hat{q}}{n}}$$ (5.4)

where

$\hat{p} =$ the sample proportion
$\hat{q} = 1 - \hat{p}$
$n =$ the sample size

The Standard Error of the Proportion Based on Sample Information

$$\hat{\sigma}_{\hat{p}} = \sqrt{\frac{\hat{p} \bullet \hat{q}}{n}} \sqrt{\frac{N - n}{N - 1}}$$ (5.5)

where

$\hat{p} =$ the sample proportion
$\hat{q} = 1 - \hat{p}$
$n =$ the sample size
Disregard FPCF when $n/N < .05$.

Review MINITAB Commands

MINITABS's selection of random numbers from 1–24. The command sequence is:

Calc > Random Data > Integer
Enter **3** into **Generate _____ rows of data**.
Enter **C1** into **Store in column(s)**.
Enter **1** into **Minimum** value.
Enter **24** into **Maximum** value.
OK
MINITAB's Standard error of the Mean.

Stat > Basic Statistic > Display Descriptive Statistics
Double click **data** into **Variables** box.
OK

5.45   The following is a population of experimental computers and their times in solving a rather complex problem.

Computer	Time	Computer	Time
#1	8.3 Seconds	#4	6.9 Seconds
#2	6.1 Seconds	#5	2.2 Seconds
#3	1.9 Seconds	#6	4.4 Seconds

a.   If we were to sample 2 computers without replacement, how many combinations are possible?
b.   Determine the mean and standard deviation of the population.
c.   Determine the mean and standard deviation (standard error) of the sampling distribution.
d.   Explain the similarities and differences between the answers to parts b and c.

5.46   What type of survey would you recommend for the following:

a.   To determine what TV shows are being watched.
b.   To determine what percentage of consumers take vacations lasting more than 5 days in duration.

5.47   You are considering opening a small business in your neighborhood. Before you do, you would certainly want to know specific facts concerning competition, failure rates, and the number of competitors a particular business can support. State how you might by looking at the phone books for the last several years for cities in your state be able to obtain some of the information.

5.48   A survey ($n = 25$) shows that the average car is driven 9,800 miles per year with $s = 2,200$ miles per year. Determine the probability of a sample average of cars driven 10,000 miles or more per year.

5.49   a.   If the information in exercise 5.48 were for an experimental car, of which there were only 100 in existence, would the probability change? Explain.
b.   Determine the new probability.

5.50   In a survey ($n = 49$) we find that 38 golfers use a cart when playing a full 18 holes of golf. What is the probability that 80% of the population actually use golf carts?

5.51   A trucking company does a survey to determine the average gallons of gas consumed commuting between two destinations. The survey information is $n = 21$, and the mean and standard deviation of the sample are 27.8 and 3.1 gallons, respectively. What is the probability that 29 or more gallons of gas will be consumed between the two destinations?

5.52   a.   Referring to exercise 5.51, how does the Central Limit Theorem impact the analysis?
b.   If $N = 100$, how would this impact the results?

5.53   Why is sampling bias a more severe problem than sampling error?

5.54   How are the terms "statistical inferences" and random sampling related?

Statistical Estimation

Where we have been

We have explained the advantages of sampling compared to census taking and have discussed the various sampling methods, the sampling distribution, and standard error of the mean and proportion. If we conduct a survey of size n, we can determine $\overline{X}$ and s for continuous data and $\hat{p}$ and n for qualitative data.

Where we are going

We sample to obtain information which we use to make inferences about the population. These inferences can be placed into two categories, statistical estimation and hypothesis testing. In this chapter, we will concentrate on statistical estimation and in the following two chapters on hypothesis testing.

In statistical estimation we will attempt to answer questions based on sample information, such as:
How many miles do tires last?
What is the President's current popularity rating?
We conclude the chapter with the determination of the proper sample sizes to yield an estimate with desired precision, confidence, and allowable error.

6.1   Introduction

Estimation is an integral part of our lives. We estimate how much time we will spend at one appointment in order to make our next appointment. We estimate when a light will turn red as we approach a traffic light. We estimate the hours of study necessary to earn and receive a particular grade in a course. All represent informal evaluations concerning the time it takes to complete certain tasks or to observe certain critical occurrences.

Similar estimates take place daily by decision-makers. Estimates have to be made concerning future interest rates, inventories, future demand, price levels, etc. The life of the company may depend on the accuracy and relevancy of such estimates.

Many such business decisions will be based on inferences from current information. It will mean that estimates are being made of population parameters based on sample statistics. Probability theory will play an important role in determining the confidence we will have in our estimates. Hence, the information covered in Chapters 3, 4, and 5 will play an important role in this (statistical estimation) and the next two chapters (hypothesis testing).

Estimates can be classified as either point or interval estimates. Envision the instructor of your class walking to the back of the classroom and placing crossed lines on the wall with a piece of chalk. The instructor then walks to the front of the room and tells you that she will throw the chalk and hit the dead-center of the crossed lines. This is a point estimate. Either she hits the center or she doesn't.

You will probably have little confidence that she would be able to hit the dead-center. If she actually made such a statement her credibility would drop sharply. However, if she told you she would hit within a yard radius of the center, your confidence would grow. If she said she would hit the back wall anywhere, your confidence will grow further; and if she said she would hit any wall, your confidence would again grow. These are now interval estimates as we are concerned with how closely bounded the estimate is. Note that having too great a confidence in the estimate would entail an interval estimate so wide as to make the information meaningless. The prediction would not be precise enough to be of any aid to us. Hence, we normally do not want too great a confidence coefficient $(1 - \alpha)$ as there is little precision in our estimates. Table 6.1 yields some examples of point and interval estimates.

Table 6.1 Examples of Point and Interval Estimates

	Point Estimate	Interval Estimate
Mean Estimates		
Car MPG Ratings	22.0	20.0–24.0
Calories in Product	432.0	412.0–452.0
Proportion Estimates		
A University Acceptance Rate	54.3%	50.3–58.3%
A Class F Rate	8.3%	5.3–11.3%

 Concept Check 6.A

An interval estimate is more precise than a point estimate. True or false? If false, explain.

Exercises

6.1 Determine if the following are point or interval estimates.

a. That the next home run hit will carry 425 feet.
b. That the next home run hit will carry between 375 and 475 feet.
c. In which of the two statements would you have more confidence? Explain.

6.2 Differentiate between point and interval estimates.

6.2 Desirable Properties of Estimators

In order to make estimates we must have estimators. An estimator is a sample statistic that is used to predict a population parameter. For example, we often use the sample mean $(\overline{X})$ as an estimator of the population mean (μ). If we surveyed and found that light bulbs in our city subways have lasted on average 275 hours (an estimator), we might then assume that the population of light bulbs we purchased have an average life expectancy of 275 hours (an estimate). Hence, an estimate is a specific observed value of, or made from, a statistic.

Statisticians prefer that estimators have certain desirable properties. These are that estimators be

- unbiased   - efficient   - consistent

Unbiased

The concept of unbiased estimators was discussed in Section 5.3. Suppose there are 24 students in our class and we want to sample their consumption of soft drink beverages in a ninety (90) day time interval. In Chapter 5, we had stratified the 24 students into 3 age groups (Table 5.3). If we incorrectly define the population as the 18–24 group instead of the entire class, we will have a bias problem.

Table 5.3 Stratified Sampling: Randomly Selected Students from Age Strata Concerning the Consumption of Soft Drinks in 3 Months ($N = 24$: $n = 3$)

YOUNG 18–25		MEDIUM AGED 26–34		OLDER 35+	
	(10) Cans		(7) Cans		(7) Cans
Age	Consumed	Age	Consumed	Age	Consumed
21	87	26	41	37	12
19*	84	29	37	49	15
18	77	27	43	48	8
21	85	31	37	39*	10
19	83	27	43	43	15
23	80	31*	41	44	7
24	85	31	40	53	16
24	82	$\overline{X} = 40.286$		$\overline{X} = 11.86$	
22	86	$s = 2.498$		$s = 3.63$	
22	77				
$\overline{X} = 82.60$					
$s = 3.57$					

The sample mean would be an **unbiased** estimator of the population mean if the mean of the sampling distribution equals the parameter value being estimated. This is true as long as we sample from the entire population rather than a subset of it.

Unbiased Estimator of the Mean

$$E(\overline{X}_i) = \mu \tag{6.1}$$

where

E = the expected value or weighted mean

$\overline{X}_i$ = the mean of all possible samples of size n

μ = the mean of the population

If we sample the age group from 18–25, we will not have an unbiased estimate of the population. For example, if we sampled all of the possible samples of a given size from the 18–25 group the

$E(\overline{X}_i) = 82.60$. Defining the entire 24 students as the population, $\mu = 49.583$. Hence, $E(\overline{X}_i) \neq \mu$, and bias exists. We can see the bias existing in Figure 6.1B as the sampling distribution is not centered around μ.

Figure 6.1 Graphing Unbiased and Biased Estimators

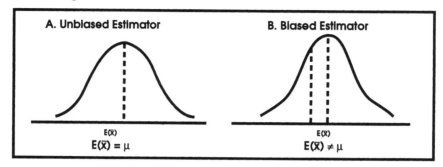

Efficiency

Efficiency deals with the dispersion of the different possible estimates of a given sample size. Assuming two sampling distributions are unbiased, the estimator with the least dispersion is considered the most efficient.

Let us view our beverage consumption problem again. Say we have two separate populations, both with $\mu = 49.583$, and one with $\sigma = 30.726$, and a second with $\sigma = 3.565$. Remember that the sampling distributions, respective standard errors are

Sampling distribution of mean, 1st population: $\sigma_{\overline{X}_1} = 30.726/\sqrt{n}$
Sampling distribution of mean, 2nd population: $\sigma_{\overline{X}_2} = 3.565/\sqrt{n}$

Ultimately, we must randomly select a single sample of size n from all those possible. Which one we actually obtain will be determined by the random numbers selected. The question of concern is: "Given a choice of selecting one survey of size n from many, would we rather select it from a tight or a wide distribution?" Logic tells us that we have a greater chance of finding a sample mean closer to μ from a smaller distribution than from a larger one, when comparing two unbiased populations. Therefore, if we had to select one sample of size n from two unbiased populations, we would prefer to make the selection from the one in which $\sigma = 3.565$ and not $\sigma = 30.726$ (Figure 6.2). This concept is known as efficiency.

Figure 6.2 Efficiency for Two Unbiased Estimators Relates to the One With
the Smaller Standard Error

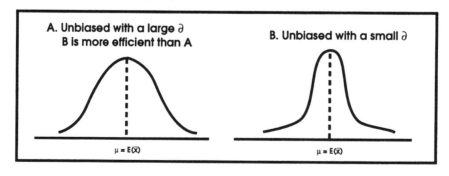

122

Consistency

A third desirable property deals with the effects of increasing the sample size (n). In dealing with bias and efficiency, we are analyzing the standard error, which measures variability in the distribution of all sample means of size n. However, with consistency we have one sample and measure the effects of increasing sample size.

As n increases to N, we desire that the $\overline{X}$ approaches μ and for the standard error to get smaller (termed **consistency**). If this is not the case, our survey results will be unreliable. This could happen if the population were not specified correctly. If we thought the population was the 18–25 age group in the beverage consumption problem, when in fact it was all 24 students, the mean of the larger sample would approach 82.60 and not the true 49.583.

Figure 6.3 Consistency; $\overline{X}$ Approaches μ and $s/\sqrt{n}$ Decreases as n Approaches N.

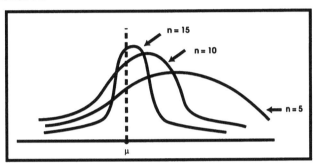

The standard error becomes smaller because the dispersion is divided by $\sqrt{n}$, and consistency involves n increasing.

 Concept Check 6.B

The term efficiency deals with taking repeated samples of a given size, whereas consistency involves a single sample which becomes larger and larger. True or false? If false, explain.

Exercises

6.3   State how the terms unbiased and efficiency differ from consistency.

6.4   Why are the terms unbiased, efficiency, and consistency considered theoretical from a sampling viewpoint?

6.5   a. If $\mu = 25$, and the mean of the sampling distribution $= 28$, what problem exists?
       b. If $\mu = 25$, $\overline{X} = 26$ when $n = 25$, and $\overline{X} = 28$ when the sample increases to $n = 49$, what problem exists?

6.6   Is it possible to obtain a biased estimate that is closer to the population parameter than an unbiased estimate? Explain.

From surveys of size n, we will obtain a mean $(\overline{X})$, and a standard deviation (s). This assumes the elements were obtained randomly, and that the data are continuous. For qualitative data we will have knowledge of only $\hat{p}$ and n. We will use $\overline{X}$ as a point estimate for μ, s as a point estimate of σ and, for qualitative data, $\hat{p}$ as an estimate of p.

Remember from Table 5.6B that none of the sample means of size 2 equaled the true population mean of 47.8. Hence, we have no confidence in making point estimates of the population mean, standard deviation, and proportion using sample information. In effect, we have no confidence in point estimates and all estimates made will be in the form of an interval.

If a survey yielded a mean $(\overline{X})$ of 74.8 and a standard deviation (s) 3.06, then 74.8 would be the point estimate of μ and 3.06 the point estimate of σ. If the survey information were qualitative, and $\hat{p} = .72$, then .72 would be the point estimate of p.

Concept Check 6.C

For most sample data, point estimates are usually obtained from either the mean or the proportion. True or false? If false, explain.

Exercises

6.7   a.   When sampling continuous data, what 3 key pieces of information will be of concern?
       b.   When sampling discrete data, what information will be available?

6.8   Why is the denominator N when tabulating σ, but $n - 1$ when computing s?

6.9   The following information is revealed from a survey: $n = 65$, $\overline{X} = 39.4$ and $s = 2.1$. What are the point estimates for μ and σ?

6.10   From a survey, 58 out of 92 favored ratification of an amendment. What is the point estimate for p?

6.4   Interval Estimates: σ Known

Interval Estimates of the Mean

An interval estimate consists of an interval that we are willing to say contains the population parameter we are trying to estimate with a specified confidence. The size of the interval will directly relate to the confidence that we wish to express in the statement. Surely we can say we are 100% confident that an automobile tire will last between 0 and 100,000 miles, or that the President enjoys between 0 and 100% popularity rating. Unfortunately, even though we are 100% confident that the population parameter lies within the interval, it will be hard to find someone willing to pay for such imprecise estimates. We will find that we are able to develop much smaller confidence intervals and only lose a small amount of our precision.

At the pivotal point of our confidence interval will be the point estimator. We can't attach any confidence in point estimates, since they do not take into account sampling error. When we randomly select the n items to be surveyed, the point estimate represents one of many samples that are possible. Hence, each different sample selected will yield a difference between the sample mean $(\overline{X})$ and the population mean (μ) due to the random generation in the selection of the elementary units themselves.

In Chapter 5, we established that when sampling occurs from a large normally distributed population, or when we sample with replacement, the sampling distribution of $\overline{X}$ is normally distributed, with a mean μ and a standard deviation $\sigma_{\overline{x}} = \sigma/\sqrt{n}$ (formula 5.1). Hence, if we take $\mu \pm \sigma_{\overline{x}} \bullet z_\alpha$, we know that the boundary just developed will contain approximately $(1 - \alpha) \bullet 100\%$ of all the possible sample means of size n. The expression $(1 - \alpha)$ is called the **confidence coefficient** and α the **significance level**.

If we desired a 90% confidence level, we state that $[(1 - \alpha = .90) \bullet 100\%]$ approximately 90% of the sample means lie within the confidence interval (CI) and 10% $[a = .10] \bullet 100\%]$ lie outside the CI. For Figure 6.4 we can see from ten confidence intervals about $\overline{X}$ that μ lies within the bounds of 9 of 10 intervals.

Figure 6.4 μ Within the Bounds of 9 of 10 Sample Confidence Intervals

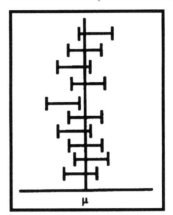

The interval, at this point, is not all that valuable, since we do not know the population mean (μ). However, if we replace μ with the estimator, then we have extremely valuable information. In the statement $\overline{X} \pm \sigma_{\overline{X}} \bullet z_\alpha$ we now have an interval estimate of μ, and with this interval can be stated a given confidence level $[(1 - \alpha) \bullet 100\%]$. We may desire any number of confidence levels, the most frequently selected and used are the 95% $(\alpha = .05)$, 99% $(\alpha = .01)$ and 90% $(\alpha = .10)$ levels. From a computational standpoint in terms of the confidence interval, changing the confidence level involves changing the z value. The specific z value is often called the reliability factor. The reliability factor depends on the confidence coefficient $(1 - \alpha)$ selected.

To find the appropriate z value (reliability factor) from the normal table, take the desired confidence coefficient and divide by 2 $[(1 - \alpha)/2]$. If we desire to have a 95% confidence level $[\alpha = .05, (1 - \alpha)/2 = .95/2 = .4750]$, we look up the body of the normal distribution (Table 6.2 and Appendix A, Table 1). The value .4750 appears in row 1.9 and column .06, yielding $z = 1.90 + .06 = 1.96$.

Table 6.2 Abbreviated Normal Distribution

z	.03	.04	.05	.06	.07	.08	.09
1.7	.4582	.4591	.4599	.4608	.4616	.4625	.4633
1.8	.4664	.4671	.4678	.4686	.4693	.4699	.4706
1.9	.4732	.4738	.4744	**.4750**	.4756	.4761	.4767
2.0	.4788	.4793	.4798	.4803	.4808	.4812	.4817
2.1	.4834	.4838	.4842	.4846	.4850	.4854	.4857

The larger the confidence coefficient the larger the z_α value, hence a larger confidence interval. A confidence coefficient of .90 equates to $z_{.10} = 1.645$, a coefficient of .95 to $z_{.05} = 1.960$, and a coefficient of .99 leads to $z_{.01} = 2.576$.

Remember that even though we have a population normality assumption in our analysis, through the Central Limit Theorem, as long as the sample size is large enough, we need not worry about the normality

125

assumption. We know that as n increases, the sampling distribution of $\overline{X}$ approaches a normal distribution. What constitutes large in terms of sample size is subject to debate. Some practitioners contend that as long as $n \geq 30$ the normality assumption applies. However, it would be foolish to state that confidence intervals involving sample sizes ≥ 30 are inherently superior to sample sizes below 30. Hence the standard deviation of the sampling distribution, the standard error of the mean, and the Central Limit Theorem are critical to the interval.

Let's illustrate what we have learned through the use of an example. Suppose we have tested 25 ($n = 25$) lightbulbs to determine their life expectancy. We believe that $\sigma = 3.06$, and survey results yield a mean of 74.8 ($\overline{X} = 74.8$). The standard error of the mean is $\sigma_{\overline{X}} = 3.06/\sqrt{25} = 0.612$.

Let's now develop our confidence interval about X.

$(1 - \alpha) \bullet 100\%$ Confidence Interval for μ: σ Known General Formula for Interval Estimates

$$\text{estimate} \pm (\text{reliability factor}) (\text{standard error}) \tag{6.2}$$

Specific Formula for Estimation of μ

$$\overline{X} \pm z_{\alpha/2} \bullet \sigma_{\overline{X}} \tag{6.3}$$

where

$z_{\alpha/2} =$ the reliability factor or appropriate z value to obtain a desired

$\quad (1 - \alpha) \bullet 100\%$ confidence level

$\sigma_{\overline{X}} = \sigma/\sqrt{n}$: the standard error or the mean.

In terms of formula 6.2, we are $(1 - \alpha) \bullet 100\%$ confident that μ will fall within the interval, and believe μ will fall outside the interval ($\alpha \bullet 100\%$ (the level of significance).

Returning to the life expectancy of our lightbulbs ($n = 25$, $\overline{X} = 74.8$, and $s = 3.06$), our 95% confidence interval is

$$\overline{X} \pm (1.96)(3.06/\sqrt{25})$$

$$\overline{X} \pm (1.96)(0.612)$$

Substituting 74.8, the numerical equivalent of $\overline{X}$ yields

$$74.8 \pm 1.1995; \text{ or } 73.6005 \leq \overline{X} \leq 75.9995$$

The 73.6005 value is often called the **Lower Control Limit** (LCL), while the 75.9995 value is called the **Upper Control Limit** (UCL). These represent the boundaries for the confidence interval. The confidence interval and appropriate z scale are shown in Figure 6.5.

Figure 6.5 95% Confidence Interval for Lightbulb Example

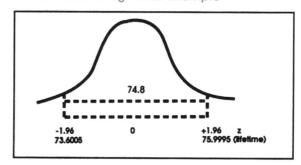

The key point to be made is that if we took 100 samples of size n, and tabulated the confidence interval, μ would be outside the interval about $\alpha \bullet 100\%$ of the time and within the interval about $(1 - \alpha) \bullet 100\%$ of the time. In our example, if we took 100 repeated samples of size 25, the population mean would fall within the computed confidence interval 95% of the time, and fall outside of it 5% of the time. The statement could be revised to say we are 95% confident that the population mean will fall within this specific interval (73.6005 to 75.9995).

To this point nothing has been stated concerning the size of the population. If $n/N \geq .05$, the finite population correction factor (formula 5.7) would be invoked. Let us suppose that in our lightbulb life expectancy problem, the size of the population (N) is $= 200$. Since $n/N = .125$, the standard error of the mean would be multiplied by

$$\sqrt{\frac{N - n}{N - 1}} = \sqrt{\frac{200 - 25}{200 - 1}} = 0.9378$$

The discounted standard error is

$$\sigma_{\overline{X}} = \frac{\sigma}{\sqrt{n}} \bullet \sqrt{\frac{N - n}{N - 1}} = (0.612)(0.9378) = 0.5739$$

and the confidence interval becomes

$$\overline{X} \pm (1.96)(0.5739)$$

or

$$74.8 \pm 1.1249; \text{ or } 73.6751 \leq \mu \leq 75.9249$$

Utilizing MINITAB to Obtain Confidence Intervals: σ Known

We can utilize MINITAB to obtain our desired confidence intervals. First we will make note of an important point.

NOTE: THE 95% CONFIDENCE LEVEL IS THE ONE PRIMARILY USED IN ACADEMIA, IN SCIENCE, AND IN THE BUSINESS WORLD. HENCE MINITAB DEFAULTS TO THE 95% CONFIDENCE INTERVAL. SHOULD ANOTHER INTERVAL BE REQUIRED CLICK TO THE CONFIDENCE INTERVAL BOX TO CHANGE IT.

Table 6.3A Using MINITAB to compute confidence intervals with the population standard
       deviation (STDEV) known to be $= 20$ (using Z-values)
       *Data File on MINITAB CD

We randomly sample 16 beverage cans and record the following volumes in ml's: 352, 358, 357, 353, 349, 352, 356, 352, 351, 348, 351, 348, 349, 355, 356, 357 enter and save data file
      The command sequence is

Stat > Basic Statistics > 1-Sample Z
Double click data column to enter it into **Variables** box.
Click **Options** to enter confidence level. Default is 95 percent.
Click **Sigma** and enter population standard deviation of 20.
OK

Table 6.3B Solution from MINITAB

One-Sample Z: Data
The assumed standard deviation $= 20.0$

Variable	N	Mean	StDev	SE Mean	95.0% CI
Data	16	352.75	3.376	5.00	(342.95, 362.55)

Concept Check 6.D

If we had a 95% confidence interval, we are 95% confident that the true population parameter lies within the specified interval. True or false? If false, explain.

Exercises

6.11   a.   Sample information from a random survey: $n = 36$, $\overline{X} = 46.9$, and $\sigma = 2.6$. Determine a 95% confidence interval for μ.
       b.   State what information the answer to part a yields.
       c.   If $N = 100$, determine the new 95% confidence interval.

6.12   Automobile producers have engineered a new oil warning light that will signal engine overheating. A random survey is taken to determine the time it takes for the light to signal an overheating problem. The results are: $\overline{X} = .89$ seconds, $n = 49$. It is believed that $\sigma = .05$ seconds. Estimate the time it takes for the oil warning lights to come on using a 99% confidence level.

6.13   A super glue has been developed that can sustain 2,000 pounds of pressure. A random sample of 45 is used to ascertain that the mean drying time to hold this pressure is 2.89 minutes ($\sigma = .19$). Estimate the mean drying time using a 99% confidence level.

6.14   A golf course manager wants to know the time it takes for the average foursome to complete a round of golf. A random survey is conducted ($n = 68$) with $\overline{X} = 4.91$ hours. It is believed that $\sigma = .68$ hours. Determine the 95% confidence interval for μ.

6.15   An airline wishes to determine the length of time it takes to service a customer at the service line. A random survey ($n = 116$) is conducted nationwide with a $\overline{X} = 12.8$ minutes ($\sigma = 2.6$ minutes). Estimate the mean service time using a 99% confidence level.

6.16   For the MINITAB data file PULSE.MTW, compute the 95% confidence intervals for the variables height and weight. Assume sigma for height to be 3 and weight to be 20.

6.5   Interval Estimates of a Proportion

For qualitative data, there will be available from survey information concerning n and $\hat{p}$ (also $\hat{q} = 1 - \hat{p}$). We discussed the binomial distribution in Section 4.3, and found the formula for the standard error of the proportion is $\sigma_p = \sqrt{p \bullet q / n}$.

When $n \bullet \hat{p}$ and $n \bullet \hat{q}$ exceeds 5, the sampling distribution of $\hat{p}$ (the sample proportion) is approximately normal with a mean of $\hat{p}$ and a standard error of $\hat{\sigma}_p = \sqrt{\hat{p} \bullet \hat{q} / n}$. The confidence interval about a specific sample proportion ($\hat{p}$) is

$(1 - \alpha) \bullet 100\%$ Confidence Interval About a Large Sample $\hat{P}$

$$\hat{p} \pm z_{\alpha/2} \bullet \hat{\sigma}_{\hat{p}} \tag{6.4}$$

where

$z_{\alpha/2} =$ the appropriate z value to obtain a desired confidence

$\hat{\sigma}_p =$ the standard error of the sample proportion $= \sqrt{\hat{p} \bullet \hat{q} / n}$

As an example, let's say market researchers conducted a survey of 100 consumers and found that 23% of them have used their product over the last 3 years. Assuming the survey selected consumers randomly, and using a confidence level of 90% (significance level of 10%; $\alpha = .10$), the standard error of the proportion is

$$\hat{\sigma}_{\hat{p}} = \sqrt{\frac{(.23)(.77)}{100}} = 0.0421$$

The appropriate confidence interval is

$$\hat{p} \pm (1.645)(0.0421)$$

or

$$.23 \pm 0.0692; \text{ or } .1608 \leq p \leq .2992$$

If 100 random surveys were taken of size 100, p would fall within the confidence interval in approximately 90 of them, and outside the interval 10 times. We think that the proportion of the population that has used our product during the last 3 years is roughly between 16% and 30%. The 16.08% is sometimes called the **lower confidence limit (LCL)** and the 29.92% value the **upper confidence limit (UCL)**.

Note, if N were known and $n/N \geq .05$, the finite population correction factor must be used. If, in our market researchers example, $N = 400$, the FPCF $= \sqrt{(400 - 100)/399} = 0.8671$, and the standard error of the proportion is 0.0365 (0.8671 $\bullet$ 0.0421); the confidence interval becomes $p \pm 0.0365 \bullet 1.645$, or $.23 \pm 0.0601$.

Confidence versus Precision

There is often a tendency to desire high confidence, which will occur at the expense of precision. In Table 6.4, we increase the confidence level from 50% to 99.9% on the marketing research problem just reviewed, and have greatly increased the confidence interval, thereby reducing the precision in the answer. The 95% confidence interval is the most widely used by practitioners, with 99% and 90% being the next most used confidence values. It is rare to desire a confidence value in excess of 99%.

Table 6.4 Confidence versus Precision: $\hat{p} = .23$, $\hat{\sigma}_p = 0.0421$

			Interval
50.0% Confidence	$\alpha = .500$	$z = 0.674$	20.16% − 25.84%
80.0% Confidence	$\alpha = .200$	$z = 1.282$	17.60% − 28.40%
90.0% Confidence	$\alpha = .100$	$z = 1.645$	16.08% − 29.92%
95.0% Confidence	$\alpha = .050$	$z = 1.960$	14.75% − 31.26%
99.0% Confidence	$\alpha = .010$	$z = 2.576$	12.16% − 33.84%
99.9% Confidence	$\alpha = .001$	$z = 3.291$	9.14% − 36.86%

 Concept Check 6.E

Whenever $p \bullet q > 5$ the sampling distribution of $\hat{p}$ is approximately normal with a mean of P and a standard error of $\sigma_p = \sqrt{p \bullet q/n}$

Exercises

6.17   a.   Random sample information $n = 89$, $p = .69$. Determine a 90% confidence interval for p.

       b.   If $N = 250$, determine a 95% confidence interval.

6.18   a.   A high tech company wishes to determine the percent of employees who have advanced degrees or certifications. It conducts an internal random survey of 370 employees and finds that 290 of them have either an advanced degree or certification. Estimate the percent of employees who have an advanced degree or certification using a 90% confidence interval.

        b.   If there are a total of 600 employees, estimate the percent of employees who have advanced degrees or certifications using a 90% confidence interval.

6.19   A market research firm desires to know the average percentage of consumer expenditure made on housing. A random survey ($n = 1,050$) is conducted with $\hat{p} = 41.9\%$. Determine the percentage of expenditures on housing using a 90% confidence interval.

6.20   A company performs a random survey ($n = 410$) to determine the number of employees who took no sick leave last year. The number is 160. Estimate the percentage of employees who took no sick leave time using a 98% confidence interval.

6.6   Interval Estimates: σ Unknown

We use a sample mean to approximate μ when it is unknown. If σ is unknown, it would seem rational to estimate it with s. However, when such a substitution is made, we are no longer involved with a standard normal random variable. It does, however, follow the attributes of another distribution called the t distribution. This distribution was developed by W. S. Gossett in 1908. The t distribution has a different value for each and every value of n. In actuality, the t value increases as n decreases.

The t distribution should be used to replace the normal distribution whenever

-   σ is unknown and must be estimated using s
-   we may assume the population is normally distributed

Since the t distribution is wider than the z distribution, the appropriate t value will always exceed the z value. In understanding the t distribution, we can view Figure 6.6. The t distribution is symmetrical, but wider or flatter than the z distribution. The flatter characteristic means that the t distribution has a greater proportion of its area in its tails than will the normal distribution. This fact ensures that $t > z$ for a specified significance level. In fact, the t distribution will become flatter as n declines. This will increase the width of the confidence interval as n declines. This is necessary as we either have less confidence with smaller sample sizes, or we must allow the interval to increase to maintain the same confidence as the sample size declines.

Figure 6.6 A Normal Distribution and t Distributions for a Given α

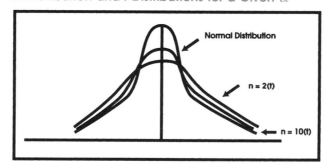

There are two factors involved in finding an appropriate *t* value. First there is the specific significance (α) level desired. For most tables a selected range of significance levels are given including the 10% ($t_{.10}$) level, the 5% ($t_{.05}$) level, and the 1% ($t_{.01}$) level. Note that our table (Appendix A: Table 3) yields *t* values for both a one- and two-tailed test. This difference will become important in the next chapter, but for now remember that we are concerned with an interval (plus or minus a selected value); hence, we are interested in the two-tailed values. Should a *t* value be desired for a one-tailed test, it would be found in the same manner as a two-tailed test.

The second factor required to use the *t* table is the number of degrees of freedom (*df*). To understand the concept of degrees of freedom, we will use an example. Suppose you are told that the mean age of you and the two students who sit on either side of you in your class is 25 ($\overline{X} = 25$: $n = 3$). The instructor asks the age of the student on your left side. Her age is a random variable as it can take on a wide range of values. Suppose she gives her age to the instructor as 20. Your instructor then asks the age of the man on your right. Again the age is a random variable with a wide range of possible values. He gives his age as 30. We know the mean age of the 3 of you to be 25, and two students' ages are 20 and 30. We need not ask you what your age is, it must be 25. Your age is fixed and is not a random variable.

For this reason the degrees of freedom is not *n*, but rather $n - 1$. The general rule for determining the degrees of freedom is the sample size minus the number of estimates that had to be made to yield the answer you have. In this example, we have made one estimate, that concerning the mean of the 3 students. In statistical estimation, our interval pivots on the estimate of the mean; hence, the degrees of freedom equals sample size minus one ($df = n - 1$).

It is now possible to look up the specific $t_{\alpha/2(df)}$ or $t_{\alpha/1(df)}$, where α = the significance level, 1 or 2 refers to a one- or two-tailed test, and df = the appropriate degrees of freedom. Let's say we want to have 95% confidence in our results ($\alpha = .05$) and that our sample size equals 26. The $df = n - 1 = 26 - 1 = 25$, and $t_{.05/2(25)} = 2.060$. For 95% confidence level; $n = 21$, $t_{.05/2(20)} = 2.086$; $n = 11$, $t_{.05/2(10)} = 2.228$; $n = 4$, $t_{.05/2(3)} = 3.182$. Note, in order to maintain the 95% confidence level, as the sample size declines, the interval increases. This means that *t* must increase to widen the interval as *n* declines.

Some statisticians use the normal distribution (*z*) rather than the *t* distribution once the sample size exceeds 31. They base this on the fact that if the *t* table is viewed (Table 6.5), there are only marginal differences between a *z* and a *t* value when *n* exceeds 31. In turn, there would only be marginal differences involving a confidence interval using a *z* instead of a *t* value. While true, we will refrain from making such a substitution because MINITAB and other computer packages consistently use the appropriate *t* value.

131

Table 6.5 Abbreviated Values of *t* for Selected Probabilities

	Probabilities		
Two tails $\alpha =$	.10	.05	.01
df		Values of t	
1	6.314	12.706	63.657
2	2.920	4.303	9.925
3	2.353	3.182	5.841
4	2.132	2.776	4.604
5	2.015	2.571	4.032
6	1.943	2.447	3.707
7	1.895	2.365	3.499
8	1.860	2.306	3.355
9	1.833	2.262	3.250
10	1.812	2.228	3.169
15	1.753	2.131	2.947
20	1.725	2.086	2.845
25	1.708	2.060	2.787
29	1.699	2.045	2.756
30	1.697	2.042	2.750
40	1.684	2.021	2.704
60	1.658	1.980	2.617
∞	1.645	1.960	2.576 z values

The appropriate confidence interval used in most applications (because σ is unknown and assuming a normal or approximately normal population) is

---

$(1 - \alpha) \bullet 100\%$ Confidence Interval for μ: σ Unknown

$$\overline{X} \pm t_{\alpha/2(df)} \bullet \hat{\sigma}_{\overline{X}} \qquad\qquad (6.5)$$

where

$t_{\alpha/2(df)} =$ the reliability factor

$\hat{\sigma}_{\overline{X}} = s/\sqrt{n}$: the standard error using s to approximate σ

A small sample will increase both the standard error and the t value involved.

Let's illustrate the process with an example. Earlier we computed the confidence interval involving the life expectancy of lightbulbs. Our survey found that the mean life expectancy $(\overline{X})$ was 74.8 and that σ was 3.06. We originally determined the interval to be 73.6005 to 75.9995 using $n = 25$ and a 95% confidence interval. Let's reanalyze the problem assuming σ is unknown and must be estimated from s. For illustration sake, let's assume $s = \sigma = 3.06$; hence, the estimated standard error of the mean equals the actual standard error of the mean at 0.612 $(3.06/\sqrt{25})$.

The appropriate t value is 2.064 $(t_{.05/2(24)} = 2.064)$. The confidence interval is

$74.8 \pm (2.064)(0.612)$

74.8 ± 1.2632

yielding a 95% confidence interval of 73.5368 to 76.0632.

Note that this interval is wider than when σ was known because that t value exceeds the z value.

Once again, we can utilize MINITAB to obtain confidence intervals.

NOTE: THE 95% CONFIDENCE LEVEL IS THE ONE PRIMARILY USED IN ACADE-MIA, IN SCIENCE, AND IN THE BUSINESS WORLD. HENCE MINITAB DEFAULTS TO THE 95% CONFIDENCE INTERVAL. SHOULD ANOTHER INTERVAL BE REQUIRED CLICK TO THE OPTIONS BOX TO CHANGE IT.

Table 6.6A Using MINITAB to compute confidence intervals with the population standard deviation unknown (using *t* values)

We randomly sample 16 beverage cans and record the following volumes in ml's: 352, 358, 357, 353, 349, 352, 356, 352, 351, 348, 351, 348, 349, 355, 356, 357 enter and save data file

Stat > Basic Statistics > 1-Sample t
Double click data column to enter it into **Variables** box.
Click **Options box** to enter confidence level as 95%. Since the default CI is 95% we proceed.
OK

Table 6.6B Solution from MINITAB

One-Sample T: Data

Variable	N	Mean	StDev	SE Mean	95.0% CI
Data	16	352.750	3.376	0.844	(350.951, 354.549)

Finite Population Correction Factor

Remember that if the population size is finite, when we sample without replacement (the norm) and when $n/N \geq .05$, the finite population correction factor must be used. The appropriate formula is

$(1 - \alpha) \bullet 100\%$ Confidence Interval for μ: σ Unknown, $n/N \geq .05$

$$\overline{X} \pm t_{\alpha/2(df)} \bullet (\hat{\sigma}_{\overline{X}}) \bullet \sqrt{(N - n)/(N - 1)} \qquad (6.6)$$

where

$t_{\alpha/2(df)} = $ the appropriate *t* value to obtain a desired confidence

$(\hat{\sigma}_{\overline{X}}) = s/\sqrt{n}$: the standard error using *s* to approximate σ

$N = $ the population size

The following information is given concerning a survey: $\overline{X} = 26.9$, $s = 0.98$, $n = 26$, $N = 100$. The appropriate confidence interval ($\alpha = .05$; $1 - \alpha = .95$) is

$$26.9 \pm 2.060 \left(\frac{0.98}{\sqrt{26}} \right) \left(\sqrt{\frac{100 - 26}{100 - 1}} \right)$$

$$26.9 \pm (2.060)(0.1922)(.8646)$$

$$26.9 \pm 0.3423 : \text{ or } 26.5577 \text{ to } 27.2423$$

For small sample sizes, we replace z with a t to widen the confidence interval. True or false? If false, explain.

Exercises

6.21 Under what conditions may we use the t distribution?

6.22 Find the appropriate t values.

    a $t_{.05/2(27)}$
    b. $t_{.01/1(8)}$
    c. $t_{.10/2(1)}$
    d. $t_{.01/1(27)}$
    e. $t_{.30/2(23)}$
    f. $t_{.005/1(4)}$
    g. $t_{.10/1(27)}$
    h. $t_{.02/2(6)}$
    i. $t_{.05/1(2)}$

6.23 A soft drink bottling distributor wants to know the mean amount of milliliters (ml) each bottle contains. They conduct a random sample of 21 bottles, and determine that $\overline{X} = 567$ with $s = 24$. Estimate the number of ml in each bottle using a 95% confidence interval.

6.24 A computer company wants to know the life expectancy of their hard drives. They perform a random survey of 9 hard drives and determine the average life expectancy to be 497.8 hours with a standard deviation of 49.3 hours. Estimate the life expectancy of the hard disks with 99% confidence.

6.25 a. A random sample of 21 cars passing a checkpoint yielded an average speed of 43.9 miles per hour with a standard deviation of 9.6. Determine a 90% confidence interval for the true mean speed.
    b. If the sample size were 210 instead of 21, how would the 90% confidence interval change?

6.26 A consumer testing company wants to know the cost of repairing a certain type of vehicle in controlled crashes of 5 miles per hour. The company performs a random survey of 23 cars with an average repair cost of $1,267 and a standard deviation of $298. Estimate the 90% confidence interval of the average cost of vehicle repair.

6.27 A company randomly selects vitamin capsules to record the correct amount of mg contained within. The results of the survey are: 205, 191, 132, 212, 219, 114, 233, 211, 168, 178, 199, 191,184, 187, 202, 207, 181, 177, 176, 200, 188, 189, 212, 124, and 206. Compute a 99% confidence interval.

6.28 In a large university 18 students are randomly selected yielding the following ages: 19, 24, 21, 34, 22, 20, 20, 19, 35, 47, 31, 19, 23, 25, 24, 28, 37, 20. Have MINITAB compute a 98.2% confidence interval.

6.29 A construction wire is made to handle 500 pounds of tensile strength. A survey of 24 cables is made with the following results: 489, 516, 551, 458, 571, 519, 490, 501, 487, 526, 537, 600, 477, 509, 511, 529, 502, 469, 488, 420, 499, 477, 500, 466. Have MINITAB compute the 95% confidence interval.

6.30   Fifteen randomly selected cans of tomato soup contain the following grams: 301, 315, 309, 289, 299, 303, 308, 297, 294, 305, 318, 310, 291, 306, 302. Have MINITAB compute the 92% confidence interval.

6.7   Determining the Sample Size: Estimation of μ

So far we have merely reported the estimates based on given samples. However, as we have seen, the sample size is critical to the precision of our estimates. Thus, we must turn our attention to the appropriate sample size necessary to yield the desired precision. Sampling is extremely costly, so over-sampling is cost prohibitive. Under-sampling will not lead to the desired information and/or the precision required. In addition, remember that all samples involve sampling error.

Formula 5.1, for the standard error of the mean ($\sigma = \sigma/\sqrt{n}$), can be algebraically rearranged and solved for n, yielding $n = \sigma^2/\sigma_{\overline{X}}^2$. In determining n, we select a specific confidence level, and set a limit on the allowable error that will yield a desired precision. In other words, we will state that we want a 95% confidence level and we desire an allowable or tolerable error ($e = z_{\alpha/2} \bullet \sigma_{\overline{X}}$). Solving for $\sigma_{\overline{X}}$ yields $e/z_{\alpha/2}$, then substituting into $n = \sigma^2/\sigma_{\overline{X}}^2$, the resulting formula is

Determining Sample Size for Estimating a Mean

$$n = \frac{z_{\alpha/2}^2 \bullet \sigma^2}{e^2} \qquad (6.7)$$

where

$z_{\alpha/2}^2 = $ the appropriate z value squared

$\sigma^2 = $ the population variance

$e^2 = $ the allowable or tolerable error squared

In review, there are three factors involved in ascertaining sample size. First would be the desired confidence in the estimate. The greater the confidence level, the greater is the required sample size. Hence, there is a direct relationship between n and the desired confidence level.

The second factor is the dispersion in the population that is being sampled as measured by σ^2. If the dispersion is small, most of the elementary units are homogenous with respect to what is being surveyed, and a small sample will suffice. If the population dispersion is larger, then the sample size will need to be increased. Hence, there is a direct relationship between σ^2 and n.

The third factor is the allowable error (e). The smaller the allowable error, the greater will be n. Conversely, the greater the allowable error, the smaller will be the necessary sample size. Hence, there is an inverse relationship between e and n.

Note that Formula 6.7 requires knowledge of the population variance prior to sampling. Normally, very little will be known concerning the population parameters. In fact, the reason for sampling is to obtain sample statistics, which are estimates of the population parameters. How then can we obtain an estimate of σ prior to sampling?

First, we may have completed a similar survey in the past involving a different site or geographical location. We may then use estimates of s^2 from that survey as an estimate of σ^2. Second, we might perform a pre-sample to provide information about dispersion. In such cases we might use s^2 from the preliminary survey as an estimate of σ^2. Third, we might estimate the largest and smallest possible observation we could obtain from the sample. The smallest estimate is subtracted from the largest to obtain an estimated range.

The estimate range is divided by 6, since within the interval of plus or minus 3 standard deviations is 99.7% of the data. This yields an estimate of σ which must be squared to obtain an estimate of σ^2.

Estimated σ Based on an Approximate Range

$$\hat{\sigma} = \frac{\text{Largest estimated observation} - \text{Smallest estimated observation}}{6} \qquad (6.8)$$

Let's illustrate the formula with the aid of an example. Suppose we wanted to estimate the mean age for your business statistics class with 95% confidence. We will allow a tolerable error of 1.5 years. We observe the class and feel that the oldest student is approximately 50 and the youngest is about 20. The estimate of (formula 6.8) is

$$\hat{\sigma} = \frac{50 - 20}{6} = \frac{30}{6} = 5.0$$

A 95% confidence interval results in a $z = 1.96$. Hence, $z^2 = 3.8416 = (1.96^2)$, $\hat{\sigma}^2 = 25 = (5.0^2)$, and $e^2 = 2.25 = (1.5^2)$. Substituting the appropriate numerical equivalents into formula 6.7 yields

$$n = \frac{3.8416 \bullet 25}{2.25} = \frac{96.04}{2.25} = 42.684$$

We must sample 43 to obtain the desired precision. Note that if the answer had been 42.001 we still would have to sample at least that many; hence, we would have to sample 43, since we could not sample a fraction of a person. We always round up when dealing with fractional samples.

 Concept Check 6.G

The sample size of a continuous distribution is directly related to the desired confidence, and inversely related to the variation in the population and the allowable error. True or false? If false, explain.

Exercises

6.31   What factors are important in ascertaining the appropriate sample size? Be sure to state if the relationship to n is direct or inverse.

6.32   When and why do we employ the finite population correction factor?

6.33   We believe $\sigma = 2.5$; we will allow an error of 0.7 and desire a 95% confidence level. Determine the appropriate sample size.

6.34   We wish to conduct a random survey in an instance where we will allow an error of 1.9. We have no knowledge of the population standard deviation, but believe the highest observation in the data set is 78 and the lowest 36. At a 90% confidence level, determine the appropriate sample size.

6.35   A company wants to determine the life expectancy of its lightbulbs. It conducted a random survey 3 years before and found the $\overline{X} = 87.9$ hours and $\sigma = 4.14$ hours. We will allow an error of 1.5 hours and desire a 99.5% confidence interval. Determine the appropriate sample size.

6.36   A golf driving range wants to conduct a random survey to determine the average length a golf ball is driven. They determine the longest ball driven was 320 yards, and the shortest was 100 yards. The golf range desires an allowable error of 3 yards and a 90% confidence level. Determine the appropriate sample size.

6.37 We desire to know the average income in your class of size 60. The σ of the entire university is $3,000. We will use this as an estimate of your class ($N = 60$). We desire a 95% confidence level and an allowable error of $1,000. Determine the appropriate sample size.

6.38 Our company has developed new standard operational procedures of which we will test our employee's knowledge. We wish to sample to ascertain the amount of time each employee studied for the exam. We desire a tolerable error of 1.0 hours and a 90% confidence level. We think the range of hours studied is from 2 to 20 hours. Determine the appropriate sample size.

6.8 Determining the Sample Size: Estimation of p

The analysis for determining sample size for a proportion is similar to that of finding n for a mean. Of course, the qualitative data, the terms mean and standard deviation of the sample have no relevance. Remember that the formula for the standard error of the proportion is $\sigma_p = \sqrt{p \bullet q/n}$. We must first solve this formula for n, $n = p \bullet q/\sigma_p^2$. If we stipulated an allowable error, $e = z_{\alpha/2} \bullet \sigma_p$. Solving for σ_p, then substituting into the $n =$ formula yields

---

Determining n for Proportions

$$n = \frac{z_{\alpha/2}^2 \bullet p \bullet q}{e^2}$$ (6.9)

where

$z_{\alpha/2}^2 =$ the appropriate z value squared

$p =$ the population proportion; usually hypothesized:

if a hypothesis is not possible assume $p = .5$

$e^2 =$ the allowable or tolerable error squared

The sample size is dependent on three factors. First is the confidence desired. There is a direct relationship between the desired confidence and the sample size. The second factor is the population proportion. A p value close to .5 ($1 - p = .5$) yields less information than $p = .9$. A population proportion near 0 or 1 says that everyone in the population is homogenous (similar) with respect to the information sought. Hence a p close to .5 needs a larger sample than a p near 0 or 1. A $p = .5$ indicates there is widespread disagreement with respect to the question asked; hence, a larger sample size is needed. If there is no way of hypothesizing p, assume the worst scenario, which is $p = 0.5$. Third is the allowable error. There is an inverse relationship as the smaller the allowable error, the greater must be n to give you the added precision.

Let us illustrate with the use of an example. We own a chain of restaurants and are interested in conducting a survey to estimate the percentage of customers who leave no tip "stiffs." Suppose that we wanted no greater than an allowable error of 1% ($e = .01$, $e^2 = .0001$) and a confidence level of 95% ($z = 1.96$, $z^2 = 3.8416$). We want to estimate the stiff rate on the high side to be sure we do not under sample. Experienced managers believe no greater than 10% of the checks are stiffed; hence, $p_o = .1 (q_o = 1 - p_o = .9)$. Substituting the appropriate numerical equivalents into formula 6.10 yields

$$n = \frac{(1.96)^2(.10)(.90)}{(.01)^2} = 3,457.44 = 3,458$$

Since sampling almost 3,500 customers would be cost prohibitive, a method must be found to reduce the sample size. If we lowered the confidence level, we will lower the required n. If the confidence level drops to 90% (from 95%), then the needed sample size is

$$n = \frac{(1.645)^2(.10)(.90)}{(.01)^2} = 2,435.42 = 2,436$$

Again, the sample size is too great. Assume that our own hypothesis concerning the stiff rate is that it is really about 5%. Hence, we will use a $p = .05$. The solution is

$$n = \frac{(1.645)^2(.05)(.95)}{(.01)^2} = 1{,}285.36 = 1{,}286$$

The sample size is still beyond being cost effective. Let us increase the allowable error from 1% to 2%. The solution is

$$n = \frac{1.645^2 \bullet .05 \bullet .95}{(.02)^2} = 321.34 = 322$$

At this point the sample size is more reasonable. Yet it is easy to understand that we have three options in reducing n should that be our goal.

If p is unknown, we may estimate it from previous studies, studies possibly performed in different regions. However, if there is no way of estimating p, we must use the most conservative estimate, which is $p = .5$. A value of .5 for p will always yield the largest value for n, given that the confidence interval and allowable error remain constant. For example, recently researchers at a prestigious medical school in California identified a new gene. If we wanted to know what percent of the population had this gene we would have no idea. Hence, we would assume $p = .5$.

 Concept Check 6.H

The sample size will be larger when the population proportion is near 1.0 or 0.0, as opposed to being near 0.5. True or false? If false, explain.

Exercises

6.39   Will n always be less than N if $n/N \geq .05$?

6.40   What factors influence the appropriate sample size when estimating a proportion?

6.41   With an allowable error of 2%, a confidence level of 95%, and a population proportion of 85.3%, determine the appropriate sample size.

6.42   With an allowable error of 1%, a confidence level of 99%, and a population proportion of 46.9%, determine the appropriate sample size.

6.43   From a nationwide study, 16.8% of the respondents favor a particular policy. A random survey is to be taken of a particular city. A 90% confidence interval is desired with a 3% allowable error. Determine the appropriate sample size.

6.44   It is believed that 64.8% of the population owns their home. We want to sample the population to test this hypothesis in a particular city. We desire to be 98% confident and will accept an allowable error of 2.5%. Determine the appropriate sample size.

6.45   A company wants to know the percent of its employees who will opt for a new retirement plan. In another company branch, 91% opted for the new program. We desire a 90% confidence level and want an allowable error of 3%. Determine the appropriate sample size.

6.46   National health data indicate that 8.23% of the population has an allergic reaction to a particular drug. We want to test our university students to determine a 95% confidence interval with a 2% tolerable error. What is the appropriate sample size?

138

We began this chapter with a discussion of the desirable properties of estimators. We then distinguished between point and interval estimates, and noted that we can't attach confidence to point estimates. The lower and upper limits of the interval estimates depend on the confidence level desired and the appropriate standard error. If σ was deemed to be unknown, we replaced z values with t values. The t values always exceed z values for a given confidence level, and t values become larger as the sample size diminishes. Larger t values mean the lower and upper limits of the confidence interval have increased.

Finally, we concluded with the determination of the needed sample size to obtain a desired confidence and precision. In dealing with continuous data, the sample size is directly related to the confidence desired and the dispersion of the population, but inversely related to the allowable error. With discrete or qualitative data, n is directly related to the confidence level and the population proportion, but inversely related to the allowable error.

Mini-case 6.1: Family Surname Distribution in the U.S.

A large insurance company does not know the exact number of accounts they have. They would like to estimate the total by surveying just one letter of the alphabet which begins surnames and using it as a basis of the estimate of their total number of accounts. The company obtains from the Social Security Administration the percentage of names and records of surnames beginning with a particular letter. For example, 5.49% of the surnames begin with the letter A (Anderson, Andrews, Anton, etc.), while 3.277% of the cumulative files of the Social Security Administration had a surname beginning with the letter B, 9.007% with the letter C, etc. Suppose we decide to survey the S records for the insurance company.

a.   Determine the appropriate sample size necessary to obtain a 95% confidence level with an allowable error of 2%.

b.   How could the sample size, obtained from Social Security data, greatly exceed the current population of the United States?

c.   Could there be a problem in applying such an analysis in areas where there is a strong ethnic concentration?

Distribution of Surnames by Initial Letter

Letter	% of Names	% of Records	Letter	% of Names	% of Records
A	5.490	3.277	N	2.984	1.833
B	6.735	9.077	O	2.845	1.471
C	5.284	7.420	P	5.380	4.933
D	5.851	4.826	Q	0.310	0.200
E	2.773	1.875	R	4.330	5.502
F	3.157	3.539	S	9.490	9.961
G	5.005	5.213	T	4.674	3.543
H	4.381	7.241	U	1.023	0.242
I	1.435	0.416	V	2.602	1.491
J	2.059	2.943	W	2.912	6.021
K	6.269	3.715	X	0.094	0.007
L	4.963	4.704	Y	1.411	0.594
M	6.442	9.413	Z	2.110	0.543

Source: Department of Health and Human Services: Social Security Administration: SSA Pub. No. 42-004, April 1985, total sample size = 346,417,726

Table 6.5: 30 Most Common Surnames in the U.S.

Surname	2000 Rank	1984 Rank
Smith	1	1
Johnson	2	2
Williams	3	3
Brown	4	4
Jones	5	5
Miller	6	7
Davis	7	8
Garcia	8	30
Rodriguez	9	18
Wilson	10	10
Martin	11	6
Anderson	12	9
Taylor	13	13
Thomas	14	12
Hernandez	15	52
Moore	16	14
Martinez	17*	
Jackson	18	15
Thompson	19	17
White	20	16
Lopez	21	46
Lee	22	26
Gonzalez	23	24
Harris	24	11
Clark	25	19
Lewis	26	21
Robinson	27	22
Walker	28	23
Perez	29	57
Hall	30	25

Source: U.S. Census; November-December 2007. The world's most common surname is Chang or Zhang. China's is Li.
*Included with Martin

Mini-case 6.2: Advertising Agency Estimate

An advertising agency wishes to know the percentage of households that have telephones in a particular geographic area. The agency knows that nationwide, 94% of the households have telephones. The agency has an allowable error of 2% and wants a 90% confidence level. Determine the appropriate sample size.

Review of Important Terms and Concepts

Point and Interval Estimates: A point estimate provides a single estimate of prediction that will either be exact or not. An interval estimate considers an allowable error, through the use of a range of values, from the point forecast that will not jeopardize our decision making skills.

An estimator and estimate: An estimator is a sample statistic used to estimate population parameters, while an estimate is a specific observed value of, or made from a statistic.

Unbiased: When the expected value of the sampling distribution (based on a standard error of repeated samples of size n) equates with the population mean.

Efficiency: In comparing two unbiased estimators (based on a standard error of repeated samples of size n), one is considered more efficient than the other if its dispersion is smaller.

Consistency: As a single sample is allowed to increase, the mean of the sampling distribution will equate with the population mean, while the distribution collapses.

Confidence interval: A confidence interval is a range of values that has a specific probability of including the population parameter.

Confidence limits: A confidence limit represents the upper and lower limits to the confidence interval.

t **distribution:** A family of probability distributions, based on the degrees of freedom, to be used in place of z when σ is unknown, and when the population may be assumed to be normal or approximately normal.

Review of Important Formulas

Unbiased Estimator of the Mean

$$E(\overline{X}_i) = \mu \tag{6.1}$$

where

$E =$ the expected value or weighted mean

$\overline{X}_i =$ the mean of all possible samples of size n

$\mu =$ the mean of the population

$(1 - \alpha) \bullet 100\%$ Confidence Interval for μ: σ Known General Formula for Interval Estimates

$$\text{estimate} \pm \text{(reliability factor) (standard error)} \tag{6.2}$$

Specific Formula for Estimation of μ

$$\overline{X} \pm z_{\alpha/2} \bullet \sigma_{\overline{X}} \tag{6.3}$$

where

$z_{\alpha/2} =$ the reliability factor or appropriate z value to obtain a desired

$(1 - \alpha) \bullet 100\%$ confidence level

$\sigma_{\overline{X}} = \sigma/\sqrt{n}$: the standard error or the mean.

$(1 - \alpha) \bullet 100\%$ Confidence Interval About a Large Sample $\hat{p}$

$$\hat{p} \pm z_{\alpha/2} \bullet \hat{\sigma}_{\hat{p}} \tag{6.4}$$

where

$z_{\alpha/2} =$ the appropriate z value to obtain a desired confidence

$\hat{\sigma}_p =$ the standard error of the sample proportion $= \sqrt{\hat{p} \bullet \hat{q}/n}$

$(1 - \alpha) \bullet 100\%$ Confidence Interval for μ: σ Unknown

$$\overline{X} \pm t_{\alpha/2(df)} \bullet \hat{\sigma}_{\overline{X}} \tag{6.5}$$

where

$t_{\alpha/2(df)} =$ the reliability factor

$\hat{\sigma}_{\overline{X}} = s/\sqrt{n}$: the standard error using s to approximate σ

$(1 - \alpha) \bullet 100\%$ Confidence Interval for μ: σ Unknown, $n/N \geq .05$

$$\overline{X} \pm t_{\alpha/2(df)} \bullet (\hat{\sigma}_{\overline{X}}) \bullet \sqrt{(N - n)/(N - 1)} \tag{6.6}$$

where

$t_{\alpha/2(df)} =$ the appropriate t value to obtain a desired confidence

$(\hat{\sigma}_{\overline{X}}) = s/\sqrt{n}$: the standard error using s to approximate σ

$N =$ the population size

Determining Sample Size for Estimating a Mean

$$n = \frac{z_{\alpha/2}^2 \bullet \sigma^2}{e^2} \tag{6.7}$$

where

$z_{\alpha/2}^2 =$ the appropriate z value squared

$\sigma^2 =$ the population variance

$e^2 =$ the allowable or tolerable error squared

Estimated s Based on an Approximate Range

$$\hat{\sigma} = \frac{\text{Largest estimated observation} - \text{Smallest estimated observation}}{6} \tag{6.8}$$

Determining n for Proportions

$$n = \frac{z_{\alpha/2}^2 \bullet p \bullet q}{e^2} \tag{6.9}$$

where

$z_{\alpha/2}^2 =$ the appropriate z value squared

$p =$ the population proportion; usually hypothesized:

if a hypothesis is not possible assume $p = .5$

$e^2 =$ the allowable or tolerable error squared

142

6.47   If $\mu = 89.2$ and the mean of the sampling distribution equaled 87.68, this would be an example of a _____ estimator.

6.48   Explain the controversy between confidence and precision in interval estimates.

6.49   Under what conditions may the t distribution be used?

6.50   Find the appropriate t values for both the one- and two-tailed tests under the following conditions:

    a. $df = 18, \alpha = .10$
    b. $df = 4, \alpha = .10$
    c. $df = 12, \alpha = .05$
    d. $df = 2, \alpha = .05$
    e. $df = 29, \alpha = .01$
    f. $df = 10, \alpha = .01$

6.51   a.   Determine a 95% confidence interval when $\overline{X} = 76.8$, $s = 4.78$ and $n = 41$.
       b.   Determine a 95% confidence interval when $\overline{X} = 76.8$, $s = 4.78$ and $n = 6$.
       c.   Comment on the size of the interval between part a and part b.

6.52   a.   A survey is taken on a new prescription medication involving its cost. The survey results are $\overline{X} = \$17.47$, $s = \$2.16$, with a random sample of size 61. Determine the 90% confidence interval.
       b.   Explain the 90% confidence interval.

6.53   A survey is taken to ascertain the average number of times in a year that cars are brought in for repair. The results of the random survey are: $\overline{X} = 2.32$, $s = 0.41$, $n = 24$. Determine the 99% confidence interval.

6.54   In a random study, 70 out of 890 students are absent on a given day. Construct the appropriate 90% confidence interval.

6.55   In a random study ($n = 260$), 70 employees expressed concern over a new evaluation process. Construct the appropriate 98% confidence interval.

6.56   A new developmental tree grows quickly. A random survey of 149 trees finds that they reach an average maturity in 19.8 years with a standard deviation of 3.0 years. Construct the 99% confidence interval.

6.57   We wish to survey patients randomly to determine the length of time they have had their current ailments. We think that $\sigma = 3$ years. We will tolerate a .5 error, and we desire a 90% confidence level. Determine the appropriate sample size.

6.58   An accountant has found that in previous years 73% of her clients owe money in taxes. This year the accountant wants to survey the clients randomly to determine the percentage that owes tax money. If an allowable error of 5% is acceptable, using a 90% confidence level, determine the appropriate sample size.

6.59   A telephone survey found that in the previous year only 4% of the calls made last more than 15 minutes. This year the company wishes to determine the 90% confidence interval with a 1.5% allowable error. What is the appropriate sample size?

6.60   A survey is taken to ascertain the average number of times in a year that consumers mow their grass in Florida. The results of the random survey are: $\overline{X} = 61.2$, $s = 12.6$, $n = 198$. Determine the 95% confidence interval.

Z Confidence Interval

Stat > Basic Statistics > 1-Sample *Z*
Double click data column to enter it into **Variables** box.
Click **Confidence interval** to enter confidence level as 95 percent. Since it is already at the 95% confidence level we will proceed.
Click Sigma and enter population **Sigma** of 20.
OK

For a *t* confidence Interval

Stat > Basic Statistics > 1-Sample *t*
Double click data column to enter it into **Variables** box.
Click **Confidence interval** to enter confidence level as 95 percent. Since the default CI is 95% we proceed.
OK

Hypothesis Testing

Where we have been

We have completed a review of one type of statistical inference, that of estimation.

Where we are going

We now turn to the second type of statistical inference, that of hypothesis testing. Every time you make a purchase, information will be supplied on the package or contract. This information will relate to total volume or weight, ingredients, and possibly a claim. These claims represent statements made by the manufacturer and/or distributor that may or may not be correct. In statistical terms, we refer to these statements as hypotheses which must be tested as to their legitimacy.

We will never actually know if these hypotheses are correct because we will not know the population parameters. We have to estimate these parameters with sample statistics. Based on the sample statistics, and with a desired confidence level, we can test the validity of such claims.

7.1   Introduction

Suppose that during a break from your class you purchase a soft drink beverage from a vending machine. You read the can and it states that there are 355 milliliters (ml) of beverage in the container. Since you have no knowledge as to the validity of this claim, it must be viewed as a hypothesis. This hypothesis may or may not be correct.

If the hypothesis is to be tested, a simple random sample must be made of n cans to ascertain if the sample information substantiates or refutes the claim. If we surveyed 100 cans and found that

$\overline{X} = 300$ ml, we would suspect the manufacturer's claim was false. With these particular results, whether we reject or do not reject the manufacturer's claim was a simple matter of intuitive and deductive logic.

However, suppose $\overline{X} = 351$ ml from a random sample of 100. Even though there was less than 355 ml in the cans, the difference might be attributable to sampling error. In fact, the distributor might have mishandled the cases of soda causing some to lose a small portion of their content. Hence, we are not totally sure if we should be rejecting the manufacturer's claim or not. The formal process of rejecting or not rejecting such a hypothesis is the function of this chapter. The major question will hinge on whether the hypothesized mean/proportion/variance ($\mu/p/\sigma^2$) is sufficiently distant from the sample mean/proportion/variance ($\overline{X}/\hat{p}/s^2$) so that the difference may or may not have been caused by sampling error. If the difference was probably caused by sampling error, we will be unable to reject the manufacturer's claim. If the difference was so great that it probably was not caused by sampling error, we will reject the manufacturer's claim.

Please note that throughout the chapter we will be referring to z values. These z values refer to the sampling distribution of the mean/proportion, the horizontal axis of which represents randomly obtained sample means/proportions and not sample observations.

 Concept Check 7.A

You are about to consume a product and read on the package that each unit contains no more than 230 calories. You sample a number of the product and find the mean to be 232 calories. You now must reject the claim of the manufacturer. True or false? If false, explain.

Exercises

7.1   Define the term "hypothesis."

7.2   If you purchase a new car, there will be a statement on the window that will inform you of the average miles per gallon of gas consumed. What is such a statement called and how would we test the claim?

7.2   Important Concepts and Terms

Null and Alternative Hypotheses

A hypothesis is a statement concerning the population or the way things are. The statement may or may not be true. In hypothesis testing we begin with a main hypothesis which is termed the **null hypothesis**, and symbolically identified by H_0. The null hypothesis represents, in effect, the status quo and will not be rejected unless sufficient statistical evidence leads us to believe it is false. If we are unable to prove that H_0 is false, we will be in a rather weak position in that we will not be able to make any really definitive statements.

In addition, to the null hypothesis, there must also be an **alternative hypothesis** (symbolically identified by H_A). The alternative hypothesis is often referred to as the hypothesis that bears the burden of proof. For example, if H_0 states that there is an average of 355 ml in a beverage can, then H_A infers that there is not. From the example, we can see that the null and alternative hypotheses are mutually exclusive and collectively exhaustive events.

A rejection of the null hypothesis (H_0) will automatically mean that there is sufficient statistical evidence to support, hence adopt, H_A. In our beverage problem, this will allow us to state that there is not an average of 355 ml in the cans. However, if there is **Insufficient Statistical Evidence to Reject** (ISER) H_0,

146

we will be able to state only that we are unable to reject the null hypothesis. We can't state that the null hypothesis is true because we simply do not know what the average ml are for all beverage cans (population).

One and Two-Tailed Tests

Our null and alternative hypothesis can involve either what are termed one- or two-tailed tests. We use the null hypothesis to explain the one- and two-tailed tests using the example of the ml volume contained in the beverage cans.

The manufacturer may claim that the average beverage can contains exactly a specified amount (e.g., 355 ml). The alternative hypothesis is that the average can does not hold the stated specified amount. The hypotheses are written generically as

Two-tailed test: H_0: $\mu = \mu_0$ H_A: $\mu \neq \mu_0$

where μ equals the unknown population mean and μ_0 is the stated or hypothesized value for the population mean. Using the specifics of our beverage example H_0: $\mu = 355$ ml and H_A: $\mu \neq 355$ ml. Ultimately we will attempt to establish statistical evidence based on a random survey to reject H_0. This is a two-sided test because we will reject H_0 if the sample mean is significantly greater or smaller than 355 ml.

If we want to know if the average beverage can contains more than ($>$) 355 ml, or less ($<$) than 355 ml, we are involved with a one-tailed test. Students must know immediately that the "equal to" symbol in a one-tailed test always falls in the null hypothesis which is always stated with $\leq$ and $\geq$ symbols. For example, if we believe that there are less than ($<$) 355 ml in the can, we would establish first the alternative hypothesis as H_A: $\mu < \mu_0$. The null hypothesis automatically becomes H_0: $\mu \geq \mu_0$. We will come to reject H_0 only if the sample mean drawn from a random survey is significantly below the stated 355 ml.

We have developed the hypotheses as though we believed that there is less than 355 ml in the cans. The hypotheses would have been the same if the manufacturer wrote on the beverage can that it contained at least 355 ml, or 355 ml or more, or $\geq$ 355 ml. Note that on the beverage can is simply reads 355 ml, signifying a two-tailed test. We made the problem a one-tailed test by stating that we believed the cans contained an average of less than 355 ml (H_A:$\mu < 355$ ml).

Note that we could have used a two-tailed test to determine if the sample mean was significantly below 355 ml. So why make a one-tailed test to our problem which could be solved using a two-tailed test? The advantage to our using a one tailed test is that, since it focuses only on one tail, we are more precisely able to determine significant differences. A difference might be significant with a one-tailed test, but not with a two-tailed test. The opposite side is that we will be unable to determine anything concerning the opposite tail. So a one-tailed test increases our chances of ascertaining significant differences. Table 7.1 reviews the symbolism used for one-/two-tailed test for the beverage problem.

Table 7.1   Null and Alternate Hypotheses for Beverage Problem

GENERAL FORMAT

	H_0	H_A
One-Tailed Test		
Left Tailed Test	$\mu \geq \mu_0$	$\mu < H_0$*
Right Tailed Test	$\mu \leq \mu_0$	$\mu > H_0$*
Two-Tailed Test	$\mu = \mu_0$	$\mu \neq \mu_0$*

BEVERAGE EXAMPLE

	H_0	H_A
One-tailed Test		
Left Tailed Test	$\mu \geq 355$ ml	$\mu < 355$ ml*
Right Tailed Test	$\mu \leq 355$ ml	$\mu > 355$ ml*
Two-Tailed Test	$\mu = 355$ ml	$\mu \neq 355$ ml

*Note that the alternative hypothesis is always stated as an inequality ($<$ or $>$) in a one-tailed test and the $=$ sign is always placed with H_0.

You might be wondering why we don't use the term accepting, rather than not-rejecting H_0. The reason is that we cannot accept any hypothesis as being true without knowledge of population parameters (μ, p, σ), which are unknown. Hence, the only statement that can be made is that there is insufficient statistical evidence available to reject (ISER) the null hypothesis. Thus, null hypotheses are not accepted, but are not-rejected in a technical sense. It is certainly easy to see that the terms rejected and not-rejected are mutually exclusive and collectively exhaustive events. Since the decision-maker's behavior often is the same regardless of whether we accept H_0 (instead of ISER), some authors and practitioners do use the words accept and reject. We will attempt to refrain from using the term accept because it is technically incorrect.

In our problem involving the beverage cans, knowledge of μ is unknown. Of all the beverage cans produced, we do not know the mean ml contents. To accept a null hypothesis, without knowledge of the population parameter, will put us in a position of possibly accepting a false hypothesis (termed a Type II error).

Type I and Type II Errors

In hypothesis testing, the analyst has two basic decisions: to have ISER or to reject the null hypothesis. There are also two possible truths: the null hypothesis is either true or it's false. This allows for 4 outcomes, 2 reflecting correct decisions, but 2 involving errors. Eventually, we will reject or state there is ISER the null hypothesis (H_0) which will either be true or false (Table 7.2). Rejecting the null hypothesis when it is true is called a **Type I error**. Accepting a null hypothesis when it is false is termed a **Type II error**.

Table 7.2   Type I and Type II Errors

	H_0: True (H_A: False)	H_A: True (H_0: False)
Accept H_0 (Reject H_A)	Correct Decision **No Error**	Incorrect Decision **Type II Error**
Reject H_0 (Accept H_A)	Incorrect Decision **Type I Error**	Correct Decision **No Error**

Type I Error (α) = Pr(Reject H_0|H_0 is True)
Type II Error (β) = Pr(Accept H_0|H_0 is False)
| is the symbolic expression for the term given

The probability of making a Type I error is α, the significance level. In our beverage problem H_0: $\mu = 355$ ml, and rejecting this hypothesis when it is true is a Type I error. If we desire a 90% confidence level ($\alpha = .10$), we will have a 10% chance of rejecting a correct null hypothesis. The difference between the population parameter under the null hypothesis and the sample statistic is so great that 10 out of 100 samples of size n, the hypothesis will be rejected. If we desire a 95% confidence level ($\alpha = .05$), we will have a 5% chance of rejecting a correct null hypothesis. Hence, the smaller the confidence level ($1 - \alpha$), the greater will be the probability of making a Type I error. The significance level (α) defines the probability of making a Type I error.

The probability of making a Type II error is called β (or beta). In the beverage problem, this is the probability of accepting a false null hypothesis. Stated more specifically, it is the probability of accepting the statement that the beverage can contains 355 ml when, in fact, it does not.

The two probabilities, α and β, involve a trade-off in terms of the type of error involved. If it is desired to reduce the probability of making one type of error, it will merely come at the expense of increasing the probability of making the other type of error. A large significance level reduces our rejection region and greatly reduces the Type II error (accepting H_0 when it is false), but will greatly increase the chance of a Type I error. Hence, a low β has created a large α. On the other hand, a smaller significance level (α) will create a greater probability of making a Type II error (β).

Courtroom Example

Since a trade-off between two types of errors must be made, it is important to review the respective consequences of both errors. In the courtroom, the null hypothesis is that the defendant is presumed innocent unless proven guilty by the weight of evidence. The jury will return a guilty or not guilty verdict. Note that the jury does not deliver an innocent verdict, rather simply stated the evidence presented is insufficient to warrant a guilty verdict. To deliver an innocent verdict, the jury would have to return to the scene of the crime, at the time the crime was committed (presumably in a yet to be invented time capsule).

In the courtroom process, we may reject a correct null hypothesis (Type I error), which means we will send an innocent person to prison. Or we may fail to reject an incorrect null hypothesis (Type II error), which means a guilty individual will be set free (Table 7.3). Our judicial system clearly believes that making a Type I error is more severe than making a Type II error. It has often been stated that the system would rather send 10 guilty individuals free than send one innocent person to prison.

Table 7.3   Court Room Scenario, H_0: The Defendant Is Innocent

	H_0: Correct	H_0: False
Not Reject H_0	Acquit innocent person No error: Correct Verdict	Acquit guilty person Type II error: β Probability
Reject H_0	Convict innocent person Type I error: α probability	Convict guilty person No error: Correct Verdict

Arguments over what constitutes a preponderance of the evidence or, in capital cases, beyond a reasonable doubt are equivalent to debating the appropriate α value to use. In a sense, if we handed down a verdict of not guilty, we ascertain that there was reasonable doubt. If the case involved statistical information, we might use the phrase there is insufficient statistical evidence to reject H_0 (ISER).

Changes in the law say legislatively limiting what evidence may be presented to the jury may reduce the probability of making a Type I error (convict innocent person). However, we probably will find that the probability of making a Type II error will be increased (releasing a guilty person).

Finally, we must realize that the prosecutor supports the alternative hypothesis (H_A), while the defense attorney argues for the presumption of innocence (H_0). Often circumstantial evidence will be presented which may be that the defendant was in the general area, or has no alibi, etc. The defense attorney must assert that any variation from that of a model innocent citizen is attributable to random chance (sampling error) and not due to guilt.

Beverage Container Example

In the beverage problem the null hypothesis was that the can contained 355 ml. A Type I error means we will reject a correct null hypothesis. We may charge the company with making false claims. A Type II error involves not rejecting a false null hypothesis, a much less serious error in terms of litigation and tarnished images. Hence, with this and in most instances, a Type I error usually involves a more severe consequence than a Type II error. However, with a sufficiently large sample size, we minimize the probabilities of making both a Type I and Type II error. Hence, the tradeoff problem between α and β is not severe for large samples.

To review the difference between Type I and II errors, let's return to our beverage problem. A Type I error involves stating that the beverage cans do not contain an average of 355 ml when they in fact do. This can be thought of as a consumer error. On the other hand, a Type II error involves not rejecting (ISER) the manufacturers labeling that the cans contain an average of 355 ml, when in fact the labeling is incorrect. This may be viewed as a producer's error.

We emphasize that to accept a null hypothesis puts us at risk of a Type II error. Hence, without knowledge of the probability of making a Type II error, we would not want to accept H_0.

Concept Check 7.B

If your instructor falsely accused you of cheating on an assignment, it would be an example of a Type II error. True or false? If false, explain.

Exercises

7.3   Do the following statements signify a one- or two-tailed test?

  a. An automobile will hold 16 gallons of gas.
  b. An automobile will hold at least 16 gallons of gas.
  c. A hard disk will hold more than 30 megabytes of information.
  d. A hard disk will hold at least 30 megabytes of information.
  e. A hard disk will hold 30 megabytes of information.

7.4   Explain the difference between one- and two-tailed tests.

7.5   Explain the term "null hypothesis" in your own words.

7.6   Explain the term "alternative hypothesis" in your own words.

7.7   What is the symbolism used for the null and alternative hypotheses?

7.8   Is it possible for survey information to fall within the bounds of both the null and alternative hypotheses?

7.9   Differentiate between a Type I and Type II error.

7.10   What symbols represent the probabilities of making a Type I and Type II error?

7.11   Why do we not use the term "accept" a null hypothesis instead of saying there is insufficient statistical information to reject the hypothesis?

7.12   Suppose your instructor accused you of cheating on an exam or assignment.

  a. What two types of errors can the instructor make?
  b. Is one error more severe than the other?

7.13   a. Does $\alpha + \beta = 1.0$?
       b. Does a relationship exist between α and β?

7.14   Can both the α and β probabilities be reduced?

7.3   Two-Tailed Hypothesis Testing About a Mean: σ Known

Using Confidence Intervals About H_0

We will begin our hypothesis testing analysis with the two-tailed test. This follows the concepts learned in Chapter 6 (Statistical Estimation) which dealt with the construction of confidence intervals. We will use these confidence intervals in our tests of hypotheses. Let's return to our beverage problem where the manufacturer made the claim that there was an average of 355 ml in the beverage containers. We are skeptical and believe this hypothesis may be false. However, even though we believe the hypothesis to be false, we are not sure if there are too many, or too few ml in the beverage cans. Assume that we desire a

95% confidence level, hence we have a 5% significance level (a 5% probability of making a Type I error). We believe that the beverage cans' population has a standard deviation of 12 ml. We survey 100 beverage cans and obtain a mean of $\overline{X} = 352$ ml. The standard error of the mean (formula 5.1;

$$\sigma_{\overline{X}} = \sigma/\sqrt{n} = 12/\sqrt{100} = 1.2) \text{ is } 1.2.$$

The appropriate critical value for z is 1.96 ($z_{.05/2} = 1.96$); hence, the 95% confidence interval about 1μ is

$$\mu \pm z_{\alpha/2} \bullet \sigma_{\overline{X}}; \ 355 \text{ ml } \pm (1.96)(1.2) = 352.65 \text{ ml to } 357.35 \text{ ml}.$$

The ISER and rejection regions can be seen in Figure 7.1. Since the sample mean (351) falls in the rejection region, we must reject the null hypothesis that there are an average of 355 ml in the beverage can.

Figure 7.1 Two-Tailed Test of the Null Hypothesis, Beverage Problem

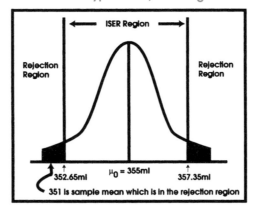

If the sample mean were 360 ml, it would still call for a rejection of the null hypothesis. This would be a much less serious rejection, from the students' viewpoint, because it would mean the company is giving you more beverage than it stated. It would be difficult to cry "foul play" under such a scenario. Hence, a rejection of a null hypothesis does not necessarily signify something inappropriate.

Using z_{test} Values

An alternative method can be used to test the null hypothesis using normal deviates.
1. We would select the desired α level (5%: $z_{.05/2} = 1.96$).
2. We compute the appropriate standard error ($\sigma_{\overline{X}} = 1.2$).
3. We would determine how many standard errors the sample mean was from the hypothesized mean. This is termed z_{test}, as this will be the test statistic used to test the null hypothesis.

The test statistic is

Test Statistic About μ: σ known

$$Z_{\text{test}} = \frac{\overline{X} - \mu_0}{\frac{\sigma}{\sqrt{n}}} \qquad (7.1)$$

where

z_{test} = the test statistic

$\overline{X}$ = the sample mean

σ = the population standard deviation

n = the sample size

Note: if sampling without replacement and $n/N \geq .05$, the finite population correction must be used to discount the standard error $\sqrt{(N - n)/(N - 1)}$.

Returning to the beverage problem, substituting the numerical equivalents into formula 7.1 yields

$$Z_{\text{test}} = \frac{352 - 355}{\frac{12}{\sqrt{100}}} = \frac{-3}{1.2} = -2.500$$

We can view the ISER and rejection regions of $z_{.05}$ in Figure 7.2. The critical values for z are ± 1.96, meaning if z_{test} falls within the critical values, we have ISER. A z_{test} of -2.500 clearly falls beyond the range of the critical values and falls within the rejection region. Hence, the null hypothesis that the beverage cans contain 355 ml is rejected. We have sufficient statistical evidence to indicate that the mean differs from 355 ml.

Most statisticians prefer to use the normal deviate of the test statistic approach than that of determining the confidence interval about the hypothesized mean, and determining if the sample mean falls inside or outside the interval. One reason for the preference is that it is possible to determine the actual area in the rejection region. Looking up the z table, associated with $z = -2.5$ is .4938; hence the area of the rejection region is 0.62% (.5 − .4948 = .0062).

Figure 7.2 ISER and Rejection Regions for Z_{test}

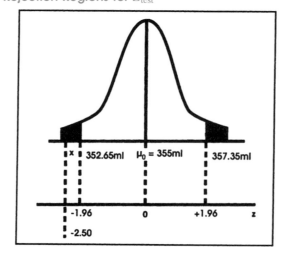

152

Reject the Null Hypothesis (Two-Tailed Test, σ Known)

The null hypothesis is rejected whenever

$$|z_{\text{test}}| > z_{\alpha/2} \tag{7.2}$$

where

$z_{\text{test}} =$ the test statistic

$z_{\alpha/2} =$ the critical value for a two-tailed test

In our beverage problem $z_{\text{test}} = -2.500$ and $z_{.05/2} = \pm 1.96$; hence $|z_{\text{test}}| > z_\alpha$, and H_0 is rejected. Thus, there is sufficient statistical evidence to state that the beverage cans do not contain 355 ml. Obviously, if $|z_{\text{test}}| \leq z_{\alpha/2}$, H_0 will have ISER.

P-Values

We have just completed a hypothesis test analyzing z_{test} (-2.5) and determining that we will reject H_0 as the desired significance level ($\alpha = .05$). The information that would prove useful to us is at what α value would we change from rejecting to having ISER H_0? To accomplish this task, we merely treat z_{test} as though it were z_a. Viewing the normal distribution in Appendix A: Table 1, a z of -2.5 corresponds to .4938, which refers to the probability from the mean to $z = -2.5$. Since we want the tail area, we will subtract from .5, yielding .0062 (.5 $-$.4938). Since we are involved in a two-tailed test (rejection occurs in both tails) we will multiply by 2, obtaining .0124 (.0062 • 2).

This *P*-value must be compared to our significance level. The rule of thumb is that if $\alpha \geq P$-value we reject H_0, or if *p*-value $< \alpha$, reject the null hypothesis. Since *P*-value $= .0124$, we would reject H_0 for alpha values of .10, .05, .0124 (corresponding to confidence levels of .90, .95, .98.6), but would have ISER H_0, for alpha values .0123, .010, .005. In effect, the *p*-value is the smallest Æ at which H_0 will be rejected.

The *P*-value approach flies in the face of traditional hypothesis testing theory which requires that you state your significance level prior to beginning the analysis. We can now scan all the Æ values that will cause rejection and ISER of H_0. The danger being that decision-makers may select the alpha value to support their own hypotheses. An advantage may come about from being able to use our own significance level as opposed to that of a researcher. A statistician may utilize a different level than you desire to use. Suppose, for example, in a courtroom case the judge decided on a 1% level compared to the normal 5% level. If the *p*-value was provided to us, we would be able to determine if H_0 is ISER or rejected at the court's chosen level of significance.

Fortunately, MINITAB will perform the hypothesis tests for us including supplying us with the appropriate *p*-values. Again note that the **95% CONFIDENCE LEVEL IS THE ONE PRIMARILY USED IN ACADEMIA, IN SCIENCE, AND IN THE BUSINESS WORLD.** Hence MINITAB defaults to the 95% confidence interval. Should another interval be required click to the Options box to change it.

We randomly select 16 beverage cans and record the following volumes in ml's: 352, 358, 357, 353, 349, 352, 356, 352, 351, 348, 351, 348, 349, 355, 356, 357.

We enter the data into a MINITAB worksheet. We will now use MINITAB to perform hypothesis testing with the population standard deviation (STDEV) known (using *z*-values). The command sequence is:

Stat > Basic Statistics > 1-Sample Z
Double click data column to enter it into **Variables** box
Click on **Standard deviation**: enter 20
Click **Test Mean** to enter μ of 355
Click **Options** and state H_A: not equal (two-tailed test)
OK

Table 7.4   One-Sample Z: Data

Test of $\mu = 355$ vs $\neq 355$
The assumed standard deviation $= 20$

Variable	N	Mean	StDev	SE Mean	95% CI	Z	P
Data	16	352.750	3.376	5.000	(342.950, 362.550)	−0.45	0.653

At any confidence level we REJECT H_0 if $\alpha \geq P$ VALUE. Since $.05 < 0.65$ we have insufficient statistical evidence (ISER) to REJECT H_0.

The computer yields the p-value $= 0.65$. If our computer yields value $= .000$, it means our test statistic is significant at any reasonable level.

As a last comment, we will state how the p-values are state as a common practice in journal articles. We must remember that we reject H_0 when the p-value $< \alpha$. Some authors after completing a test will state ($p > 0.05$), which refers to H_0 not being significant at the 5% level. If we see ($p < 0.01$), this refers to rejecting H_0 at the 1% level.

A Point of Clarification

Some practitioners use z_{test} (instead of the appropriate t_{test}) even for cases where σ is unknown if $n > 31$. In fact, if you look up the t table, we note there are a few t values for instance where $n > 31$ ($df \leq 31$). The reason z has been used to replace t is because the differences between z and t are negligible when $n > 31$. Also, the Central Limit Theorem uses this sample size to state that the sampling distribution about $\overline{X}$ is approximately normal. However, since most computer software use the appropriate t_{test}, we use z_{test} only when σ is known (which will be a rare situation in practice), not when σ is unknown and when $n > 31$.

  Concept Check 7.C

The hypothesis test just described essentially involves finding the appropriate confidence interval, then determining if the hypothetical parameters falls within it. If it does, we will have ISER the hypothesis. True or false? If false, explain.

Exercises

7.15   A survey is taken and the following information obtained: $n = 65$, $\overline{X} = 39.4$, and it is believed that $\sigma = 2.1$.

    a.   Determine the 95% confidence interval for μ.
    b.   If the manufacturer claimed the mean to be 42 (H_0: $\mu_0 = 42$), would it fall within the 95% confidence interval?
    c.   Do we fall in the rejection region?
    d.   From the normal table, obtain the p-value.
    e.   Obtain the p-value (PROB) using MINITAB.

7.16   a.   In exercise 7.15, test the manufacturer's claim using the test statistic rule of formula 7.2.
    b.   Are the results between Exercises 7.15b and 7.16a the same? Explain.
    c.   Recompute the test statistic given $N = 300$.

7.17   Automobile producers have engineered a new oil warning light that will signal engine overheating. The producers believe that the light will come on 90 seconds of engine overheating. A survey is taken to test the hypothesis with the following results: $n = 49$, $\overline{X} = 89$ seconds. It is believed that $\sigma = 5$ seconds. Use a 99% confidence level to determine if the hypothesis is correct (cannot be rejected).

7.18   In Exercise 7.17, test the manufacturer's claim using the test statistic rule of formula 7.2.

154

7.19   a.   A super glue has been developed that can sustain 2,000 pounds of pressure. The company claims that 1 minute of drying time is required for the glue to set. A survey is conducted and the following results obtained: $n = 79$, $\overline{X} = 53$ seconds. It is believed that $\sigma = 11$ seconds. Using z_{test} and .99 confidence level, will we reject H_0?

        b.   Determine the probability of making a Type I error.

7.20   a.   The owner of a golf course believes that it takes a foursome 5 hours to complete 18 holes of golf. A study of 36 foursomes is made with $\overline{X} = 5.2$ hours. It is believed that $\sigma = .9$ hours. Using z_{test}, and a .95 confidence level, will we reject H_0?

        b.   Use MINITAB to obtain the p-value.

7.4   One-Tailed Hypothesis Testing About a Mean: σ Known

Using Confidence Intervals About a H_0.

In many business applications of hypothesis testing, we are interested in whether the mean of a population is smaller or larger than some specified value. As an example, suppose we believe that the average beverage container contains less than 355 ml, and that the manufacturer is misleading consumers by their labeling practices. We state our belief in the form of an alternative hypothesis, namely $H_A: \mu < 355$ ml (remember the alternative hypothesis is not stated using $\leq$ or $\geq$), which we are really attempting to support by survey information. Since we have specified our alternate hypothesis, our null hypothesis is also specified and is $H_0: \mu \geq 355$ ml. Note that the null hypothesis could have come directly from the manufacturer if the claim on our beverage can read "contents: ≥ 355 ml." The hypothesis, in effect, states there are at least 355 ml in the can.

Whether the claim is initiated by the researcher (playing the devil's advocate) or the manufacturer matters not, we are involved with a one-tailed test as opposed to a two-tailed test. In terms of the intervals, one-tailed tests do not involve rejection regions greater than and less than μ_0, but rather a rejection region either greater than or less than μ_0, but not both.

The critical values for a right tail and left tailed test are given in Figure 7.3. The critical z value for a greater than or equal to test situation is in the left tail of the distribution. This is logical because if our sample from the beverage problem yielded a $\overline{X} = 357$ ml, the result would support the null hypothesis ($\mu \geq 355$ ml) and we would automatically be unable to reject the null hypothesis as being false. Hence, the only opportunity to reject the null hypothesis is when the survey mean is significantly below 355 ml. Note that the tail of rejection follows the sign of the alternative hypothesis which states $H_A: \mu < 355$ ml.

Figure 7.3   Left- and Right-Tailed Critical Values

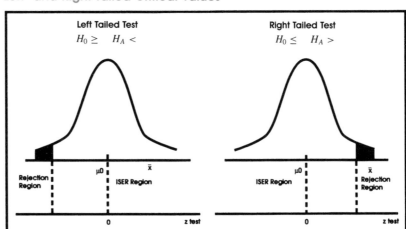

155

To obtain the correct z value for a one-tailed test, we subtract half of the normal distribution because we are only concerned with one tail. Hence, if we desire a .95 confidence level, $.95 - .50 = .45$ ($\alpha = .05$). We look up .4500 in the body of the normal distribution (Table 7.5 and Appendix A, Table 1). The value falls exactly between $z = 1.6 + .04 = 1.64$ and $z = 1.6 + .05 = 1.65$; hence we may extrapolate $z_{.05/1} = 1.645$ ($[1.64 + 1.65]/2$). Such extrapolations yield an approximate z value. Remember that the normal distributions area is greatest the closer we are to μ; hence, extrapolation yields only approximations.

Table 7.5   Abbreviated Normal Distribution

z	.01	.02	.03	.03	.05	.06	.07
1.4	.4207	.4222	.4236	.4251	.4265	.4279	.4292
1.5	.4345	.4357	.4370	.4382	.4394	.4406	.4418
1.6	.4463	.4474	.4484	.4495	.4505	.4515	.4525
1.7	.4564	.4573	.4582	.4591	.4599	.4608	.4616
1.8	.4649	.4656	.4664	.4671	.4678	.4686	.4693

Most Commonly Used z_α Values

α	One-Tailed Test	Two-Tailed Test
.10	1.282	1.645
.05	1.645	1.960
.01	2.326	2.576

Returning now to our beverage problem where $n = 100$, $\overline{X} = 352$, $\sigma = 12$, $\alpha = .05/1$, the lowest tailed critical value is

$$H_0: \mu_o \geq 355 \text{ Critical value } \mu_o - z_{\alpha/1} \bullet \sigma_{\overline{X}}$$

or

$$355 - (1.645)(1.2) = 353.03$$

The rejection region is shown in Figure 7.4, and the sample mean (352) is clearly in the rejection region. Hence, we reject the hypothesis that there is an average of at least 355 ml in the beverage cans.

Having shown how to find the appropriate z value for a greater than or equal to null hypothesis, we will turn to a less than or equal to example. If we believed that the average ml was more than 355 (H_A: μ_o: >355 ml), or if the beverage container read "contents: ≤ 355," we would be involved in a right-tail test. If the survey results determine that the sample mean is 352 ml, we would be unable to reject H_0. The only chance to reject H_0 is if the sample mean is more than 355 ml. Of course, a right-tailed test makes little sense in this particular example.

Figure 7.4 ISER and Rejection Regions for Beverage Problem

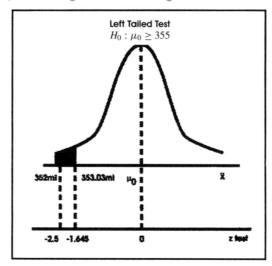

Using z_{test} Values

We may again use z_{test} values to ascertain the rejection or non-rejection of the null hypothesis. In the two-tailed test, if $|z_{\text{test}}| \leq z_{\alpha/2}$, we will be unable to reject the null hypothesis. Or stated another way, if $|z_{\text{test}}| > z_{\alpha/2}$, the null hypothesis will be rejected. In the one-tailed test there is no plus or minus z. It will either be plus or minus z, but not both. The appropriate test is given in formula 7.3

Reject the Null Hypothesis (One-Tailed Test, s Known)

Left Tailed Test,	$H_0: \mu \geq \mu_0$	Right Tailed Test,	$H_0: \mu \leq \mu_0$	
	$H_A: \mu < \mu_0$		$H_A: \mu > \mu_0$	
	$z_{\text{test}} < -z_{\alpha/1}$		$z_{\text{test}} > +z_{\alpha/1}$	(7.3)

where

μ_0 = some specific value for the population parameter
z_{test} = the test statistic
$z_{\alpha/1}$ = the critical value for a one-tailed test

After computing the standard error of the mean (1.2) and determining our significance level (5%), we must determine how many standard errors apart are the hypothesized and sample mean. Substituting the numerical equivalent into formula 7.1 yields

$$Z_{\text{test}} = \frac{352 - 355}{\frac{12}{\sqrt{100}}} = \frac{-3}{1.2} = -2.500$$

Note that the same z_{test} exists for the one- or two-tailed test. The only difference is we will compare z_{test} to a one-tailed $z_{\alpha/1}$ critical value. The critical value is $z_{.05/1} = -1.645$ (we make the critical value negative z because we are involved with a left tailed test). Since z_{test} (-2.500) is less than $z_{.05/1}$ (-1.645), the null hypothesis must be rejected. The beverage containers apparently do not hold an average of at least 355 ml, but possibly something less.

157

MINITAB will also perform an analysis for us with either a left- or right-tailed test. The process is essentially the same as it was with a two-tailed test, the only difference is in the alternative selected. The command sequence is:

Stat > **Basic Statistics** > **1-Sample** z
Double click data column to enter it into **Variables** box
Click **Test Mean** to enter μ of **355**
Click **Options for Alternatives** for H_A: **not equal** (two-tailed test)
                                            less than (left-tailed test)
                                            greater than (right-tailed test)
Click on **Sigma**: enter 20
OK

Table 7.6   One-Sample Z: Data

Test of $\mu = 355$ vs < 355
The assumed standard deviation $= 20$

Variable	N	Mean	StDev	SE Mean	95% Upper Bound	Z	P
Data	16	352.750	3.376	5.000	360.974	−0.45	0.326

At any confidence level we REJECT H_0 if $\alpha \geq P$ VALUE. Since $.05 < 0.326$ we have insufficient statistical evidence (ISER) to REJECT H_0.

Test of $\mu = 355$ vs > 355
The assumed standard deviation $= 20$

Variable	N	Mean	StDev	SE Mean	95% Lower Bound	Z	P
Data	16	352.750	3.376	5.000	344.526	−0.45	0.674

At any confidence level we REJECT H_0 if $\alpha \geq P$ VALUE. Since $.05 < 0.674$ we have insufficient statistical evidence (ISER) to REJECT H_0.

 Concept Check 7.D

The only difference in determining z_{test} for a one- or two-tailed test is that a two-tailed test involves a $\pm$ with a one-tailed test either $+$ or $-$, but not both. True or false. If false, explain.

Exercises

7.21   Find the appropriate z values for an upper tailed test for the following confidence levels using both the normal tables and MINITAB:

   a. .02   b. .80   c. 98   d. 94

7.22   In which tail are the appropriate critical values for an upper and lower tailed test? Explain.

7.23   An airline wishes to ensure that the length of time it takes to service a customer does not exceed 10 minutes. It conducts a random survey of 116 customers and finds $\overline{X} = 9.4$ minutes. The airline believes that $\sigma = 1$ minute. Determine the critical value for μ_0 (.95 confidence level) and ascertain if the hypothesis should be rejected.

7.24   In exercise 7.23, change the mean from 9.4 to 10.6 and test the hypothesis.

7.25 a. A survey of 43 (out of 1,000) different types of basic math textbooks is taken. One publisher believes the average at least 900 pages long. The survey results in a sample mean = 863 pages. The company believes that $\sigma = 81$ pages. Determine the critical value for μ_0 (.95 confidence level) and ascertain if the hypothesis should be rejected.

b. Test the manufacturer's claim using the test statistic rule of formula 7.3.

7.26 A manufacturer claims that a meal contains on average 210 calories. However, a consumer group maintains that it contains more than 210 calories. A survey of 35 is taken with a sample mean of 224 calories. It is believed that σ is 13.0.

a. State the alternative and null hypotheses.

b. Is the null hypothesis rejected at the 5% level?

7.27 A major highway is developed and it is important that motorists travel at least 50 miles per hour (H_0: $\mu \geq 50$ mph) for safety reasons. A survey is conducted with the following results: $n = 1,200$, $\overline{X} = 51.8$ mph. It is believed that $\sigma = 11.8$. Using a .99 confidence level and z_{test}, determines if H_0 is correct.

7.28 In Exercise 7.27, change $\overline{X}$ to 47.9 mph.

a. Using a .99 confidence level and z_{test}, determine if H_0 is correct.

b. How are Exercises 7.27 and 7.28a different?

7.5 Hypothesis Testing: σ Unknown

Two-Tailed Test Using t_{test} Values

When σ is unknown, the population standard deviation must be estimated using s, and when the population can be assumed to be normal (or approximately normal), the test statistic will be t and not z. The t_{test} statistic is

---

The t Test Statistic (σ Unknown but Normally Distributed)

$$t_{test} = \frac{\overline{X} - \mu_0}{\frac{s}{\sqrt{n}}} \qquad (7.4)$$

where

t_{test} = the test statistic

$\overline{X}$ = the sample mean

μ_0 = the hypothesized population mean

s = the sample standard deviation

n = the sample size

Note: if sampling without replacement and $n/N \geq .05$, the finite population correction must be used to discount the standard error $\sqrt{(N-n)/(N-1)}$.

Reject the Null Hypothesis (Two-Tailed Test, σ Unknown)

We will reject the null hypothesis if

$$|t_{\text{test}}| > t_{\alpha/2(d(f))} \qquad\qquad (7.5)$$

where

$t_{\text{test}} =$ the test statistic

$t_{\alpha/2(d(f))} =$ the critical value for a two-tailed test and specific df

---

Let us illustrate with the use of an example involving a sample of beverage cans. Suppose we sample 16 beverage cans and find the following ml: 352, 358, 357, 353, 349, 352, 356, 352, 351, 348, 351, 348, 349, 355, 356, and 357. We can input the data to MINITAB to obtain the summary statistics (STATS command, specifically $\overline{X} = 352.75$ and $s = 3.376$). The beverage can says it contains an average of 355 ml (H_0: 355 ml; a two-tailed test). Substituting the appropriate numerical equivalents into formula 7.4,

$$t_{\text{test}} = \frac{352.75 - 355.00}{\dfrac{3.376}{\sqrt{16}}} = \frac{-2.25}{0.844} = -2.666$$

To test the null hypothesis we need a critical value for t which is $t_{.05/2(15)} = 2.131$. Note that the degrees of freedom (df) is enclosed within the parenthesis in the subscript. Since $|t_{\text{test}}|$ (2.666) exceeds $t_{\alpha/2(d(f))}$ (2.131), we reject the null hypothesis that the mean ml is 355.

Using MINITAB to Obtain the Desired Results

We can utilize MINITAB to yield the desired results. Remember our rejection rule.

Reject H_0 if $\alpha \geq P$ value

If we desire a .95 confidence level, $\alpha = .05$. Since $.05 \geq .018$, we must reject the claim that the average beverage can has 355 ml. The average beverage container does not contain 355 ml, but rather something less than 355 ml. MINITAB will again do all the work for us. Again we note that 95% CONFIDENCE LEVEL IS THE ONE PRIMARILY USED IN ACADEMIA, IN SCIENCE, AND IN THE BUSINESS WORLD. Hence MINITAB defaults to the 95% confidence interval. Should another interval be required, click to the Confidence interval box to change it. We will use the same data set as before involving 16 randomly selected beverage cans and record the following volumes in ml's: 352, 358, 357, 353, 349, 352, 356, 352, 351, 348, 351, 348, 349, 355, 356, 357.

The MINITAB command sequence and output is:

Stat > Basic Statistics > 1-Sample *t*
Double click data column to enter it into **Variables** box
Click **Test Mean** to enter μ of 355
Click under **Alternatives** for H_A: **not equal** (two-tailed test)
                                     less than (left-tailed test)
                                     greater than (right-tailed test)

OK

Table 7.7   One-Sample T: Data

Test of $\mu = 355$ *vs* $\neq 355$

Variable	N	Mean	StDev	SE Mean	95% CI Bound	T	P
Data	16	352.750	3.376	0.844	(350.951, 354.549)	−2.67	0.018

At any confidence level we REJECT H_0 if $\alpha \geq P$ VALUE. Since .05 ≥ 0.018 we REJECT H_0.

Test of $\mu = 355$ *vs* < 355

Variable	N	Mean	StDev	SE Mean	95% Upper Bound	T	P
Data	16	352.750	3.376	0.844	354.230	−2.67	0.009

At any confidence level we REJECT H_0 if $\alpha \geq P$ VALUE. Since .05 ≥ 0.0088 we REJECT H_0.

Test of $\mu = 355$ *vs* > 355

Variable	N	Mean	StDev	SE Mean	95% Lower Bound	T	P
Data	16	352.750	3.376	0.844	351.270	−2.67	0.991

At any confidence level we REJECT H_0 if $\alpha \geq P$ VALUE. Since .05 < 0.99 we have insufficient statistical evidence (ISER) to REJECT H_0.

One-Tailed Test Using t_{test} Values

For a one-tailed test, t_{test} is found using formula 7.4; however, it is compared to a one-tailed critical value for t. The decision rule is

---

Reject the Null Hypothesis (One-Tailed Test, σ Unknown)

Left-Tailed Test, $H_0: \mu \geq \mu_0$ Right-Tailed Test, $H_0: \mu \leq \mu_0$

$H_A: \mu < \mu_0$ $H_A: \mu > \mu_0$ (7.6)

$t_{test} < -t_{\alpha/1(d(f))}$ $t_{test} > t_{\alpha/1(d(f))}$

where

μ_0 = some specific value for the population parameter

t_{test} = the test statistic

$t_{\alpha/1(d(f))}$ = the critical value for a one-tailed test

---

Let's return to the beverage problem just completed. Suppose the manufacturer claimed that there are 355 or more ml as the average container content or that we believed there are less than 355 ml in the cans ($H_0: \mu \geq 355$ ml; $H_A: \mu < 355$ ml; a left-tailed test). The test statistic remains the same ($t_{\text{test}} = -2.666$), the only change that occurs is in the critical value. The critical value is $-1.753 = t_{.05/1(15)}$. We must make the critical value negative because we are involved with a left tailed test. Since t_{test} (-2.666) $< t_{.05/1(15)}$ (-1.753), we must reject H_0. We do not believe there are 355 or more ml in the cans based on the survey results.

When the sample size is small we must use z_{test} in lieu of t_{test}. True or false? If false, explain.

Exercises

7.29   Why do we substitute t_{test}, for z_{test} when σ is unknown?

7.30   What are the appropriate degrees of freedom in utilizing t_{test}?

   a. $n = 12$ b. $n = 3$ c. $n = 19$
   d. $n = 29$ e. $n = 21$ f. $n = 10$

7.31   What are the appropriate $t_{\alpha(df)}$ values for a one-tailed test?

   a. $n = 17, \alpha = .05.$ b. $n = 7, \alpha = .01$ c. $n = 27, \alpha = .10$

7.32   What are the appropriate $t_{\alpha(df)}$ values for a two-tailed test?

   a. $n = 15, \alpha = .05.$ b. $n = 4, \alpha = .01$ c. $n = 23, \alpha = .10$

7.33   A university believes that all word processing packages will use 110,000 bytes of memory to store a manuscript. They conduct a survey of 7 word processing packages and determine that the mean storage for a manuscript is 112,569 bytes. The sample standard deviation is 7,298 bytes.

   a.   Does the null hypothesis involve a one- or two-tailed test?
   b.   Test the null hypothesis ($\alpha = .05$).
   c.   Test the null hypothesis ($\alpha = .05$) under the belief that the population contains 25 word processing packages.

7.34   A soft drink beverage container is said to hold an average of at least 355 ml. A survey of 22 cans finds a mean of 353.7 ml and a standard deviation of 1.0. Using a 10% significance level, determine if the manufacturer's claim should be rejected.

7.35   A strong wire cable used by construction crews is guaranteed to withstand at least 500 pounds of tensile strength by the manufacturer. A survey is conducted of 24 cables with the following results: 489, 516, 551, 458, 571, 519, 490, 501, 487, 526, 537, 600, 477, 509, 511, 529, 502, 469, 488, 420, 499, 477, 500, 466.

   a.   Does the null hypothesis involve a one- or two-tailed test?
   b.   Test the null hypothesis ($\alpha = .01$) utilizing MINITAB.

7.36   A can of tomato soup states that it contains an average of 308 grams. A survey of 15 cans yields: 301, 315, 309, 289, 299, 303, 308, 297, 294, 305, 318, 310, 291, 306, 302.

   a.   Does the null hypothesis involve a one- or two-tailed test?
   b.   Suppose a consumer advocate group believed that the soup contains on the average less than 308 grams. Does this alter the null or alternative hypotheses?
   c.   Test the null hypotheses at the 10% level ($\alpha = .10$) using MINITAB.

7.37   A diet frozen dinner says it contains at most 270 calories. A survey of 28 frozen dinners yields a mean of 274 calories with an $s = 12$ calories.

   a.   Does the null hypothesis involve a one- or two-tailed test?
   b.   Test the null hypothesis at the 5% level ($\alpha = .05$).

7.38   A can of tomato soup states that it contains no more than 660 mg of sodium. A survey of 9 cans reveals the following mg of sodium: 667, 661, 654, 665, 663, 659, 665, 663, 661.

       a.   Does the null hypothesis involve a one- or two-tailed test?
       b.   Test the null hypothesis at the 10% level ($\alpha = .10$) using MINITAB.

7.6   Hypothesis Testing About a Proportion, Large Sample

When hypothesis testing about a proportion, the binomial assumptions outlined in Section 4.3 must be met. First an outcome must be placed into one of two mutually exclusive categories (such as defective or not defective), the probability for success must remain constant over time, and that there is no relationship (independence) between successive trials.

If these conditions are met, and $n \bullet p > 5$, $n \bullet q > 5$, the normal distribution may be used to approximate the binomial distribution.

Two-Tailed Test using z_{test} Values

Hypothesis testing about a proportion is similar to that about a mean. The z_{test} is the difference between a sample proportion and hypothesized population proportion in terms of standard errors. The formula is

---

Test Statistic About $p(n \bullet p \ \& \ n \bullet q > 5)$

$$z_{\text{test}} = \frac{\hat{p} - p_0}{\sqrt{\dfrac{p_0 \bullet q_0}{n}}} \tag{7.7}$$

where

$z_{\text{test}} = $ the test statistic z

$\hat{p} = $ the sample proportion

$p_0 = $ the hypothesized population proportion

$q_0 = 1 - p_0$

$n = $ the sample size

Note: if $n/N \geq .05$ the finite population correction must be used to discount the standard error $\sqrt{(N - n)/(N - 1)}$.

The test statistic rejects the null hypothesis whenever $|z_{\text{test}}| > z_{\alpha/2}$ (formula 7.2).

Let's illustrate with the use of an example. A pharmaceutical company believes a new medication is effective 80% of the time (H_0: $p = .8$). A survey of 100 reveals that in 76 causes the medication is effective, but in 24 cases it is not. In order to test the hypothesis, we use formula 7.7 ($\hat{p} = 76/100 = .76$).

$$Z_{\text{test}} = \frac{.76 - .80}{\sqrt{\dfrac{.8 \bullet .2}{100}}} = \frac{-.04}{.04} = -1.000$$

Since $|z_{\text{test}}|$ (1.000) is less than $z_{.05/2}$ (1.96), at the 5% level of significance, we have ISER H_0. Given the survey results, we are unable to reject the manufacturer's claim.

163

One-Tailed Test Using z_{test} Values

For a one-tailed test, z_{test} is computed as in formula 7.7. The only difference is in the critical value and the rejection rule. Let's return to our pharmaceutical company example. Let's say the company publicist takes on the role of consumer advocate in believing the new medication to be effective less than 80% of the time (H_A: $p < .80$). If the publicist believes H_0: $\geq .80$, we are involved in a left tailed test.

Let's utilize the same sample information as before, $n = 100$, and $\hat{p} = .76$. We will use formula 7.3 to test the hypothesis. The appropriate critical value is $z_{.05/1} = -1.645$ (a negative z because it is a lower tailed test). Since z_{test} (-1.000) is not less than $z_{.05/1}$ we have ISER H_0.

 Concept Check 7.F

The normal distribution may be used to approximate the binomial distribution, for hypothesis testing purposes, only when the specified assumptions are met. True or false? If false, explain.

Exercises

7.39   When may the normal distribution be allowed to approximate the binomial distribution?

7.40   A company believes at most 40% of its employees will take no sick leave this year. A survey of 41 is taken with $p = .39$.

   a.   Does the null hypothesis involve a one- or two-tailed test?
   b.   Test the null hypothesis ($\alpha = .01$) utilizing z_{test}.

7.41   A company believes that 40% of its employees will take sick leave this year. A survey of 410 is taken with 180 having taken sick leave.

   a.   Does the null hypothesis involve a one- or two-tailed test?
   b.   Test the null hypothesis ($\alpha = .05$) utilizing z_{test}.

7.42   A consumer group believes that the average consumer spends at least 42% of his or her budget on their homes. A survey of 1,050 consumers is taken with 429 of them spending at least 42% on housing. Test the null hypothesis ($\alpha = .05$) utilizing z_{test}.

7.43   A major military contracting company believes that they will lose at least 50% of their degreed and professional certified engineers within 24 months. It conducted a survey of 610 qualified engineers and found that 320 surveyed left in less than two years. Test the company hypothesis ($\alpha = .05$) z_{test}.

7.44   A publishing company thinks that 60% of the adopters of a science text will drop it after the initial year of use. A survey is taken after the year of 170 adopters with 80 dropping the text. Test the null hypothesis ($\alpha = .10$) utilizing z_{test}.

7.7   Hypothesis Testing Comparing Two Means from Independent Large Samples: σ Unknown

Before we begin our analysis it will be useful to review the rules of hypothesis testing involved. Most of our analyses will be comparing two or more columns of data. When making comparisons between two columns of data we may be involved with a one- or two-tailed test. For a two-tailed test, the null hypothesis states that whatever statistic we are comparing (mean, median, standard deviation, etc.) are statistically the same in both columns. For a one-tailed test, we are stating that one of the column statistics

164

is either greater than or less than the other. This establishes the alternate hypothesis. To determine if a greater than or less than arrow is appropriate we simply need to understand which data set is in which column, and whether the largest or the smallest statistic is optimum.

We will start by analyzing independent samples. Suppose we have two divisions of our pharmaceutical company producing an identical medication by chemical formula, but by different mechanical processes. We want to be sure that both divisions produce medications of equal effectiveness. The medication is designed to kill a certain type of bacteria in a prescribed time limit. We randomly survey patients who have received the medication from both divisions and record the time (in days) it takes the medication to kill the bacteria. The summary statistics for both surveys are:

Survey #1: $n_1 = 15$, $\overline{X}_1 = 8.573$, $s_1 = 2.039$
Survey #2: $n_2 = 11$, $\overline{X}_2 = 8.209$, $s_2 = 0.470$

Table 7.8   Comparing the Time it Takes a Drug to Kill a Bacteria
*Data File on MINITAB CD

	Survey #1	Survey #2
	7.9	8.1
	9.6	9.1
	9.1	8.0
	10.6	7.9
	12.8	8.6
	4.1	7.4
	8.8	8.2
	9.5	8.7
	6.9	7.8
	7.3	8.4
	8.5	8.1
	8.7	
	9.9	
	5.9	
	9.0	
n	15	11
$\overline{X}$	8.573	8.209
s	2.039	0.470

We think that both plants are producing equal medications, so our null hypothesis is that there is no (null) difference between the two medications ($\mu_1 = \mu_2$). If our sample mean difference is positive, it indicates $\overline{X}_1 > \overline{X}_2$, and if negative, that $\overline{X}_2 > \overline{X}_1$. Remember that our example is something analogous to a golf score. The lower the score, the better we are. If we reject H_0, it means that one of the drugs may be more effective than the other. The null and alternative hypothesis are

H_0: $\mu_1 = \mu_2$; or $\mu_1 - \mu_2 = 0$

H_A: $\mu_1 \neq \mu_2$; or $\mu_1 - \mu_2 \neq 0$

Fortunately MINITAB will compute confidence intervals, develop test statistics, and obtain p-values for us. The data would be entered exactly as it appears in Table 7.8. The MINITAB command sequence and output for both one- and two-tailed tests is as follows:

Stat > Basic Statistics > 2-Sample t
Click on **Samples in different columns**
Double click **SURVEY1** to place in **First**
Double click **SURVEY2** to place in **Second**
not equal to for a two-tailed test
less than for a left-tailed test

Table 7.9   Two-Sample *T*-Test and CI: Survey1, Survey2

Two-sample *T* for Survey1 vs Survey2

	N	Mean	StDev	SE Mean
Survey1	15	8.57	2.04	0.53
Survey2	11	8.209	0.470	0.14

Difference = μ (Survey1) − μ (Survey2)
Estimate for difference: 0.364242
95% CI for difference: (−0.797876, 1.526361)
T-Test of difference = 0 (vs not =): *T*-Value = 0.67 *P*-Value = 0.514 DF = 15

Two-sample *T* for Survey1 vs Survey2

	N	Mean	StDev	SE Mean
Survey1	15	8.57	2.04	0.53
Survey2	11	8.209	0.470	0.14

Difference = μ (Survey1) − μ (Survey2)
Estimate for difference: 0.364242
95% upper bound for difference: 1.320049
T-Test of difference = 0 (vs <): *T*-Value = 0.67 *P*-Value = 0.743 DF = 15

Two-sample *T* for Survey1 vs Survey2

	N	Mean	StDev	SE Mean
Survey1	15	8.57	2.04	0.53
Survey2	11	8.209	0.470	0.14

Difference = μ (Survey1) − μ (Survey2)
Estimate for difference: 0.364242
95% lower bound for difference: −0.591564
T-Test of difference = 0 (vs >): *T*-Value = 0.67 *P*-Value = 0.257 DF = 15

We can see that our test statistic = .67, $df = 15$, and our *p*-value varies depending if we are involved with a two-tailed or a one-tailed test. If $\alpha \geq$ *p*-value, we reject our null hypothesis. This does not happen at the 95% confidence level for either a one or a two-tailed test.

Special Case Involving Equal Population Variances

For some examples we may assume equal population variances. For example, the variance in grades between two classes randomly drawn would be expected to be the same. Unless, of course, one class was an honors class. Also, random sampling from production lines using the same equipment would be expected to have equal variances. If we are able to assume equal population variances, we will pool the data and perform a somewhat stronger and more powerful hypothesis test. Power is defined as a greater likelihood of rejecting H_0 when it is in fact false. The pooled variance formula, test statistic, and confidence interval are provided by MINITAB.

MINITAB will solve all the information for us. The MINITAB commands and output is:

Stat > Basic Statistics > 2-Sample *t*
Click on **Samples in different columns**
Double click **SURVEY1** to place in **First**
Double click **SURVEY2** to place in **Second**
Alternative
        not equal to for a two-tailed test
        less than for a left-tailed test
        greater than for a right-tailed test
Click on **Assume equal variances**
OK

Table 7.10	Two-Sample *T*-Test and CI: Survey1, Survey2			
Two-sample *T* for Survey1 vs Survey2				
	N	*Mean*	*StDev*	*SE Mean*
Survey1	15	8.57	2.04	0.53
Survey2	11	8.209	0.470	0.14

Difference = μ (Survey1) $- \mu$ (Survey2)
Estimate for difference: 0.364242
95% CI for difference: $(-0.935664, 1.664149)$
T-Test of difference $= 0$ (vs not $=$): *T*-Value $= 0.58$ *P*-Value $= 0.568$ DF $= 24$
Both use Pooled StDev $= 1.5866$

With $P = .57$ we are unable to reject the null hypothesis.

Which Test Statistic to Use?

Even though the pooled variance approach is a more powerful test, it is also more risky. The pooled variance approach is unreliable if the assumption of equal population variances is not true. Hence, we recommend using the nonpooled approach unless there is strong evidence to indicate equal variances. In Section 7.9 we will learn to test to see if the two population variances are equal using the *F* distribution.

Analyzation of a Single Variable

MINITAB will allow us to analyze a single variable using a two-tailed test. For example let's open a MINITAB data file GRADES. In this file is a sample of 200 for three variables. One of the variables is the grade point average (GPA) of students. Another variable is the student math score on a standardized test. Suppose we wanted to determine if students' GPAs were higher for students who scored above 650 on the standardized test were significantly above the GPAs for students who scored 649 or below. We can do this by a coding process.

First open the MINITAB file.
Open grades.mtw
Select **Manip > Code > Numeric to Numeric**
Double-click **Math** to enter in the **Code data from column** box
Type **C4** to the **Into columns** box

Type **200:649** in the first **Original Values** box. Type **1** in the corresponding **New** box. What we are doing is saying that any math score between 200 and 649 is to be recorded as a 1.

Type **650:800** in the second **Original Values** box. Type **2** in the corresponding **New** box. What we are doing is saying that any math score above **650** is to be recorded as a 2.

Select Stat > Basic Statistics > 2-Sample *t*
Click to **Samples in one column**.
Double-click the variable **GPA** into the **Samples** box.
Double-click the variable **C4** into the **Subscripts** box.
OK

Since $P = 0.042$ we may reject the hypothesis that the GPA's of students verbal score below 650 are equal to those 650 or above at the 5% level of significance.

 Concept Check 7.G

If we pool the data when comparing two means from independent samples, we are developing a less powerful but riskier test. True or false? If false, explain.

Exercises

7.45   A country club has two golf companies wanting to be their exclusive supplier. Company A has quoted prices which are less expensive for what is believed to be products of equal quality from Company B. The country club is recording the driving distance obtained by randomly selected golfers. The recorded information is:

	Company A						Company B		
213	245	201	224	191	200	178	278	196	231
199	208	178	243	196	171	215	179	243	266
218	197	212	267	212	188	261	161	208	203
230	190	212	181	219					

The country club will purchase from company A if its product is better than that of product B. Using MINITAB, at the 5% level, do we reject H_0?

7.46   A professor has two identical classes of a required course. Hence, the professor feels that the assumption of equal variances applies. Grades are recorded for the two classes as follows:

	Class A						Class B		
79	81	68	95	87	64	71	89	73	54
74	98	78	72	91	51	82	73	74	69
94	67	78	71		62				

a.   Using MINITAB at the 1% level of significance, are the mean grades the same?
b.   Compare the confidence interval for the difference between the two means ($\alpha = .05$).

7.47   A scientist views the 1989 infant mortality rates per 1,000 births for randomly selected developing and developed countries. The data are:

Developing Countries	Deaths	Developed Countries	Deaths
Afghanistan	173	West Germany	7
Bangladesh	138	U.S.S.R.	25
Iraq	69	Great Britain	9
India	91	Switzerland	6
Laos	128	U.S.	0
Pakistan	20	Belgium	8
Angola	161	Denmark	7
Bolivia	23	Greece	11

Developing Countries	Deaths		Developed Countries	Deaths
Ecuador	62		Italy	8
Haiti	92		Sweden	6
Brazil	67		France	9
Mexico	42			
Peru	69			

The scientist believes that the developed nations have superior infant mortality rates.

a. Should we pool the data? Explain.

b. Using MINITAB, at the 5% level, is the scientist correct?

7.48   A personnel department is developing a screening test for applications. The company wants to determine if minorities' scores are equal to those of non-minorities. In presenting the following scores are recorded

		Minorities							Non-Minorities			
87	62	17	74	91	87		76	41	82	71	66	78
64	82	91	61	59	67		71	56	82	94	74	88
							55	73	65	39	53	99
							81					

a. Should we pool the data?

b. Using MINITAB, at the 1% level, is the H_0 rejected?

c. If H_0 were to be rejected, to what does it refer?

d. Compute the confidence interval for the difference between the two means ($\alpha = .01$).

7.49   The following data represents the number of sick days for employees under and over 40 years of age, during the last year. It is hypothesized that the number of sick days is the same between the two groups.

		Age $\leq$ 40						Age $\geq$ 40			
12	8	5	0	1	7		2	15	8	2	0	7
23	7	0	2	6	2		3	0	2	0	0	
9	2										

a. Should we pool the data?

b. Using MINITAB, at the 5% level, is H_0 rejected?

c. If H_0 were to be rejected to what does it refer?

d. Assume that the data may be pooled. Test the hypothesis at the 5% level.

7.50   A company decides to test the time its lightbulbs last as measured in hours. It has two crews, a day and nighttime shift, operating from the same machine; hence, it feels the equal variance assumption applies and it can pool the data. It randomly samples lightbulbs coming from both crews with the following results:

	Day Crew				Night Crew		
36.4	62.1	9.8	5.3		65.9	46.3	77.9	62.8
29.1	45.8	67.0	38.9		43.2	71.8	39.3	55.3
49.3	55.6	40.3	61.2		68.9	65.8	52.9	77.0
36.2	44.8	61.0					

Use MINITAB at the 10% level to determine if the day and night crews perform equally.

All business majors have probably heard of Elton Mayo's Hawthorne studies of the 1920's. Researchers selected individuals from a large Chicago plant to participate in an experiment. Mayo had a theory that lighting, or lack thereof, affected productivity. He selected workers and changed their work environments. He placed the workers into two groups. The first group (#1) would have lighting similar to what was experienced in the main plant. The second group (#2) would have its lighting raised and lowered.

Group #1 was the control group, and any differences in output between the two groups would be attributable to illumination, as that appeared to be the only difference between the groups. As workers were selected for the two groups, it was important to match each worker in terms of their demographic and psychographic makeup. It was important that neither a demographic nor psychographic difference could cause the productivity difference. All differences between the groups were attempted to be blocked out, except for illumination. The company was trying to minimize the variation in data by filtering or blocking certain factors so it could more carefully evaluate the impact of illumination. In this example, illumination is termed a treatment.

Suppose the following results were obtained from the Mayo studies with the measured output being per hour for 21 pairs of employees (Table 7.11).

Table 7.11   21 Paired Employees Output per Hour
Data File on MINITAB CD

Paired Employees	Output: #1	Output: #2	Difference
1	100	89	+11
2	95	96	−1
3	97	84	+13
4	98	81	+17
5	89	91	−2
6	92	93	−1
7	89	90	−1
8	89	89	0
9	99	90	+9
10	91	92	−1
11	88	92	−4
12	94	96	−2
13	94	95	−1
14	96	88	+8
15	99	92	+7
16	95	96	−1
17	90	93	−3
18	88	90	−2
19	89	90	−1
20	94	89	+5
21	94	91	+3
$\overline{X}$	93.333	90.810	2.524
s	3.929	3.710	5.988

The null hypothesis is that the output of both groups is the same; hence, illumination is not significant in terms of output. The alternative hypothesis is that illumination is significant in terms of measured output. This is a two-tailed test because if the output of #1 exceeds #2, or if the output of #2 exceeds #1, the null hypothesis is incorrect.

H_0: $\mu_1 - \mu_2 = 0$

H_A: $\mu_1 - \mu_2 \neq 0$

Let's develop an alternate example using the same data set. Our firm sells a five blade razor and we want to consider producing and selling a six blade razor. We would like to prove that a six blade razor shaves closer than a five blade razor. Hence we will design an experiment to test this hypothesis.

The problem is that different men have very different beards that grow at different rates and widths. However, we believe that our beards on the right sides of our faces grow at the same rates as does the left side. Each day we will randomly select to shave one side of our face with a six blade razor and one side with a five blade razor.

We would want to make sure that our participants would not shave harder with a six blade razor (to please the company) so both razors would contain six blades; however, one of the blades would be retracted from one of the razors so that the razor would actually only be shaving with five blades. This retraction would not be visible with the naked eye.

We then would use a sensitive microphone to determine which razor shaved closer. The results are shown in Table 7.12. The null hypothesis is that there is null (no) difference in the shaving outcomes for a five or six blade razor. If this hypothesis is rejected then there is a difference. From our results table (Table 7.12) both a five and six blade razor shave equally close. This is probably not the result we wanted to obtain.

We will assume that the population in question follow the normal distributions. The formula for the test statistic and confidence interval is provided by MINITAB.

Stat > Basic Statistics > Paired t
Click **Output1** into **First sample** box.
Click **Output2** into **Second sample** box.
Click **Options** to change confidence level and type of test
OK

Table 7.12   Paired T-Test and CI: Output1–Output2

Paired T for Output1–Output2

	N	Mean	StDev	SE Mean
Output1	21	93.3333	3.9285	0.8573
Output2	21	90.8095	3.7097	0.8095
Difference	21	2.52381	5.98848	1.30679

95% CI for mean difference: $(-0.20211, 5.24973)$
T-Test of mean difference = 0 (vs not = 0): T-Value = 1.93 P-Value = 0.68

Since the p-value $> .05$ we are unable to reject H_0 at the 5% level.

 Concept Check 7.H

In comparing two means from matched pair samples we are attempting to block out the influences of other factors that may be distorting our analysis. True or false? If false, explain.

7.51   University students are asked to evaluate a new ball point pen. The students are asked to record the length of time it takes for them to run out of ink. Each student is to record the length of time for two pens, one the old model and one the new developmental pen. The students don't know which pen is which, because they both have similar appearance (except color). The results are shown in hours.

Student	Old Pen	New Pen
1	19.6	28.9
2	17.6	21.7
3	15.1	24.9
4	16.2	16.1
5	21.9	37.8
6	22.4	24.8
7	14.6	16.4
8	17.6	17.4
9	25.0	28.7
10	13.9	27.3
11	28.2	21.3
12	22.0	23.8
13	17.1	16.4
14	29.8	23.6
15	18.9	18.3
16	19.9	19.3
17	21.9	23.4
18	21.9	21.2
19	16.9	27.9
20	26.7	23.4

a. The manufacturer will only produce the developmental pen if it lasts longer than the original model. Using MINITAB, at the 5% level, test the null hypothesis.

b. Develop the appropriate 95% confidence interval in comparing the difference between the two means.

7.52   An advertising firm wants to compare sales when products at grocery stores are and are not at eye level. The same merchandise is stored at eye level at one store and not at eye level at another store. The stores were selected because their demographic and psychographic profiles of their customer bases matched. Fifteen randomly selected hours are recorded in terms of sales as:

Hour	Sales Eye Level	Sales Not Eye Level
1	43	26
2	66	49
3	11	2
4	19	15
5	39	22
6	72	28
7	29	15
8	21	9
9	56	21
10	38	33

11	23	26
12	44	41
13	33	15
14	21	24
15	46	18

a. The manufacturer will pay for eye level space only if it produces sales greater than the non-eye-level space. Using MINITAB at the 10% level test the null hypothesis.

b. Develop the appropriate 90% confidence interval on comparing the difference between the two means.

7.53 Two friends have taken a number of identical classes. The grades the two friends received from the same courses are:

Course	Friend 1	Friend 2
Psychology	76	81
Biology	92	71
Calculus	98	67
Sociology	75	87
Anthropology	81	93
World History	83	95
Art I	87	96
Statistics	91	64
Finance	86	81
Economics I	89	77
Law I	76	98
Marketing	81	86
Management I	83	91
Language I	72	93
Accounting I	88	77
Accounting II	84	77
Computer Science	98	85
International Business	84	84
Report Writing	74	87
Logistics	91	83
Political Science	81	99

a. Why did we only record grades for identical classes?

b. Using MINITAB at the 5% level, did the two friends receive the same mean grades?

7.54 A sports fan wishes to see how she performed compared to a local sports reporter during a college basketball season. She randomly selects 15 days and records the number of winning selections made by herself and the reporter. The record is

Days	Sports Reporter	Fan
1	11	8
2	13	10
3	6	9
4	10	8
5	8	8
6	21	12
7	5	7
8	13	9
9	17	13

Days	Sports Reporter	Fan
10	6	9
11	19	15
12	14	6
13	15	14
14	7	3
15	11	7

Using MINITAB at the 2% level, did the fan's selection equal that of the reporter?

7.55 Two statistical packages are to be evaluated on the basis of speed of computation using an identical data base. The time it takes to manipulate the data bases, on exactly the same computer, is recorded as:

Data Base	Statistical Package #1	Statistical Package #2
1	0.6 min	1.1 min
2	7.8	7.2
3	24.9	31.3
4	6.2	6.7
5	121.1	112.6
6	0.2	0.1
7	19.8	27.5
8	4.3	4.4
9	5.1	5.5

a. Why is it important that we use exactly the same computer when comparing the analytical speed of the two statistical packages?

b. Use MINITAB to determine if the two statistical packages are equally fast ($\alpha = .10$) in processing the different data bases.

7.56 A new stain is developed that is believed to last longer on a wooden house than the old stain. Matched houses are found in 8 geographic climates and one is stained with the new product and one with the old. The results are given in terms of years of duration.

Geographic Region	New Stain	Old Stain
1	5.4 years	5.1 years
2	4.8	5.1
3	4.1	3.9
4	2.1	1.7
5	9.4	9.5
6	7.7	7.9
7	6.3	6.9
8	2.7	2.5

a. Why is it important that we use two wooden houses in each geographic region when comparing the lasting power of the two stains?

b. Use MINITAB to test the hypothesis that the new stain lasts longer than the old ($\alpha = .05$).

7.9 Hypothesis Testing Comparing Variances of Two Normal Populations: Independent Samples

In Section 7.7 we discussed the possibility of combining the data from two samples in order to make the analysis a more powerful test. In order to do this we need to make the assumption that the two populations have equal variances. This is not true in most cases.

We can engage MINITAB to test the main hypothesis that the two populations are indeed equal.

$H_0: \sigma_1 - \sigma_2 = 0$
$H_A: \sigma_1 - \sigma_2 \neq 0$

Utilizing the same data set in Table 7.8 the MINITAB commands are:

Stat > Basic Statistics > 2 Variances
Click on **Samples in different columns** and enter data
Options to establish confidence levels
OK

Figure 7.5

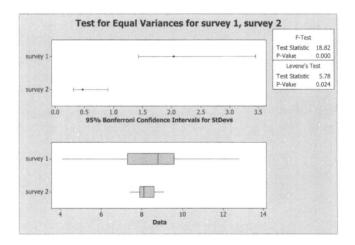

MINITAB uses two hypothesis tests (F-Test and Levene's Test) to test the main hypothesis. At the 95% confidence level we would reject the main hypothesis using both tests, hence that data may not be pooled. The two populations have different variances.

Exercises

7.57   A country club has two golf companies wanting to be its exclusive supplier. Company A has quoted prices which are less expensive for what is believed to be products of equal quality from Company B. The country club is recording the driving distance obtained by randomly selected golfers. The recorded information is:

Company A					Company B				
213	245	201	224	191	200	178	278	196	231
199	208	278	243	196	171	215	179	243	266
218	197	212	267	212	188	261	161	208	203
230	190	212	181	219					

At the 5% level are we involved with equal population variances?

7.58   A professor has two identical classes involving a required class. Hence, the professor feels that the assumption of equal variances applies. Grades are recorded for the two classes are as follows:

		Class A					Class B		
79	81	68	95	87	64	71	89	73	54
74	98	78	72	91	51	82	73	74	69
94	67	78	71		62				

At the 1% level are we involved with equal population variances?

7.59   A scientist views the 1989 infant mortality rates per 1,000 births selected developing and developed countries. The data are:

Developing Countries	Deaths	Developed Countries	Deaths
Afghanistan	173	West Germany	7
Bangladesh	138	U.S.S.R.	25
Iraq	69	Great Britain	9
India	91	Switzerland	6
Laos	128	U.S.	10
Pakistan	120	Belgium	8
Angola	161	Denmark	7
Bolivia	123	Greece	11
Ecuador	62	Italy	8
Haiti	92	Sweden	6
Brazil	67	France	9
Mexico	42		
Peru	69		

At the 5% level are we involved with equal population variances?

7.60   A personnel department is developing a screening test for applicants. The company wants to determine if minorities' score is equal to that of non-minorities. In pretesting the following scores are recorded:

		Minorities						Non-Minorities			
87	62	17	74	91	87	76	41	82	71	66	78
64	82	91	61	59	67	71	56	82	94	74	88
						55	73	65	39	53	99
						81					

At the 1% level are we involved with equal population variances?

7.61   The following data represent the number of sick days for employees under and over 40 years of age, during the last year.

		Age ≤ 40						Age ≥ 40			
12	8	5	0	1	7	2	15	8	2	0	7
23	7	0	2	6	2	3	0	2	0	0	
9	2										

At the 5% level are we involved with equal population variances?

7.62   A company decides to test the time its lightbulbs last as measured in hours. It has two crews, a day and nighttime shift, operating the same machine; hence, it feels the equal variance assumption applies and it can pool the data. It randomly samples lightbulbs coming from both crews with the following results:

Day Crew				Night Crew			
36.4	62.1	9.8	5.3	65.9	46.3	77.9	62.8
29.1	45.8	67.0	38.9	43.2	71.8	39.3	55.3
49.3	55.6	40.3	61.2	68.9	65.8	52.9	77.0
36.2	44.8	61.0					

At the 1% level are we involved with equal population variances?

7.10 Summary

We have reviewed the concepts involved with testing hypotheses. Every time we make a purchase we can read claims made by the manufacturer in terms of how much (the exact weight, volume, etc.) of the product is contained in the package. These claims represent hypotheses which can be tested. It is hoped that the manufacturers themselves would check their own quality control standards and make tests as outlined in this chapter. Yet sometimes pressure from competitors makes this impractical.

Companies should realize the problems that can develop from making false claims. Imagine the problems the Federal Drug Administration (FDA) has to deal with when pharmaceutical companies make claims about miraculous drugs. The public sometimes pressures the agency into releasing a drug before the appropriate hypothesis testing can occur. Often, other countries have less stringent hypothesis testing procedures, making experimental drugs (hope) available in these nations first. Many drug tests involve control groups to compare differences. This takes a great deal of time and resources. Therefore, companies must expend both time and money to ensure that claims they make are statistically valid.

We have reviewed the concepts involved with testing hypotheses and developing confidence intervals involving situations dealing with dual populations. At the pivot of the confidence interval is the difference between two population means, proportions, or variances. The formula for confidence interval is the same as when dealing with a single population. We multiply the appropriate z_α or $t_{\alpha(df)}$ by the estimated standard deviation of the sampling distribution.

 Mini-case 7.1: Should I Take This Class?

A student registers late for his or her classes. He or she can only get into one section of a required class and that section has an unknown instructor. The student can't afford to have a low grade, and hence will not take this instructor if the instructor's average grade point average is not equal to that of other instructors at the university. The student has been told that the average grade point given for all sections of the class over the last several years was 2.30 with a standard deviation of .62. The student belongs to a fraternity. He contacts the fraternity members at the university from which the new instructor has come. The student is given the following GPA's for classes taught by the instructor involve: 1.96, 1.87, 2.37, 2.19, 2.01, 2.07, 2.27, 2.29, 2.06, 2.19, 2.22, 2.36.

a.   Are we involved in a one- or two-tailed test? Explain.
b.   Use MINITAB and test the null hypotheses at the 5% and 1% levels of significance.
c.   What is the lowest α value or largest $1 - \alpha$ values, which would cause us to reject H_0?
d.   What should the student do?

Mini-case 7.2: Do Students Want Friday Off in Summer Schedule?

A university runs accelerated 6-week summer semesters. The courses meet for two hours per day, four days a week. A particular college claims that students would prefer a mid-week day off. It claims that 65% of the students prefer this to having Friday off. Students conduct a random survey and find that 54 out of 100 students prefer Friday off. Is the null hypothesis that the students prefer a mid-week day off true at the 5% level?

Mini-case 7.3: Household Cleaning: 1890 & 1990

Researchers have heard two theories concerning the number of weekly hours spent on house cleaning in the nineteenth and twentieth centuries. One hypothesis states that labor saving cleaning equipment (vacuums, washing machines, dishwashers) did not exist in 1890; hence, a greater number of hours were devoted to cleaning. A second hypothesis says that even though labor saving devices were developed, the definition of cleanliness was raised to new heights by the year 1990. This increased level of cleanliness has fostered an increase in home cleaning hours as opposed to a decrease.

The scientists have found an old university study that monitored the weekly cleaning and cooking time in old New England households in 1890. They repeat the study, in the same geographic area, but not the same households, in the year 1990. Households were matched on the basis of square feet and reported house structure. The results of the studies are as follows:

Square feet	1890	1990
800–850	12.6	14.8
100–1050	14.9	15.7
720–750	11.6	12.4
1250–1275	14.8	17.1
1750–1775	17.9	21.2
1960–1975	16.6	17.2
675–700	10.1	11.3
1200–1225	14.1	13.7
705–720	10.3	10.5
835–855	12.4	12.1
900–920	13.5	13.2
940–955	13.3	14.6
980–995	14.6	14.8
770–785	11.9	12.5

a. Why were the homes matched in terms of the houses' square footage and structure?
b. Using MINITAB test both hypotheses at the 10% level.
c. Relating the two hypotheses to computers, do you think they will reduce the recording and processing time? Or will it raise recording and processing data to new levels thereby increasing time spent with data?

Mini-case 7.4: Test Scores: 1930 and 1990

An established university finds an old test administered to seniors in 1930. Administrators decide to give the same test to its seniors in 1990, some 60 years later. They have the student profiles which they attempted to match with profiles of the earlier class. The administrators felt that current students would perform as well as past students. The matched profiles and scores are:

Profiles	1930	1990
1	650	590
2	520	485
3	715	615
4	480	510
5	720	700
6	615	595
7	695	615
8	585	525
9	785	775
10	665	605
11	775	605
12	440	415
13	635	625
14	715	695
15	595	565

a. Why did the administrators attempt to match student profiles before comparing results?
b. What factors would be unable to be blocked which would probably render any analysis useless?
c. Use MINITAB and test the null hypothesis at the 5% level.

 Mini-case 7.5: Do Men Earn More Than Women and Does Education Pay (1987)?

Based on a casual observation of the data supplied by the Census Department in 1991, concerning a 1987 data base, do men earn more than women when compared to their educational backgrounds? Are there advantages to be gained from advanced education? Note that we are dealing with large sample sizes.

Both Sexes: Mean Monthly Earning ($\geq$ 18 years old)

Degrees Attained	Earnings	Standard Error
Professional	$4,003	$369
Master's	$2,378	$78
Bachelor's	$1,829	$41
Associate	$1,458	$54
Vocational	$1,088	$65
Some college: no degree	$1,088	$23
High school graduate only	$921	$14
Not a high school graduate	$452	$15
Grand Mean	$1,075	$14

Men: Mean Monthly Earning (≥ 18 years old)

Degrees Attained	Earnings	Standard Error
Professional	$4,480	$449
Master's	$2,901	$110
Bachelor's	$2,471	$71
Associate	$1,977	$94
Vocational	$1,699	$129
Some college: no degree	$1,483	$42
High school graduate only	$1,350	$23
Not a high school graduate	$709	$25
Grand Mean	$1,540	$25

Women: Mean Monthly Earning (≥ 18 years old)

Degrees Attained	Earnings	Standard Error
Professional	$2,311	$346
Master's	$1,733	$91
Bachelor's	$1,136	$30
Associate	$1,022	$60
Vocational	$773	$49
Some college: no degree	$710	$18
High school graduate only	$583	$13
Not a high school graduate	$207	$9
Grand Mean	$652	$10

Note: For Ph.D. degrees, there were not enough women to list their mean monthly earnings. For men the mean monthly earnings with a Ph.D. degree was $3,950 with a standard error of $667.

Source: What's it Worth? Educational Background and Economic Status: Spring 1987, Department of the Census, 1991.

Mini-case 7.6: Age Distribution of World Population, 1990 (000)

Do the developed nations in the world have a greater percentage of their population over 65 years of age than do the developed nations? Do we even need to make any computations to test the hypothesis?

Age	WORLD POPULATION		DEVELOPING NATIONS		DEVELOPED NATIONS	
	Number	%	Number	%	Number	%
0–4 years	638,777	12.0	551,173	13.4	87,604	7.2
5–14 years	1,093,732	20.5	920,539	22.3	173,194	14.3
15–19 years	523,192	9.8	434,683	10.5	88,509	7.3
20–44 years	1,965,085	36.9	1,509,779	36.6	455,306	37.6
45–65 years	792,922	14.9	533,120	12.9	259,802	21.5
65–79 years	264,866	5.0	151,479	3.7	113,344	9.4
80+ years	52,928	1.0	19,916	0.5	33,011	2.7
Totals*	5,331,503	100.0	4,120,732	100.0	1,210,771	100.0

*May not total due to rounding error
Source: World Population Profile: 1989, Bureau of the Census

7.63   Do the following statements signify a one- or two-tailed test (if a one-tailed test signify if upper or lower tailed).

    a.   The output of a stereo is 50 watts.
    b.   The weight of a can is approximately 5.2 pounds.
    c.   If you stick to this diet we guarantee you will lose 10 pounds in 7 days.
    d.   This tire will last at least 37,000 miles.
    e.   If you take lessons from the golf pro, your score will not exceed 90.

7.64   A roll of dental floss states there are 60 yards in the container. A consumer group believes it contains an average of less than 60 yards. They conduct a survey of 25 containers, which yields: 58.3, 59.5, 60.8, 54.9, 58.7, 56.6, 67.1, 58.8, 59.1, 60.1, 58.8, 58.2, 62.1, 59.9, 58.3, 61.9, 58.2, 55.6, 59.9, 60.3, 61.2, 55.3, 58.6, 59.6 and 60.0 yards.

    a.   What are the null and alternative hypotheses?
    b.   Using the .95 confidence level, is the statement on the container correct?

7.65   A floppy disk is advertised to hold at least 720k of memory. A survey of 17 disks yields: 721, 732, 714, 728, 724, 717, 700, 733, 721, 731, 722, 719, 748, 712, 731, 717, and 709. Using the .90 confidence level, is the hypothesis correct?

7.66   A college administrator believes at least 50% of students taking a statistics class have had calculus, even though it is not a prerequisite. The administrator surveys 550 students and finds that 220 have had calculus. Is the hypothesis correct at the 5% level?

7.67   Find the appropriate $t_{\alpha/1 \text{ or } 2(df)}$ values.

    a. $t_{.05/1(17)}$ b. $t_{.01/2(9)}$
    c. $t_{.10/1(25)}$ d. $t_{.05/2(5)}$

7.68   The output of a stereo is stated to be 100 watts. A survey of 22 stereos yields: $\overline{X} = 98.2$ watts, $s = 7.5$ watts. Is the statement concerning the watt output correct at the 10% level?

7.69   The current going through residential lines is stated by a Municipal Power Company to be 120 volts. A survey of 55 homes found a mean of 118 volts and a standard deviation of 8.3 volts. Is the hypothesis of 120 volts correct at the 5% significance level?

7.70   a.   For exercise 7.63 determine the critical voltages.
    b.   What is the probability of making a Type II error if $\mu_0 = 119$ or 121 watts, if $\mu_0 = 118$ or 122 watts, if $\mu_0 = 117$ or 123 watts?

7.71   The current going through residential lines is stated by a Municipal Power Company to be at least 120 volts. A survey of 55 homes finds a mean of 118 volts and a standard deviation of 8.3 volts. Is the hypothesis of 120 volts correct at the .95 confidence level?

7.72   a.   For exercise 7.65, determine the critical voltage.
    b.   What is the probability of making a Type II error if $\mu_0 = 119$, or $\mu_0 = 118$, or if $\mu_0 = 117$, or if $\mu_0 = 116$?

7.73   The leader of a political party will push for legislation only if at least 80% of the voters favor it. A poll is taken of 2000 voters and 1570 favor this legislation. Using the 5% level of significance, should the political leader push for the legislation?

7.74   a.   If we are comparing two μs from independent samples, is it necessary to have equal sample sizes?
       b.   If we are comparing two μ's from paired data, is it necessary to have equal sample sizes?

7.75   A new machine (#1) is supposed to produce parts quicker than an older machine (#2). A sample of the output is taken from each machine during different operational hours:

Machine #1: 17, 19, 15, 17, 17, 20, 19, 14, 22, 16
Machine #2: 21, 19, 16, 29, 19, 11, 17, 18
Use MINITAB to test H_0 at the 5% level.

7.76   A company has two plants which are filling containers of tomato soup. The label on all cans reads contents 305 grams. The company believes that both plants fill the containers with the same grams. A survey is conducted in both plants with the following results:

Survey #1: 307g, 304g, 301g, 307g, 301g, 316g, 310g
Survey #2: 299g, 311g, 304g, 319g, 301g, 310g, 312g, 309g, 311g
   a.   Are these paired data?
   b.   Use MINITAB to test H_0 at the 1% level

7.77   An agricultural specialist is comparing the growth ability of two strains of grass seed. The specialist wants to see how the two strains grow in different soils but with the same amounts of moisture and fertilizer. The growth measured in inches per month for each strain is:

Type of Soil	Strain #1	Strain #2
1	7.8 inches	8.3 inches
2	4.8	5.1
3	6.9	6.8
4	1.7	1.4
5	9.4	10.5
6	3.3	3.9
7	8.1	6.9
8	12.4	17.2
9	6.4	8.3
10	15.7	15.4
11	9.3	9.7
12	0.9	0.9
13	14.8	16.2

   a.   Why is it important that we use exactly the same moisture and fertilizer when comparing the growth of the two strains?
   b.   Use MINITAB to test the hypothesis ($\alpha = .05$) that the growth rates of both strains are equal.

7.78   Two computer printers are set to print the same chapters from this textbook and are monitored to determine the time to complete the process. The publishing company believes the two printers have equal speed. Using MINITAB at the 5% level, test the hypothesis.

Chapter	Printer #1	Printer #2
1	2.3 min	1.9 min
2	4.8	4.4
3	3.1	3.2
4	4.6	4.2
5	6.9	6.4
6	6.1	6.4

Chapter	Printer #1	Printer #2
7	8.1	6.9
8	4.3	3.9
9	7.3	6.7
10	10.5	9.4
11	9.3	9.1

7.79   A company is comparing two machines, one made at home (#1) and one abroad (#2). The company will buy the machine made at home if it is better or as good as the machine made abroad. However, if the machine made abroad is better in terms of output, the company will purchase it. A sample of the product output is taken from each machine during different operational hours:

Machine #1: 161, 179, 147, 167, 152, 189
Machine #2: 175, 185, 149, 151, 168, 185, 178, 181, 160
Use MINITAB to determine which machine should be purchased at the 5% level.

A Review of Hypothesis Testing

Facts Known for Survey

Quantitative Data: n, $\overline{X}$, s, N?
Qualitative Data: n, p, $q = (1 - p)$, N?

Facts known about hypothesis test to be performed

Quantitative Data: α, μ_0 (hypothesized μ), one or two-tailed test
Qualitative Data: α, p_0 (hypothesized p), one- or two-tailed test

In differentiating between a one- and two-tailed test in a stated problem, look for the definitive statement that would be necessary to make it a one-tailed test. Statements such as at least ($\geq$), at most ($\leq$), greater than or equal to ($\geq$), less than or equal to ($\leq$), greater than ($>$), less than ($>$), we guarantee, etc., are all indicators of a one-tailed test. In the absence of such statements we are usually involved in a two-tailed test. If you are making your own hypothesis test, ask yourself if these statements are necessary to state your hypothesis. If they are, we are involved in a one-tailed test. Also, if an adversary relationship is established it makes the alternative hypothesis have a $>$ or $<$ sign, making it a one-tailed test.

The Hypothesis Test: Comparing Test Statistic to Critical Value

σ Known: Compare z_{test} to $z_{\alpha/1}$ or $z_{\alpha/2}$
σ Unknown: Compare t_{test} to $t_{a/1(df)}$ or $t_{a/2(df)}$

Decision Rules for One- and Two-Tailed Tests

One-tailed test
    Left tail: if Test Statistic $< -$ critical value, REJECT H_0
    Right tail: if Test Statistic $> +$critical value, REJECT H_0
Two-tailed test: if | Test Statistic | $>$ critical value, REJECT H_0

p-Values as a Decision Rule

If $\alpha \geq p$-Value, REJECT H_0

Null Hypothesis (H_0): The main hypothesis being tested.

Alternative Hypothesis (H_A): Whatever sample information that will not fall under the null hypothesis must fall under the alternative hypothesis. Sample data will fall into one and only one of the hypotheses.

Type I Error: Rejecting a true null hypothesis.

Type II Error: Accepting a false null hypothesis.

Alpha (α): Pr(Reject H_0 | H_0 is True)*, the Pr(Type I Error)

Beta (β): Pr(Accept H_0 | H_0 is False)*, the Pr(Type II Error)

*| is the symbolic expression for the term Given

ISER and Rejection Regions: Regions in which hypotheses fall. A hypothesis can only fall into one of the regions. Either we will have insufficient statistical evidence to reject H_0 or we will reject H_0.

p-Value: The smallest value for α for which we will reject H_0.

Blocking: Blocking in an attempt to minimize the variation in a data set to aid in evaluating a treatment factor.

A Review of Important Formulas

The Statistic About μ: σ Known

$$Z_{\text{test}} = \frac{\overline{X} - \mu_0}{\frac{\sigma}{\sqrt{n}}} \tag{7.1}$$

where

z_{test} = the test statistic

$\overline{X}$ = the sample mean

μ_0 = the hypothesized population mean

σ = the population standard deviation

Note: if sampling without replacement and $n/N \geq .05$, the finite population correction must be used to discount the standard error $\sqrt{(N-n)/(N-1)}$.

Reject the Null Hypothesis (Two-Tailed Test, σ Known)

Left-Tailed Test,   Right-Tailed Test,   (7.2)
$|t_{test}| > t_{\alpha/2}$

where

$$z_{test} = \text{the test statistic}$$

$$z_{\alpha/2(df)} = \text{the critical value for a two-tailed test}$$

Reject the Null Hypothesis (One-Tailed Test, σ Known)

Lower Tailed Test, $H_0: \mu \geq \mu_0$ Upper Tailed Test, $H_0: \mu \leq \mu_0$
                          $H_A: \mu < \mu_0$ $H_A: \mu > \mu_0$
                          $z_{test} < -z_{\alpha/1}$ $z_{test} > +z_{\alpha/1}$

                                                              (7.3)

where

$\mu_0 = $ some specific value for the population parameter
$z_{test} = $ the test statistic
$z_{\alpha/1} = $ the critical value for a one-tailed test

The t Test Statistic (σ Unknown but Normally Distributed)

$$t_{test} = \frac{\overline{X} - \mu_0}{\frac{s}{\sqrt{n}}} \tag{7.4}$$

where

$t_{test} = $ the test statistic
$\overline{X} = $ the sample mean
$\mu_0 = $ the hypothesized population mean
$s = $ the sample standard deviation
$n = $ the sample size

Note: if sampling without replacement and $n/N \geq .05$, the finite population correction must be used to discount the standard error $\sqrt{(N - n)/(N - 1)}$.

Reject the Null Hypothesis (Two-Tailed Test, σ Unknown)

$$|t_{test}| > t_{\alpha/2(df)} \tag{7.5}$$

where

$t_{test} = $ the test statistic
$t_{\alpha/2(df)} = $ the critical value for a two-tailed test and specific df

Reject the Null Hypothesis (One-Tailed Test, σ Unknown)

Left Tailed Test, $H_0: \mu \geq \mu_0$ Right Tailed Test, $H_0: \mu \leq \mu_0$

                             $H_A: \mu < \mu_0$ $H_A: \mu > \mu_0$

                             $t_{test} < -t_{\alpha/1(df)}$ $t_{test} > +t_{\alpha/1(df)}$ (7.6)

where

     $\mu_0 =$ some specific value for the population parameter

     $t_{test} =$ the test statistic

     $t_{\alpha/1(df)} =$ the critical value for a one-tailed test

---

Test Statistic About p ($n \bullet p$ & $n \bullet q > 5$)

$$z_{test} = \frac{\hat{p} - p_0}{\sqrt{\dfrac{p_0 \bullet q_0}{n}}} \tag{7.7}$$

where

     $z_{test} =$ the test statistic z

     $\hat{p} =$ the sample proportion

     $p_0 =$ the hypothesized population proportion

     $q_0 = 1 - p_0$

     $n =$ the sample size

Note: if $n/N \geq .05$ the finite population correction must be used to discount the standard error $\sqrt{(N - n)/(N - 1)}$.

Hypothesis Test for Equal Population Variances: Independent Samples

$$F_{test} = \frac{\text{larger of } s_1^2 \text{ or } s_2^2}{\text{smaller of } s_1^2 \text{ or } s_2^2} \tag{7.8}$$

where

     s_1^2 & $s_2^2 =$ the respective sample variances

A Review of MINITAB Commands

The MINITAB command sequence for t_{test} is:

Stat > **Basic Statistics** > **1-Sample** t
Double click data column to enter it into **Variables** box
Click **Test Mean** to enter μ of 355
Click under **Alternatives** for H_A: **not equal** (two-tailed test)
                                             less than (left-tailed test)
                                             greater than (right-tailed test)

OK

For a z_{test} enter the numeric value of sigma.

MINITAB Commands two sample t test.

Stat > **Basic Statistics** > **2-Sample** t
Click on **Samples in different columns**
Double click **SURVEY1** to place in **First**
Double click **SURVEY2** to place in **Second**
Alternative

        not equal to for a two-tailed test
        less than for a left-tailed test
        greater than for a right-tailed test

leave at default 95% confidence level
OK

The MINITAB commands two sample t test assuming equal variances:

Stat > **Basic Statistics** > **2-Sample** t
Click on **Samples in different columns**
Double click **SURVEY1** to place in **First**
Double click **SURVEY2** to place in **Second**
Alternative

        not equal to for a two-tailed test
        less than for a left-tailed test
        greater than for a right-tailed test

Click on **Assume equal variances**
OK

MINITAB commands for a paired t test

Stat > **Basic Statistics** > **Paired** t
Click **OUTPUT1** into **First** sample box
Click **OUTPUT2** into **Second** sample box
Click **Option** to change confidence and test
OK

MINITAB commands for equal variances

Stat > **Basic Statistics** > **2 Variances**
Click on **Samples in different columns** and enter data
Options to establish confidence levels
OK

Analysis of Variance

Where we have been

In the last chapter, we used F_{test} to test hypotheses comparing variances of two normal populations from independent samples.

Where we are going

We now will utilize the F distribution to test hypotheses involving more than two populations. The null hypothesis will be that all the means emanate from the same population. Hence, there is no (or null) difference between the various population means. The alternative hypothesis is that at least two of the means differ.

We also will try to account for some external factors as we make our analyses. Hence, we may want to determine if the mean grades from three or more statistics classes are the same while we account for factors such as different instructors, different texts, the time the class is taught, etc. The process that will be used in this chapter to make such analyses is called analysis of variance (ANOVA). The analysis of variance process does require stringent assumptions. Hence, later in the text (Chapter 14), we will learn other techniques to test such hypotheses should the ANOVA requirements not be met.

8.1   Introduction

Analysis of variance techniques had their origins in agricultural research. Different land units were **treated** with different fertilizers and/or different amounts of fertilizers. A treatment involves an experiment to ascertain if differences in results can be achieved to make one alternative superior to others. In the agricultural research, the researchers wanted to know if different fertilizers and different quantities of fertilizers would yield superior growth rates for agricultural products. The desired goal was to make agricultural production more efficient and profitable.

With increased international competition, firms are always faced with having to increase efficiency. A company may want to determine if new preservatives will extend the shelf life of merchandise.

Computer companies must continually develop machines that can process information at quicker rates. Automobile firms must produce cars that are more economically efficient to operate while maintaining comfort levels. All of these examples represent experimentation with alternatives to ascertain if one choice is superior to others.

One of the techniques used to handle such analysis is called **analysis of variance**, and is often referred to by the acronym **ANOVA** (AN = analysis, O = of, VA = variance). From the acronym itself (ANOVA), it is clear we will be comparing or analyzing more than one measure of variation.

In addition to needing a minimum of two populations, the analysis of variance technique assumes the populations are normally distributed and that the standard deviations (σ) of the populations are identical. A final assumption required in an ANOVA analysis is that the sample elements chosen from each population are independent of each other.

In review, the ANOVA assumptions are
- At least two normally distributed populations
- The populations have identical standard deviations
- The elementary units selected from each population are random and independent. No dependence between the elementary units exists.

If these conditions are not met, we must use techniques that do not require such stringent assumptions. We will cover such techniques in Chapter 14.

 Concept Check 8.A

The term ANOVA implies that we are going to analyze or compare more than one variation to test a hypothesis. True or false? If false, explain.

Exercises

8.1   What does the acronym ANOVA stand for?

8.2   Explain the experimentation process involved with ANOVA and how the term **treatments** applies.

8.3   If there were only two means involved in an analysis, what would be our hypothesis testing procedure?

8.4   State the assumptions necessary to use an ANOVA.

8.2   Analysis of Variance: Completely Randomized Design

As usual with statistical methods, they can best be explained through the use of examples. Suppose we are a pharmaceutical company that has developed a new medication to combat a specific virus. The medication can't be taken orally; hence, a visit to the physician's office is required to obtain the drug. We are experimenting with taking the medication in one dose of 1.2cc, in three doses of .4cc each, or in six doses of .2cc each. These are referred to as levels of treatment. Hence we have $k = 3$ levels of treatment in the medication problem.

If there is no difference in the medication effectiveness, we will recommend that physicians administer one 1.2cc dose to reduce patient costs and time involvement. However, if the medication is superior for one of the other treatment methods, we will recommend that level. We would like to keep patient costs down, but combating the disease is the main concern.

Our experiments are conducted in a hospital environment. Earlier experiments have proven that total doses greater than 1.2cc may prove harmful to the patient. Hence, the total dosage can't exceed 1.2cc without fear of harm to the patient and long term and costly litigations. We use an unrestricted random sample process to select patients infected with the virus, for treatment. In Table 8.1 are the days it takes the medication to eliminate the virus for randomly selected patients.

Table 8.1   18 Patients Stratified into 3 Treatment Levels: Data Yield the Number of Days Until Virus Is Eliminated

# of Patients	1 dose (1/1.2cc)	3 doses (3/.4cc)	6 doses (6/.2cc)
1	11.6	18.3	8.8
2	7.3	12.4	16.8
3	13.8	7.8	16.6
4	15.4	8.1	10.2
5	9.7	10.2	7.1
6	8.2	21.2	12.5
	$\overline{X}_1 = 66.0/6 = 11$	$\overline{X}_2 = 78.0/6 = 13$	$\overline{X}_3 = 72.0/6 = 12$

In ANOVA, we will again be testing a null hypothesis. The null hypothesis for the ANOVA problems is always the same. The null hypothesis states that there is no (or null) statistical difference between the means of the different populations. There is no difference between the treatment levels.

H_0: $\mu_1 = \mu_2 = \mu_3$

H_A: At least two means differ

As always, with all hypothesis testing, the appropriate test statistic will either allow us to reject H_0, or we will have insufficient statistical evidence to reject H_0 (ISER). The appropriate test statistic in an ANOVA analysis is F_{test}.

Of course, the means from the 3 treatment levels differ on an absolute scale. Yet because of the variation in the 3 treatment levels, the mean differences may not be great enough to state that at least 2 mean differences are significantly different at a specific confidence level (they differ taking into account sampling variation).

Our test statistic (F_{test}) is a ratio of important variations that must be reviewed. First there is a variation that is explained by the different treatment levels. Remember our treatments involved the administering of a given amount of medication during three time intervals. This variation is called SSTR for the treatment sum of squares. A second variation is called SSE, named such because it is the sum of the squares, which we will be unable to say was caused by the levels of treatment involved. It is an error sum of squares that cannot be explained by the treatment; hence, is unexplained to us. Finally, there is SST, which measures a total variation about the pooled, or overall, mean.

We will ultimately compare the ratio between SSTR and SSE to determine if our treatment is significant. If our treatment was effective, we would expect the variance due to treatment to be significantly greater than the variance due to other factors.

Computing SSTR

The variation in SSTR is caused by the different levels of treatment under investigation. We have administered a constant amount of medication to three populations of patients differently and we may suspect that because of it, the death of the virus may occur at varying rates. Because of this SSTR is sometimes referred to as an explained variation, explained by the different treatment levels. SSTR involves the variation between the individual population means ($\overline{X}_T$) and the pooled data mean ($\overline{X}_p$). The formula is

Sum of the Squares Due to Treatment

$$\text{SSTR} = n_1 \left(\overline{X}_1 - \overline{X}_p^2 \right) + n_2 \left(\overline{X}_2 - \overline{X}_p \right)^2 + \bullet\bullet\bullet + n_k \left(\overline{X}_k - \overline{X}_p \right)^2 \qquad (8.1)$$

where

k = total number of treatments

n_1, n_2, n_k = the respective treatment sample sizes

$\overline{X}_1, \overline{X}_2, \overline{X}_k$ = the respective treatment sample means

$\Sigma X_1, \Sigma X_2, \Sigma X_k$ = the sum of the raw data for each treatment

$\overline{X}_p$ = the pooled data sample mean found by the formula

$$\overline{X}_p = \frac{\Sigma X_1 + \Sigma X_2 + \bullet\bullet\bullet + \Sigma X_k}{n_1 + n_2 + \bullet\bullet\bullet + n_k} \qquad (8.2)$$

For our medication problem, the pooled mean is

$$\overline{X}_p = \frac{66 + 78 + 72}{6 + 6 + 6} = 12$$

SSRT equals

$$\text{SSRT} = [6(11 - 12)^2 + 6(13 - 12)^2 + 6(12 - 12)^2] = 12$$

Computing SSE

Any statistically significant variance between populations can be explained by the treatment levels. However, variations within each population could not be explained away by the treatment levels, because each population received exactly the same treatment. The variation within populations is often termed the unexplained variation or the sum of squares due to error (SSE). The formula for SSE is

Sum of the Squares Due to Error

$$\text{SSE} = \Sigma(X_1 - \overline{X}_1)^2 + \Sigma(X_2 - \overline{X}_2)^2 + \bullet\bullet\bullet + \Sigma(X_k - \overline{X}_k)^2 \qquad (8.3)$$

where

X_1, X_2, X_k = the raw data points for the respective treatments

$\overline{X}_1, \overline{X}_2, \overline{X}_k$ = the respective treatment sample means

k = number of treatment levels

For our medication problem, SSE is obtained from computing the sum of the squares independently for each treatment, then summing to obtain SSE = 287.30 (see Table 8.2, SSE = 50.78 + 154.58 + 81.94).

Table 8.2   Computing SSE for the Medication Problem

$(11.6 - 11)^2 = 0.36$	$(18.3 - 13)^2 = 28.09$	$(8.8 - 12)^2 = 10.24$
$(7.3 - 11)^2 = 13.69$	$(12.4 - 13)^2 = 0.36$	$(16.8 - 12)^2 = 23.04$
$(13.8 - 11)^2 = 7.84$	$(7.8 - 13)^2 = 27.04$	$(16.6 - 12)^2 = 21.16$
$(15.4 - 11)^2 = 19.36$	$(8.1 - 13)^2 = 24.01$	$(10.2 - 12)^2 = 3.24$
$(9.7 - 11)^2 = 1.69$	$(10.2 - 13)^2 = 7.84$	$(7.1 - 12)^2 = 24.01$
$(8.2 - 11)^2 = 7.84$	$(21.2 - 13)^2 = 67.24$	$(12.5 - 12)^2 = 0.25$
$\Sigma(X_1 - \overline{X}_1)^2 = 50.78$	$\Sigma(X_2 - \overline{X}_2)^2 = 154.58$	$\Sigma(X_k - \overline{X}_k)^2 = 81.94$

SST is the sum of the squares of the pooled data. SST measures all of the variation in the pooled data regardless of whether it is caused by treatment levels or unknown factors. The formula for SST is

Total Sum of the Squares

$$SST = \Sigma(X_i - \overline{X}_p)^2 \tag{8.4}$$

where

X_i = each and every data point from all treatments

$\overline{X}_p$ = the pooled data sample mean

The computations necessary to solve for SST are given in Table 8.3. SST equals the sum of all squared deviations about the pooled mean (299.30).

Table 8.3   Computing SST for the Medication Problem

$(11.6 - 12)^2 = 0.16$	$(18.3 - 12)^2 = 39.69$	$(8.8 - 12)^2 = 10.24$
$(7.3 - 12)^2 = 22.09$	$(12.4 - 12)^2 = 0.16$	$(16.8 - 12)^2 = 23.04$
$(13.8 - 12)^2 = 3.24$	$(7.8 - 12)^2 = 17.64$	$(16.6 - 12)^2 = 20.16$
$(15.4 - 12)^2 = 11.56$	$(8.1 - 12)^2 = 15.21$	$(10.2 - 12)^2 = 3.24$
$(9.7 - 12)^2 = 5.29$	$(10.2 - 12)^2 = 3.24$	$(7.1 - 12)^2 = 24.01$
$(8.2 - 12)^2 = 14.44$	$(21.2 - 12)^2 = 84.64$	$(12.5 - 12)^2 = 0.25$

It should be evident that
$$SST = SSTR + SSE$$

This relationship holds because either the variation is being caused by the treatment levels (in which case it will be picked up by SSTR) or it is caused by unknown factors (in which case it will be picked up in SSE). Either a factor is accounted for or it is not. Hence, if we have any two of the sum of the squares, it is simple to obtain the third. Note that the formula SST = SSTR + SSE assumes that the impact on the treatment variable (often called a dependent variable) is additive. Each observation equals the mean of the population + the effect of the treatment + a random or chance impact.

Computing Mean Squares

To make the sum of the squares comparable, we normalize the values by dividing the appropriate degrees of freedom to obtain mean squares. The mean squares for treatments (MSTR), for error (MSE), and for total (MST) are as follows.

Mean Squares (Variances) for ANOVA Model: Completely Randomized Design

$$\text{MSTR} = \frac{\text{SSTR}}{k-1} \quad \text{MSE} = \frac{\text{SSE}}{n_p - k} \quad \text{MST} = \frac{\text{SST}}{n_p - 1} \qquad (8.5)$$

where

$\text{SSTR} = $ sum of the squares treatment

$\text{SSE} = $ sum of the squares error

$\text{SST} = $ total sum of the squares

$n_p = $ pooled sample size

$k = $ number of treatments

The mean squares for the medication problem are

$$\text{MSTR} = \frac{12}{2} = 6 \quad \text{MSE} = \frac{287.3}{15} = 19.153 \quad \text{MST} = \frac{299.3}{17} = 17.606$$

It should be noted that, when using ANOVA, we believe the populations have a common variance (σ^2). To estimate σ^2 we use an estimate that does not require equal means. This involves the variation within each sample, which is MSE. Hence, the pooled variance s_p^2 of formula 8.3B is MSE.

The F_{test} Statistic

To test the null hypothesis that there is no (or null) difference between the sample means of the populations, we use the F_{test} statistic. This test statistic is the ratio of MSTR to MSE.

The ANOVA Test Statistic

$$F_{\text{test}} = \frac{\text{MSTR}}{\text{MSE}} \qquad (8.6)$$

where

$\text{MSTR} = $ mean square treatment

$\text{MSE} = $ mean square error

For convenience, we have established the test statistic as an upper tailed test. The null hypothesis is that the treatment means are statistically identical, meaning that $\text{MSTR} \leq \text{MSE}$ or that MSTR is not significantly greater than MSE. If we have ISER, we are stating that the treatments had no more impact on the variances of the populations than did the cumulative impact of the other factors. Hence, the treatment is ineffective. However, if we reject the null hypothesis at a given confidence level, then we believe that the treatment may have a significant impact.

The test statistic for the medication problem is

$$F_{\text{test}} = \frac{6}{19.153} = 0.313$$

The *F* distribution has distinct characteristics which are:
- The curve of the *F* distribution is positively skewed, continuous, and the values go from 0 to infinity (no negative values)
- Like the *t* distribution, there is a different *F* distribution for each number of degrees of freedom involved. Since F_{test} is a ratio, there is a degree of freedom in the numerator and in the denominator. Hence, there is a different *F* distribution based on the paired degrees of freedom.

In our medication experiment, F_{test} is a ratio of MSTR to MSE. The degrees of freedom used to obtain the numerator MSTR is $k - 1$, where k equals the number of treatment levels. Since there are 3 treatment levels, the degrees of freedom in the numerator is $3 - 1 = 2$. The denominator of the test statistic is MSE. In order to obtain the denominator MSE, it was necessary to divide SSE by $n_p - k$. The degrees of freedom in the denominator is $18 - 3 = 15$.

Hence, in comparing the test and critical value of *F*, we must look up 2 degrees of freedom in the numerator and 15 in the denominator, at a specified significance level (say 10%). This will be symbolically designated as $F_{.10(2, 15)}$. This is read as the critical value for *F*, at the 10% level of significance ($\alpha = .10$), with 2 degrees of freedom in the numerator and 15 in the denominator. In Table 8.4 we see an abbreviated version of the *F* distribution at the 10% significance level. We read over to df numerator to 2, and df denominator to 15, and $F_{.10(2, 15)} = 2.70$.

Table 8.4 Abbreviated *F* Distribution Table ($\alpha = .10$)

		$d(f)$ NUMERATOR				
d		*1*	*2*	*3*	*4*	*5*
(f)	13	3.14	2.76	2.56	2.43	2.35
	14	3.10	2.73	2.52	2.39	2.31
D	15	3.07	**2.70**	2.49	2.36	2.27
E	16	3.05	2.67	2.46	2.33	2.24
N	17	3.03	2.64	2.44	2.31	2.22
O						
M						
I						
N						
A						
T						
O						
R						

The rejection rule for F_{test} is

Rejection of the Null Hypothesis

$$F_{test} > F_{\alpha, (d(f)num, d(f)den)} \qquad (8.7)$$

where

α = the significance level

$d(f)num$ = degrees of freedom in the numerator

$d(f)den$ = degrees of freedom in the denominator

Since F_{test} (0.313) in our medication problem is less than $F_{.10/2,\,15}$ (2.70), we are unable to reject the null hypothesis. There is no significant difference in medication effectiveness if we administer 1.2cc in one dose, in three doses, or in six doses. If this were true, we might tell the physicians using our medication to administer it in one dose. However, before we are willing to make such a definitive statement, we must learn more advanced procedures.

Normally, an ANOVA table is used for easily viewing the important information. The format of the ANOVA table follows that of Table 8.5.

Table 8.5   General Format for an ANOVA Table: Completely Randomized Design

Source	$d(f)$	SS	MS	F_{test}
Treatment	$k - l$	SSTR	MSTR = SSTR/$(k - 1)$	MSTR/MSE
Error	$n_p - k$	SSE	MSE = SSE/$(n_p - k)$	
Total	$n_p - 1$	SST	MST = SST/$(n_p - 1)$	

For the medication problem it would be

Table 8.6   An ANOVA Table for the Medication Problem

Source	$d(f)$	SS	MS	F_{test}
Treatment	2	12	6	0.313
Error	15	287.3	19.153	
Total	17	299.3	17.606	

MINITAB Application

The hand computation process in utilizing ANOVA is quite burdensome and is easiest to perform on a computer. MINITAB performs an ANOVA for us. In order to use MINITAB, the data must be input in a slightly different manner than how they were originally listed. The data must be input where the treatment factor is a separate variable to be placed alongside all of the recorded output. Table 8.7A reveals the input process. The MINITAB output follows the general format of an ANOVA table.

Table 8.7A   Editing Data Base for MINITAB Run
*Data File on MINITAB CD

vn1 (Dependent or Data Variable)	vn2 (Treatment Variable)
11.6	1
7.3	1
13.8	1
15.4	1
9.7	1
8.2	1
18.3	2
12.4	2
7.8	2
8.1	2
10.2	2
21.2	2
8.8	3
16.8	3
16.6	3
10.2	3
7.1	3
12.5	3

Stat > ANOVA > Oneway
Double click **Data** to enter to **Response** box.
Double click **Treatment** to enter to **Factor** box.
OK

Table 8.7B   MINITAB ANOVA Output: Completely Randomized Design

One-way ANOVA: Data versus treatment

ANALYSIS OF VARIANCE FOR DATA

Source	DF	SS	MS	F	P
Treatment	2	12.0	6.0	0.31	0.736
Error	15	287.3	19.2		
Total	17	299.3			

S = 4.376   R-Sq = 4.01%   R-Sq(adj) = 0.00%

INDIVIDUAL 95% CIS FOR MEAN
BASED ON POOLED STDEV

Level	N	Mean	StDev	
1	6	11.000	3.187	(——————*——————)
2	6	13.000	5.560	(——————*——————)
3	6	12.000	4.048	(——————*——————)

Pooled StDev = 4.376   7.5   10.0   12.5   15.0

In addition to MINITAB tabulating F_{test} for us, it also looks up the critical value of F. The decision rule is if $\alpha \geq P$, we will reject the null hypothesis. Since our alpha is .10 and $P = .736$, we have ISER and consequently there is no statistical difference between the treatment levels or population means.

Confidence Levels: Multiple Comparisons

We have insufficient statistical evidence to reject the null hypothesis. Hence, all the means are statistically identical. Had we rejected the null hypothesis, we would have had to select the mean which was different from the rest. We could simply select the optimal mean (the smallest in our example because we are measuring the time a medication takes to kill a deadly virus), but such an evaluation is subject to sampling error interpretations. We must learn to compute confidence intervals and ascertain where the differences actually lie had H_0 been rejected.

Confidence intervals involving multiple populations are extremely complicated since we must evaluate a number of combinations involving two populations at a time. Ultimately, we have a combination problem of taking two out of as many populations that are involved. The number of combinations is $c = k(k-1)/2$, where $k = $ the number of treatment levels. So the number of combinations in our medication problem is 3 ($c = 3 \bullet 2/2$).

In our particular example, we have no need to compute confidence intervals because the F test failed to reject H_0 (all the means are equal). We will proceed with computing the confidence interval anyway, just to establish procedural steps. Should the following t test reject H_0, while the F test has ISER H_0, the F test takes precedence.

The probability of any single interval containing the true population difference is $1 - \alpha$, but the probability that all confidence intervals contain the true population difference is considerably less than $1 - \alpha$.

To deal with multiple comparisons, we need to use a multiple comparison procedure. Multiple comparison procedures allow us first to compute all confidence intervals and view which are significant in a post-hoc fashion. Such a procedure was developed by J. W. Tukey in the early 1950's. Tukey's multiple comparison confidence intervals can also be obtained using MINITAB. The sequence and output are as follows:

Stat > ANOVA > Oneway
Check to see that **Data** is in the **Response** box and **Treat** in the **Factor** box.
Be sure **Store Fits** and **Store residuals** options are not selected.
Click **Tukey's, family error rate.**
OK twice.

Table 8.8   MINITAB's Multiple Comparison Confidence Intervals: Post-Hoc Analysis Using
            MINITAB

Intervals for (column level mean)—(row level mean)

	1	2
2	−8.557	
	4.557	
3	−7.557	−5.557
	5.557	7.557

Since all of the intervals include 0, none of the means are statistically significantly different at the specified confidence level.

 Concept Check 8.B

In an ANOVA completely randomized design: SSE = SSTR − SST. True or false? If false, explain.

Exercises

8.5   Why does SST = SSTR + SSE?

8.6   Define

    a.   SST
    b.   SSTR

8.7   To make the sum of the squares comparable between SSTR and SSE, we _____.

8.8   In ANOVA, what is H_0 and H_A?

8.9   What are the characteristics of the F distribution?

8.10   Can F_{test} or $F_{\alpha(d(f))}$ be negative or zero?

8.11   Find the appropriate critical values of F.

    a. $F_{.05(2/8)}$ b. $F_{.05(4/20)}$ c. $F_{.05(6/24)}$ d. $F_{.05(2/22)}$
    e. $F_{.01(2/8)}$ f. $F_{.01(4/20)}$ g. $F_{.10(2/10)}$ h. $F_{.10(2/22)}$

8.12   In comparing F_{test} and $F_{\alpha(d(f)num/d(f)den)}$,

    a.   under what conditions will we have ISER H_0?
    b.   under what conditions will we reject H_0?

8.13   A company is experimenting with 4 new strains of pine trees which will grow at accelerated rates. Based on preliminary research the company wants to know which strain to develop. Strain A is the cheapest; hence, if there is no differences in the 4 growth patterns, this is the one with which it will go. However, if one of the strains does yield superior growth, this is the one with which it will go. The growth in inches per year for a randomly selected tree from each strain:

	Strain A	Stain B	Strain C	Strain D
Case 1	2.3	3.3	2.6	3.1
Case 2	2.7	3.4	2.3	3.3
Case 3	2.1	3.3	2.8	3.4
Case 4	2.7	3.6	2.7	3.6
Case 5	2.6	3.5	2.4	3.1
Case 6	2.5	3.3	2.9	3.5
Case 7	2.4	3.6	2.4	3.5

a. State the null and alternative hypotheses.
b. How many treatments, and how many levels of the treatments are involved?
c. At the 5% level, test the null hypothesis using this completely randomized design.
d. If H_0 is rejected, compute Tukey's multiple comparison confidence intervals ($\alpha = .05$) and ascertain which differences are significant.
e. Can you state what other factors need be accounted for before a determination of strain superiority can be made?

8.14   A scientist has developed five alternative assembly line methods for producing a product. She randomly selects workers to try each method and records the number of defective parts per hour for six hours. The results are

Method A	Method B	Method C	Method D	Method E
18	10	16	13	11
16	12	8	20	17
12	15	13	13	16
11	11	15	10	14
14	17	15	9	15
13	15	14	16	12
	14	17	17	
		12		
		18		

a. Statistic the null and alternative hypotheses.
b. At the 1% level are the mean errors per hour the same for all 5 assembly line methods (completely randomized design)?

8.15   A hardware store carries three different brands of equally priced hammers. The manager records the number of each unit sold over the last two weeks, as follows:

Brand A: 12, 8, 7, 16, 5, 9, 3, 1, 9, 0
Brand B: 6, 7, 2, 9, 10, 4, 1, 3, 1, 7
Brand C: 15, 8, 9, 5, 21, 16, 11, 13, 10, 17
a. State the null and alternative hypotheses.
b. At the 5% level are the same number of the three brands of hammers sold in the store using the completely randomized design?

8.16   A company that makes fishing lures wants to test three new varieties. It randomly selects three individuals to fish with a different lure. The results in terms of the number of fish caught per day days are:

Lure #1:   6, 9, 3, 4, 7, 5, 1, 6, 12, 10, 16
Lure #2:   3, 4, 1, 0, 2, 4, 7, 1
Lure #3:   0, 3, 2, 4, 5, 2, 1, 4, 6
a. State the null hypothesis.
b. Test the null hypothesis at the 5% level using the completely randomized design.
c. Can you state what other factors need to be accounted for before a determination of lure superiority can be made?

8.17 Consumer researchers are interested in 3 different displays for a grocery store product. They use one display, then count the number of customers between purchases, for a number of sales. They then change to a second display and repeat the process. They then change to the third display and again repeat the process. The results are:

Display A: 41, 62, 98, 12, 26, 61, 57, 16, 19
Display B: 9, 108, 36, 56, 43, 77, 98
Display C: 77, 12, 45, 67, 31, 29, 84, 66, 14, 29, 71, 69

  a.   State the null hypothesis.
  b.   Is the null hypothesis rejected at the 1% level using the completely randomized design?

8.18 If we reject the null hypothesis, why do we develop elaborate confidence intervals to tell which means differ?

8.19 A surfboard shop sells three surfboards priced from expensive to inexpensive. The number of boards sold each day for the last week is:

	M	T	W	TH	F	S	SU
Expensive:	5	8	9	15	9	2	2
Less expensive:	2	0	1	3	2	4	1
Inexpensive:	9	12	7	17	8	3	2

  a.   State the null hypothesis.
  b.   Will you have ISER or reject the null hypothesis at the 5% level using the completely randomized design?
  c.   If the null hypothesis is rejected, use a dual comparison confidence intervals to determine if the expensive and less expensive boards differ ($\alpha = .05$). Even though we are only supposed to deal with two pre-established means, compare all mean differences.
  d.   If the null hypothesis is rejected, use Tukey's confidence intervals to determine statistical significant differences between all means ($\alpha = .05$).

8.20 Suppose over the last seven weeks two sports fans and two sports experts have been selecting the winning teams in the National Football League. The number of winning selections for the last seven weeks is:

Fan A: 11, 6, 4, 9, 10, 7, 9
Fan B: 13, 9, 7, 5, 8, 6, 10
Expert A: 12, 8, 6, 9, 11, 6, 10
Expert B: 13, 7, 9, 7, 11, 10, 7

  a.   State the null hypothesis.
  b.   Will you have ISER or reject the null hypothesis at the 10% level using the completely randomized design?

8.3   Analysis of Variance: Randomized Block Design

Our experiments were conducted in a hospital environment. Earlier experiments have proven that total doses greater than 1.2cc may prove harmful to the patient. Hence, the total dosage can not exceed 1.2cc without fear of long term litigations. Our earlier studies have also shown that the patient's age might be a factor in treating the virus. Hence, we will find patients in similar age categories to use age as a blocking variable. Note that we now require equal sample sizes in each treatment, a condition not necessary in the completely randomized design.

Blocking variables involve an attempt to reduce or eliminate at least one factor that might influence our results. Our blocking variable will be age. We will not test for the significance of age, but rather simply want to reduce its influence over the treatment variable (dosage). We have given the medication to the randomly selected patients who have contracted the virus and have recorded the time it takes for the virus no longer to appear in tissue analysis (see Table 8.8).

Table 8.8   Number of Days Until Virus Is Eliminated*

10–< 20	7.3	7.8	7.1	$\overline{X}_{b1} = 7.400$
20–< 30	8.2	8.1	8.8	$\overline{X}_{b2} = 8.367$
30–< 40	9.7	10.2	10.2	$\overline{X}_{b3} = 10.033$
40–< 50	11.6	12.4	12.5	$\overline{X}_{b4} = 12.167$
50–< 60	13.8	18.3	16.6	$\overline{X}_{b5} = 16.233$
≥ 60	15.4	21.2	16.8	$\overline{X}_{b6} = 17.800$
	$\overline{X}_1 = 11.0$	$\overline{X}_2 = 13.0$	$\overline{X}_3 = 12.0$	

*This is the same data as Table 8.1, just rearranged by age

The blocking variable can be qualitative or quantitative. If quantitative, it is analyzed in blocks or groups and not as a continuous variable. In this example, the ages were grouped in decades. The sample means are tabulated for each population and are used in the ANOVA process.

In our analysis involving blocking variable, we are assuming that there is no interaction between the treatment and blocking variable. In the next section, we will deal with the possibility of such an interaction.

Since the data set of Table 8.8 is identical to that of Table 8.1, the values for SSTR (12) and SST (299.3) will remain the same. There will, however, be a new sum of the squares relating to the blocking variable (age). In a sense, there will be a new explained variation, explained by age, though, and not by medication dosage. The new sum of the squares is SSB, or the sum of the squares due to blocks. The formula for SSB is

Sum of the Squares Due to Blocks

$$SSB = n_{B1}(\overline{X}_{B1} - \overline{X}_p)^2 + n_{B2}(\overline{X}_{B2} - \overline{X}_p)^2 + \bullet\bullet\bullet + n_{Bk}(\overline{X}_{Bk} - \overline{X}_p)^2 \quad (8.8)$$

where

$b = $ total number of blocks

$n_{B1}, n_{B2}, n_{Bk} = $ the respective block sample sizes

$\overline{X}_{B1}, \overline{X}_{B2}, \overline{X}_{Bk} = $ the respective block sample means

SSB for the medication problem is

$$SSB = 3(7.4 - 12)^2 + 3(8.367 - 12)^2 + 3(10.033 - 12)^2 +$$
$$3(16.233 - 12)^2 + 3(17.8 - 12)^2 = 269.453$$

SSE is now computed as a residual value. Since

$$SST = SSTR + SSB + SSE$$

then

$$SSE = SST - SSTR - SSB$$

or numerically for the medication problem

$$SSE = 299.3 - 12 - 269.453 = 17.846$$

The formulas for MSB and MSE are

MSB and MSE ANOVA Model: Randomized Block Design

$$MSB = \frac{SSB}{b-1} \quad MSE = \frac{SSE}{n_p - k - b + 1} \tag{8.9}$$

where

SSB = sum of squares due to blocks

SSE = sum of squares due to error

b = number of blocks

k = number of treatment levels

n_p = the pooled data sample size

MSTR and MST formulas remain unchanged from completely randomized design

MSB and MSE for the medication problem are

$$MSB = \frac{269.4533}{6-1} = 53.891 \quad MSE = \frac{17.8467}{18 - 3 - 6 + 1} = 1.785$$

The general format for the ANOVA table is given in Table 8.9.

Table 8.9   General Format for an ANOVA Table: Randomized Block Design

Source	df	SS	MS	F_{test}
Treatment levels	$k-1$	SSTR	MSTR = SSTR/$(k-1)$	MSTR/MSE
Blocks	$b-1$	SSB	MSG = SSB/$(b-1)$	
Error	$n_p - k - b + 1$	SSE	MSE = SSE/$(n_p - k - b + 1)$	
Total	$n_p - 1$			

For the medication problem the specific ANOVA table is given in Table 8.10.

Table 8.10   An ANOVA Table for the Medication Problem: Block Design

Source	df	SS	MS	F_{test}
Treatments	2	12	6	3.362
Blocks	5	269.4533	53.8907	30.20
Error	10	17.8467	1.7847	
Total	17	299.3	17.606	

Comparing F_{test} (3.3672) to $F_{.10(2, 10)}$ (2.92) now reveals that H_0 must be rejected ($F_{\text{test}} > F_{(\alpha(df num, df den))}$). There is a difference in results when the dosage of 1.2cc is given in one, three, or six injections. We can now see the problem with the completely randomized design. SSE is so large that it will be difficult to reject the null hypothesis. Blocking allowed us to provide for one factor (age) and, because of it, we went from having ISER the null hypothesis to rejecting it.

MINITAB Application

Again, the hand computational burden is unnecessary. We will allow MINITAB to make all the data manipulations for us. The appropriate MINITAB data entry and output are shown in Table 8.11.

Table 8.11A MINITAB Data Entry for Randomized Block Design: Medication Problem
***Data File on MINITAB CD**

	Data	Treatment	Age
Case 1	7.3	1	1
Case 2	7.8	2	1
Case 3	7.1	3	1
Case 4	8.2	1	2
Case 5	8.1	2	2
Case 6	8.8	3	2
Case 7	9.7	1	3
Case 8	10.2	2	3
Case 9	10.2	3	3
Case 10	11.6	1	4
Case 11	12.4	2	4
Case 12	12.5	3	4
Case 13	13.8	1	5
Case 14	18.3	2	5
Case 15	16.6	3	5
Case 16	15.4	1	6
Case 17	21.2	2	6
Case 18	16.8	3	6

Analysis of Variance: Randomized Block Design (Table 8.10)

MINITAB Commands for ANOVA Output: Randomized Block Design

Stat > ANOVA > Twoway
Double click **Data** into **Response** box.
Double click **block variable** (age) into **Row Factor** box.
Double click **treatment variable** into **Column Factor** box.
Click on **Display Means** from both the **Row** and **Column Factor** boxes.
OK

Table 8.11B Two-way Analysis of Variance

TWO-WAY ANOVA: DATA VERSUS AGE, TREATMENT

Source	DF	SS	MS	F	P
Age	5	269.453	53.8907	30.20	0.000
Treatment	2	12.000	6.0000	3.36	0.076
Error	10	17.847	1.7847		
Total	17	299.300			

S = 1.336   R-Sq = 94.04%   R-Sq(adj) = 89.86%

203

INDIVIDUAL 95% CIs FOR MEAN
BASED ON POOLED STDEV

Age	Mean
1	7.4000
2	8.3667
3	10.0333
4	12.1667
5	16.2333
6	17.8000

```
                    ——–+———–+———–+———-+———
                  (———*———)
                  (———*———)
                    (———*———)
                      (———*———)
                                      (———*———)
                                        (———*———)
                    ——–+———–+———–+———-+———
                    7.0       10.5      14.0      17.5
```

INDIVIDUAL 95% CIs FOR MEAN
BASED ON POOLED STDEV

Treatment	Mean
1	11
2	13
3	12

```
                    ——–+———–+———–+———-+———
                  (———*———)
                              (———*———)
                      (———*———)
                    ——–+———–+———–+———-+———
                    10.8      12.0      13.2      14.4
```

Concept Check 8.C

The purpose of a blocking variable is to allow for a second treatment variable to aid in explaining the relationships involved. True or false? If false, explain.

Exercises

8.21 Differentiate between the randomized block and completely randomized designs.

8.22 Define a blocking variable.

8.23 Why was it that our medication problem had a much smaller SSE and MSE for the randomized block design as compared to the completely randomized design?

8.24 Does the randomized block design require equal sample sizes for the population?

8.25 A company is experimenting with 4 new strains of pine trees which will grow at accelerated rates. Based on preliminary research the company wants to know which strain to develop. Strain A is the cheapest; hence, if there is no differences in the 4 growth patterns, this is the one with which it will go. However, if one of the strains does yield superior growth, this is the one that will be selected. The growth in inches per year for a randomly selected tree from each strain are shown below. The company wants to block combined levels of moisture and fertilizer. The moisture and fertilizer combinations increase with the block levels.

Blocks	Strain A	Strain B	Strain C	Strain D
Level 1	1.9	3.0	2.2	3.1
Level 2	2.1	2.9	2.3	3.3
Level 3	2.7	3.3	2.8	3.4
Level 4	2.4	3.6	2.7	3.6

Blocks	Strain A	Strain B	Strain C	Strain D
Level 5	2.8	3.5	3.4	3.9
Level 6	2.7	3.7	3.3	3.5
Level 7	3.4	3.9	3.5	4.1

a. State the null and alternative hypotheses.
b. At the 5% level, test the null hypothesis is based on the randomized block design.

8.26 Two new cardboard boxes are designed to hold weight while wet. An experiment is made using the old design and the two new designs. The blocking factor is four levels of wetness. The packages are picked up and the weight necessary to break the box is recorded. The results are:

Wetness Levels	Old Box	New Box #1	New Box #2
Level 1	41 lbs	37 lbs	40 lbs
Level 2	36	32	33
Level 3	29	34	29
Level 4	17	31	27

a. State the null and alternative hypotheses.
b. At the 1% level, test the null hypothesis is based on the randomized block design.

8.27 Why is it necessary formally to test which means are different (after we have rejected H_0) when a visual glance can tell you which is different?

8.28 You have a major league baseball team. You want to know if your team obtains the same number of hits during a day ball game, a night ball game, or at an enclosed stadium. You randomly select days when your club played against four specific pitchers, under the three conditions, and find:

Pitcher	Day Game	Night Game	Indoor Game
#1	6	12	7
#2	8	9	5
#3	5	8	5
#4	8	10	4

a. Why is it important to pick days when your club was facing the same pitcher under the 3 treatment levels?
b. Test the null hypothesis at the 5% level using the randomized block design.

8.29 Consumer researchers are interested in 3 different displays for a grocery store product. They randomly select 5 stores for each demographic and psychographic mix in the region and record the sales of consumers going by the isle. An observer waits for a customer to pick up the product, then counts the number of customers who walk by until the next customer buys a box. The results are:

	Display A	Display B	Display C
Store type 1:	46	26	68
Store type 2:	75	34	49
Store type 3:	51	49	77
Store type 4:	89	31	99
Store type 5:	74	43	52

a. State the null hypothesis.
b. Why is it important to block the variable demographic and psychographic mix?
c. Is the null hypothesis rejected at the 10% significance level using the randomized block design?
d. Use Tukey's multiple confidence interval technique to determine which sample means are significantly different ($\alpha = .05$).

8.30   A surfboard shot sells three surfboards priced from expensive to inexpensive. The number of boards sold each day for the last week is:

	M	T	W	TH	F	S	SU
Expensive:	5	8	9	15	9	2	2
Less expensive:	2	0	1	3	2	4	1
Inexpensive:	9	12	7	17	8	3	2

a.   State the null hypothesis.
b.   Will you have ISER or reject the null hypothesis at the 5% level using the randomized block design?
c.   Use Tukey's multiple confidence interval technique to determine which sample means are significantly different ($\alpha = .05$).

8.4   Factorial Experiments

In some experiments we may wish to analyze two treatment variables (called factors) rather than one. It may have seemed that we did have two treatment variables when we used the randomized block design. However, this was not the case. We merely attempted to block age (involving 6 levels) impact on the treatment variable, medication dosage (involving 3 levels). Age is not a treatment variable, but it may influence the results of a treatment variable. Hence, we wanted to block its impact. If we wanted to design an experiment that included more than one treatment variable, we would want to analyze every possible combination of factor levels. It would then be called a factorial experiment.

Suppose we wanted to analyze our medication dosage and the taking of aspirin daily as treatment variables. The consumption of aspirin will be in two levels. Either the patient consumes an aspirin a day or consumes no aspirin. Now, not only do we have to deal with the independent impact of the two treatment variables, but also the possible combined or joint impact (called interaction) of both treatments needs to be analyzed.

If a statistically significant interaction is involved, then interpretation of the individual factors is clouded. If interaction is absent, then the interpretation of the independent variable is clearer. The treatment variables have an independent impact on the virus.

A significant interaction would suggest a relationship between our medication dosage and the consumption of aspirin. The mean of each medication dose and aspirin cell would show a trend if graphed. In our problem of 3 medication doses and 2 aspirin levels, we have a constant 3 data points within each cell. Hence, we have 6 cell means, all of size 3. If the trend lines has a zero slope, then no such trend exists. The MINITAB graph of the trend lines is given in Figure 8.1. There does not appear to be a clear indication of trend, but a limited sample size can cloud the picture. Therefore, to be sure, we will determine if a cross relationship exists between medication dosage and aspirin consumption using hypothesis testing techniques.

Figure 8.1 Ascertaining If Trend Exists

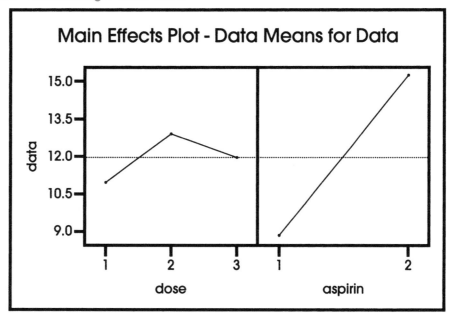

Remember that two medications can act together either negatively or positively. In a negative sense, dual medications can create a toxicity level that would not exist if the medications were taken independently. In a positive sense, two medications can act as a catalyst to increase the rate of effectiveness of both or one of the medications.

Factorial experiments can involve either the completely randomized or randomized block designs. We will analyze the former with our medication example. We have 3 treatment levels for **Factor A** (our medication dosage) and 2 treatment levels for **Factor B** (aspirin consumed or not). This is termed a 3 × 2 factorial design involving 6 combinations of the two treatments. Since there has been no attempt to pair the data, we are involved with a completely randomized design. We have recorded the data from 18 patients in Table 8.12.

Table 8.12   **Number of Days Until Virus Is Eliminated**

Aspirin a Day	1 dose	3 doses	6 doses	
Yes	7.3	7.8	7.1	
Yes	8.2	8.1	8.8	
Yes	9.7	10.2	10.2	$\overline{X}_{B2} = 8.6$
No	11.6	12.4	12.5	
No	13.8	18.3	16.6	
No	15.4	21.2	16.8	$\overline{X}_{B2} = 15.4$
	$\overline{X}_{A1} = 11.0$	$\overline{X}_{A2} = 13.0$	$\overline{X}_{A3} = 12.0$	

The basic sum of the squares formula is

$$\mathbf{SST = SSTR(A) + SSTR(B) + SSTR(AB) + SSE}$$

where SST(AB) represents the interaction between treatments A and B.

207

The general format for the ANOVA design is given in Table 8.13.

Table 8.13   General Format for a Factorial Design: Two Treatments; Factorial Design

Source	df	SS	MS	F_{test}
Treat: A	$T(A)^* - 1$	SSA	$MSA = SSA/(T(A) - 1)$	MSA/MSE
Treat: B	$T(B)^* - 1$	SSB	$MSB = SSB/(T(B) - 1)$	MSB/MSE
Treat: AB	$(T(A) - 1)(T(B) - 1)$	SSAB	$MSAB = SSAB/(T(A) - 1)(T(B) - 1)$	MSAB/MSE
ERROR	$n_p - T(A) \bullet T(B)$	SSE	$MSE = SSE(n_p - T(A) \bullet T(B))$	
Total	$n_p - 1$	SST		

$^*T(A)$ = levels of treatment A, $T(B)$ = levels of treatment B.

We will not attempt any hand computations since we have MINITAB to do them for us. The data entry process closely follows that of the randomized block design. Note the only change would be that vn3 would only have 2 levels instead of 6. The appropriate MINITAB data entry, commands, and output is:

Table 8.14A MINITAB Data Entry of Table 8.12
*Data File on MINITAB CD

Data	Dose	Aspirin
7.3	1	1
8.2	1	1
9.7	1	1
7.8	2	1
8.1	2	1
10.2	2	1
7.1	3	1
8.8	3	1
10.2	3	1
11.6	1	2
13.8	1	2
15.4	1	2
12.4	2	2
18.3	2	2
21.2	2	2
12.5	3	2
16.6	3	2
16.8	3	2

MINITAB Commands for ANOVA table:

Stat > ANOVA > Balanced ANOVA
Click **Data** into **Responses** box
Click to **Model** box, then click **Dose Aspirin**, into **Model** box. Then click **Dose** and **Aspirin** into **Response** box again, then manually place a * symbol between the **Dose** and **Aspirin**.
Click to **Results**, in **Display means corresponding to the terms**:
    enter **Dose, Aspirin, Dose * Aspirin**.
OK twice

208

Table 8.14B MINITAB ANOVA Output

ANOVA: Data versus Dose, Aspirin

Factor	Type	Levels	Values
Dose	fixed	3	1, 2, 3
Aspirin	fixed	2	1, 2

ANALYSIS OF VARIANCE FOR DATA

Source	DF	SS	MS	F	P
Dose	2	12.000	6.000	1.02	0.389
Aspirin	1	208.080	208.080	35.44	0.000
Dose*Aspirin	2	8.760	4.380	0.75	0.495
Error	12	70.460	5.872		
Total	17	299.300			

$S = 2.42315$ R-Sq = 76.46%   R-Sq(adj) = 66.65%

MEANS

Dose	N	Data
1	6	11.000
2	6	13.000
3	6	12.000

Aspirin	N	Data
1	9	8.600
2	9	15.400

Dose	Aspirin	N	Data
1	1	3	8.400
1	2	3	13.600
2	1	3	8.700
2	2	3	17.300
3	1	3	8.700
3	2	3	15.300

We will first analyze the interaction of the two treatments. Since our significance level ($\alpha = .05$) is less than P, we have ISER the hypothesis that the true interaction between treatments A and B is 0. If we had rejected the null hypothesis (meaning treatment AB is significant), we would not have been able to analyze and isolate the individual effects of treatments A and B.

From Table 8.14B we can see that the Aspirin treatment is significant; however, our dose is not.

 Concept Check 8.D

If the interaction between two factors is statistically significant, it will be difficult to ascertain the independent impact of the factors. True or false? If false, explain.

Exercises

8.31   How is the two-factor ANOVA process different from that of the randomized block design one-factor analysis?

8.32   Define the term "factorial experiment."

8.33   When the interaction factor is not significant, what do we normally do with the sum of the squares of the interaction [SS(AB)]?

8.34   What function is served by graphing the respective cell means?

8.35   If interaction exists between the factors, what complications arise in terms of stating hypotheses?

8.36   Factor A has 5 levels and factor B has 3 levels. Within each cell is an equal sample size of 4. How many degrees of freedom are involved with the

a.   mean square for factor A?
b.   mean square for factor B?
c.   mean square for factor AB?
d.   mean square for error?

8.37   An experiment involving two factors, each with two levels, yields the following table:

Factor A	Factor B: Level 1	Factor B: Level 2
Level 1:	88	78
	76	78
	71	82
	92	94
Level 2:	67	69
	62	58
	48	57
	64	61

a.   Perform an ANOVA analysis and determining if H_0 is significant at the 5% level.
b.   Is there interaction between the two factors?
c.   Plot the cell means. Does the graph support the ANOVA conclusion on interaction?

8.38   The following is an ANOVA table from a computer output.

Source	Sum-of-Squares	DF	Mean-Source	F-Ratio
vn2	100.000	2	———	1.500
vn3	300.080	—	———	9.000
vn2 * vn3	200.000	2	———	3.000
ERROR	400.000	12	33.333	
Total	1000.000	17		

a.   How many treatments or factors are involved?
b.   Fill in the blanks.

8.39   Consumer researchers are interested in 3 different displays for a grocery store product. They randomly select 2 stores to represent each demographic mix in the region and record the sales of consumers going by the aisle. An observer waits for a customer to pick up a product, then counts the number of customers who walk by until the next customer buys a box. The results are:

	Display A	Display B	Display C
Store type 1:	46	26	68
	75	34	49
	51	49	77
	89	31	99
	74	43	52
Store type 2:	71	62	65
	102	67	115
	111	73	94
	68	64	71
	101	68	89

a. State the null hypothesis.

b. Is the null hypothesis rejected at the 1% level using the two-factor ANOVA procedure?

c. Even if the interaction between the two treatments is not significant, compute Tukey's confidence intervals for all the cell differences and attempt to ascertain significant cofactors ($\alpha = .01$).

8.40 A company is deciding on which of 3 word processing packages to buy. It wants to compare the three packages with employees who are already skilled on other word processing packages and those who have no word processing experience. The company randomly selects individuals in all categories and records the output in number of words per minute. The output is:

	Processor A	Processor B	Processor C
Experienced:	116	126	101
	109	131	113
	98	137	97
	89	123	110
	121	119	92
	117	126	129
Inexperienced:	71	62	65
	102	67	58
	111	73	74
	78	64	71
	101	68	79
	93	67	72

a. State the null hypothesis.

b. Is the cross factor AB significant at the 1% level using the two-factor ANOVA procedure?

c. If factor AB is significant, what problems does this cause in determining the individual impact of the factors?

d. Compute confidence intervals for the cells using Tukey's multiple confidence intervals ($\alpha = .05$).

8.5 Summary

The ANOVA process utilizes the F distribution in comparing whether the means of multiple populations are identical. The hypothesis testing procedures to this point do not allow for testing of three or more populations. We began the analysis with one treatment variable to ascertain if the treatment affected the outcome of the data. We then proceeded to block the influence of other variables which might distort our analysis. Finally, we analyzed two treatment variables to determine if their impact is additive and independent, and to determine if they significantly affect our results. Through ANOVA, we can test more than two treatment means; however, the process is beyond the scope of this text.

If we found that the means of at least two populations were in fact different, confidence interval techniques are utilized to ascertain exactly which two means differ. Such an analysis might appear easy, but the process is clouded by sampling error.

Mini-case 8.1: Different Textbooks?

A professor wants to experiment with textbooks. She selects three textbooks for her three business statistics classes. She fears that student skills may differ between classes so she groups students by grade point average (GPA). Then she randomly selects students within each group to represent the group. She will use the final class average as the measure of student skills learned. The resulting data for her experiment are:

GPA	Textbook A	Textbook B	Textbook C
≤ 2.0	63.8	71.2	59.8
2.01–2.39	71.9	68.7	64.3
2.40–2.79	74.1	74.9	70.5
2.80–3.19	79.3	82.4	76.2
3.20–3.59	87.5	89.3	81.1
≥ 3.60	94.2	98.1	86.3

a. State the null and alternative hypotheses.
b. Why did the professor group students by GPA prior to the random selection process?
c. At the 5% level, test the null hypothesis.
d. If the null hypothesis is rejected, use confidence intervals to determine exactly which means differ.

Mini-case 8.2: Are Automobiles Affected by Their Day of Assembly?

Our company is engaged in the production of automobiles. Consumer groups hypothesize that cars assembled immediately before or following a weekend have more assembly line defects than those produced mid-week. We decide upon randomly selecting 10 cars each day during the week and meticulously record the defects. The number of defects per day is:

	Monday	Tuesday	Wednesday	Thursday	Friday
Car #1	11	9	8	3	15
Car #2	7	12	4	5	19
Car #3	10	5	2	7	22
Car #4	12	8	1	9	21
Car #5	5	5	7	4	16
Car #6	9	6	6	2	19
Car #7	10	7	4	8	20
Car #8	8	3	9	4	18
Car #9	14	1	6	3	24
Car #10	7	4	7	2	21

a. Test the null hypothesis (5% level) using the completely randomized design.
b. At the 5% level, are any days different than the rest in terms of producing defects?
c. How could you utilize the information as a manager?

212

Treatment: A treatment involves an experiment to ascertain if differences in results can be achieved to make one alternative superior to others.

Level: The different categories into which the treatment variable falls.

ANOVA: Analysis of variance.

Blocking variable: A variable that would distort the treatment variable if not taken into account.

Factorial Experiment: An experiment involving two or more treatment variables.

Cell: The data set involving two or more treatment variables.

Interaction: The combined relationship between two treatment variables.

Review of Important Formulas

Sum of the Squares Due to Treatment

$$\text{SSTR} = n_1 \left(\overline{X}_1 - \overline{X}_p^2 \right) + n_2 \left(\overline{X}_2 - \overline{X}_p \right)^2 + \bullet\bullet\bullet + n_k \left(\overline{X}_k - \overline{X}_p \right)^2 \qquad (8.1)$$

where

$k = $ total number of treatments

$n_1, n_2, n_k = $ the respective treatment sample sizes

$\overline{X}_1, \overline{X}_2, \overline{X}_k = $ the respective treatment sample means

$\Sigma X_1, \Sigma X_2, \Sigma X_k = $ the sum of the raw data for each treatment

$\overline{X}_p = $ the pooled data sample mean found by the formula

$$\overline{X}_p = \frac{\Sigma X_1 + \Sigma X_2 + \bullet\bullet\bullet + \Sigma X_k}{n_1 + n_2 + \bullet\bullet\bullet + n_k} \qquad (8.2)$$

Sum of the Squares Due to Error

$$\text{SSE} = \Sigma (X_1 - \overline{X}_1)^2 + \Sigma (X_2 - \overline{X}_2)^2 + \bullet\bullet\bullet + \Sigma (X_k - \overline{X}_k)^2 \qquad (8.3)$$

where

$X_1, X_2, X_k = $ the raw data points for the respective treatments

$\overline{X}_1, \overline{X}_2, \overline{X}_k = $ the respective treatment sample means

$k = $ number of treatment levels

Total Sum of the Squares

$$\text{SST} = \Sigma (X_i - \overline{X}_p)^2 \qquad (8.4)$$

where

$X_i = $ each and every data point from all treatments

$\overline{X}_p = $ the pooled data sample mean

Mean Squares (Variances) for ANOVA Model: Completely Randomized Design

$$\text{MSTR} = \frac{\text{SSTR}}{k-1} \quad \text{MSE} = \frac{\text{SSE}}{n_p - k} \quad \text{MST} = \frac{\text{SST}}{n_p - 1} \tag{8.5}$$

where

SSTR = sum of the squares treatment

SSE = sum of the squares error

SST = total sum of the squares

n_p = pooled sample size

k = number of treatments

The ANOVA Test Statistic

$$F_{\text{test}} = \frac{\text{MSTR}}{\text{MSE}} \tag{8.6}$$

where

MSTR = mean square treatment

MSE = mean square error

Rejection of the Null Hypothesis

$$F_{\text{test}} > F_{\alpha,\,(dfnum,\,dfden)} \tag{8.7}$$

where

α = the significance level

$dfnum$ = degrees of freedom in the numerator

$dfden$ = degrees of freedom in the denominator

Sum of the Squares Due to Blocks

$$\text{SSB} = n_{B1}(\overline{X}_{B1} - \overline{X}_p)^2 + n_{B2}(\overline{X}_{B2} - \overline{X}_p)^2 + \bullet\bullet\bullet + n_{Bk}(\overline{X}_{Bk} - \overline{X}_p)^2 \tag{8.8}$$

where

b = total number of blocks

n_{B1}, n_{B2}, n_{Bk} = the respective block sample sizes

$\overline{X}_{B1}, \overline{X}_{B2}, \overline{X}_{Bk}$ = the respective block sample means

MSB and MSE ANOVA Model: Randomized Block Design

$$MSB = \frac{SSB}{b-1} \quad MSE = \frac{SSE}{n_p - k - b + 1} \tag{8.9}$$

where

SSB = sum of squares due to blocks

SSE = sum of squares due to error

b = number of blocks

k = number of treatment levels

n_p = the pooled data sample size

MSTR and MST formulas remain unchanged from completely randomized design

---

Review of MINITAB Commands

MINITAB Commands for ANOVA Output: Completely Randomized Design

Stat > ANOVA > Oneway
Double click **Data** to enter to **Response** box.
Double click **Treatment** to enter to **Factor** box.
OK

Tukey's multiple comparison confidence intervals can be obtained using MINITAB. The sequence and output are as follows:

Stat > ANOVA > Oneway
Check to see that **Data** is in the **Response** box and **Treat** in the **Factor** box.
Be sure **Store Fits** and **Store residuals** options are not selected.
Click **Tukey's, family error rate**.
OK twice.

MINITAB Commands for ANOVA Output: Randomized Block Design

Stat > ANOVA > Twoway
Double click **Data** into **Response** box.
Double click **block variable** (row) into **Row Factor** box.
Double click **treatment variable** (column) into **Column Factor** box.
Click on **Display Means** from both the **Row** and **Column Factor** boxes.
OK

MINITAB Commands for ANOVA table

Stat > ANOVA > Balanced ANOVA
Click **Data** into **Response** box.
Click to **Model** box, then click **Dose Aspirin**, into **Model** box. Then click **Dose** and **Aspirin** into **Response** box again, then manually place a * symbol between the **Dose** and **Aspirin**.
OK

ANOVA Plots

Stat > ANOVA > Main Effects Plot
Click **Data** into **Response** box.
Click **Dose** and **Aspirin** into **Factors** box.
OK

End of Chapter Exercises

8.41   Differentiate between a one-factor completely randomized design, a one-factor randomized block design, and a two-factor completely randomized design.

8.42   Differentiate between the MINITAB commands when dealing with a one-factor completely randomized design, a one-factor randomized block design, and a two-factor completely randomized design.

8.43   A major housing development allows 5 companies to build on their sites. It wants to see if the number of complaints is the same between them. It randomly selects home owners from homes in the 1600–1999 sq. ft., 2000–2399 sq. ft., and 2400–2800 sq. ft. ranges. The number of complaints is as follows:

Company	1600–1999 sq. ft.	2000–2399 sq. ft.	2400–2800 sq. ft.
#1	7	10	9
#2	17	22	26
#3	6	8	9
#4	3	3	5
#5	14	20	24

Using the completely randomized design at the 10% level, are the mean complaints the same?

8.44   a.   For problem 8.43, do the randomized block design (5% level). State if the means are the same for each builder.

b.   Do you think you were more justified in using the completely randomized or the randomized block design on the data set?

8.45   A major housing development allows two companies to build on its sites. It wants to see if the number of complaints is the same between them. It randomly selects 5 homeowners from homes in the 1600–1999 sq. ft., 2000–2399 sq. ft., and 2400–2800 sq. ft. ranges. The number of complaints is as follows:

Company	1600–1999 sq. ft.	2000–2399 sq. ft.	2400–2800 sq. ft.
#1	7	10	9
	8	10	12
	6	8	9
	3	3	5
	9	7	3
#2	17	22	16
	14	20	17
	21	17	11
	16	15	16
	20	14	9

Based on the two-factor ANOVA procedure, will we reject the null hypothesis at the 5% level?

216

8.46   Three computer printers are set to print the same chapters from this textbook and are monitored to determine the time to complete the process. The publishing company believes the three printers have equal speed. Using the randomized block design, at the 5% level, test the null hypothesis.

Chapter	Printer #1	Printer #2	Printer #3
1	2.3 min	1.9 min	2.0 min
2	4.8	4.4	4.5
3	3.1	3.2	2.8
4	4.6	4.2	4.7
5	6.9	6.4	6.2
6	6.1	6.4	6.7
7	8.1	6.9	7.3
8	4.3	3.9	4.0
9	7.3	6.7	7.3
10	10.5	9.4	9.8
11	9.3	9.1	9.0

8.47   Four suppliers of floppy disks claim their product will hold 720k of data. We randomly survey disks from each supplier and record the data capacity. The results are:

Disc	Company A	Company B	Company C	Company D
1	689	715	745	722
2	718	722	736	719
3	712	724	751	726
4	702	718	739	721
5	716	716	744	718
6	690		751	712
7	716			720

a. Are all of the floppy disks equivalent, at the 10% level, using the completely randomized design?
b. If treatment is significant, determine the confidence intervals and ascertain if Company A and D are different.

8.48   An individual is comparing general 15-year home mortgage rates of three lending institutions for last year. Because rates increased during the second half of the year, 6 days are randomly selected from the first and second half of the year. The results are:

Half Year	Mortgage Co. #1	Mortgage Co. #2	Mortgage Co. #3
1st	8.9%	8.7%	9.0%
	9.2	9.3	9.5
	8.6	8.6	8.8
	8.4	8.2	8.7
	9.1	9.4	9.5
	9.5	9.4	9.7
2nd	12.3	11.7	11.8
	14.1	12.7	13.4
	14.3	13.9	14.0
	15.6	14.7	14.3
	13.5	12.4	12.8
	12.3	12.1	12.0

a. Based on a two-factor ANOVA test, would you have ISER or reject the null hypothesis (5% level).
b. If the null hypothesis is rejected, use confidence intervals to ascertain if the first half of the year differs from the second ($\alpha = .05$).
c. Construct Tukey's confidence intervals and compare all cell means.

8.49   A company is thinking about opening a branch in one of three countries in Europe. The company has a great deal of computer equipment that is sensitive to voltages different from 220 volts. Engineers monitor the voltage output in the three countries and randomly select a point in time to measure the voltage. The following is the results of the survey:

Day	Country A	Country B	Country C
Monday	220.6	221.2	191.8
Tuesday	220.1	220.2	228.5
Wednesday	220.4	221.6	194.7
Thursday	219.3	222.1	231.2
Friday	220.0	219.5	234.1
Saturday	217.1	217.3	186.9
Sunday	216.9	217.1	184.1

Based on the completely randomized design, are the voltage levels the same for all countries (5% level)?

8.50   a.   Repeat exercise 8.49 based on the randomized block design (5% level).
        b.   If the null hypothesis is rejected, utilize the pre-established means confidence intervals to determine which sample means are different. (Remember, in actuality, you would only test to see if two means differ).
        c.   Use Tukey's confidence intervals to determine which sample means differ.

Regression and Correlation Analysis

Where we have been

To this point we have concentrated on analyzing sample statistics concerning a single variable.

Where we are going

We will now concentrate on developing techniques to analyze the relationship between two variables. The implication in the analysis is that changes in one variable can be associated with changes in another variable. If this is the case, we may be able to develop models to aid us in understanding the association existing between variables and in possibly predicting such variables as sales, profits, etc. If such predictions prove to be reliable, they could aid us in our decision-making process.

9.1   Introduction

For the next two chapters, we will develop models the purpose of which is to predict the value of a variable based on knowledge of other variables. All well-managed organizations have goals that they constantly strive to attain. Attainment of these goals requires reliable forecasts of variables such as sales, interest rates, exchange rates, and labor costs. For instance, if sales are overestimated, inventory accumulates and handling and storage costs increase, diminishing profits or increasing losses. Without accurate forecasts, a rational decision concerning an optimal choice among available options would be impossible.

Firms succeed by making forecasts that are superior to, and more timely than, those of their competitors. Even when the purpose of our statistical model is not to forecast, regression models are useful due to their ability to quantify the relationship between variables. In economics, we learn about the theory of demand and the importance of price. However, for a specific firm, only through statistical modeling can we be precise about the extent that price affects the number of units demanded. The following examples illustrate typical organizational problems which can be analyzed with the regression models that we are developing.

Example 1

A management specialist wants to develop a screening device to help select new employees. Since morale and productivity problems are associated with high turnover and poor attendance, the screening device should identify candidates most likely to perform successfully on the job. The specialist first surveys successful employees to determine which of their traits might be factors in their success. Then a demographic and psychographic profile of these employees is developed and candidates are matched against the profile.

The personnel manager must make sure the model measures what it is supposed to ensure and does not violate the rights of minority candidates. The specialist might have to appear in court on an Equal Employment Opportunity Commission (EEOC) charge of discrimination and the model must withstand the rigors of an alternative (adversary) analysis. While it is possible for the specialist to discriminate against minorities without realizing it, ignorance is no defense.

Example 2

A marketing specialist wants to determine how consumers will respond to a new humorous ad developed to boost sales for an aging product. Although a new advertising approach is necessary, if it's too bold, it may alienate potential consumers. A pretest is needed, but it must only include consumers in the targeted sales market. The sample group's response to the ad will determine whether the company runs the humorous ad or one that is more reserved.

Example 3

An accountant wants to forecast yearly demand so an EOQ (economic order quantity) inventory model can be used to minimize inventory carrying costs.

Example 4

An economist wants to forecast changes in the interest rates so that she can analyze future investment and consumption patterns.

Example 5

A financial expert wants to predict the exchange rate so that a foreign acquisition can be analyzed.

 Concept Check 9.A

In regression models we are attempting to forecast an important variable that affects us personally or our business activities. True or false? If false, explain.

Exercises

9.1   Provide three variables relevant to your career five years from now, which you would like to predict.

9.2   Provide three variables relevant to your success in five years, which your parents, spouse, or friends would like to predict.

When we develop a regression model, we are actually hypothesizing a mathematical relationship. In the relationship

$$Y = f(X)$$

Y is called the **dependent** (also called an **explained** or **response** variable), and X is called the **independent** (synonyms include **explanatory** or **predictor** variable). The mathematical relationship indicates that changes in the independent or predictor variable, X, are associated with changes in the dependent variable, Y. Graphically, the dependent variable (Y) is measured on the vertical axis and the independent variable (X) is measured along the horizontal axis. If the two variables were smoking and cancer, the Surgeon General of the United States believes a causal relationship exists between them.

We need to know which variable exerts influence over the other. If we think smoking either directly causes or acts as a catalyst to make cancer cells grow, then smoking is the independent or the predictor variable (it attempts to predict changes in the rate of growth in cancerous cells). Cancer, which is affected by smoking, is termed the dependent variable.

Assume the two variables are spending and income. External evidence supports a hypothesis that they are related. If so, which of the following two equations is correct?

$$spending = f(income)$$

or

$$income = f(spending)$$

Is either correct or are they both correct? If the second equation were correct, there probably would be very few students who would be taking this class and reading this textbook. For those of you who are now employed, you could just increase your spending by buying whatever you wanted, then notify your employer that your expenses have increased and your salary should be adjusted accordingly. Unfortunately, it is unlikely your employer will increase your wages based upon an increase in your consumption. Of course, it sometimes seems as if this is how our government operates: more spending requires more revenue, which necessitates a tax increase.

We must note that traditional regression analysis assumes that we can differentiate between the dependent and independent variable. This identification may not be as easy as it appears. For example, for many years now we have believed that world climatic conditions impact the world's population [population $= f$(climatic conditions)]. A new theory suggests this may be incorrect. The new theory states that the size and distribution of the world population (approximately 6.5 billion) actually influences world climatic conditions [climatic conditions $= f$(population)].

In this chapter, all analyses are limited to a single independent or predictor variable and to a linear relationship existing between X and Y. Such models are often termed **bivariate** models or **simple linear regression models**. In Chapter 10 the number of independent variables will increase and the models are called multiple regression models.

When dealing with a simple linear regression model, the equation involved is

$Y = a + bX$ (using statistical notation)

$Y = mX + b$ (using mathematical notation)

Y represents the dependent (explained/response) variable and X the independent (predictor/explanatory) variable. Two constants distinguish one linear equation from all others: the slope of the equation (b using statistical notation) and the Y intercept (a using statistical notation).

A linear relationship in a business problem reflects levels of proportionality. For example, if $Y =$ profits, $X =$ advertising, $b = 3$, and $a = 0$, then for every advertising dollar, the return in profits would be three times as large. The change in Y is directly proportional to the change in X [sometimes written $Y(X)$]. The key to the linear relationship is that the Y variable increases or decreases by a constant amount with respect to changes in the independent variable.

Concept Check 9.B

The independent variable is the variable to be predicted. True or false?
If false, explain.

Exercises

9.3   There certainly is a relationship between the chicken and the egg. Which is the dependent and
       which the independent variable?

9.4   How are multiple regression models different from simple linear regression models?

9.5   We believe that inventory carrying costs are linearly related to the inventory carried. Explain.

9.6   If we had a linear regression equation where Y = weights and X = ages for children between the
       ages of 6 and 15, and found a slope of 3.66 pounds, how could the result be interpreted?

9.3   Model Building

Business firms are always trying to discover relationships that will be used to ensure greater
accuracy in their forecasts. Regression analysis helps formalize this thought process. Suppose you notice
a vacant lot on a major roadway near where you live. You might envision purchasing the lot, buying a franchise (such as McDonald's), and making a great deal of money. Further investigation might uncover lot,
franchise, and commercial construction costs. These costs could easily amount to several million dollars,
which makes monthly expenses quite high. These expenses, however, are acceptable as long as potential
revenues exceed these costs.

You may ask: "Is there any way to forecast revenue for a vacant lot?" Fortunately, the answer is
"yes." There are numerous fast food restaurants we can use to help identify which factors (variables) determine good sales. These variables then could be used in a predictive equation or model. Our model might
look like

$$\text{Sales} = f(X_1, X_2, X_3, X_4, X_5, X_6)$$

where

$X_1 =$ Population density within a short radius of the vacant lot. Remember that a fast food fran-
        chise will not draw from great distances due to the inexpensive price and the large num-
        ber of competitors.

$X_2 =$ The actual traffic flow in front of the vacant lot. Many of us have busy schedules and, as
        we travel, our stops for food are brief and not planned.

$X_3 =$ The ease of entry and exit. People usually will not cross dangerous intersections to go to
        a fast food restaurant, especially if a competitor is more accessible and equally close. An
        inaccessible location can easily negate the advantages of a high traffic flow if competitors
        are closely located.

$X_4 =$ The number of competitors in the immediate vicinity of the vacant lot. This factor not only
        includes hamburger competitors, but other fast food restaurants as well.

$X_5 =$ Some of the demographics of the population that surround the vacant lot. Of particular
        importance is the life cycle of the population. No longer is the age of the population
        all important, but instead where the residents are in terms of the life cycle. College stu-
        dents are an excellent illustration. Undergraduate students typically consume a great many
        hamburgers during their academic careers as they rush between studying, earning money
        for college, and socializing. After graduation, they may have more time to develop their

culinary pallets and may avoid fast foods; but later, when they get married and have children, they again find themselves under extreme time constraints and are likely to take advantage of a quick meal. A captive young population is one of the best markets for fast food franchisers. That's why franchisers like to be close to universities and military bases. In fact, McDonald's currently has the Navy contract and Burger King the Army contract, which means they can be found on military installations all over the world.

$X_6 = $ The prices of the competing fast food products. If all other factors are equal, consumers are most likely to go to the fast food restaurant with the lowest prices.

Such models are called site location models and virtually all chains have their own version of them. Historically, fast food chains develop their own models to predict the demand for a product at a vacant site. The six variables given above represent a few of the possible independent (explanatory or predictor) variables. A more complete model must consider additional factors.

The franchising model is similar to other models we will discuss in this chapter. Also, regression models are generally the most important statistical model used in business applications. As mentioned earlier, our models in this chapter are limited to a single predictor or independent variable, where we predict the dependent (response) variable, Y, based on a single X. Some traditional models are:

Spending $= f$(Income)

Graduate School Performance $= f$(GMAT/LSAT/GRE Scores)

Span of Control $= f$(Levels of Management)

Loanable Funds $= f$(Interest Rates)

Sales $= f$(Advertising)

Advertising $= f$(Products Competition)

Reorder Inventory Point $= f$(Rate of Inventory Depletion)

Employee Evaluation $= f$(Score on Employee Evaluation Form)

Imports/Exports $= f$(International Exchange Rates)

The empirical foundations for these different models are established in finance, accounting, economics, marketing, and management courses. Our task is to analyze and evaluate the statistical models rather than to develop their theoretical foundations.

 Check Concept 9.C

The model; Spending $= f$(Income), is identical with the model; Income $= f$(Spending). True or false? If false, explain.

Exercises

9.7 A university admissions officer wants to predict enrollments for the next ten years. What do you believe will be some of the relevant explanatory variables?

9.8 A chain of fast food restaurants wants to predict the availability of a certain age group to meet their labor supply. What might be some of the relevant explanatory variables?

223

Fitting Straight Lines to Data

A manager may believe a straight line represents the relationship between two variables. Remember this merely means that a proportional relationship exists. As the independent variable changes (X), the dependent variable (Y) changes proportionally to the changes in X. We may ask how many straight lines may represent a data set? Figure 9.1 demonstrates that there are an infinite number of lines. Therefore, we must determine which of these lines represents the optimum, or "best," choice.

Figure 9.1   Fitting Straight Lines to a Data Set

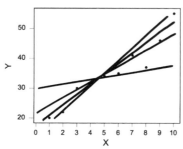

The Best Fitting Line: The Least Squares Method

The most widely accepted method for determining a line of "best fit" is the method of least squares. The method of least squares uses a specific rationale to determine that one line is superior or "fits" the data best. The line tends to be centered among a plot of the data, with some of the data points above the line and some below it. This idea can be expressed mathematically. Figure 9.2 shows that for each value of $X(X_i)$ there are actually two values of Y. First, there is the actual value (termed Y_i). Second, there is the estimated value of Y that lies directly on the line (termed $\hat{Y}$). The $\hat{Y}$ symbol indicates that this value of Y is computed, estimated, or fitted.

Figure 9.2   Least Squares Residual Values

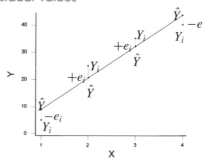

The difference between the Y_i and the $\hat{Y}$ is important. This difference is sometimes referred to as a residual or error term and is symbolically defined as e. To determine a specific residual or e value we simply subtract $\hat{Y}$ from Y_i,

$$e_i = Y_i - \hat{Y}$$

Note that e represents the vertical difference between Y_i and the regression equation, and not a perpendicular or horizontal difference. This fact is particularly important in regression analysis.

For a best fitting line, the sum of the positive errors should be equal to the sum of the negative errors, which causes a cancellation effect. Mathematically, this is expressed as the sum of e equaling 0,

$$\Sigma e_i = 0$$

Although this criterion appears logical, there is an inherent flaw in using it to select the "line of best fit." Specifically, numerous lines can satisfy this condition. In fact, any line passing through the mean of Y ($\overline{Y}$) will have a zero sum of the deviation. In Figure 9.3 we have three graphs, each illustrating the same five observations. To make the pictorial comparison simpler, we have drawn three straight lines with different slopes and intercepts, so that each is centered among the data points. We can actually see that line 1 is superior to line 2, and line 2 is superior to line 3. Superior as used here means a better fit or better representation of the relationship that exists between the variables. We now need to eliminate the lines that are poorer representations of the data. This process eventually results in the determination of the line of best fit, often called the regression equation.

Figure 9.3 Three Lines Representing a Data Set Where $\Sigma e_i = 0$.

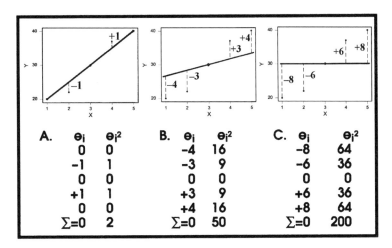

The term **regression** (part of the title of the chapter) originates from the research of Sir Francis Galton, who observed that children of very tall parents were usually shorter than their parents and children of very short parents were generally taller than their parents. In other words, children "regressed" (height-wise) toward the mean or average height. Since his analysis was for a simple linear regression model (X = height of parents; Y = height of children), the term regression began to be used generically to represent the analysis of relationship between variables.

In Figure 9.3, the sum of the error or residual values for each graph is 0. Thus, there are a number of lines that satisfy this condition, but as before we want to determine which line is optimum. To help answer this question, we must recall that both statisticians and mathematicians avoid zero sums since we cannot multiply or divide by 0 and obtain meaningful results. To avoid the 0 sum, we can evaluate the absolute value of the errors or their squares. Either method eliminates negative values and avoids the 0 sum. Recall that we used similar logic in the development of the variance in Chapter 2.

When we square the residual values and find their sum, the size of that sum is very important. The larger the sum of the residuals squared, the less the regression equation represents the pattern in the data and the poorer the fit of the equation. The converse is also true: the smaller the sum of the residuals squared, the better the regression equation represents the pattern in the data. Therefore, we are interested in the smallest possible sum of residuals squared. Mathematically, we seek to determine the regression equation that minimizes the sum of the squared residuals and refer to the result as the least squares equation.

Least squares defines the best fitting function as the one which meets the following criteria:

1. $\Sigma e_i = 0$
2. $\Sigma e_i^2 =$ minimum value

The second condition indicates how the name "least squares" was chosen.

A basic knowledge of calculus is needed to understand the mathematics of finding the least squares line since it requires a minimization procedure. For those students proficient in calculus, we leave the derivation as an exercise. Through the differentiation process, the solution equations, called the **normal equations**, are obtained.

These are

$$\Sigma Y = na + b\Sigma X$$
$$\Sigma XY = a\Sigma X + b\Sigma X^2$$

The solution equations are called the normal equations due to their mathematical properties, not because they are related to the normal distribution.

Once statisticians have obtained a solution equation, they often algebraically rearrange them in order to minimize hand calculations. This was particularly important prior to the proliferation of inexpensive, yet powerful statistical packages. The most common solution equations are

---

Estimated Linear Regression Coefficients

$$b = \frac{\Sigma XY - n\overline{X}\,\overline{Y}}{\Sigma X^2 - n\overline{X}^2} \tag{9.1}$$

$$a = \overline{Y} - b\overline{X}$$

where

$X =$ independent variable values, $i = 1, 2, \ldots, n$

$Y =$ dependent variable values, $i = 1, 2, \ldots, n$

$n =$ sample size

$\overline{Y} =$ arithmetic mean of Y

$\overline{X} =$ arithmetic mean of X

Note that $\overline{X}^2$ is read "the (mean of X) squared" not "the mean (of X squared)." The second equation is often called the equation of the means. Since the second equation involves b, we must solve the first equation for b before we can determine a.

Applying Least Squares to a Data Application

We can now apply the normal equations to data. We first use Equations 9.1 to solve for a and b. In addition to the sample size, Equations 9.1 require four summations (ΣX, ΣY, ΣXY, ΣX^2). Table 9.1 shows the necessary calculations for our next example. Note that the sum of Y^2 is also computed. Although the ΣY^2 is not required to calculate a or b, we will need it later, and so it is computed at this time.

The data in Table 9.1 are used by a university to predict student performance in graduate school (as defined by graduate GPA) based on standardized GMAT (Graduate Management Admission Test) scores. The GMAT score is a scale from 200 to 800. Very few students score outside the 300 to 700 range. The mean score is about 500, and about two-thirds of the students score between 400 and 600. In our model, Y represents first year GPA in graduate school (GGPA) and X represents the score on the GMAT exam. The data given are realistic, but fictitious, and are not meant to represent any real situation. Note that the independent variable, X, is a composite of two factors. It combines the scores on the quantitative and verbal sections of the exam. Thus, even a high score on the standardized exam might not fully reveal a student who has strong quantitative skills, but has weak verbal communicative skills, or the opposite.

Table 9.1   Calculations for Estimated Regression Coefficients

Student	GMAT Score	GGPA		
	X	Y	XY	X^2
1	560	3.05	1,708.00	313,600
2	640	4.00	2,560.00	409,600
3	580	3.55	2,059.00	336,400
4	480	3.53	1,694.40	230,400
5	637	3.58	2,280.46	405,769
6	610	3.21	1,958.10	372,100
7	430	3.50	1,505.00	184,900
8	400	2.80	1,120.00	160,000
9	450	3.44	1,548.00	202,500
10	525	3.17	1,664.25	275,625
11	330	2.46	811.80	108,900
12	620	2.75	1,705.00	384,400
SUMS	6,262	39.04	20,614.01	3,384,194

Mean of $X = \overline{X} = \Sigma X/n = 6262/12 = 521.8333$

Mean of $Y = \overline{Y} = \Sigma Y/n = 39.04/12 = 3.2533$

We next substitute the appropriate values into equation 9.1 and obtain the following estimated regression coefficients:

$$b = \frac{\Sigma XY - n\overline{X}\ \overline{Y}}{\Sigma X^2 - n\overline{X}^2} = \frac{20,614.01 - 12(521.8333)(3.2533)}{3,384,194 - 12(521.8333)^2}$$

$$b = 241.6367/116,473.668 = +0.0020746$$

$$a = \overline{Y} - b\overline{X} = 3.2533 - (.0020746)\ 521.8333 = 2.170736$$

Note that the estimated regression slope, b, is close to 0. For this reason we carry the numeric answers to seven decimal places to avoid serious rounding errors. If the slope were computed to the nearest hundredth, it would equal 0. The specific slope implies that for each additional point added to a GMAT score, .0020746 is added to the graduate GPA. An improvement of a GMAT score by 100 points increases the graduate GPA by a 0.20746.

Graduate GPA scores are less dispersed than undergraduate GPA scores due to two factors. In graduate school a "B" average must be maintained to graduate, while in undergraduate school, a "C" grade is sufficient. Also it's typical for a student who obtains two "C" grades in graduate school to be placed on probation or dismissed from the program.

As mentioned earlier, the regression slope (b) tells us how much a GGPA would increase (or decrease if the slope were negative) if the GMAT scores were increased by a single unit. The regression intercept (a) tells us the expected GGPA if the GMAT score $X = 0$. Since a 0 is not even a possible GMAT score, the intercept has little meaning to our problem. Since the lowest GMAT score for our twelve students was 330, substituting 0 for X places the observation outside the bounds of the data set. For an undergraduate GPA, the intercept would probably be 1.00 lower than the graduate GPA because the passing grade is 1.00 point lower.

An interesting feature of a regression equation is that it always passes through the point of intersection of the means of Y and X. To test this, just substitute the mean of X into the regression equation.

The result is the mean of Y. This can easily be seen from the equation of the means. Hence, substituting the values for a, b, and the mean of X, we obtain

$$Y = a + b\overline{X} = 2.170736 + .0020746(521.8333) = 3.2533$$

The University Admissions Committee might use the equation and the GMAT score to predict the performance of a new student. If a student obtained 640 on the GMAT, the regression model yields

$$\text{Graduate GPA} = 2.170736 + .0020746(640) = 3.498 \approx 3.5$$

The committee might conclude this student would be an excellent addition to the student body. Since a 3.0 grade point must be maintained, the university could rearrange the equation to determine what GMAT score would be expected to ensure that average. This is done as follows:

$$3.0 = 2.170736 + .0020746(X)$$
$$= (3.0 - 2.170736)/.0020746 = 399.7 \approx 400$$

The university then set a minimum score of 400 on the GMAT for incoming graduate students. Of course, factors other than GMAT scores should be considered. Other variables might be the quality of a student's undergraduate education, such as undergraduate grade point average (UGPA), quality of the school and the programs complete, student involvement with those programs, work experience, ability to add to the knowledge of the class, and leadership. Studies have found that the score on the quantitative section of the GMAT test is a better predictor of GGPA than either the verbal scores or the combined verbal and quantitative scores. The reason for this is difficult to understand. Perhaps it is more difficult to measure the contributions of verbal skill excellence than quantitative skills. It also might indicate an enormous increase in the use of multiple choice tests, which provide students with little opportunity to demonstrate their verbal skills.

Using MINITAB to Determine the Regression Equation

The regression equation can be obtained from MINITAB and is given in Table 9.2. The regression equation is printed as GGPA = 2.17 + 0.00207 GMAT, and the coefficients are again listed to more decimal places under the column.

Stat > Regression > Regression
Double click **GGPA** into **Response** box.
Double click **GMAT** into **Predictors** box.
OK

Table 9.2   MINITAB Abbreviated Output for Regression Analysis

THE REGRESSION EQUATION IS
GGPA = 2.17 + 0.00207 GMAT

Predictor	Coef	Stdev	t-ratio	p
Constant	2.1707	0.6149	3.53	0.005
GMAT	0.002075	0.001158	1.79	0.103

 Concept Check 9.D

The Least Squares Method always selects the equation that minimizes the sum of the residuals squared, when the residuals are measured vertically. True or false? If false, explain.

9.9   The following linear equation explains the relationship between X and Y: $Y = 40 + 3.2(X)$.

     a.   when $X = 0$, $Y = ?$
     b.   When $X = 40$, $Y = ?$
     c.   When $Y = 40$, $X = ?$
     d.   Is it possible that $Y = X = 40$?

9.10   Explain the term "least squares" in your own words.

9.11   Why is least squares considered a "best fit" equation?

9.12   In the derivation of least squares, why does the equation have to be place in the form of $\Sigma e^2 = ?$

9.13   In the data set, we are given the following information: $\Sigma Y = 229$, $\Sigma X = 99$, $\Sigma XY = 4416$, $\Sigma X^2 = 2251$, $\Sigma Y^2 = 9431$, $\Sigma X^2 Y^2 = 5436138$, $n = 6$

     a.   What summations are necessary in computing the least squares linear equation?
     b.   In computing ΣX^2, do we ΣX then square, or do we square the X's first and then sum? Would it make a difference?
     c.   Find the slope and the intercept for the least squares linear equation.
     d.   Halving the least squares linear equation, if $X = 66$, $Y = ?$

9.14   In a data set, we are given the following information: $\Sigma Y = 60$, $\Sigma X = 76$, $\Sigma XY = 591$, $\Sigma X^2 = 1438$, $\Sigma Y^2 = 1106$, $n = 5$.

     a.   Find the slope and intercept for the least squares linear equation.
     b.   Halving the least squares linear equation, if $X = 30$, $Y = ?$

9.15

Y	X
27	4
14	10
12	16
6	21
1	25

     a.   Are X and Y directly or inversely related?
     b.   Does your answer to part a affect the sign of the slope?
     c.   For the data, compute all the summations necessary to solve the normal equations.
     d.   Find the numerical values for the slope and intercept of the least squares linear equation.
     e.   Having obtained the least squares linear equation, if $X = 1$, $\hat{Y} = ?$
     f.   Have MINITAB determine the regression equation.

9.16

X	Y
1	4
6	10
12	16
14	21
27	25

     a.   Are X and Y directly or inversely related?
     b.   For this data, compute all the summations necessary to solve the normal equations.
     c.   Find the numerical values for the slope and intercept of the least squares linear equation.
     d.   Is your answer to part a consistent with the sign of the slope?
     e.   Having obtained the least squares linear equation, if $X = 1$, $\hat{Y} = ?$
     f.   Is the small sample size a consideration when making forecasts?
     g.   Have MINITAB determine the regression equation.

9.17

Y	X
1	4
6	10
12	16
14	21
27	25

a. Are X and Y directly or inversely related?
b. For the data, compute all the summations necessary to solve the normal equations.
c. Find the numerical values for the slope and intercept of the least squares linear equation.
d. Check your answers with the MINITAB solution.
e. Since exercises 9.16 and 9.17 are identical except for the reversing of X with Y, will it be necessary to input both data sets to the MINITAB editor?

9.18

X	Y
3	26
5	14
10	11
21	7

a. Are X and Y directly or inversely related?
b. For the data, compute all the summations necessary to solve the normal equations.
c. Find the numerical values for the slope and intercept of the least squares linear equation.
d. Check your answers with the MINITAB solution.

9.5   Measuring Variability in the Dependent Variable

Residual values are extremely important in linear regression analysis. Not only are they the basis for establishing the normal equations, but also they represent the impact of omitted variables from the regression model. Residuals represent changes in the Y variables caused by omitted variables from the model. Hence, the larger our residuals are, the smaller is the association existing between X and Y.

We can learn a great deal about the relationship between two variables by visually observing their association, or lack of association. A graphical plot of a two variable data set is referred to as a scatter diagram or scattergram. Figure 9.4 shows a series of six such scattergrams. In Figure 9.4A and 9.4B, the data points are fairly close to the regression line, while in Figures 9.4C and 9.4.D the spread of the data is more pronounced. The first two functions have small residual values (e), while the second two have larger residual values.

Although scattergrams yield an easy-to-understand visual interpretation of the size of the residual values, they are not as effective or as precise as mathematically determining their numeric values. If we were to examine nonlinear functions (and we will in Chapter 10), viewing a scattergram can be misleading. A data point can actually be close to a regression line if measured perpendicularly, but far away from the line if measured vertically. Thus, a visual interpretation might lead us to believe an e value is small, when it actually is quite large (as in Figure 9.4E and 9.4F).

Figure 9.4 Scatter Diagrams

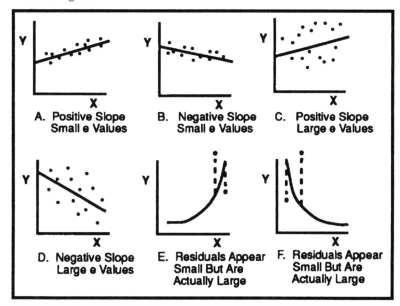

From scatter diagrams we can learn something about the variation in the dependent variable. To be more precise; however, we can think of the simple linear regression model as an analysis of three sum-of-squares involving the dependent variable (Y). This is precisely the approach that all statistical software utilizes. The three sum-of-squares are:

1. $SST = \Sigma(Y_i - \overline{Y})^2 = \Sigma Y_i^2 - n\overline{Y}^2$, the squared deviation of Y about its mean. This variation is called the total sum-of-squares (SST) because it measures all the variation in Y, regardless of its cause.
2. $SSR = \Sigma(\hat{Y} - \overline{Y})^2 = \Sigma \hat{Y}^2 - n\overline{Y}^2$, the sum of the squares between $\hat{Y}$ and the mean of Y. This variation is the regression sum-of-squares (SSR), the sum-of squares attributed to or explained by the independent (predictor) variable within the regression equation. This variation reflects the variation in Y associated with changes in X, the variable contained in the regression equation.
3. $SSE = \Sigma(Y_i - \hat{Y})^2 = \Sigma e^2$, the sum of the residuals squared. This variation is often called the error sum-of-squares (SSE) or residual sum-of-squares, because it is the variability in Y that is not explained by the regression equation. This variation is caused by independent variables external to, or outside of, the regression model.

Since either an independent variable is within the regression equation (in which case the variation associated with Y is SSR) or it's outside the regression equation (in which case the variation associated with Y is within SSE), hence,

$$SST = SSR + SSE; \; \Sigma(Y_i - \overline{Y})^2 = \Sigma(\hat{Y} - \overline{Y})^2 + \Sigma(Y_i - \hat{Y})^2$$

Rather than getting bogged down in hand computations, we will call on MINITAB to yield all of our sum-of-squares (Table 9.3).

231

Stat > Regression > Regression
Double click **GGPA** into **Response** box.
Double click **GMAT** into **Predictors** box.
Click on the **Storage** box
Click on the **Fits** box. (To obtain the estimated Y values)
Click on **Residuals** box. (To obtain the residuals)
OK.

Note: an alternate approach would be to click the **Results** box, then click on **In addition, the full table of fits and residuals**

Table 9.3 MINITAB Output Plus Residuals

THE REGRESSION EQUATION IS

GGPA $= 2.17 + .00207$ GMAT

Predictor	Coef	Stdev	T	P
Constant	2.1707	0.6149	3.53	0.005
GMAT	0.002075	0.001158	1.79	0.103

$S = 0.3952$ R–Sq $= 24.3\%$ R–Sq (adj) $= 16.7\%$

Analysis of Variance

Source	DF	SS	MS	F	P
Regression	1	0.5013	0.5013	3.21	0.103
Residual Error	10	1.5616	0.1562		
Total	11	2.0629			

MINITAB Printout of Estimated or Fitted Y Values Plus Residuals.

	C1 GMAT	C2 GGPA	C4 RESI1	C3 FITS 1
1	560	3.05	−0.282514	3.33251
2	640	4.00	0.501518	3.49848
3	580	3.55	0.175994	3.37401
4	480	3.53	0.363454	3.16655
5	637	3.58	0.087741	3.49226
6	610	3.21	−0.226244	3.43624
7	430	3.50	0.437184	3.06282
8	400	2.80	−0.200577	3.00058
9	450	3.44	0.335692	3.10431
10	525	3.17	−0.089903	3.25990
11	330	2.46	−0.395355	2.85536
12	620	2.75	−0.706990	3.45699

Note: If we sum the residuals equal 0, and if we square, then sum the residuals it equals SSE (1.5616).

If we want a scatter plot with regression equation we use the following command sequence:

Stat > Regression > Fitted Line Plot
Double click **GGPA** into **Response (Y)** box.
Double click **GMAT** into **Predictor (X)** box.
Click on **Linear Model**
OK

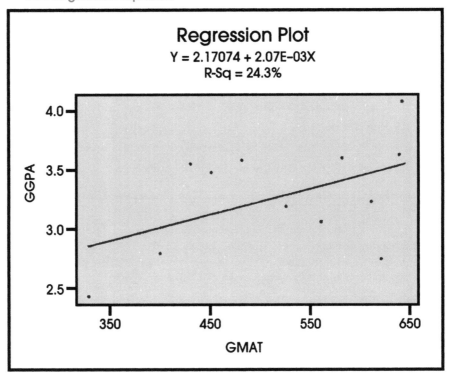

We can see from the printout that SSR = 0.5013 and that SSE = 1.5616 (remember that the terms error and residual are synonyms).

It is useful to know that MINITAB is using the regression equation to compute $\hat{Y}$ and e. Suppose we wanted to hand compute the first values for $\hat{Y}$ and e. Our regression equation is

$$\hat{Y} = 2.1707 + 0.002075(X)$$

and substituting our first X value of 560 ($X_1 = 560$) yields

$$\hat{Y}_1 = 2.1707 + 0.002075(560) = 3.3327$$

and

$$e_1 = Y_1 - \hat{Y}_1 = 3.05 - 3.3327 = -0.2827$$

In a similar manner, we could compute all $\hat{Y}_i$ and e_i values.

From our sum-of-squares we will now develop several important statistics including the standard error of the estimate, and the coefficients of determination and correlation.

The Standard Error of the Estimate

We are about to estimate the error variance for our regression model. Remember that the residuals measure the impact of omitted variables from our regression model. Hence, if our error variance is large, it will leave us unable to use our regression model as a predictor. The square root of the error variance is large, it will leave us unable to use our regression model as a predictor. The square root of the error variance is often called the **standard error of the estimate** and is symbolized by $s_{Y \bullet X}$ (or in the more general format σe). The subscript $Y \bullet X$ indicates that the deviations are around a regression line that yields values of Y, based on specific values of X.

233

The formula for the standard error of the estimate is

The Standard Error of the Estimate

$$S_{Y \bullet 12} = \hat{\sigma}_e = \sqrt{\frac{\text{SSE}}{n - m}} \qquad\qquad (9.2)$$

where

SSE = the error sum-of-squares

n = the sample size

m = the number of coefficients in the regression equation: in a linear two variable
model there are 2 estimated parameters (a & b).

Substituting the numerical equivalents yields $S_{Y \bullet X} = \sqrt{(1.5616/10)} = 0.3952$, which is the numerical reading given on the MINITAB output as $S = 0.3952$. Since the GGPA can't exceed 4.0, and 3.0 must be maintained for graduation, we can see how the numerical value for the standard error of the estimate would be small in an absolute sense. We will learn shortly if it is small in a relative sense.

The standard error of the estimate is analogous to the standard deviation in the sense that one measures dispersion about a regression line, and the other measures dispersion about the mean. Table 9.3 converts the residuals to a Z or standardized scale 68.3% of the residuals are between $\pm 1S$, 95.5% between $\pm 2S$, and 99.7% between $\pm 3S$.

The Coefficient of Determination (R^2)

When a regression model is developed, we usually want to know how much of the changes in Y are explained by the independent (predictor) variable in the regression model. If models are meticulously developed, they might be reliable and useful to decision makers. If a firm develops a model for their most productive employees, they would like to be able to use it to screen job applicants and anticipate how those hired will perform.

Many statistics developed are merely indices with some finite range and frequently the scale (or range) is from 0 to 1. The **coefficient of determination** (symbolized by R^2) measures the proportion of variability in Y that is associated with variability in the independent variable, X. It uses a scale from 0 to 1 and serves to measure the percent of the change in Y that is associated with X. A coefficient of determination of 0 indicates no association exists between X and Y, and a 1 indicates a perfect association between X and Y. Thus, if the coefficient of determination is 0, none of the variability in Y is associated with X and the estimated regression line has no predictability. However, if R^2 is 1, all of the variability in the dependent response variable is associated with the independent predictor variable and the sample results are completely predictable through the regression equation.

The formula for the coefficient of determination is

Sample Coefficient of Determination: Expressed by Sum of Squares

$$R^2 = 1 - \frac{\text{SSE}}{\text{SST}} = \frac{\text{SSR}}{\text{SST}} \qquad (9.3)$$

where

$\quad$ SSE = errors sum of squares (Σe_i^2)

$\quad$ SSR = regression sum of squares

$\quad$ SST = total sum of squares

Substituting numerical equivalents for our example yields $R^2 = 0.5013/2.0629 = 0.243$ (which appears on the MINITAB printout as R-sq). We now believe that 24.3% of the variation in the dependent variable (Y) is explained by the independent variable (X). This is not a particularly large value for R^2; however, in a later section we will learn to test to determine if it is significant at a specific confidence level.

$\qquad$ Please note that even if we obtain an R^2 from the computer near 1, this does not necessarily imply causality. We may be having interference from a third variable which is distorting our results. We will expand on this thought process in Section 9.9.

A Zero or One Coefficient of Determination

$\qquad$ The coefficient of determination is an index that ranges between 0 and 1. A 0 reading indicates none of the changes in Y are attributable to changes in X, while a reading of 1 means all of the changes in Y are attributable to changes in X. Let us examine these extreme cases. If $R^2 = 0$ in a model, then

$\qquad$ SST = SSE and SSR = 0

The model has no explanatory value since the sum of squares due to regression (SSR) is 0 and all variability in Y is associated with variables omitted from the model. We should note that in this case the regression line would have a 0 slope and pass through a single Y, which must be the mean of Y (Figure 9.6). Since the mean of Y is constant, the data would simply be dispersed about this constant. Thus, a 0 coefficient of determination denotes the horizontal regression line (0 slope).

$\qquad$ However, if the slope of the estimated regression line is non-zero the coefficient of determination is also non-zero. This will become important when we test the hypothesis concerning the true slope and coefficient of determination that is estimated from the sample results. If we test the hypothesis that the true slope is 0, we are simultaneously testing the hypothesis that the true coefficient of determination is also 0. Of course, if we test that the hypothesis concerning the population coefficient of determination equals 0, we are also testing the hypothesis that the population slope (B) equals 0.

Figure 9.6 $\quad R^2$ Values of 0 and 1

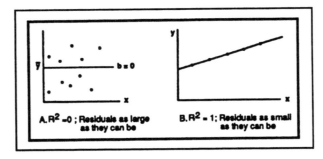

If the coefficient of determination were 1, then

$$SST = SSR \text{ and } SSE = 0$$

All explanation for the changes in Y would be provided by the independent variable in the model (due to regression and the model). No omitted variable(s) would have an impact on the predictability. Also, the sum of the squared residuals (SSE) must equal 0. Thus all the residual values (e) have to equal 0 as well. Since the squares of a variable can have no negative values, positive and negative readings will not cancel each other. Therefore, all of the data points must lie directly on the regression line and each and every e value will equal 0 (Figure 9.6B). Since there is no outside influence or disturbance, the explanation of the changes in Y attributable to changes in X is perfect.

Suppose all of the data points fall on a horizontal line ($b = 0$). Is there perfect or zero predictability? In such a case we would find that $SST = SSR = SSE = 0$. There is no vertical variation of any kind and dividing by 0 is undefined.

The Coefficient of Correlation

The **coefficient of correlation**, developed by Karl Pearson (1857–1936), is the statistic that measures the degree of linear association between X and Y. It is the square root of the coefficient of determination. Since the square root of a number that ranges from 0 to 1, will range from -1 to $+1$, we obtain

---

Sample Coefficient of Correlation

$$R = \pm\sqrt{R^2} \qquad\qquad (9.4)$$

where $R^2 =$ coefficient of determination

If we substitute numerical equivalents into our formula, $R = \sqrt{.243} = .493$. However, this formula will not tell us whether R is positive or negative. To determine the sign, simply look at the sign of the regression slope (b). If we have a $+b$ we have a direct relationship between Y and X and we have a $+R$, and if we have an inverse relationship between Y and X then we have $-b$ and a $-R$. Our regression slope is $+.002$, hence $R = +.493$.

MINITAB will perform a correlation of any two variables by using the following steps:

Stat > Basic Statistics > Correlation
Double click **GMAT** and **GGPA** into **Variables** box
OK

The MINITAB output is
Correlations, (Pearson)
Correlation of GMAT and GGPA $= 0.493$, P-value $= 0.103$

We will use an example to illustrate what it would mean to have a $+1$, -1, or 0 coefficient of correlation. In the U.S., prior to 1950 there was a yearly average of 16,000 cases of paralytic poliomyelitis (polio: a dreaded disease). Since 1961 health officials vaccinate with a live oral poliomyelitis vaccine. Hence, there is a $+1$ correlation between taking the vaccine and having a virus in our system (the vaccine is a live virus). From 1980–1989 there had been no reported cases of epidemic paralytic polio in the U.S. This represents a -1 correlation. You take the vaccine and you will not contract the disease in question.

A 0 coefficient of correlation would indicate that no linear association exists between the vaccine and contract of the disease.

Figure 9.7 shows scatter diagrams for different coefficients of correlation. In Figures 9.7A and 9.7B, examples of perfect linear association between X and Y are shown. The two examples differ not in terms of the degree of association but only in the direction of the relationship. In Figure 9.7A, X and Y are inversely related (negative slope) and in 9.7B, X and Y are directly related (positive slope).

If we observe the scatter diagrams in Figure 9.7C and 9.7D, we see that the correlation coefficient for the data in 9.7C is larger than in 9.7D (assuming X and Y scales are identical). This observation is due to the smaller residual values in Figure 9.7C. The scattergrams in Figure 9.7E and 9.7F both show examples with zero correlation coefficients. However, we must be careful in our interpretation of each. Figure 9.7E is typical of situations with zero linear association. Since the unexplained variation equals the total variation, the explained variation equals 0 and its square root R, is 0. Figure 9.7F illustrates a situation in which the association between X and Y is quite well defined but is definitely not linear. Using linear regression and correlation in this case is an application of an improper functional form. The data are in the basic form of a second-degree polynomial or parabola.

Fitting a straight line to parabolic data is inappropriate. If a parabola were fit to this data using the least squares technique, the appropriate correlation coefficient would be close to 1 because the residual (e) values about a parabola are relatively small. We can distinguish between the two cases simply by examining the residual values. In Figure 9.7E, the signs of the residuals are random. In Figure 9.7F, the residuals generated from the fit of a linear equation are clumped or grouped together, where the first group contains positive residuals, the second group contains negative residuals, and the final group contains positive residuals. Whenever the signs of the residuals are not random, it can be a sign of an improper specification of the model. In this case, we should determine if a different functional form for our model would yield a considerably higher R^2. If we can't find a better model, we will have to use techniques more advanced than those converted in this text to alleviate the problem of clumped residuals.

Figure 9.7 Scatter Diagrams for Different Values of R

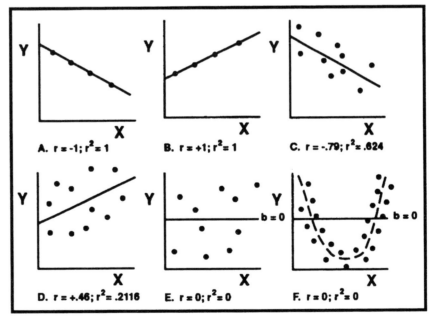

Care must be taken in comparing two coefficients of correlation. If one is .2, and the other is .8, we could not say that the latter coefficient represents a linear association four times stronger than the former. Instead we must examine the coefficient of determination, which is .04 and .64 respectively. Thus, the latter case reflects a model that explains percentage-wise 16 times more variability in Y than does the former.

 Concept Check 9.E

The larger the residual values the smaller the values for $S_{Y \bullet X}$ and R^2. True or false? If false, explain.

Exercises

9.19

Y	X
27	4
14	10
12	16
6	21
1	25

a. After estimating the regression equation, how many residual (e) values will there be in the data set?

b. If the regression equation is $= 29.253 - 1.135(X)$ tabulate each residual value.

c. Are the residual values (e) a vertical reading, a horizontal reading, or a perpendicular reading?

d. From an intuitive standpoint, do you believe these residual values are relatively large or small?

9.20   For the data set in Exercise 9.19, answer the following using a MINITAB printout:

a. Check your residuals computed in Exercise 9.19.b with those tabulated by MINITAB.

b. From MINITAB: What is SSR, SSE, and SST?

c. Use SSE and formula 9.2 to check MINITAB's answer for the standard error of the estimate.

d. Is $R^2 = $ SSR/SST?

e. Is the value for R positive or negative?

9.21

X	Y
1	4
6	10
12	16
14	21
27	25

a. How many residual (e) values will there be in the data set?

b. If the regression equation is $= 5.469 + 0.811(X)$, tabulate each residual value.

c. Are the residual values (e) a vertical reading, a horizontal reading, or a perpendicular reading?

d. From an intuitive standpoint do you believe these residual values are relatively large or small?

e. Compute the standard error of the estimate assuming $\Sigma e^2 = 28.994$.

9.22   For the data set in Exercise 9.21, answer the following using a MINITAB printout:

a. Check your residuals computed in Exercise 9.21.b with those tabulated by MINITAB.

b. From MINITAB: What is SSR, SSE, and SST?

c. Use SSE and formula 9.2 to check MINITAB's answer for the standard error of the estimate.

d. Is $R^2 = $ SSR/SST?

e. Is the value for R positive or negative?

9.23
Y	X
1	4
6	10
12	16
14	21
27	25

Have MINITAB perform a regression analysis and interpret the regression slope, standard error of the estimate, R^2 and R.

9.24　a.　In your own words explain R^2.

b.　In your own words explain R.

9.25　a.　Explain the differences between R^2 and R.

X	Y
1	7
7	7
10	7
24	7
39	7
49	7
51	7
77	7

b.　From observing the data, what do you suspect about SSR, SSE, and SST? Confirm with MINITAB.

9.26　a.
X	Y
1	7
7	7
10	7
24	7
39	7
49	7
51	7
77	7

b.　From observing the data, what do you suspect about SSR, SSE, and SST? Confirm with MINITAB.

9.27
X	Y
1	4
2	6
3	8
4	10
5	12
6	14
7	16
8	18

a.　From observing the data, what do you suspect about a, b, SSR, SSE, SST, R, and R^2?

b.　Use MINITAB to confirm or deny your suspicions.

9.28

X	Y
1	4
2	6
3	8
4	10
5	8
6	6
7	4

    a. From observing the data, what do you suspect about the linear R, and R^2?
    b. Use MINITAB to confirm or deny your suspicions.
    c. Have MINITAB list the residuals. Evaluate.

9.29   Is it possible that SST = SSR = SSE? Explain.

9.30   What are the underlying assumptions of least squares?

9.6   Hypothesis Testing Involving the Regression Model

We now turn to hypothesis testing involving the regression model. The question arises as to whether the regression model is significant at a specific level of confidence. Two approaches can be taken towards answering this question. The first is called **global testing**, which attempts to determine if the entire model is significant. The second attempts to determine if the independent variables in the model are significant. Of course, in a simple linear regression model, there is but one independent variable; hence, both approaches yield exactly the same conclusion. However, in the next chapter, there are multiple independent variables; hence, the model may be significant, but all of the independent variables may not necessarily be significant.

Testing for R^2: Global Testing With ANOVA

We now will use an **analysis of variance** (ANOVA) test to determine if the model has predictability. The null hypothesis will be that the true predictability of the model is 0 (H_o: Population $R^2 = 0$; H_A: Population $R^2 \neq 0$). This null hypothesis places the burden of proof on the researcher to prove that the model they created is significant. Recall that three types of variation are possible. SST measures changes in Y about its own mean. SSE measures changes in Y not associated with X and presumably associated with omitted variables. Finally, SSR measures changes in Y due to X, which is included in the model. Therefore,

SST = SSR + SSE

The general format of the ANOVA table is

Table 9.4 General Format for the Anova Table

Source	Sum of Squares	Degrees of Freedom	Mean Square	F_{test}
Regression-SSR	$\Sigma(\hat{Y} - \overline{Y})^2$	$df = m - 1$	MSR = SSR/(m − 1)	MSR/MSE
Residual-SSE	$\Sigma(Y_i - \hat{Y})^2$	$df = n - m$	MSE = SSE/(n − m)	
Total-SST	$\Sigma(Y_i - \overline{Y})^2$	$df = n - 1$		

Note that if the square root of MSE is taken (called the root mean square error: RMSE = $\sqrt{MSE}$), it is the standard error of the estimate ($S_{Y \bullet X}$).

As was the case when we introduced the ANOVA concepts in Chapter 8, the test statistic is F_{test}, and is defined as

---

The Regression Model Test Statistic: F_{test}

$$F_{test} = \frac{MSR}{MSE}$$

(9.5)

where

$MSR = SSR/(m-1)$

$MSE = SSE/(n-m)$

$n = $ sample size

$m = $ the number of coefficients in the regression model

$H_o = $ population $R^2 = B = 0$; $H_A = $ population R^2 & $B \neq 0$.

Remember that we are trying to estimate the true regression equation

$Y = A + BX$ based on a randomly selected survey.

Returning to our GMAT/GGPA data set, we will take the ANOVA results directly from MINITAB (Table 9.5).

Table 9.5   Abbreviated MINITAB Results: Analysis of Variance

Source	DF	SS	MS	F	p
Regression	1	0.5013	0.5013	3.21	0.103
Residual Error	10	1.5616	0.1562		
Total	11	2.0629			

We must compare F_{test} (MINITAB's F) to the $F_{\alpha(df)}$ value found in Appendix A, Table 4. If we assume a 5% level of significance, 1 degree of freedom in the numerator $(m-1)$ and 10 degrees of freedom in the denominator $(n-m)$, we obtain $F_{.05(1/10)} = 4.96$. Since the test statistic, F_{test} (3.210), is less than the critical F (4.96), we are unable to reject the null hypothesis that the model is inadequate $(R^2 = 0)$. To reject the null hypothesis, the condition that must be met is $F_{test} > F_{\alpha(df)}$.

Note that we favor the hypothesis that $R^2 = 0$ for a linear model only. If we view Figure 9.7F, we can see that a nonlinear relationship exists. For this data set, MINITAB would probably tell us that there is no linear relationship between X and Y. However, if we fit a quadratic equation to the data set (Section 10.9), we would find a significant R^2.

Since there is Insufficient Statistical Evidence to Reject (ISER) the null hypothesis, we must conclude our model is not significant, neither is it currently useful as a predictive tool. The true predictability of the model is 0, even though the sample predictability coefficient indicated that 24.3% of the changes in Y are explained by changes in X. The 24.3% association could have occurred because of the random selection of the sample; hence, is attributable to sampling error.

p-Values

If we use MINITAB, it is not necessary to use the F table since the computer program automatically provides the relevant information. The p-value (0.103) tells us that F_{test} is significant for all significance levels at .103 or above. Hence, the p-value is the smallest value for a for which we will reject H_0. Since we desire a 5% level $(\alpha = .05)$ of significance, we have ISER H_0. **The decision rule is if $\alpha \geq P$, we reject the null hypothesis that the population $R^2=0$. If $\alpha < P$, we have ISER for the null hypothesis.**

241

We turn from the global approach of looking at the entire regression model to looking at the individual independent variables within the model. Of course, a linear bivariate regression model contains but one independent variable; hence, in this chapter, the two approaches yield identical results. This will not be the case in the next chapter.

We are testing the hypothesis that the population slope (B) equals 0. Since the true linear equation is in the form $\hat{Y} = A + B \bullet X$, if $B = 0$, $B \bullet X = 0$, and X drops from the regression model leaving us without a model.

The null and alternative hypotheses concerning B may be a one- or two-tailed test. A one-tailed test would be employed if there is empirical evidence that would support the hypothesis that X and Y should be directly related ($+b$) or inversely related ($-b$). The respective tests are

TWO-TAILED TEST	ONE-TAILED TEST	
	Direct relationship	*Inverse relationship*
H_o: $B = 0$	H_o: $B \leq 0$	H_o: $B \geq 0$
H_A: $B \neq 0$	H_A: $B > 0$	H_A: $B < 0$

In a sense, the null hypothesis places the burden of proof on the researcher. It is up to the researcher to disprove the null hypothesis. The sample slope (b) must be significantly different from 0 to lead to a rejection of the null hypothesis. It is normal to use a two-tailed test in the analysis and that is what will be concentrate in our analyses. The test statistic is

Test Statistic for B

$$t_{\text{test}} = \frac{b}{\dfrac{S_{Y \bullet X}}{\sqrt{\Sigma X^2 - n\overline{X}^2}}} = \frac{b}{S_b} \tag{9.6}$$

where

b = estimated slope

S_b = standard error of the slope = $S_{Y \bullet X} \Big/ \sqrt{(\Sigma X^2 - n\overline{X}^2)}$

n = the sample size

H_o: $B = 0$; H_A: $B \neq 0$. If theoretical knowledge exists that the slope should be

positive H_o: $\leq 0\,(H_A > 0)$, and if negative H_o: $\geq 0\,(H_A < 0)$.

Applying formula 9.6 to our graduate GPA example, we obtain

$$S_b = \frac{.3951}{\sqrt{3,384,194 - 12(6262/12)^2}} = 0.0011579$$

and

$$t_{\text{test}} = \frac{.0020746}{.0011579} = 1.792$$

If this problem is treated as a two-tailed test, the critical value for $t_{.05/2(10)}$ (from Appendix A, Table 3 at $n - 2$ degrees of freedom because we are using estimates of A and B in our computations) is $t_{.05/2(10)} = 2.228$. If $|t_{\text{test}}| > t_{\alpha/2(df)}$, we would reject H_o. Since $1.792 \leq 2.228$, we have ISER H_o; GMAT is not a significant predictor of GGPA.

It is more appropriate to employ a one-tailed test in our example because it is assumed that graduate GPA varies directly (positive relationship) with GMAT scores. We place the burden of proof on the researcher to prove that his or her model does have a positive relationship; hence, $H_A: B > 0$, making $H_o: B \leq 0$. Remember, as the creator of the model, we will want to reject H_o in favor of H_A. To reject H_o means that a significant association exists between X and Y and maybe we can utilize the model as a predictive tool. Remember from Chapter 7 that the equal sign must appear only in the null hypothesis, never in the alternate hypothesis.

The critical or tabular value for a 5 percent level of significance is $t_{.05/1(10)} = 1.812$. For the upper-tailed test, we reject H_o when $t_{test} > t_{\alpha/1/(df)}$. Since $1.792 \leq 1.812$, we are unable to reject H_o. We must assume at this point that the graduate GPA model is not significant and applicants' GMAT scores are not a good predictor of graduate GGPA.

In a linear equation, the slope is more important than the intercept. If the slope equals 0, there is no simple linear regression model.

MINITAB performs all of the computational work to test hypotheses concerning the intercept and slope of the regression equation. It also provides estimates of the coefficients and their standard errors if we desire to formulate the interval estimates. The abbreviated MINITAB output is given in Table 9.6.

Table 9.6 Abbreviated MINITAB Output

Regression Analysis

THE REGRESSION EQUATION IS

GGPA $= 2.17 + 0.00207$ GMAT

Predictor	Coef	StDev	T	P
Constant	2.1707	0.6149	3.53	0.005
GMAT	0.002075	0.001158	1.79	0.103

From Table 9.6, if we divide the coefficient by its standard error, we obtain t_{test} ($t_{test} =$ MINITAB's $T = .002075/.0011158$). With MINITAB, and with most statistical packages, there is no need to look up the $t_{\alpha(df)}$ in the back of the text because we are directly supplied with all pertinent information. MINITAB yields the P-**Value** for a two-tailed test P. The rules for rejecting the null hypothesis using p-values are as follows:

P-**Value Rules for Rejecting the Hypothesis That** $B_i = 0$, $B_i \geq 0$, **&** $B_i \leq 0$

Two-tailed test: If $\alpha \geq P$, rejection $H_0: B = 0$.

One-tailed test: If in the tail of Rejection, rejection when $\alpha \geq P/2$. You are in the tail of rejection when your alternate hypothesis is $<$ and your test statistic is negative, and when your alternate hypothesis is $>$ and the test statistic is positive.

In our example involving GGPA and GMAT scores, we expected a positive slope; hence, with respect to B we are involved in a one-tailed test. If we desire a 95% confidence level ($\alpha = .05$), we would not reject the hypothesis that $B = 0$ ($.05 < .103/2$). Since we can assume that $B = 0$, GMAT is not a significant predictor of GGPA at the 5% level. Had we selected a 90% confidence level, we would have rejected the hypothesis that $B = 0$ ($.10 \geq .103/2$).

Confidence Interval for B

Since we know S_b, it is an easy process to compute the $(1 - \alpha) \bullet 100\%$ confidence interval of the population slope (B).

$(1 - \alpha) \bullet 100\%$ Confidence Interval for the Population Slope (B)

$$b \pm t_{\alpha/2(df)} \bullet S_b \qquad (9.7)$$

where

$$b = \text{estimated slope}$$

$$t_{\alpha/2(df)} = \text{critical value of } t, \text{ two-tailed test}$$

$$S_b = \text{standard error of the coefficient (slope)}$$

Using our graduate GPA example, we obtain the following 95% confidence interval of B:
$.002075 \pm (2.228)(.001158); \ -.000505 \le B \le +.004654$

Remembering the topic of interval estimation (Chapter 6), if 100 different samples of size 12 are taken, approximately 95 of the confidence intervals would include the population slope B. In the graduate GPA example, the interval estimate of B has a negative lower limit and a positive upper limit. Thus, with 95 percent confidence, we can't even conclude that increases in the GMAT score are associated with increases in graduate performance as shown by graduate grade point average.

Concept Check 9.F

If the confidence interval about b includes 0, we have ISER the hypothesis that the true slope (B) is 0; hence, the independent variable is significant to the regression model. True or false? If false, explain.

Exercises

9.31   What is the difference between testing to determine if the true $R^2 = 0$ or if $B = 0$ in a linear bivariate regression model?

9.32 $F_{\text{test}} = \text{SSR/SST}$ If false, explain.

9.33   a.   If we expect a direct relationship between X and Y, what is our null hypothesis concerning B?
        b.   If we expect an inverse relationship between X and Y, what is our null hypothesis concerning B?

9.34   a.   For a two-tailed test, what is our rejection of $H_o: B = 0$ rule for our p-value?
        b.   For a one-tailed test, what is our rejection of $H_o: B \ge 0$ rule for our p-value?

9.35

Y	X
27	4
14	10
12	16
6	21
1	25

Answer the following using a MINITAB printout:
a.   From a global perspective, is the linear model between X and Y significant at the 5% level?
b.   Since we do not know anything about the actual data, we can't assume a direct or inverse relationship. Hence, we are involved with a two-tailed test. At the 5% level, is the slope significant?
c.   Compare your answers from 9.35.a and 9.35.b Explain.
d.   Compute the 95% confidence interval for the regression slope. Does it contain $B = 0$?

9.36

X	Y
1	4
6	10
12	16
14	21
27	25

Answer the following using a MINITAB Printout:

a. From a global perspective, is the linear model between X and Y significant at the 1% level? What is the smallest α value for which the model is significant?

b. Since we do not know anything about the actual data, we can't assume a direct or inverse relationship. Hence, we are involved with a two-tailed test. At the 1% level, is the slope significant?

c. Compare your answers from 9.36.a and 9.36.b. Explain.

d. Compute the 99% confidence interval for the regression slope. Does it contain $B = 0$?

9.37

X	Y
3	26
5	14
10	11
21	7

Answer the following using a MINITAB printout:

a. From a global perspective, is the linear model between X and Y significant at the 10% level?

b. Since we do not know anything about the actual data, we can't assume a direct or inverse relationship. Hence, we are involved with a two-tailed test. At the 10% level, is the slope significant?

c. Compare your answers from 9.37.a and 9.37.b. Explain.

d. Compute the 90% confidence interval for the regression slope. Does it contain $B = 0$?

9.38

Student	GGPA	UGGPA
#1	3.86	3.91
#2	3.05	2.77
#3	2.65	2.10
#4	3.50	3.68
#5	3.00	2.79
#6	4.00	3.81
#7	3.10	2.75
#8	3.89	3.89
#9	3.21	3.07
#10	3.45	3.61
#11	2.80	2.19
#12	3.30	3.24
#13	3.12	3.38
#14	3.44	3.63
#15	3.59	3.41
#16	3.16	3.04
#17	3.22	3.67

a. A university admissions committee believes there is a direct relationship between a student's undergraduate grade point (UGGPA) and his or her graduate grade point average (GGPA). What are the null and alternate hypotheses concerning the true slope?

b. Using MINITAB is H_o rejected at the 5% level?

245

9.39	Year	Consumption	GNP
	1965	440.7	705.1
	1966	477.3	772.0
	1967	503.6	816.4
	1968	552.5	892.7
	1969	597.9	963.9
	1970	640.0	1,015.5
	1971	691.6	1,102.7
	1972	757.6	1,212.8
	1973	837.2	1,359.3
	1974	916.5	1,472.8
	1975	1,012.8	1,598.4
	1976	1,129.3	1,782.3
	1977	1,257.2	1,990.5
	1978	1,403.5	2,249.7
	1979	1,566.8	2,508.2
	1980	1,732.6	2,732.0
	1981	1,915.1	3,052.6
	1982	2,050.7	3,166.0
	1983	2,234.5	3,405.7
	1984	2,430.5	3,772.2
	1985	2,629.0	4,014.9
	1986	2,807.5	4,240.3
	1987	3,012.1	4,526.7
	1988	3,226.0	4,861.8

a. We have the Gross National Product and Personal Consumption expenditures in billions of current dollars in the U.S. between 1965–1988. Would we expect a positive or negative linear relationship for the model: Consumption $= f(\text{GNP})$?

b. Use MINITAB to ascertain if the true R^2, and $B = 0$ at the 1% level of significance.

9.40	Individual	Hours of Overtime	Defective Parts
	#1	1	3
	#2	17	40
	#3	5	10
	#4	15	36
	#5	10	24
	#6	7	16
	#7	11	23
	#8	6	8
	#9	0	3
	#10	4	12
	#11	9	26
	#12	20	51
	#13	8	18
	#14	12	33
	#15	3	9

A company fears that a linear relationship exists between employees' hours of overtime work and their defective parts produced. It monitors all 15 of its employees in a week's period of time. Are the company's fears founded ($\alpha = .01$)?

Confidence Intervals for $\mu_{Y|X_o}$

The sample intercept and slope are determined by the specific sample that was randomly selected. If the estimated parameters can change due to sample selection, then certainly the confidence and prediction intervals based on those estimated parameters can also change.

Using the data from the graduate GPA example, suppose the admissions committee wanted to estimate the average graduate GPA for all students with a 500 ($X_o = 500$) score on the GMAT. Using the regression equation, given that the mean of all X values is 500 (symbolized by $\mu_{Y|500}$), the mean of Y is estimated to be

$$Y = 2.170736 + .00207469(500) = 3.208 \approx 3.21$$

If there were 100 applicants with a GMAT score of 500, we might expect that their mean grade-point average would not always exactly equal 3.21. Therefore, a $(1 - \alpha) \bullet 100\%$ confidence interval about the predicted value for the dependent variable is required. This confidence interval depends on $t_{\alpha2(df)}$ and the standard deviation of the fit.

The $(1 - \alpha) \bullet 100\%$ confidence interval for the mean of Y, given a particular value of X is

---

$(1 - \alpha) \bullet 100\%$ Confidence Interval for $\mu_{Y|500}$

$$\hat{Y} \pm t_{\alpha/2(n-m)}\text{stdev.fit} \tag{9.8}$$

where

$$\text{Stdev.fit} = S_{Y \bullet X}\sqrt{\frac{1}{n} + \frac{(X - \overline{X})^2}{\Sigma X^2 - n\overline{X}^2}}$$

Stdev.fit = Standard Deviation of the Fit

$\hat{Y}$ = estimated Y value

$t_{\alpha/2(n-m)}$ = critical two-tailed t-value

n = sample size

m = number of estimated parameters

$S_{Y \bullet X}$ = standard error of the estimate

For our GGPA example, if we use a GMAT score of 500 ($X = 500$), we obtain

$$3.208 \pm 2.228(.395)\sqrt{\frac{1}{12} + \frac{(500 - 521.833)^2}{3,384,194 - 12(521.833)^2}}$$

$$3.208 \pm (2.228)(.395)(.296)$$

$$3.208 \pm .260; \ 2.948 \le \hat{Y} \le 3.468$$

Note that since a grade-point average of 3.0 is required, the lower value of the interval is just slightly below what is required for graduation. Hence, the admissions committee may reject any applications whose GMAT score is ≤ 500.

MINITAB will print $\hat{Y}$ and stdev.fit values for all X values contained in the data base and for any specified value for X. The confidence and prediction intervals for the 95% level for X values within and without the data set can be obtained using the following procedure.

Stat > Regression > Regression
Double click **GGPA** to enter in **Response** box.
Double click **GMAT** to enter in **Predictors** box.
Click in **Options**.
Click on the **Predication intervals for new observations** text box.
If you want the intervals for all X values in the data set double click **GMAT** into the box.
If you want the intervals for X values not included in the data set (say $X = 500$) enter that value into the box
OK twice.

Table 9.7A Abbreviated MINITAB Output Yielding 95% Confidence and Prediction Intervals for all values of GMAT.

Fit	Stdev.Fit	95% C.I	95% P.I
3.333	0.122	(3.060, 3.605)	(2.411, 4.254)
3.498	0.178	(3.101, 3.896)	(2.532, 4.465)
3.374	0.132	(3.079, 3.669)	(2.445, 4.303)
3.167	0.124	(2.890, 3.443)	(2.244, 4.090)
3.492	0.175	(3.101, 3.883)	(2.529, 4.456)
3.436	0.153	(3.095, 3.777)	(2.492, 4.381)
3.063	0.156	(2.715, 3.410)	(2.116, 4.010)
3.001	0.181	(2.596, 3.405)	(2.031, 3.970)
3.104	0.141	(2.790, 3.419)	(2.169, 4.040)
3.260	0.114	(3.006, 3.514)	(2.343, 4.177)
2.855	0.250	(2.299, 3.412)	(1.814, 3.897)
3.457	0.161	(3.098, 3.816)	(2.506, 4.408)

Table 9.7B Abbreviated MINITAB Output Yielding 95% Confidence and Prediction Intervals when GMAT = 500.

Predicted Values

Fit	SE Fit	95% C.I		95% P.I	
3.208	0.117	2.948	3.468	2.290	4.126

Let's duplicate MINITAB's output for the first student in the data set. This student had 560 for their GMAT score. For $X = 560$, the 95% confidence interval ($\mu_{Y|560}$) is

$\hat{Y} \pm 5_{.05/2(10)}$(Std.fit); $3.333 \pm 2.228(.122)$; $3.333 \pm .2718$

So, the average GGPA, for all students whose GMAT = 560, is expected with 95 percent confidence to fall between 3.0612 and 3.6048.

Note from Table 9.7A that St.dev.fit is smallest the closer the chosen value for X is to ($\overline{X} = 521.833$), and increases the selected value for X departs from $\overline{X}$. If St.dev.fit increases under this condition, so will the upper and lower confidence limits. This is because the estimate is less reliable as we depart from X. The upper and lower confidence limits can be seen in Figure 9.8.

If we desire a graph of the 95% confidence and predictive bands MINITAB will supply it to us. The commands and graph are:

Stat > Regression > Fitted Line Plot
Double click **GGPA** into **Response (Y)** box.
Double click GMAT into **Predictor (X)** box.
Click **Options** box
Click on **Display confidence and prediction interval**
OK twice

248

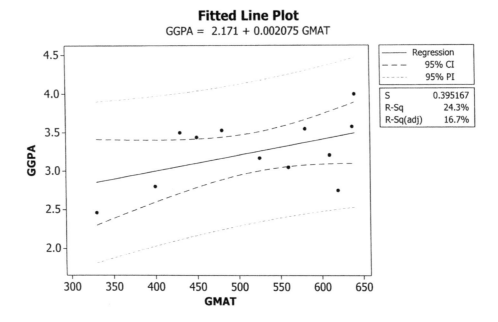

Fitted Line Plot
GGPA = 2.171 + 0.002075 GMAT

Let's duplicate the confidence interval involved when $X = 500$.

$$\hat{Y} \pm t_{.05/2(10)}(\text{St.dev.fit}); \ 3.208 \pm 2.228(.117); \ 3.208 \pm .261$$

We must be careful not to compute confidence intervals too far from $\overline{X}$, as the interval may be so large as to render it meaningless. Extrapolation beyond the bounds of the data base is rarely recommended since the dispersion and potential for error increase. Also linear analysis over a specified range of X values may become nonlinear over a larger range.

$(1 - \alpha) \bullet$ 100% Prediction Interval for $Y_{|X_o}$

More often than not, regression analysis is used to predict an individual value of Y for a given value of X (rather than the mean value of X). The prediction of an individual Y, given a particular value of X, is symbolized by $Y_{|X_o}$. As before, the prediction interval will pivot on $\hat{Y}$. Note that we do not use the term "confidence interval" because we are not trying to estimate a parameter. When trying to predict the value of a random variable, we use the term prediction interval.

249

Since we are predicting the value of a random variable, the variability is much greater than it was in formula 9.9. The prediction interval for $Y_{|X_o}$ is

---

$(1 - \alpha) \bullet 100\%$ Prediction Interval for $Y_{|X_o}$

$$\hat{Y} \pm t_{\alpha/2(n-m)} \bullet \sqrt{\left[\text{MSE} + (\text{Stdev.Fit})^2\right]} \qquad (9.9A)$$

$$\hat{Y} \pm t_{\alpha/2(n-m)} \bullet S_{Y \bullet X} \sqrt{1 + \frac{1}{n} + \frac{\left(X - \overline{X}\right)^2}{\Sigma X2 - n\overline{X}^2}} \qquad (9.9B)$$

where

$n = $ sample size

$\hat{Y} = $ estimated Y-value for a specified X-value

$t_{\alpha/2(df)} = $ critical two-tailed t-value

$n = $ sample size

$m = $ number of estimated parameters

$S_{Y \bullet X} = $ standard error of the estimate

The only difference between formulas 9.8 and 9.9B is the addition of $+1$ to formula 9.9B. It might appear that this will result in a small increase in the interval, but it actually represents a sizeable increase.

Let's return to our graduate GGPA/GMAT example and compute the 95% prediction interval for $X = 500$.

$$3.208 \pm 2.228(.3951)\sqrt{1 + \frac{1}{12} + \frac{(500 - 521.833)^2}{3,384,194 - 12(6262/12)^2}}$$

$$3.208 \pm 0.918; \ 2.290 \leq \hat{Y} \leq 4.126$$

We will now compute the prediction interval using formula 9.9A and MINITAB's MSE $= .156$ and St.dev.fit $= 0.117$. The 95% prediction interval is

$$3.208 \pm (2.228) \bullet \sqrt{[0.156 + (0.117)^2]}; \ \text{Or } 3.208 \pm 0.918$$

Note that this interval is considerably wider than our previous interval for the conditional mean $(2.948 \leq \hat{Y} \leq 3.468)$. The wider interval resulted from our predicting the GGPA for a specific person as opposed to predicting the average GGPA for a group of persons all with 500 GMAT scores. The prediction of an average (mean) value should always be more precise than predicting an individual value. In Figure 9.8 we have graphed both intervals.

 Concept Check 9.G

If the estimated parameters of a regression equation can change due to sample selection, then certainly the predictions based on these estimated parameters can change. True or false? If false, explain.

9.41

Y	X
1	4
6	10
12	16
14	21
27	25

a. Using MINITAB predict Y when $X = 20$.
b. Calculate the 95% confidence interval for $\mu_{Y|20}$.
c. Calculate the 95% prediction interval for $Y_{|20}$.
d. Between the 95% confidence and prediction intervals, which is larger? Explain.

9.42

X	Y
3	26
5	14
10	11
21	7

a. Using MINITAB predict Y when $X = 20$.
b. Calculate the 95% confidence interval for $\mu_{Y|20}$.
c. Calculate the 95% prediction interval for $Y_{|20}$.

9.43

Student	GGPA	UGGPA
#1	3.86	3.91
#2	3.05	2.77
#3	2.65	2.10
#4	3.50	3.68
#5	3.00	2.79
#6	4.00	3.81
#7	3.10	2.75
#8	3.89	3.89
#9	3.21	3.07
#10	3.45	3.61
#11	2.80	2.19
#12	3.30	3.24
#13	3.12	3.38
#14	3.44	3.63
#15	3.59	3.41
#16	3.16	3.04
#17	3.22	3.67

a. Using MINITAB predict GGPA when UGGPA $= 3.00$.
b. Calculate the 99% confidence interval for $\mu_{Y|3.00}$.
c. Calculate the 99% prediction interval for $Y_{|3.00}$.

9.44	Year	Consumption	GNP
	1965	440.7	705.1
	1966	477.3	772.0
	1967	503.6	816.4
	1968	552.5	892.7
	1969	597.9	963.9
	1970	640.0	1,015.5
	1971	691.6	1,102.7
	1972	757.6	1,212.8
	1973	837.2	1,359.3
	1974	916.5	1,472.8
	1975	1,012.8	1,598.4
	1976	1,129.3	1,782.8
	1977	1,257.2	1,990.5
	1978	1,403.5	2,249.7
	1979	1,566.8	2,508.2
	1980	1,732.6	2,732.0
	1981	1,915.1	3,052.6
	1982	2,050.7	3,166.0
	1983	2,234.5	3,405.7
	1984	2,430.5	3,772.2
	1985	2,629.0	4,014.9
	1986	2,807.5	4,240.3
	1987	3,012.1	4,526.7
	1988	3,226.0	4,861.8

a. Using MINITAB, predict consumption when GNP = 5,000.
b. Calculate the 90% confidence interval for $\mu_{Y|5000}$.
c. Calculate the 90% prediction interval for $Y_{|5000}$.

9.45	Individual	Hours of Overtime	Defective Parts
	#1	1	3
	#2	17	40
	#3	5	10
	#4	15	36
	#5	10	24
	#6	7	16
	#7	11	23
	#8	6	8
	#9	0	3
	#10	4	12
	#11	9	26
	#12	20	51
	#13	8	18
	#14	12	33
	#15	3	9

a. Using MINITAB, predict defective parts when overtime = 25 hours.
b. Calculate the 95% confidence interval for $\mu_{Y|25}$.
c. Calculate the 95% prediction interval for $Y_{|25}$.

252

9.46
X	Y
1	4
2	6
3	8
4	10
5	12
6	14
7	16
8	18

   a. Using MINITAB, predict Y when $X = 20$.
   b. Calculate the 45% confidence interval for $\mu_{Y|20}$.
   c. Calculate the 95% prediction interval for $Y_{|20}$.
   d. Is there anything unusual concerning the confidence and prediction intervals? Explain.

9.8   An Analysis of Outliers

One of the most nagging problems in applying regression analysis to business oriented problems involves unusual data points. These unusual observations can involve X, Y, or both X & Y. These unusual data points are known through many synonyms including **maverick** data points, **extreme** data points, or most often as **outliers** because they lie outside of normal bounds.

Let's return to our GMAT/GGPA example and add a new twist. Suppose after the drop date without penalty, our University Admissions Committee had one graduate student who was called out of town because of a family emergency and had to accept an F in all class work (4 courses). Suppose, too, that the student had a GMAT score of 595. Table 9.8 shows the data with this student added to the original 12 observations.

Table 9.8   GMAT and GGPA Data Set with an Outlier

Student	GMAT Score X	Graduate GPA Y
1	560	3.05
2	640	4.00
3	580	3.55
4	480	3.53
5	637	3.58
6	610	3.21
7	430	3.50
8	400	2.80
9	450	3.44
10	525	3.17
11	330	2.46
12	620	2.75
13	595	0.00

The MINITAB output for the data set without this 13th student appears in Table 9.9A, and with this student included in Table 9.9b. We can note the enormous changes in the output particularly in the p value following F and in the coefficient of determination. Fortunately, MINITAB also warns us of the presence of the outlier when it states that the symbol R denotes an observation with a large standardized or studentized residual. We are told that the residual involved, on a t scale, is more than 3 standard deviates below the norm. MINITAB will list any studentized residual with greater than an absolute value of

2 as an outlier. With the addition of this outlier the value for R-sq decreased from 24.3% to 0.0%. The addition of an outlier can have the opposite effect on R-sq, it can cause it to greatly increase in value. For example, if our 13th student had GMAT = 10,000 and GGPA = 22.921, the R-sq value would increase from 24.3% to 99.6%. This would lead us to believe that our model essentially had perfect predictability. This is not the case, the data was simply distorted by the outlier which greatly increased SSR, and made SSR/SST almost 1. This happened because the outlier was with respect to X (GMAT), while Y (GGPA) was in line with the original regression equation. This would cause SSR to increase dramatically while SSE would remain relatively unchanged.

In Table 9.9C we have changed our 13th student to have a normal reading for GGPA (Y) but is an outlier with respect to their GMAT (X) score (GGPA = 3.4; GMAT = 200). The warning we receive concerning the unusual observation for X, is X denotes an observation whose X value gives it large influence. Finally, we entered our 13th student to have an unusual observation for both GGPA and GMAT (GGPA = 0.0; GMAT = 200), MINITAB informs us that we have an outlier with respect to both X and Y.

Table 9.9   MINITAB Printout Without Outliers, then with Various Outliers

9.9A MINITAB output with original 12 students (no outliers)

THE REGRESSION EQUATION IS GGPA = 2.17 + 0.00207 GMAT

Predictor	Coef	Stdev	T	p
Constant	2.1707	0.6149	3.53	0.005
GMAT	0.002075	0.001158	1.79	0.103

$s = 0.3952$ R-sq = 24.3% R-sq(adj) = 16.7%

Analysis of Variance

Source	DF	SS	MS	F	p
Regression	1	0.5013	0.5013	3.21	0.103
Error	10	1.5616	0.1562		
Total	11	2.0629			

9.9B MINITAB output with 13th student, an outlier with respect to Y (13th student GMAT = 595; GGPA = 0.0)

THE REGRESSION EQUATION IS GGPA = 2.91 + 0.00018 GMAT

Predictor	Coef	Stdev	T	p
Constant	2.908	1.596	1.82	0.096
GMAT	0.000180	0.002976	0.06	0.953

$s = 1.037$ R-sq = 0.0% R-sq(adj) = 0.00

Analysis of Variance

Source	DF	SS	MS	F	p
Regression	1	0.004	0.004	0.00	0.953
Residual Error	11	11.829	1.075		
Total	12	11.833			

Unusual Observations

Obs.	GMAT	GGPA	Fit	Stdev.Fit	Residual	St.Resid
13	595	0.000	3.015	0.351	−3.015	−3.09R

R denotes an observation with a large standardized residual.

9.9C MINITAB output with 13th student as outlier with respect to X (13th student GMAT = 200; GGPA = 3.4).

THE REGRESSION EQUATION IS GGPA = 2.80 + 0.000934 GMAT

Predictor	Coef	Stdev	T	p
Constant	2.8004	0.4629	6.05	0.000
GMAT	0.0009339	0.0009019	1.04	0.323

$s = 0.4154$ R-sq = 8.9% R-sq(adj) = 0.6%

Analysis of Variance

Source	DF	SS	MS	F	p
Regression	1	0.1850	0.1850	1.07	0.323
Residual Error	11	1.8977	0.1725		
Total	12	2.0827			

Unusual Observations

Obs.	GMAT	GGPA	Fit	Stdev.Fit	Residual	St.Resid
13	200	3.400	2.987	0.292	0.413	1.40X

X denotes an observation whose X value gives it large influence.

9.9D MINITAB output with 13th student an outlier with respect to both Y and X (13th student GMAT = 200; GGPA = 0.0).

THE REGRESSION EQUATION IS GGPA = 0.171 + 0.00570 GMAT

Predictor	Coef	Stdev	T	p
Constant	0.1715	0.7476	0.23	0.823
GMAT	0.005696	0.001457	3.91	0.002

$s = 0.609$ R-sq = 58.2% R-sq(adj) = 54.4%

Analysis of Variance

Source	DF	SS	MS	F	p
Regression	1	6.8821	6.8821	15.29	0.002
Residual Error	11	4.9508	0.4501		
Total	12	11.8329			

Unusual Observations

Obs.	GMAT	GGPA	Fit	Stdev.Fit	Residual	St.Resid
13	200	0.000	1.311	0.471	−1.311	−2.74RX

R denotes an observation with a large standardized residual.

X denotes an observation whose X value gives it large influence.

Since the impact of outliers can be devastating, they should be evaluated carefully. After identification, decision-makers must attempt to determine the cause of the outlier. Were the data incorrectly recorded or incorrectly entered into the computer program? If so, merely edit the file and return the program. Did an unusual condition distort the data point? Perhaps a student was called away by an emergency out of state. If this occurred after the allowable drop date, the student might have received 12 credit hours of "F" grades, which do not reflect the student's true capabilities. In cases such as this, it might be reasonable to delete this data point from the analysis.

Although it may seem logical to eliminate most outliers, extreme care should be taken. An extreme data point may represent the effect of a variable omitted from the model. If so, the proper procedure would be to expand the model to include the effect of this factor. Of course, adding variables to our regression models is the subject of Chapter 10 on multiple regression analysis.

Not all outliers are considered problems. The Internal Revenue Service (IRS) uses outliers to determine which tax returns have unusually large deductions. These deductions are flagged by the computer since they are so many standard deviations from the mean, and so many standard deviations from the predicted value based on the regression model where X = the income level involved. These outliers are selected to be audited to explain the legitimacy of their claims of being an outlier.

The impact on the coefficient of determination of an outlier depends on whether it is close to the original regression equation or not. If it is close to the original regression equation, the outlier will cause R-sq to approach 100%. This is because SSE will remain basically unchanged, while SSR (hence SST) will increase greatly in value. For example, if we add a thirteenth point where GMAT = 100,000 and GGPA = 209.67 we would find $R0$-sq = 100%. This does not mean we have 100% predictability, rather that our analysis has been distorted by an outlier. Note that a GGPA of 209.67 looks like an outlier, but it is not with respect to Y because it is in line with the original regression equation (YFit = 2.1707 + 0.002075(100,000) = 209.67).

There are three analyses performed to determine if an outlier is present. After the command sequence Stat > Regression > Regression we would click on storage, then click on the options Standardized residuals, Hi (leverage), and Cook's distance boxes. The standardized residuals command finds outlies with respect to the dependent or response variable, and places the residuals on a z scale. MINITAB flags any such values over 2.0. For example, for Table 9.9B, if we clicked on Standard residuals option we would have received a value of -3.08996. Hence we know this value for the 13th students GGPA is far below the norm. It is the standardized residual command which triggers the sentence "R denotes an obs. with a large st. resid."

If we have an outlier with the independent or predictor variable then this would be picked up the Hi (leverage) process. A large leverage reading means our predictor variables is an outlier. For example, for Table 9.9C we would receive a leverage reading of 0.493056, which is more than twice that of any other value. It is the Hi (leverage) command that triggers the sentence "X denotes an obs. whose X value gives it large influence."

If we were to have a data point which was an outlier with respect to both dependent (response) and independent variables we would receive a Cook's distance (click on Cook's distance box). For Table 9.9D we would receive Cook's distance value of 3.66206, which is almost eighteen times greater than the next greatest value. It is the Cook's distance command which triggers the combined commands "R denotes an obs. with a large st. resid." and "X denotes an obs. whose X value gives it large influence."

 Check Concept 9.H

A company has a model: Salary = f(Term of Employment), and finds a standardized residual off MINITAB to be +4. This refers to the fact that this individual's salary is considerably below fellow workers with similar tenure at the company. True or false? If false, explain.

Exercises

9.47   Explain in general terms the impact that an extreme point or outlier can have on regression analysis.

9.48   Explain the outlier warnings that MINITAB yields.

9.49
Y	X
27	4
14	10
12	16
6	21
1	25

   a.   Are any MINITAB warnings given for the linear model $Y = f(X)$? Explain.
   b.   The regression equation is = 29.253 − 1.135(X), the standard error = 2.686, and R^2 = 0.944. A sixth data point is added to the data set (X = 100, Y = −69). Is the new point close to the original regression equation?

c. Would you expect the regression equation to change significantly?
d. Compute the new regression analysis, and ascertain what MINITAB warnings are given. Explain.

9.50

X	Y
3	26
5	14
10	11
21	7

a. Are any MINITAB warnings given for the linear model $Y = f(X)$? Explain.
b. The regression is $\hat{Y} = 22.535 - 0.824(X)$, the standard error $= 5.862$, and $R^2 = 0.658$. A sixth data point is added to the data set ($X = 1000$, $Y = -801.6$). Is the new point close to the original regression equation?
c. Would you expect the linear regression equation and R^2 to change significantly? Explain.
d. Have MINITAB confirm/deny your hypotheses.

9.51

Student	GGPA	UGGPA
#1	3.86	3.91
#2	3.05	2.77
#3	2.65	2.10
#4	3.50	3.68
#5	3.00	2.79
#6	4.00	3.81
#7	3.10	2.75
#8	3.89	3.89
#9	3.21	3.07
#10	3.45	3.61
#11	2.80	2.19
#12	3.30	3.24
#13	3.12	3.38
#14	3.44	3.63
#15	3.59	3.41
#16	3.16	3.04
#17	3.22	3.67
#18	3.52	37.10

a. Can you see a problem with the given data set?
b. What MINITAB warnings do you predict that you will get?
c. Run MINITAB to confirm deny your predictions.

9.52

Individual	Hours of Overtime	Defective Parts
#1	1	3
#2	17	40
#3	5	10
#4	15	36
#5	10	24
#6	7	16
#7	11	23
#8	6	8
#9	0	3
#10	4	12
#11	9	26

Individual	Hours of Overtime	Defective Parts
#12	20	51
#13	8	18
#14	12	33
#15	3	9
#16	2	69

a. Can you see a problem with the given data set?
b. What MINITAB warnings do you predict that you will get?
c. Run MINITAB to confirm/deny your predictions.

9.9   A Word of Caution

We must remember that when we attempt to develop predictive models, we may make erroneous assumptions which can distort our conclusions. There is the story of the scientist who had trained a frog to jump over an obstacle in response to commands. The scientist then records the height and angle of the jump. The scientist surgically removes one of the frog's limbs. At the command, the frog still jumps over the obstacles and the scientist records the new height and angle of the jump. The scientist then removes a second and third limb, and at the command the frog still manages to jump over the obstacle, although with considerably more difficulty than before. Once again the scientist records the height and angle of each jump. Finally the scientist removes the last limb from the frog. Now, however, the frog does not jump over the obstacle after the repeated commands to do so. This too is recorded, Finally, the scientist records the conclusion of the experiment: "When you remove all the limbs from a frog, it becomes stone deaf!"

Although ridiculous, if you were to compute an R^2 for the scientist's data, it probably would read a perfect 1. The result is due to the way the experiment was set up: when one event happened, the other event automatically followed. When you removed the limbs from the frog (X), the frog failed to respond to the command (Y).

We must always be careful to avoid making erroneous correlations between variables. For example, we sometimes read the newspaper and hear of a promising anti-cancer drug, only to discover later no cause-and-effect relation between them. Similarly, during the late 1950's there was an isometric craze, which made incredible claims that the exercises strengthened muscles as never done before. Later it was found that only parts of the muscles were strengthened, causing imbalances, and that isometrics caused blood pressure problems for certain individuals. So, care must be taken when making claims in the absence of substantial evidence. Even if a relationship exists, it may be difficult to know precisely which variable influences which. The sun rises when the rooster crows. Or does the rooster crow when the sun rises? Many absurd associations exist between variables. One such relationship suggests there is a relationship between whether the AFC or NFC wins the Super Bowl and which political party will obtain the office of president.

It is important to learn to differentiate between possible real associations and superficial ones. As an example, Table 9.10 lists the winner and the average winning speeds of the Indianapolis 500 motor car race between 1955 and 1972. Also listed is the Gross National Product (GNP) of the United States for the same years. The model to be tested is that

(GNP) $= a + b$(INDY 500 Speeds)

or that the United States economy is dependent on the winning INDY 500 speeds. If the speeds increase, so does GNP. If the speeds decrease, so does GNP (since the data are directly related). Recall that the GNP datum is the Y variable and the INDY 500 datum is the X variable. You might be surprised to discover that the coefficient of determination is extremely high ($R^2 = 0.913$ using MINITAB). Does this mean that the president should be informed that the economy is now predictable? At this point the claim of predictability is probably premature.

258

Table 9.10 Indianapolis 500 winners, Speeds, and GNP*

Year	Winner	MPH	GNP
1955	Bob Sweikert	128.209	$405.9
1956	Pat Flaherty	128.490	428.2
1957	Sam Hanks	135.601	451.0
1958	Jimmy Bryan	133.791	456.8
1959	Roger Ward	135.875	495.8
1960	Jim Rathman	138.767	515.3
1961	A. J. Foyt	139.130	533.8
1962	Roger Ward	140.293	574.6
1963	Parnelli Jones	143.137	606.9
1964	A. J. Foyt	147.350	649.8
1965	Jim Clark	151.388	705.1
1966	Graham Hill	144.317	772.0
1967	A. J. Foyt	151.207	816.4
1968	Bobby Unser	152.882	892.7
1969	Mario Andretti	156.867	963.9
1970	Al Unser	155.749	1,015.2
1971	Al Unser	157.735	1,102.7
1972	Mark Donahue	162.962	1,212.8

*GNP Listed in billions of dollars.

You might be wondering why these specific years were selected. It just so happens that these years result in the highest possible value for R^2. Basically, the average speeds increased proportionately during these years. In fact, the average speeds declined after 1972 for four consecutive years, because in three of those four years the race had to be shortened due to the fuel shortage of the time. Most likely, these two variables (GNP and INDY 500 speeds) are both increasing somewhat proportionately over time. In a growing economy, it would be expected that GNP increases from year to year. Also, it is common for average Indy 500 speeds to increase each year due to the work of automotive engineers. However, if it rains, or if there are major accidents during the race, the average speeds decrease. Sometimes race officials attempt to reduce speeds by such measures as adding new pit restrictions in hope that reduced speeds might save lives. Although their actions might reduce speeds for that year, the following year the automotive engineers invariably discover how to overcome the restriction and, once again, the speeds will increase. If the INDY 500 speeds and GNP both moved in phase with time, they might appear to be related to each other even though no relation might exist.

The computer and statistical software make it possible for us to perform statistical procedures that are quite complex. However, there is a tremendous risk in using statistical techniques with which we are unfamiliar. MINITAB is able to provide statistics in the regression area that we have not yet developed. However, some of these topics will be introduced in Chapter 10 and we will have a working knowledge of the entire regression output.

 Concept Check 9.1

If we obtain a significant R^2 from a regression model, it does not refer to the fact that a significant cause and effect relationship exists. True or false? If false, explain.

Exercises

9.53   If we were to hear about a new cancer cure, why would our first thought involve skepticism?

9.54   Why did we receive a R^2 near 1 when we regressed the GNP with the winning speeds of the Indy 500 race?

259

In this chapter we analyzed linear regression models. The analysis involved two variables (X and Y). We tried to develop an equation that would allow us to predict a value for the Y variable based on information from an X variable. The residual values (e_i) were extremely important in determining the least squares best fit regression equation and in the ability of the model to explain an association between variables or to predict what it is supposed to.

We also tested hypotheses concerning the model's coefficients and developed confidence and prediction intervals. The two variable model provides us a foundation for developing more elaborate regression models which contain more than one independent variable.

We conclude the chapter with a problem that frequently appears in business applications: that is the problem caused by outliers. We also noted that even if our results strongly support that we have a valid regression model, we have not proven that a causal relationship exists.

Mini-case 9.1: Household Size and Median Age of the Population

The marketing department of a large U.S. home builder has analyzed average household size approximately during the 1900's and has observed a decrease in each of the last seven census years. Some theories suggest a positive correlation of household size with the life expectancy of the population. The greater the life expectancy, the greater the possibility of the death to one spouse, and so the greater the incidence of single member households. The model to be developed and analyzed is $\hat{Y}$ (Average Household Size) $= a + bX$ (Population Life Expectancy)

    a.   Do you believe a linear relationship if existing between 1920 and 2000, can continue into the future?

    b.   Compute the linear regression equation, the standard error and R^2.

    c.   Is the information obtained from such an analysis important for marketing specialists?

Table 9.11   Life Expectancy to Household Size: 1920–2000

Year	Average Life Expectancy X	Household Size Y
1920	54.1	4.34
1930	59.7	4.11
1940	62.9	3.67
1950	68.2	3.37
1960	69.7	3.33
1970	70.8	3.14
1980	73.8	2.76
1990	75.4	2.63
2000	76.9	2.59

Note: 2004 life expectancy, Women 80.4; Mean 75.2.

Mini-case 9.2: Continental Statistics

The National Geographic Society located in Washington D.C., has estimated the world land mass and populations in the early 1980's (Table 9.12). A hypothesis claims that the dispersion of the population is determined by the land mass necessary to sustain it. The model is

Population % $= a + b$(Area %)

    a.   If we are to test the significance of the independent variable, are we involved with a one- or a two-tailed test?

    b.   Is the model significant at the 5% level?

    c.   Could other factors explain population distribution? Name some.

Table 9.12   Continental Statistics

	Continents	Area Sq. Mi.	Area %	Population	Population %
1	Asia	16,999,000	29.7	2,738,718,000	59.7
2	Africa	11,688,000	20.4	498,000,000	9.9
3	North America	9,366,000	16.3	381,000,000	8.3
4	South America	6,881,000	12.0	252,000,000	5.5
5	Europe	4,017,000	7.0	690,282,000	15.1
6	Australia	2,966,000	5.2	15,000,000	0.3
7	Antarctica	5,100,000	8.9	negligible	0.0

Mini-case 9.3: Predicting Student Performance

Assume that the level of education at high school is not what it should be. Use the student's SAT scores as a measure of performance. Only 22 states require their students to take SAT tests, 1 state requires its own test, and the remainder requires the ACT (Table 9.13). Some educators believe two variables that might contribute to higher/lower SAT scores are teacher salaries and the pupil–teacher ratios.

    a.   In what ways would teacher salaries and pupil–teacher ratios impact SAT scores?

    b.   Are SAT scores a good indicator of what students learn in high school? Explain. What variables do you think would be a better measure of what students learn in high school?

    c.   If you compute the coefficient of correlation for SAT versus Teacher Salaries and SAT versus Student–Teacher Ratio, which do you feel would be larger? Explain why.

    d.   Can you think of other independent variables that could affect SAT scores and maybe even be more important than the two listed?

    e.   Besides SAT scores, what factors would be important to competitive schools in determining admittance of a student?

    f.   Use MINITAB and complete linear models of SAT scores $= f$(average teacher salary), and SAT scores $= f$(pupil–teacher ratio). Are the models significant at the 5% level?

Table 9.13   1998 Education Statistics

State	Average SAT scores	Average Teacher Salary($)	Pupil–Teacher Ratio
California	1013	42,992	21.5
Connecticut	1019	51,181	13.4
Delaware	994	41,436	16.9
Dist. of Columbia	964	42,424	17.5
Florida	1001	33,885	18.1
Georgia	968	35,679	16
Hawaii	996	38,105	17.8
Indiana	997	38,772	17.1
Maine	1005	33,676	13
Maryland	1014	41,257	16.9
Massachusetts	1016	44,101	14.1
New Hampshire	1043	36,029	15.6
New Jersey	1005	49,786	13.9
New York	998	48,000	14.2
North Carolina	982	31,019	16.1
Oregon	1056	41,093	19.9
Pennsylvania	992	47,147	16.8
Rhode Island	996	43,083	14.4
South Carolina	951	32,659	15.3

State	Average SAT scores	Average Teacher Salary($)	Pupil–Teacher Ratio
Texas	995	32,426	15.3
Vermont	1012	36,053	13.1
Virginia	1006	36,116	14.7

Sources: South Carolina Information Highway for SAT (www.sciway.net) www.aft.org for salaries
National Center for Education Statistics for Pupil–teacher ratios

Review of Important Terms and Concepts

Dependent/explained/response variable: The variable we try to predict or explain is termed the dependent variable.

Independent/predictor/explanatory variable: The variables we believe explain changes in the dependent variable.

Least squares method: The technique used to find the best equation that most appropriately represents the data set. It minimizes the sum of the squared vertical distances between the data points and the fitted line.

Residual: The difference between an actual (observed) value of Y (Y_i) and an estimated value of Y ($\hat{Y}$) based on least squares.

Normal equations: The least squares solution equations.

Estimated regression coefficients: The estimates for the population parameters derived from the normal equations or their algebraic equivalent.

Scatter diagram (scattergram): The pictorial representation of the spread of the data points of Y on X.

Standard error of the estimate: The measure of dispersion of the data points about a regression line. Plus or minus 1 standard error about the regression line is expected to contain about 68.3% of the data. The percentage is 95.5 for 2 standard errors, and for 3 standard errors it is 99.7%.

Coefficient of determination: The explained variation as a percentage of the total variation.

Residuals or errors: Residual values (e) are changes in the dependent variable caused by variables external to the regression model.

SSR, SSE, and SST: SSR is the variation in the dependent variable (Y) associated with the independent variable(s) contained within the model. SSE is the variation in the dependent variable (Y) associated by variables omitted from or external to the regression model. SST is the variation in the dependent variable (Y) regardless of cause.

Coefficient of correlation: A measure of association (from -1 to $+1$) between the dependent and independent variables. A positive value of R means that the association between the variables is direct. If the relationship is inverse, the coefficient of correlation is negative.

p-Values: The smallest value for α for which H_o will be rejected.

Outliers: Outliers are sometimes called extreme values or maverick points. They can greatly distort regression analyses.

A word of caution: We must be reminded that just because a computer program yields good statistical results, does not mean that a true cause-and-effect relationship exists. It only represents a starting point from which to begin a more detailed analysis.

Estimated Linear Regression Coefficients

$$b = \frac{\Sigma XY - n\overline{X}\ \overline{Y}}{\Sigma X^2 - n\overline{X}^2}$$ (9.1)

$$a = \overline{Y} - b\overline{X}$$

where

X = independent variable values, $i = 1, 2, \ldots, n$

Y = dependent variable values, $i = 1, 2, \ldots, n$

n = sample size

$\overline{Y}$ = arithmetic mean of Y

$\overline{X}$ = arithmetic mean of X

The Standard Error of the Estimate

$$s_{Y \bullet 12} = \hat{\sigma}_e = \sqrt{\frac{SSE}{n - m}}$$ (9.2)

where

SSE = the error sum-of-squares

n = the sample size

m = the number of coefficients in the regression equation: in a linear two variable model there are 2 estimated parameters ($a \& b$).

Sample Coefficient of Determination: Expressed by Sum of Squares

$$R^2 = 1 - \frac{SSE}{SST} = \frac{SSR}{SST}$$ (9.3)

where

SSE = errors sum of squares (Σe_i^2)

SSR = regression sum of squares

SST = total sum of squares

Sample Coefficient of Correlation

$$R = \pm\sqrt{R^2}$$ (9.4)

where

The Regression Model Test Statistic: F_{test}

$$F_{\text{test}} = \frac{\text{MSR}}{\text{MSE}}$$
(9.5)

where

$\text{MSR} = \text{SSR}/(m - 1)$

$\text{MSE} = \text{SSE}/(n - m)$

$n = $ sample size

$m = $ the number of coefficients in the regression model

$H_o = $ population $R^2 = B = 0$; $H_A = $ population R^2 & $B \neq 0$.

Remember that we are trying to estimate the true regression equation

$Y = A + BX$ based on a randomly selected survey.

Test Statistic for B

$$t_{\text{test}} = \frac{b}{\dfrac{S_{Y \bullet X}}{\sqrt{\Sigma X^2 - n\overline{X}^2}}} = \frac{b}{S_b}$$
(9.6)

where

$b = $ estimated slope

$S_b = $ standard error of the slope $= S_{Y \bullet X} \left/ \sqrt{(\Sigma X^2 - n\overline{X}^2)} \right.$

$n = $ the sample size

H_o: $B = 0$; H_A: $B \neq 0$. If theoretical knowledge exists that the slope should be
positive H_o: $\leq 0 (H_A > 0)$, and if negative H_o: $\geq 0 (H_A < 0)$.

$(1 - \alpha) \bullet 100\%$ Confidence Interval for the Population Slope (B)

$$b \pm t_{\alpha/2(df)} \bullet S_b$$
(9.7)

where

$b = $ estimated slope

$t_{\alpha/2(df)} = $ critical value of t, two-tailed test

$S_b = $ standard error of the coefficient (slope)

264

$(1 - \alpha) \bullet 100\%$ Confidence Interval for $\mu_{Y|500}$

$$\hat{Y} \pm t_{\alpha/2(n-m)}\text{stdev.fit} \tag{9.8}$$

where

$$\text{Stdev.fit} = S_{Y\bullet X}\sqrt{\frac{1}{n} + \frac{(X - \overline{X})^2}{\Sigma X^2 - n\overline{X}^2}}$$

Stdev.fit = Standard Deviation of the Fit

$\hat{Y}$ = estimated Y value

$t_{\alpha/2(n-m)}$ = critical two-tailed t-value

n = sample size

m = number of estimated parameters

$S_{Y\bullet X}$ = standard error of the estimate

$(1 - \alpha) \bullet 100\%$ Prediction Interval for $Y_{|X_o}$

$$\hat{Y} \pm t_{\alpha/2(n-m)} \bullet \sqrt{\left[\text{MSE} + (\text{Stdev.Fit})^2\right]} \tag{9.9A}$$

$$\hat{Y} \pm t_{\alpha/2(n-m)} \bullet S_{Y\bullet X}\sqrt{1 + \frac{1}{n} + \frac{\left(X - \overline{X}\right)^2}{\Sigma X2 - n\overline{X}^2}} \tag{9.9B}$$

where

n = sample size

$\hat{Y}$ = estimated Y-value for a specified X-value

$t_{\alpha/2(df)}$ = critical two-tailed t-value

n = sample size

m = number of estimated parameters

$S_{Y\bullet X}$ = standard error of the estimate

Review MINITAB Commands

MINITAB Commands for Regression Analysis

Stat > Regression > Regression
Double click **GGPA** into **Response** box.
Double click **GMAT** into **Predictors** box.
Click on **Storage**.
Click on the **Fits** box. (To obtain the estimated Y values)
Click on **Residuals** box. (To obtain the residuals)
OK

Note: An alternate approach would be to click the **Results** box, then click on **in addition, the full table of fits and residuals.**

MINITAB scatter plot with regression equation.

Stat > Regression > Fitted Line Plot
Double click **Y** into **Y variable** box.
Double click **X** into **X variable** box.
OK

MINITAB correlation analysis.

Stat > Basic Statistics > Correlation
Double click **GMAT** and **GGPA** into **Variables** box
OK

MINITAB's confidence and prediction intervals.

Stat > Regression > Fitted Line Plot
Double click **Y** to enter in **Response** box.
Double click **X** to enter in **Predictors** box.
Click on **Options**.
Click on display **confidence** and **prediction** bands.
OK twice.

End of Chapter Exercises

9.55   A personnel manager wants to determine if an internally administered job evaluation is related to salary increases. The evaluation is an index which varies on a 0–100 scale and relates to the employee evaluation for the past year. The salary increases are listed in thousands. All the employees have exactly the same job category, so differences in raises can't be explained by superior skills. Ten employees are sampled with the following results:

Eval: 87, 62, 91, 89, 77, 69, 86, 81, 79, 94

Sal+: 3.2, 1.9, 3.6, 3.0, 2.3, 2.0, 3.1, 2.6, 2.5, 3.7

    a.   If you were the personnel manager, would you want to find that a linear relationship exists between the two data sets? Which should be the independent (explanatory) variable?
    b.   Use MINITAB and ascertain if the model is significant at the 5% level.
    c.   Determine the 95% confidence interval for B.
    d.   If the model is significant, predict when evaluation = 91.
    e.   If the model is significant, have MINITAB define the 95% confidence and prediction intervals for an evaluation = 91.

9.56   A karate instructor takes her class into a meet for competition. As the students go through their skills they are subjectively graded by the grand master on a scale from 0–100. The instructor wants to know if there is any relationship between the student's age and performance. The results of scores and ages are given for 12 students.

Eval: 89, 42, 98, 67, 78, 13, 65, 91, 93, 56, 64, 88

Age: 16, 67, 56, 13, 38, 51, 7, 9, 16, 41, 26, 10

    a.   If you were the instructor, would you expect that a relationship will exist between the two data sets? Which variable would be classified as the independent variable?
    b.   Do a MINITAB regression analysis and comment on the output.

9.57   The owner of an apartment complex wishes to know if they are charging competitive rates for their apartments based on the square feet involved. The owner does a study of nine competitors with the following results:

Sq.Ft.: 1000, 1200, 2000, 900, 1700, 1400, 1450, 1250, 700

Rent: 485, 600, 800, 500, 900, 620, 650, 575, 375

a. Would you expect a relationship to exist between the two data sets? If so, which would be the independent variable?
b. Do a MINITAB regression analysis and comment on the output.
c. Predict rent for 1900 square feet.

9.58   A golf course wishes to establish whether better average scores (lower scores) are associated with the number of times one plays the game during one year. It would like to advertise that performance is based on playing time. It samples 14 golfers and obtains the following information:

Golfer	# of times played a year	Average Score
#1	52	87
#2	10	81
#3	105	90
#4	5	91
#5	19	67
#6	75	61
#7	22	71
#8	49	57
#9	1	98
#10	17	65
#11	33	72
#12	29	84
#13	41	59
#14	87	72

a. What is the model that the golf course believes? What is the fallacy involved with the logic?
b. Using MINITAB complete a linear regression analysis and comment on the results.
c. Predict golf score with 75 hours of practice.

9.59   The magazine Surfing (February 1989, Vol. 25, No. 2, pp. 149–156) supplies a rough idea of the relationship between surf board length and surfer height. The data are as follows:

Board Length	Surfer Height
5.50′	5.00′
5.83′	5.33′
6.00′	5.50′
6.17′	5.67′
6.25′	5.83′
6.33′	6.00′
6.50′	6.33′
6.67′	6.50′

a. Assuming a relationship exists, which is the independent (or predictor) variable?
b. Use MINITAB and ascertain if the model is significant at the 5% level.
c. Determine the 95% confidence interval for B.
d. If the model is significant, predict $\hat{Y}$ when evaluation surfer height $= 6.75$ ft.
e. If the model is significant, have MINITAB define the 95% confidence and prediction intervals about $\hat{Y}$ for a surfer height $= 6.75$ ft.

9.60   A table yields the relationship between output and cost for a particular firm.

Output	Costs
0	0
10,000	28,000
20,000	62,000
30,000	96,000
40,000	119,000
50,000	154,000
60,000	185,000
70,000	221,000

a. Assuming a relationship exists, which is the independent variable? Use MINITAB to perform a complete regression analysis.

b. Evaluate F_{test} and t_{test}. With t_{test} are we involved with a one- or two-tailed test? Are our test statistics significant at the 10% level?

c. Forecast costs when output = 80,000. Also, have MINITAB define the appropriate confidence and prediction intervals.

9.61   A table yields data for output and profits for a small firm.

Output	Profits
0	0
10,000	28,000
20,000	62,000
30,000	96,000
40,000	119,000
50,000	154,000
60,000	185,000
70,000	221,000
80,000	212,000
90,000	200,000
100,000	187,000

Note: Enter the data in thousands.

a. Make a rough plot of the data and determine if you believe a linear relationship exists.

b. Have MINITAB determine the least squares linear equation and associated residual values. Comment on the residual values.

9.62   Inventory holding costs for a product historically has been believed to be $1.00 per unit. This cost is to be rechecked so that accounting obtains the following information:

Holding Costs	Units Held
1,150	1,000
1,960	2,000
3,210	3,000
3,972	4,000
5,580	5,000
5,839	6,000
6,552	7,000
8,344	8,000
9,324	9,000
9,640	10,000
11,660	11,000

a. Is there a sound theoretical basis for assuming a linear relationship between the two variables?

b. Using MINITAB evaluate the regression analysis assuming a 5% level of significance.

9.63 A student records the miles driven and the gas consumed for a ten day period of time. The data are as follows:

Day	Miles Driven	Gas Consumed
#1	17	0.63
#2	160	6.32
#3	280	9.56
#4	24	1.25
#5	67	3.20
#6	112	5.71
#7	97	5.95
#8	241	8.86
#9	348	11.23
#10	16	0.94

a. Is there a sound theoretical basis for assuming a linear relationship between the two variables?
b. Using MINITAB evaluate the regression analysis assuming a 1% level of significance.

9.64 A restaurant wants to know if there is any relationship between the tip rate received and the hours of actual work. The company fears that fatigue may be affecting some of their employees. The company obtains the following information from a market study:

Server	Tip Rate	Hours Worked
#1	9.78%	6.88
#2	11.44	40.00
#3	7.78	11.13
#4	10.22	28.90
#5	10.60	31.62
#6	10.24	32.15
#7	8.23	40.00
#8	11.91	32.83
#9	11.54	29.25
#10	13.01	37.52
#11	9.78	32.42
#12	11.63	31.90
#13	9.35	40.00
#14	11.16	9.80
#15	12.86	5.00
#16	10.97	34.05
#17	13.45	35.91
#18	6.55	22.27
#19	8.26	28.70
#20	9.82	12.98
#21	10.78	19.60
#22	13.90	39.63
#23	11.52	38.08
#24	11.42	20.25
#25	13.65	23.07
#26	11.22	16.25

a. Would you expect an association to exist between the two data sets?
b. Using MINITAB evaluate the regression analysis assuming a 5% level of significance.
c. Are there any outlier warnings?

9.65 a. For the tip rate problem of Exercise 9.64, add a 27th surver who worked 40 hours and had a tip rate of 94.5%, and repeat the MINITAB analysis. Comment on the impact of the outlier.

b. For the tip rate problem of Exercise 9.64, add a 27th server who worked 200 hours and had a tip rate of 94.5%, and repeat the MINITAB analysis. Comment on the impact of the outlier.

9.66 The following are the data set's personal consumption expenditures (in billions of current dollars) and the consumer price index (1967 = 100) between 1939 and 1959.

Year	Personal Consumption Expenditures	CPI
1939	67.0	41.6
1940	71.0	42.0
1941	80.8	44.1
1942	88.6	48.8
1943	99.5	51.8
1944	108.2	52.7
1945	119.6	53.9
1946	143.9	58.5
1947	161.9	66.9
1948	174.9	72.1
1949	178.3	71.4
1950	192.1	72.1
1951	208.1	77.8
1952	219.1	79.5
1953	232.6	80.1
1954	239.8	80.5
1955	237.9	80.2
1956	270.6	81.4
1957	285.3	84.3
1958	294.6	86.6
1959	316.3	87.3

Have MINITAB perform a regression analysis (CPI = f(expenditures) and comment on the results (5% level of significance).

9.67 A company has developed the following cost structure for transporting heavy objects.

Cost per 100 lbs.		Distance
$41	between	0—300 miles, plus
36	between	301—600 miles, plus
30	between	601—900 miles, plus
24	between	901—1,200 miles, plus
19	between	1,201—1,500 miles, plus
12	between	1,501—1,800 miles, plus
6	between	1,801—2,100 the limit

Note: Enter distance as the average distance involved.

Have MINITAB perform a regression analysis and comment on the results (5% level of significance).

270

In the late eighteenth century, a famous economist, Thomas Malthus, predicted gloom for the world. He believed the food supply could only increase in an arithmetic relationship. Only so much food could be added each year. The basis of his theory was that the major resource used to produce agricultural products was fixed (land), while labor could increase almost without bound. The growth in the number of people could increase by a constant percentage rate. It therefore would only be a matter of time before the population would outgrow the food supply.

Since Thomas Malthus developed his theory in 1798, agricultural technology has increased rapidly. These agricultural improvements prevented Malthus's prediction from becoming fact for much of the world. Yet some people believe his hypothesis is essentially correct and Malthus only miscalculated when the problem would occur.

We introduce the Malthusian thesis to explain the basic difference between arithmetic and geometric growth rates. While arithmetic growth increases steadily, geometric growth increases at accelerating rates. High school students often discover the explosive nature of a geometric series when asked: "Would you work for someone for one month (31 days) if they paid you a penny the first day and doubled your pay each day thereafter?" The student learns the nature of geometric growth by computing the actual earnings, which are quite substantial.

Arithmetic Relationships and Polynomials

If data increase or decrease arithmetically, we can describe the change using a family of functions known as polynomials. The simplest is a zero-degree polynomial since the exponent of the independent variable is zero. Thus, a zero order polynomial is a constant function: a function that has a constant value with respect to the independent variable, X.

The next order of polynomial is a first degree (the exponent of the variable is one) or linear function. These functions graph as a straight line with a non-zero slope.

First-Degree or Linear Equation

An equation that expresses a relationship between arithmetic progressions that never changes directions.

$Y = a + bX$ (Statistical notation) or

$Y = mX + b$ (Mathematical notation)

Y represents the dependent (explained) variable and X the independent (explanatory) variable. Two constants differentiate one line from all others: the slope of the equation (b using business notation) and the Y intercept (a using business notation).

A linear relationship in a business problem reflects proportionality. For example, if Y = profits, X = advertising, $b = 3$, and $a = 0$, then for every advertising dollar, the return in profits would be three times as large. The change in Y is directly proportional to the change in X [sometimes written $Y(X)$]. The key to the linear relationship is that the Y variable increases or decreases by a constant amount with respect to the independent variable.

If a firm continues putting money into advertising, it would eventually reach diminishing returns. That is, despite the initial advantage of increased advertising expenditures, these benefits could not continue indefinitely. Therefore, profits might be expected eventually to increase at diminishing rates with respect to advertising and then even to decrease. This relationship, which rises and then falls, can be described by a **second-degree polynomial** or **quadratic** equation (often called a **parabola**). The graph of a second-degree polynomial is not linear due to the "cX^2" term, which causes the graph to change

271

directions once. In other words, if the domain of a second-degree polynomial is not restricted it will either increase initially and then decrease, or decrease initially and then increase.

A second-degree polynomial, also called a quadratic equation or parabola is an equation that expresses a relationship between arithmetic progressions that changes directions once $(Y = a + bX = cX^2)$.

If the graph of the data were to change directions twice, we could add a "dX^3" term and form a third-degree polynomial. A third-degree polynomial, also called a cubic equation, is an equation that expresses a relationship between arithmetic progressions that changes directions twice $(Y = a + bX = cX^2 + dX^3)$.

If the graph of the data changed directions a third time, an "eX^4" term could be added. This convenient property of polynomials makes them a useful device for representing relationships between variables. Graphs of the first-, second-, third-, and fourth-degree polynomial are given in Figure 9.9A, 9.9B, 9.9C, and 9.9D, respectively.

Figure 9.9   Graphs of Various Functional Forms

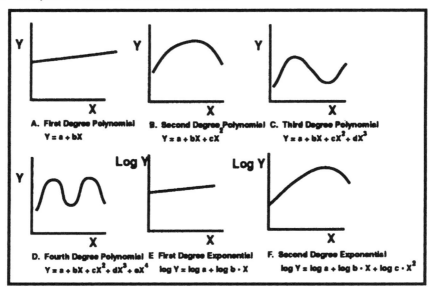

A. First Degree Polynomial
$Y = a + bX$

B. Second Degree Polynomial
$Y = a + bX + cX^2$

C. Third Degree Polynomial
$Y = a + bX + cX^2 + dX^3$

D. Fourth Degree Polynomial
$Y = a + bX + cX^2 + dX^3 + eX^4$

E. First Degree Exponential
$\log Y = \log a + \log b \cdot X$

F. Second Degree Exponential
$\log Y = \log a + \log b \cdot X + \log c \cdot X^2$

Geometric Relationships and Exponentials

Sometimes data change quickly, either increasing or decreasing at a constant percentage rate. For such changes, linear and quadratic equations are inappropriate. In these cases, we need the family of equations known as exponential. The formula for a first-degree exponential is

$$Y = a \bullet b^X$$

or

$$Y = a \bullet b^{-X}$$

If graphed on semilog paper, first-degree exponentials appear as a straight line (Figure 9.9F). These equations often appear in time series data, which will be discussed in Chapter 11. We convert exponential equations to their logarithmic counterparts to make analysis and computation simpler. The logarithmic format of the first degree exponential provides a linear equation in the form

$$\log Y = \log a + \log b \bullet X$$

272

Multiple Regression and Correlation Analysis

Where we have been

In Chapter 9, we used models to explain relationships and to predict a given variable (Y) based upon information from a single independent variable (X). These bivariate, or two-variable, models may have unusually large residuals (e_i) because of the influence of important variables not included in the model. For this reason, in the simple two-variable model, the sum of the squares due to regression (SSR) can be small compared to the total sum of squares (SST). Thus, a large portion of the variability in the dependent variable about its own mean cannot be associated with the single independent variable.

Where we are going

However, before concluding that this portion of the variability is purely due to chance phenomena or random effects, we should try to expand the model to include the effects of other independent variables. Such regression models containing two or more independent variables are referred to as multiple regression models.

We can apply many of the concepts discussed in linear regression analysis (Chapter 9) to multiple regression and correlation analysis. However, some additional statistical tools will be introduced in this chapter, as well as the generalizations of numerous concepts from the simpler bivariate methods. As you might expect, the computational complexity will increase. While hand computations are possible for simple linear regression models (unless the sample size is large), multiple regression analysis requires the analysis of data with the aid of a computer and statistical software.

If one additional independent variable is added to the bivariate regression model of Chapter 9, it would be termed a multiple regression or trivariate model, and the equation would be

$$Y = a + b_1 X_1 + b_2 X_2$$

The equation is still linear, but is now three-dimensional because there are three variables involved (Y, X_1, and X_2). The predicted regression equation represents a plane which is tilted to provide the best fit according to the least squares criteria. Even with the best-fitting plane there will generally be residual values and dispersion about the plane as indicated in Figure 10.1.

Figure 10.1 Trivariate Regression Plane and Scatter Diagram

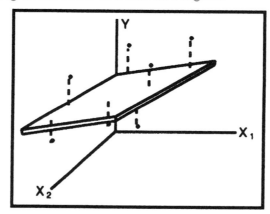

A linear multiple regression equation will generally have an intercept and separate slope coefficients for each independent variable contained in the model. We have chosen to use "a" for the intercept and "b's" for the coefficients of the independent variables of the estimated regression equation. Since in the multiple regression model there is more than one X and thus more than one "b", we use subscripts to differentiate symbolically between the coefficients. Some computer programs and texts also use "b" for the intercept. If this notation is chosen, b_0 is used for the intercept and the coefficients of the independent variables will have integer subscripts beginning at 1 and continuing consecutively. We will always use Y as the dependent variable and X_i will refer to the ith independent variable.

Multiple regression models can be quite large and contain many independent variables. All variables, however, will not necessarily contribute to the explanation of the model and some might be eliminated after initial entry. In Chapter 9, we discussed a model to predict the sales of a fast food franchise. We selected the variables: population density (X_1), traffic flow (X_2), ease of entry and exit (X_3), the number of fast food competitors (X_4), population life cycle (X_5), and the product price for competing products (X_6). We could also have included such variables as the age and income of the population around the site, whether the site was near a military base, university, or interstate highway, and the mobility of the population.

 Concept Check 10.A

A multiple regression model with 6 independent variables would have 6 estimated parameters. True or false? If false, explain.

Exercises

10.1 A multiple linear regression analysis involves a linear two-dimensional analysis. If false, explain.

10.2 In most business regression models there is probably more than a single independent or predictor variable. Explain.

10.2 The Building of a Model: Selection of Independent Variables

An important aspect of building a regression model is the selection of the independent variables. The choice should be based on the logic of the disciplines involved in the application. Although the focus of this text is the statistical analysis of the model once it has been developed, we should review the thought processes common to some of the business disciplines. However, we will first discuss the classification of variables found in many business problems.

After selection of the independent (predictor) variables we should categorize them as qualitative (categorical) or quantitative. For example, marketers might be interested in targeting a product for a certain gender, or for people over 40 years of age. Hence, an observation would be in one category or another and the variable would be qualitative. Either a sampled individual is over 40 or they're not. When a variable is categorical, dummy variables are created to distinguish the effect of the various categories on the dependent variable. These variables will be discussed in more detail in Section 10.6.

In some instances, we may not be able to measure directly an important variable. For example, in economics it is important to predict what expectations are concerning changes in interest or foreign exchange rates. If interest rates are expected to drop, people would wait to purchase homes. Yet, if interest rates are expected to rise, the same people would move quickly into the market. Likewise, if the dollar is expected to devalue compared to the German D-Mark, consumers planning to buy a BMW would be wise to act immediately.

However, how do we actually measure such perceptions? There are normally two ways to handle such data. First, national surveys that answer these questions are frequently performed and the changes in response percentages from previous surveys are usually important. Second, a proxy variable can be used in place of a variable that cannot be measured. A proxy variable is a variable that can be measured and can serve as a substitute for a specific variable that may be unmeasurable, or expensive to measure. The proxy variable, and the variable for which it substitutes, should be highly correlated to justify the substitution. Since in many real-world situations there is insufficient or no data available for the original variable, we must use subjective judgment. Of course, if we have sufficient time and money, a survey might enable the variables to be measured directly.

A Management Model

Pay scales are very important to businesses. If new employees are being hired at starting salaries equal to or above those of valued employees who have been with the firm for many years, a severe morale problem may result. Or, if a few employees have been overlooked in the evaluation process, again a morale factor can develop which may deter productivity. Companies must make sure that their compensation package is consistently applied.

To ensure this consistency, a model is often developed to determine salary outliers. Once identified, these outliers can be qualitatively reviewed to see if the salaries are appropriate. The dependent variable in this case would be current salary. The important independent variables we would use to determine salary would be such factors as:

- employee evaluations (better evaluations should translate to higher income)
- tenure with the company and tenure in their current job category (service to the company and profession)
- formal education and professional certifications (as with a P.E. in engineering or a C.P.A. in accounting)

Thus, the relevant personnel model might be

$$Y = a + b_1 X_1 + b_2 X_2 + b_3 X_3 + b_4 X_4 + b_5 X_5$$

where

Y = current salary

X_1 = personnel evaluations

X_2 = years with firm

X_3 = years in current position/profession/rank

X_4 = academic degrees held

X_5 = certifications attained

This model is not meant to be the only means to determine salary, but merely the starting point and the method to identify outliers or unusual salaries. Even questions concerning which variables are important to the model are bound to occur as well as whether the model is being implemented correctly. Employees might believe that their personnel evaluations are more political than analytical, or there may be a question about the validity of a certain degree or certification. Despite such concerns, the model represents a starting point for the valuative process.

Suppose a firm's data indicate a negative correlation between an employee's current salary (Y) and tenure with the company (X_2), with degrees held (X_4), or with certifications attained (X_5). Such a relationship would surely have a long-term negative impact on morale and productivity of that employee. Thus, a firm should decide what variables it wants to affect salaries in a wage determination model, then ensure that these variables are indeed important in practice.

A Legal Model

Many families have to go through the trauma of divorce. However, divorce is more complex when children are involved in the dissolution of marriage. Normally, the parent who has custody of the children will be given child support payments. The determination of the size of these payments is often the source of many legal battles. What factors should determine that support payment? Consider the following child support payment model:

$$Y = a + b_1 X_1 + b_2 X_2 + b_3 X_3 + b_4 X_4$$

where

Y = the actual child support payment

X_1 = the number of children

X_2 = the duration of the marriage

X_3 = the income and/or net worth of both parties

X_4 = the needs of both parties

These represent only some of the important variables to be considered. Models such as this would help maintain consistency within the judicial system. Judges should not select their own variables, because the amount of the child support payment would then depend on the random selection of which judge was selected to hear the case.

276

One of the most important variables in an economy is current spending (or consumption), which depends on numerous factors. Hence, consumption (symbolically designated as C by the profession) is the dependent variable. Yet, what factors influence our spending behavior? We would all probably give income as our answer. Not only would our current incomes be important, but also our perceptions of what our incomes will be in the near future. In the military, promotions in rank are sometimes given, but the subsequent pay adjustments may not occur for up to a maximum of one year later. Performance is rewarded even though funding may be delinquent. Military personnel call this practice frocking. When personnel are frocked, it is normal for them to spend as though they were at the higher rank. Their perception of future income has changed, and so their spending habits also change. Expectations of increases in income, however, are often not realized. When anticipated raises do not materialize, short-term indebtedness may turn into long-term financial problems.

In our model for predicting spending, other variables would certainly be evaluated, such as:
- interest rates on indebtedness (the higher the rates, the lower the spending)
- perceptions concerning inflation (the higher the inflation rates are, the greater is the urge to spend and not to save)
- perceptions concerning upturns and downturns in the economy (the down turns might require greater liquidity and lower spending and personal spending)

Since this model is based upon economic theory, an economics text might be consulted to review economic theories of consumption for additional variables to include in the model. Hence, the initial model to be evaluated might be

$$Y = a + b_1 X_1 + b_2 X_2 + b_3 X_3 + b_4 X_4 + b_5 X_5$$

where

$Y = $ consumption

$X_1 = $ current income

$X_2 = $ expected future income

$X_3 = $ expected change in the interest rate

$X_4 = $ expected change in the inflation rate

$X_5 = $ expectations of general business conditions

This model would require the use of proxy variables in order to incorporate the effects of the perceptual factors. A possible proxy for X_5 is the monthly change in the Index of Leading Economic Indicators, and/or a barometer of business executives, responses to upcoming economic changes.

 Concept Check 10.B

The selection of the specific independent or predictor variables for the respective multiple regression models is determined by statisticians. True or false? If false, explain.

Exercises

10.3   You are currently attending a community college and/or a university. What do you believe are some of the factors (independent variables) that would make a university successful?

10.4 You either have a selected major or are thinking about one. Using a textbook from that major, develop a multiple regression model to forecast a critical variable within that discipline.

10.5 List eight or more independent variables you believe will determine your final grade in this course. Place an asterisk next to those variables that you believe will be important to all the students in the class, and a double asterisk next to those variables that may be germane only to you. Which set of factors do you feel will have a greater impact on predicting the average grade for the class?

10.6 Identify relevant independent variables to predict the college grade point average of high school seniors applying to a college.

10.7 What factors might be important in a model used to predict sales of a retail clothing store?

10.8 Suppose an NFL team decided to base initial salaries offered to players on a regression model. Identify some of the factors that might determine the offer. Which variables will be easy to measure? Comment on the difficulty of quantifying the other variables.

10.3 Linear Trivariate Model

Suppose we are hired to develop a site location model for a fast food franchise. The franchise has a dozen sites in operation and has tabulated the weekly sales volume, the average hourly traffic flow, and the number of fast food competitors within a mile and a half of the current operation (Table 10.1). The model chosen to predict weekly sales volume is

$$Y = a + b_1 X_1 + b_2 X_2$$

where

Y = weekly sales volume

X_1 = average hourly traffic flow during operational hours

X_2 = number of fast food competitors within a mile and a half

Table 10.1 Sales Volume Model: Traffic Flow, Number of Competitors

#	Y	X_1	X_2
1	78000	640	3
2	61000	410	8
3	93000	818	5
4	48000	416	4
5	72000	549	5
6	51000	479	6
7	87000	822	5
8	98000	784	3
9	66000	499	4
10	77000	510	4
11	86000	800	2
12	46000	387	3
13	94000	875	4
14	49000	452	9
15	72000	602	3

If we compare this model to the models of Chapter 9, the only differences are the addition of a second independent variable (X_2) and the inclusion of its coefficient (b_2). For multiple regression analysis

278

and nonlinear equations, it is impractical to use hand computations to determine the coefficients of the least squares equation. Hence, MINITAB will be used to obtain the relevant statistics (Table 10.2).

Using MINITAB for Trivariate Model

Stat > Regression > Regression
Double click **SALES** into **Response** box.
Double click both **TFLOW** and **NUMCOMP** into **Predictors** box.
If you desire to see the **Residuals** in the worksheet click on **Options**, then **Residuals**.
Click on the **Fits** box. (To obtain the estimated Y values).
Click on the **Residuals** box. (To obtain the residuals).
OK

Table 10.2   Regression Analysis: Sales versus TFLOW, NUMCOMP

THE REGRESSION EQUATION IS

SALES = 19136 + 92.2 TFLOW − 636 NUMCOMP

Predictor	Coef	SE Coef	T	P
Constant	19136	10613	1.80	0.097
TFLOW	92.25	12.31	7.49	0.000
NUMCOMP	−636	1110	−0.57	0.577

S = 7371   R-Sq = 85.4%   R-Sq(adj) = 82.9%

ANALYSIS OF VARIANCE

Source	DF	SS	MS	F	P
Regression	2	3809681124	1904840562	35.06	0.000
Residual Error	12	652052209	54337684		
Total	14	4461733333			

Source	DF	Seq SS
TFLOW	1	3791831024
NUMCOMP	1	17850100

Obs	TFLOW	Sales	Fit	SE Fit	Residual	St Resid
1	640	78000	76267	2476	1733	0.25
2	410	61000	51870	4129	9130	1.50
3	818	93000	91416	3457	1584	0.24
4	416	48000	54967	3210	−6967	−1.05
5	549	72000	66601	2017	5399	0.76
6	479	51000	59507	2587	−8507	−1.23
7	822	87000	91785	3498	−4785	−0.74
8	784	98000	89551	2929	8449	1.25
9	499	66000	62624	2487	3376	0.49
10	510	77000	63639	2408	13361	1.92
11	800	86000	91663	3490	−5663	−0.87
12	387	46000	52928	4129	−6928	−1.13
13	875	94000	97310	3697	−3310	−0.52
14	452	49000	55108	4958	−6108	−1.12
15	602	72000	72762	2556	−762	−0.11

Note: The interpretation of SEQ SS (sequential sum-of-square) is in order. It is the value for SSR that would be obtained using the independent variables in sequence. For example, if we perform the regression equation SALES = f(TFLOW), SSR = 3791831024. The regression equation SALES f(TFLOW,NUMCOMP) yields an SSR = 3809681124. Adding NUMCOMP to the regression equation increased our SSR by 17850100.

The least squares equation is

$$\hat{Y} = 19,136 + 92.25(X_1) - 636(X_2)$$

Assuming the other variable remains constant, each unit increase in hourly traffic flow increases sales revenue by $92.25 and each new fast food competitor reduces sales revenue $636.

Suppose management wants to open a franchise on a site with an average traffic flow of 600 cars per hour and 5 competitors in the immediate vicinity. Then the forecast of sales revenue is

$$\hat{Y} = 19,136 + 92.25(X_1) - 636(X_2)$$

If you desire that MINITAB make this computation for us we would place a 600 and a 5 into the **Prediction interval for new observations** box (after we click on the **Options** box) and we would obtain:

Fit	St.DevFit	95% C.I.	95% P.I.
71305	1969	(67015, 75596)	(54681, 87930)

 Concept Check 10.C

A linear trivariate model utilizes three independent variables in addition to the single dependent variable. True or false? If false, explain.

10.9 Suppose the following linear regression equation has been estimated for a community of homes:

$$\hat{Y} = 3,000 + 35.75(X_1) + 4,986(X_2)$$

The dependent variable is the selling price of the home and the independent variables are the square footage (X_1) and the number of bedrooms (X_2) in the home.

a. Using this information interpret the coefficients 35.75 and 4,986.
b. Predict the selling price of a 2,000 square foot home with 4 bedrooms.

10.10 Explain in simple terms why a trivariate linear regression equation necessitates three normal equations.

10.11 Suppose that a corporation wants to estimate a trivariate linear regression equation that relates the firm's output of defective parts (Y) to the number of days to complete the production cycle (X_1) and the number of employees (X_2). A cross section of data from 12 production cycles is presented below.

Cycle	Defects	Number of Days to Complete	Number of Employees
A	100	2	7
B	120	3	6
C	125	2	8
D	130	4	12
E	132	2	10
F	140	5	12
G	160	7	12
H	162	4	18
I	165	6	14
J	180	7	12
K	190	7	13
L	200	10	14

a. Establish the normal equations necessary to solve the coefficients.
b. Have MINITAB compute the least squares linear regression equation [Defects $= f(X_1$: # of days to complete, X_2: # of employees)].
c. Have MINITAB forecast for $X_1 = 8$ and $X_2 = 14$.

10.12 Suppose that a corporation wants to estimate a trivariate regression equation that relates the total salary for an auditing department (Y) to the number of employees in the department (X_1) and the organization's size as measured by total assets (X_2). A cross section of data from 15 firms is presented below.

Firm	Total Salary	Number of Employees	Total Assets
A	2.0	100	50
B	2.3	94	60
C	2.5	102	90
D	3.0	108	100
E	3.7	142	120
F	5.1	200	125
G	6.5	190	130
H	8.0	350	225
I	8.1	400	140
J	8.3	422	180
K	8.3	388	190
L	8.5	416	200
M	8.9	340	250
N	9.2	410	240
O	9.4	408	240

* Note total salary and total assets are in millions of dollars.

a. From casual observation of the data, do you believe the slope coefficients will be positive or negative?
b. Based on this information, determine the linear multiple regression equation.

10.13 A data set is:

Y	X_1	X_2
1	10	100
2	11	95
3	12	90
4	11	85
5	10	80
6	9	75
7	8	70
8	9	65
9	10	60
10	11	55

a. What slope values might you expect for the linear regression model $Y = a + b_1 X_1 + b_2 X_2$?
b. Use MINITAB to confirm or reject your expectations, and to forecast Y when $X_1 = 10$ and $X_2 = 85$.

281

10.14   A university graduate admissions committee is attempting to predict graduate GPA ($Y =$ GGPA) based on the GMAT score (X_1) and on undergraduate GPA ($X_2 =$ UGPA). Data for twelve randomly selected graduate students are as follows:

Student	Y	X_1	X_2
1	3.05	560	3.33
2	4.00	640	3.79
3	3.55	580	3.57
4	3.53	480	3.23
5	3.58	637	3.92
6	3.21	610	3.09
7	3.50	430	3.18
8	2.80	400	2.48
9	3.44	450	3.31
10	3.17	525	3.26
11	2.46	330	2.56
12	2.75	620	3.58

Use MINITAB to perform a regression analysis. Forecast the grade of an incoming student who received a 3.40 UGPA and a 518 on the GMAT.

10.4 Measuring Variability in the Dependent Variable

The analysis of residuals is still of paramount importance. The residual is the difference between the actual values for Y (Y_i) and the predicted values of Y ($\hat{Y}$) obtained by the regression equation ($e_i^2 = Y_i - \hat{Y}$). The least squares methodology still assures that Σe_i^2 (SSE) is the smallest possible value; hence, we have the optimal fitting function.

We will proceed to duplicate the first Y estimated and error term from the MINITAB output. The numeric value for the first X_1 value is 640, for the first X_2 is 3, and for Y is 78,000. Utilizing our regression equation yields:

$$\hat{Y}_1 = 19,136 + 92.25(640) - 636(3) = 76,267.5$$

$$e_i = Y_1 - \hat{Y}_1 = 78,000 - 76,267.5 = 1,732.5$$

If we squared all of the residuals and then summed, they would equal SSE (652,052,209).

As we saw in Section 9.5, regression analysis hinges on 3 sum-of-squares. These are:
1.   SST, which measures all changes in Y regardless of the cause.
2.   SSR, which measures all changes in Y associated with the independent variables contained within the regression equation.
3.   SSE (Σe_i^2) which measures all changes in Y associated with independent variables omitted from the regression model or by random phenomena.

282

The standard error analysis and formula is unchanged from Chapter 9, and is as follows:

The Standard Error of the Estimate

$$S_{Y \bullet 12} = \hat{\sigma}_e = \sqrt{\frac{SSE}{n - m}} \qquad (9.2)$$

where

SSE = sum-of-squares due to error $= \Sigma e_i^2$

n = sample size

m = the number of coefficients in the regression equation; in a linear trivariate

---

Note the subscript change in the standard error formula ($Y \bullet 12$). The symbol to the left of the dot represents the dependent variable in the regression model, and the numbers to the right of the dot indicate the specific independent variables to be used in the analysis. Hence, $Y \bullet 12$ states that this is the standard error of the estimate in a multiple regression model with the dependent variable Y, and the independent variables X_1 and X_2. If we had three independent variables within the model, our subscript would be $Y \bullet 123$.

Also note that the numerical equivalent for the degrees of freedom (the denominator) would change. In the simple linear regression model there were two estimated coefficients (a & b). However, in the linear trivariate model, there are three estimated coefficients (a, b_1, & b_2).

The MINITAB output yields SSR = 3,809,681,124, SSE = 652,052,209, and $S_{Y \bullet 12}$ = 7,371. By adding SSE and SSR we obtain SST = 4,461,733,333. If we weren't given $S_{Y \bullet 12}$ we could utilize formula 10.2, $S_{Y \bullet 12} = \sqrt{652,052,209/(15 - 3)}$.

If we developed the appropriate bands plus or minus the multiple regression model, we would find that 68.3% of our data is within one standard error, 95.5% within two standard errors, and 99.7% within three standard errors.

The Coefficient of Multiple Determination

With the coefficient of multiple determination, we are attempting to determine what percentage of the total variation in the Y variable is explained by the independent variables within the regression model. Again, the formula and logic remain unchanged from Chapter 9. The formula is as follows:

Sample Coefficient of Multiple Determination

$$R^2 = 1 - \frac{SSE}{SST} = \frac{SSR}{SST} \qquad (9.3)$$

where

$R_{Y \bullet 12}^2$ = multiple R^2 between Y and both X_1 and X_2

SSE = error sum-of-squares

SSR = regression sum-of-squares

SST = total sum-of-squares

Note that the R^2 subscript ($Y \bullet 12$) matches that of the standard error of the estimate. Utilizing our formula and the appropriate sum of the squares yields

$$R^2_{Y\bullet12} = 3,809,681,124/4,461,733,333 = 0.854$$

Of the variation in Y, 85.4% is explained by the predictor variables in the regression equation.

 Concept Check 10.D

The standard error of the estimate measures the variability about the regression plane in a trivariate model. True or false? If false, explain.

Exercises

10.15 Explain SST, SSR, and SSE.

10.16 Are the formulas and logic for the standard error of the estimate and r^2 the same in the multiple regression model as in the simple linear regression model?

10.17 (Continuation of exercise 10.11.) Suppose that a corporation wants to estimate a trivariate linear regression equation that relates the firm's output of defective parts (Y) to the number of days to complete the production cycle (X_1) and the number of employees (X_2). A cross section of data from 12 production cycles is presented below.

Cycle	Defects	Number of Days to Complete	Number of Employees
A	100	2	7
B	120	3	6
C	125	2	8
D	130	4	12
E	132	2	10
F	140	5	12
G	160	7	12
H	162	4	18
I	165	6	14
J	180	7	12
K	190	7	13
L	200	10	14

a. What are the numerical equivalents to SST, SSE, and SSR?
b. Even though the solutions are on the MINITAB printout, use SSE to compute $S_{Y\bullet12}$ and SSR and SST to obtain R^2.

10.18 (Continuation of exercise 10.12.) Suppose that a corporation wants to estimate a trivariate regression equation that relates the total salary for an auditing department (Y) to the number of employees in the department (X_1) and the organization's size as measured by total assets (X_2). A cross section of data from 15 firms is presented below.

Firm	Total Salary	Number of Employees	Total Assets
A	2.0	100	50
B	2.3	94	60
C	2.5	102	90
D	3.0	108	100
E	3.7	142	120
F	5.1	200	125
G	6.5	190	130
H	8.0	350	225
I	8.1	400	140
J	8.3	422	180
K	8.3	388	190
L	8.5	416	200
M	8.9	340	250
N	9.2	410	240
O	9.4	408	240

*Note total salary and total assets are in millions of dollars.

a. What are the numerical equivalents to SST, SSE, and SSR?

b. Even though the solutions are on the MINITAB printout, use SSE to compute $S_{Y \bullet 12}$ and SSR and SST to obtain R^2.

10.19 (Continuation of Exercise 10.13.) A data set is:

Y	X_1	X_2
1	10	100
2	11	95
3	12	90
4	11	85
5	10	80
6	9	75
7	8	70
8	9	65
9	10	60
10	11	55

Using MINITAB, obtain and explain the sample estimates for $S_{Y \bullet 12}$ and R^2.

10.20 (Continuation of Exercise 10.14.) A university graduate admissions committee is attempting to predict graduate GPA (Y = GGPA) based on the GMAT score (X_1) and on undergraduate GPA (X_2 = UGGPA). Data for twelve randomly selected graduate students are as follows:

Student	Y	X_1	X_2
1	3.05	560	3.33
2	4.00	640	3.79
3	3.55	580	3.57
4	3.53	480	3.23
5	3.58	637	3.92
6	3.21	610	3.09
7	3.50	430	3.18
8	2.80	400	2.48
9	3.44	450	3.31
10	3.17	525	3.26
11	2.46	330	2.56
12	2.75	620	3.58

Using MINITAB, obtain and explain the sample estimates for $S_{Y \bullet 12}$ and R^2. 285

As was the case for the simple linear regression model, we need to ascertain if our model, and the variables within it, are significant at a specified confidence level.

Testing for R^2: Global Testing with ANOVA

To test if the entire model is significant (global approach), we view the ANOVA table (Table 10.3) from MINITAB. The general format for the ANOVA table again is identical to that of the simple linear regression model:

Table 10.3   General format for the ANOVA Table

Source	Sum-of-squares	df	Means Square	F_{test}
Regression	SSR	$m-1$	SSR/$(m-1)$	MSR/MSE
Residual Error	SSE	$n-m$	SSE/$(n-m)$	
Total	SST	$n-1$		

n = sample size, m = the # of estimated parameters

Abbreviated MINITAB output for Sales, Traffic Flow and Number of Competitors Model—Analysis of Variance

Source	DF	SS	MS	F	P
Regression	2	3809681124	1904840562	35.06	0.000
Residual Error	12	652052209	54337684		
Total	14	4461733333			

From MINITAB we learn that $R^2_{Y\bullet 12} = .854$ and $F_{test} = 35.06$. Let's assume we desire a 95% confidence level. We will reject the null hypothesis (H_0: $R^2_{Y\bullet 12} = 0$) if $F_{test} > F_{\alpha(dfnnm,dfden)}$. Since $F_{test}(35.06) > F_{.05(2.12)}$ (3.89), we reject the null hypothesis that the population $R^2 = 0$. This means that at least either B_1 or B_2 does not equal 0. At least one of the variables, traffic flow and/or number of competitors, is significant.

p-Values

In actuality, the F table need not be consulted as the MINITAB P reading (p-Values) yields all the needed information. The null hypothesis is rejected if $\alpha \geq P$-value. Since .05 exceeds 0.000, the null hypothesis must be rejected. The model is significant, based on the argument that the sample coefficient of determination is sufficiently different from zero and it is unlikely that this difference is the result of sampling error.

Testing Hypotheses Concerning the Population Slopes (B_1)

The ANOVA indicates the model
$$Y = a + b_i X_i + b_2 X_2$$
where

$$Y = \text{sales}$$

$$X_1 = \text{traffic flow}$$

$$X_2 = \text{number of competitors}$$

was significant, since we rejected the hypothesis that the true $R^2_{Y\bullet 12} = 0$. Hence, at least one of the two slopes must be significant.

As we saw in Chapter 9, a test of the statistical significance of individual variables is a t_{test} on the partial slope(s) of the regression equation. In other words, the null hypothesis for each variable is:

| | Two-Tailed Test | One-Tailed Test | |
| | | *Direct Relationship* | *Inverse Relationship* |

| H_0: $B_i = 0$ | H_0: $B_i \leq 0$ | H_0: $B_i \geq 0$ |
| H_A: $B_i \neq 0$ | H_A: $B_i > 0$ | H_A: $B_i < 0$ |

The test statistic (t_{test}) is the appropriate sample slope coefficient divided by its appropriate standard error ($t_{test} = b_i/S_{bi}$; Formula 9.6).

The rejection rules are summarized as follows:

Rules for Rejecting the Hypothesis that $B_i = 0$, $B_i \geq 0$, and $B_i \leq 0$

Two-tailed test: If $\alpha \geq P$, reject H_0: $B_i = 0$

One-tailed test: If $\alpha \geq P/2$, reject null hypothesis if in the tail of rejection.

You are in the tail of rejection when your alternate hypothesis is $<$ and your test statistic is negative, and when your alternate hypotheses is $>$ and the test statistic is positive.

Table 10.4   The Theoretical Relationship between the Variables

Variables	*Expected Relationship*
Sales and Traffic Flow	Direct
Sales and Number of Competitors	Inverse

Note that the expected relationships involve the assumption that the impact of the remaining independent variables are being held constant. For example, we expect a direct relationship between sales and traffic flow if the number of competitors is held constant. This may not be the case. For example, increases in traffic flow will draw competitors like a magnet.

In addition, a statistical problem called multicollinearity (Section 10.9) can cause irregularities even in the signs of the regression coefficients. Hence, these t-tests are often performed as a two-tailed test, at least initially.

We will use the MINITAB printout and perform both one- and two-tailed tests on the null hypothesis (Table 10.5). Our rejection rules yield

Table 10.5   MINITAB Testing of H_0

Two-tailed test $B_i = 0$ ($\alpha = .05$)		
$t_{i,test} = P$		Decision for Null Hypothesis
$t_{1,test} = 7.49$	$P = 0.000$	$\alpha \geq P$: reject H_0: $B_1 \neq 0$
$t_{2,test} = -0.57$	$P = 0.577$	$\alpha < P$: ISER H_0: $B_2 = 0$
One-tailed test $B_i \geq 0$ and $B_i \leq 0$ ($\alpha = .05$)		
$t_{i,test} = P/P$		Decision for Null Hypothesis
$t_{i,test} = 7.49$	0.000	$\alpha \geq P/2$: reject H_0: $B_i \neq 0$
$t_{2,test} = -0.57$	0.2885	$\alpha < P/2$: ISER H_0: $B_2 = 0$

Regardless of whether we use the one- or two-tailed test, B_1 is significantly different from 0 and independent variable X_1 is significant. However, we cannot reject the null hypotheses that $B_2 = 0$. Thus, X_1 is the only significant variable in the trivariate regression model. In essence, the multiple regression model reduces to a bivariate regression model. The model becomes $Y = f(X_1)$. When we remove X_2 from the model, we must recompute a new regression equation to obtain the estimated linear bivariate intercept and slope. Of course, before variable X_2 is removed from the model, we might try to obtain additional data and reestimate the model with a larger sample size.

We will learn in a later section that X_1 may not be significant when analyzed as part of a larger model; hence, we must be very careful about the statements we make.

An alternate way of writing the null hypothesis for the Global approach is simply to say that all of the slope coefficients equal to zero. If we had two predictor variables it would be H_O :$b_1 = b_2 = 0$. The alternative hypothesis is that at least one of the slope coefficients does not equal to 0.

The confidence interval formula is again identical to that of the simple linear regression model, $b_i \pm t_{\alpha/2(\mathrm{df})} \bullet S_{bi}$ (Formula 9.7). The 95% confidence interval with respect to B_1 is

$$92.25 \pm 2.179 \bullet 12.31; \ 92.25 \pm 26.823: 65.427 \text{ to } 119.073$$

The 95% confidence interval with respect to B_2 is

$$-636 \pm 2.179 \bullet 1110: -3690.69 \text{ to } 1782.69$$

Since this interval includes $B_2 = 0$, we have insufficient statistical evidence to reject (ISER) the hypothesis that $B_2 = 0$ at a 5% level of significance.

 Concept Check 10.E

The formula for the coefficient of determination used in a multiple regression analysis is the same as given in the linear bivariate models of Chapter 9. True or false? If false, explain.

Exercises

10.21   For $R^2_{Y \bullet 12}$, what does the subscript $Y \bullet 12$ refer to?

10.22   For the linear regression model $Y = f(X_1, X_2)$, if $n = 41$, the degrees of freedom for MSR and MSE are _____ and _____?

10.23   a.   For F_{test}, if our p-value $= .037$, would we reject H_0 at the 95% confidence level?
        b.   What is H_0?

10.24   In Chapter 9, our p-values for our F_{test} and t_{test} were the same. Is this true in a three variable model? Explain.

10.25   Review the p-value rejection rules for H_0: $B_i \geq 0$ or $B_i \leq 0$.

10.26   Review the p-value rejection rules for H_0: $B_i = 0$.

10.27   (Continuation of Exercise 10.11.) Suppose that a corporation wants to estimate a trivariate linear regression equation that relates the firm's output of defective parts (Y) to the number of days to complete the production cycle (X_1) and the number of employees (X_2). A cross section of data from 12 production cycles is presented below.

Cycle	Defects	Number of Days to Complete	Number of Employees
A	100	2	7
B	120	3	6
C	125	2	8
D	130	4	12
E	132	2	10
F	140	5	12
G	160	7	12
H	162	4	18

Cycle	Defects	Number of Days to Complete	Number of Employees
I	165	6	14
J	180	7	12
K	190	7	13
L	200	10	14

a. Is F_{test} significant at the 5% level?
b. Will we expect the relationships between $Y - X_1$, and $Y - X_2$ to be direct or inverse?
c. Are independent variables X_1 and X_2 significant at the 5% level?
d. Compute the 95% confidence intervals for B_1 and B_2.

10.28   (Continuation of Exercise 10.12.) Suppose that a corporation wants to estimate a trivariate regression equation that relates the total salary for an auditing department (Y) to the number of employees in the department (X_1) and the organization's size as measured by total assets (X_2). A cross section of data from 15 firms is presented below.

Firm	Total Salary	Number of Employees	Total Assets
A	2.0	100	50
B	2.3	94	60
C	2.5	102	90
D	3.0	108	100
E	3.7	142	120
F	5.1	200	125
G	6.5	190	130
H	8.0	350	225
I	8.1	400	140
J	8.3	422	180
K	8.3	388	190
L	8.5	416	200
M	8.9	340	230
N	9.2	410	240
O	9.4	408	240

*Note total salary and total assets are in millions of dollars.

a. Is F_{test} significant at the 1% level?
b. Will we expect the relationships between $Y - X_1$, and $Y - X_2$, be direct or inverse?
c. Are independent variables X_1 and X_2 significant at the 1% level?
d. Compute the 99% confidence intervals for B_1 and B_2.

10.29   (Continuation of Exercise 10.13.) A data set is:

Y	X_1	X_2
1	10	100
2	11	95
3	12	90
4	11	85
5	10	80
6	9	75
7	8	70
8	9	65
9	10	60
10	11	55

a. For the model $Y = f(X_1, X_2)$, what is SSE?
b. What is SSR and SST?

10.30 (Continuation of Exercise 10.14.) A university graduate admissions committee is attempting to predict graduate GPA ($Y = $ GGPA) based on the GMAT score (X_1) and undergraduate GPA ($X_2 = $ UGPA). Data for twelve randomly selected graduate students are as follows:

Student	Y	X_1	X_2
1	3.05	560	3.33
2	4.00	640	3.79
3	3.55	580	3.57
4	3.53	480	3.23
5	3.58	637	3.92
6	3.21	610	3.09
7	3.50	430	3.18
8	2.80	400	2.48
9	3.44	450	3.31
10	3.17	525	3.26
11	2.46	330	2.56
12	2.75	620	3.58

a. For the model $Y = f(X_1, X_2)$, is F_{test} significant at the 5% level?
b. Will we expect the relationships between $Y - X_1$, and $Y - X_2$ to be direct or inverse?
c. Are independent variables X_1 and X_2 significant at the 5% level?

10.6 Adding Variables to an Existing Model

In the business world, organizations are always in a quest to improve their models to obtain an edge over their competitors. We begin our analysis of this quest by attempting to improve our site location model by adding predictor (independent) variables to the model.

Adding X_3

In our fast food franchise model, the regression equation yielded a $R^2_{Y \bullet 12} = .853$. This result, although significant, may mean that some important variables have not been included in the regression model. We will try to include another variable to reduce the error and improve the predictability of the model. If an important variable is added to the regression equation, the errors should be reduced. Hence, the standard error of the estimate and the unexplained variation (SSE) will be smaller, and the coefficient of determination will be larger. If the variable does not add significantly to the model, there will probably be little change in the coefficient of determination.

The fast food industry believes that its franchises do particularly well with the younger generation. This explains why hamburger franchises want to locate next to or on military bases and universities. In our model, we will use age as a proxy for the changes in eating habits over one's life cycle. The regression equation is

$$Y = a + b_1 X_1 + b_2 X_2 + b_3 X_3$$

where

$Y = $ sales

$X_1 = $ traffic flow

$X_2 = $ number of competitors

$X_3 = $ average age of the surrounding population

Sometimes it is necessary to work with a variable that either does or does not have a certain attribute. For example, either a part is within specified tolerances or it is not. In Chapter 1, we introduced qualitative variables. As we saw, qualitative variables are categorical and reflect non-numeric characteristics.

In our fast food model, a potentially important variable is the ease of entry and exit from the restaurant. Either there is free access to the site, or there are hindrances such as oncoming traffic that must be crossed. In Table 10.6, X_3 is the median age of the surrounding population and X_4 is the dummy (or binary) variable for ease of entry or exit. A 1 for X_4 indicates sites where there is no hindrance to entry or exit and a 0 indicates that a hindrance exists. Computationally, dummy variables are easier to work with than continuous data because 1 and 0 are simple numbers to use in calculations. For example, the sum of X_4 equals 5 (the sum of 5 ones and 7 zeros).

Table 10.6 Data Set for Fast Food Regression Model

Site#	Y	X_1	X_2	X_3	X_4
1	78000	640	3	27.1	0
2	61000	410	8	41.2	1
3	93000	818	5	21.8	1
4	48000	416	4	43.1	0
5	72000	549	5	32.7	1
6	51000	479	6	42.3	0
7	87000	822	5	22.6	1
8	98000	784	3	21.9	1
9	66000	499	4	36.0	0
10	77000	510	4	27.3	0
11	86000	800	2	26.1	1
12	46000	387	3	46.2	0
13	94000	875	4	20.9	1
14	49000	452	9	39.8	0
15	72000	602	3	32.0	0

The MINITAB computer printout for the multiple regression model is shown in Table 10.7. Using MINITAB for a Linear Multiple Regression Model

Stat > Regression > Regression
Double click **SALES** into **Response** box.
Double click **TFLOW, NUMCOMP, AGE, ENTRY** into **Predictors** box.

Table 10.7   Regression Analysis: Sales versus TFLOW, NUNCOMP, AGE, ENTRY
*Data File on MINITAB CD

The regression equation is

SALES = 138315 − 11.6 TFLOW − 1128 NUMCOMP − 1814 AGE + 8125 ENTRY

Predictor	Coef	SE Coef	T	P
Constant	138315	14750	9.38	0.000
TFLOW	−11.56	13.13	−0.88	0.399
NUMCOMP	−1127.7	463.2	−2.43	0.035
AGE	−1813.7	227.4	−7.98	0.000
ENTRY	8125	2155	3.77	0.004

S = 2818   R-Sq = 98.2%   R-Sq(adj) = 97.5%

Analysis of Variance

Source	DF	SS	MS	F	P
Regression	4	4382337848	1095584462	137.99	0.000
Residual Error	10	79395485	7939549		
Total	14	4461733333			

Source	DF	Seq SS
TFLOW	1	3791831024
NUMCOMP	1	17850100
AGE	1	459749465
ENTRY	1	112907259

The regression equation is

$$\hat{Y} = 138,315 - 11.56(X_1) - 1127.7(X_2) - 1813.7(X_3) + 8125(X_4)$$

where

Y = sales

X_1 = traffic flow (Tflow)

X_2 = number of competitors (NUMCOMP)

X_3 = age (AGE)

X_4 = entry dummy variable (ENTRY)

To make a forecast of Y, specific values for X_1, X_2, X_3, and X_4 are substituted into the estimated regression equation. There are only two possible values for X_4, 1 or 0. If $X_4 = 0$, then the equation reduces to

$\hat{Y}$ = 138,315 − 11.56TFLOW − 1127.7NUMCOMP − 1813.7AGE

However, if $X_4 = 1$, then 8125(b_4) must be added to the intercept to obtain a new intercept. Therefore, the new predictive equation is

$\hat{Y}$ = 146,440 − 11.56TFLOW − 1127.7NUMCOMP − 1813.7AGE

As an example, suppose our model is significant and we want to predict the sales of a fast food franchise for a particular vacant site. From public sources we discover that the traffic flow (X_1) is 750, there are seven fast food competitors (X_2), and the median age of the adjacent population (X_3) is 24.5. Then the predicted sales for a site with an entry or exit problem is

$\hat{Y}$ = 138,315 − 11.56(750) − 1127.7(7) − 1813.7(24.5) 77,315.45

When there is no problem with entering or exiting the restaurant ($X_4 = 1$), the predicted level of sales is

$\hat{Y}$ = 146440 − 11.56(750) − 1127.7(7) − 1813.7(24.5) = 85, 440.45

The difference between the two forecasts is the estimated coefficient of the dummy variable (8125). If there is no problem with entry or exit, the forecasted sales is 8125 higher than when a potential problem exists.

We decided to place a "1" for X_4 when there was no hindrance and a "0" for problems with entry or exit. This process could have been reversed, with a "0" for restaurants with entry or exit problems and a "1" for restaurants with no such problems. The only difference would be that b_4 would be $-\$8125$ instead of $+\$8125$. If we graph the equations, there would be two parallel planes, where the graph of the equation assuming no problems with entry or exit located $\$8125$ above the graph of the equation where there is an entry or exit problem.

Are All B_1's Significant?

The theoretical relationship between sales and the four independent variables is given in Table 10.8.

Table 10.8 The Theoretical Relationship between the Variables

Variables	Expected Relationship
Sales and Traffic Flow	Direct
Sales and Number of Competitors	Inverse
Sales and age of surrounding population	Inverse
Sales and ease of entry/exit	Direct*

*Direct because we assigned a 1 where there were no entry/exit problems and a 0 where there were problems. If the assignments were reversed the relationship would be inverse.

Note that the expected relationships involve the assumption that the effect of the remaining independent variables are being held constant. For example, we expect a direct relationship between sales and traffic flow if the number of competitors, age, and ease of entry/exit are held constant. This may not be the case. For example, increases in traffic flow will draw competitors like a magnet, and will affect entry/exit problems.

In addition, a statistical problem called multicollinearity (Section 10.9) can cause irregularities even in the signs of the regression coefficients. Hence, often t-tests are performed as a two-tailed test, at least initially.

We will use the MINITAB printout and perform both one- and two-tailed tests on the null hypothesis (Table 10.9). Our rejection rules yield:

Table 10.9 MINITAB Testing of H_0

Two-tailed test: $B_i = 0\ (\alpha = .05)$		
$t_{i,\text{test}} = P$		Decision for Null Hypothesis
$t_{1,\text{test}} = -0.88$	0.399	$\alpha < P$: ISER H_0: $B_1 = 0$
$t_{2,\text{test}} = -2.43$	0.035	$\alpha \geq P$: Reject H_0: $B_2 \neq 0$
$t_{3,\text{test}} = -7.98$	0.000	$\alpha \geq P$: Reject H_0: $B_3 \neq 0$
$t_{4,\text{test}} = 3.77$	0.004	$\alpha \geq P$: Reject H_0: $B_4 \neq 0$
One-tailed test: $B_i \leq 0$ and $B_i \geq 0\ (\alpha = .05)$		
$t_{1,\text{test}} = P/2$		Decision for Null Hypothesis
$t_{t,\text{test}} = -0.88$	0.199	$\alpha < P/2$: ISER H_0: $B_1 = 0$
$t_{2,\text{test}} = -2.43$	0.018	$\alpha \geq P/2$: Reject H_0: $B_2 \neq 0$
$t_{3,\text{test}} = -7.98$	0.000	$\alpha \geq P/2$: Reject H_0: $B_3 \neq 0$
$t_{4,\text{test}} = 3.77$	0.002	$\alpha \geq P/2$: Reject H_0: $B_4 \neq 0$

Note: You are in the tail of rejection when your alternate hypothesis is $<$ and your test statistic is negative, and when your alternate hypotheses is $>$ and the test statistic is positive.

Regardless of whether we use the one- or two-tailed test, B_2, B_3 and B_4 are significantly different from 0. However, we cannot reject the null hypothesis that $B_1 = 0$.

Concept Check 10.F

If F_{test} is significant in a model with two predictor variables, it means that both predictor variables are significant in the model. True or false? If false, explain.

Exercises

Use MINITAB to perform all computations.

10.31 Adding independent or predictor variables to a multiple regression model will always raise R^2. Explain.

10.32 In your own words explain dummy variables.

10.33 The multiple regression model of Exercise 10.11 [defects = f(# of days to complete, # of employees)] is to include a third independent variable, reflecting the number of electrical surges occurring during the cycle (X_3). This additional variable for each of the twelve cycles is listed in the following table. Based on the expanded data set, completely analyze the statistical results.

Cycle	Defects	Number of Days to Complete	Number of Employees	Surges
A	100	2	7	1.5
B	120	3	6	2.1
C	125	2	8	2.1
D	130	4	12	2.0
E	132	2	10	2.5
F	140	5	12	1.8
G	160	7	12	1.9
H	162	4	18	2.0
I	165	6	14	2.1
J	180	7	12	2.0
K	190	7	13	2.4
L	200	10	14	2.0

10.34 The trivariate linear model of Exercise 10.12 [Salary = f(# of employees, total assets)] is to include a third independent variable reflecting the average age of the auditing department's employees (X_3). This additional variable for each of the fifteen firms is listed in the following table. Based on the expanded data set of Exercise 10.11, completely analyze the statistical results.

Firm	Total Salary	Number of Employees	Total Assets	Mean Age
A	2.0	100	50	35
B	2.3	94	60	37
C	2.5	102	90	43
D	3.0	108	100	41
E	3.7	142	120	44
F	5.1	200	125	45
G	6.5	190	130	49
H	8.0	350	225	52
I	8.1	400	140	51
J	8.3	422	180	54
K	8.3	388	190	56
L	8.5	416	200	57

		Total	Number of	Total	Mean
Firm	Salary		Employees	Assets	Age
M	8.9		340	250	53
N	9.2		410	240	58
O	9.4		408	240	58

*Note total salary and total assets are in millions of dollars.

10.35   (Continuation of Exercise 10.13.) A data set is:

Y	X_1	X_2	X_3
1	10	100	17
2	11	95	28
3	12	90	7
4	11	85	19
5	10	80	4
6	9	75	16
7	8	70	29
8	9	65	17
9	10	60	14
10	11	55	31

a.   For the model $Y = f(X_1, X_2, X_3)$, is F_{test} significant at the 10% level?
b.   Are independent variables X_1, X_2, and X_3 significant at the 10% level?

10.36   (Continuation of Exercise 10.14.) A university graduate admissions committee is attempting to predict graduate GPA (Y = GGPA) based on the GMAT score (X_1), undergraduate GPA (X_2 = UGGPA), and the average number of absences from class at the undergraduate level (X_3). Data for twelve randomly selected graduate students are as follows:

Student	Y	X_1	X_2	X_3
1	3.05	560	3.33	15
2	4.00	640	3.79	1
3	3.55	580	3.57	4
4	3.53	480	3.23	3
5	3.58	637	3.92	2
6	3.21	610	3.09	9
7	3.50	430	3.18	3
8	2.80	400	2.48	14
9	3.44	450	3.31	6
10	3.17	525	3.26	7
11	2.46	330	2.56	21
12	2.75	620	3.58	18

a.   For the model $Y = f(X_1, X_2, X_3)$, is F_{test} significant at the 5% level?
b.   Are independent variables X_1, X_2, and X_3 significant at the 5% level?

10.37   Suppose the following linear regression model was estimated by the quality control department of an automobile manufacturing plant:

$$\hat{Y} = 3.2 - 1.2(X_1) + 2.4(X_2)$$

where

Y = number of defective components produced in an eight hour shift

X_1 = dummy variable that equals 1 if the shift is on Monday and 0 otherwise

X_2 = dummy variable that equals 1 if the shift is on Friday and 0 otherwise.

Interpret the regression coefficients. If this result reflects the true relationship, on which day would you want this component produced for your car?

10.38 Suppose a publishing house believes the following equation represents their true costs of publishing a textbook:

$$\hat{Y} = \$75,000 + \$50(X_1) + \$30,000(X_2) + \$10,000(X_3)$$

where

Y = the cost of publishing a textbook hour shift

X_1 = number of pages in text

X_2 = dummy variable that equals 1 if the text is quantitative and 0 otherwise

X_3 = dummy variable that equals 1 if the text requires computer software and 0 otherwise.

a. If a 1,000-page text is proposed that is both quantitative and requires computer software, determine the cost.
b. If a 1000-page text is proposed that is not quantitative and does not require computer software, determine the cost.

10.7 Stepwise Regression Analysis

Model building and estimation is critical for most business decision-makers. It is important to know what variables are significant to a model and which are not. There are several options available to the decision-maker including forward, backward, and stepwise regression.

All of the options attempt not only to determine the R^2 for the overall model, but to aid in the decision of which variables to include in the model. They do so by entering/deleting a different independent variable on each step or iteration of the process based on that variable's importance to the model. Thus, the procedures build the model one variable at a time.

As an example, we will return to our fast food franchise model. The regression equation is

$$Y = a + b_1 X_1 + b_2 X_2 + b_3 X_3 + b_4 X_4$$

where

Y = Sales

X_1 = Traffic flow

X_2 = Number of Competitors

X_3 = Median age

X_4 = Ease of entry or exit

Since there are four independent (predictor) variables, there will be four iterations or steps in the case of this model.

Stat > Regression > Stepwise
Double click **SALES** into **Response** box.
Double click **TFLOW, NUMCOMP, AGE, ENTRY** into **Predictors** box.

Table 10.10 Stepwise Regression: Sales versus TFLOW, NUMCOMP, AGE, ENTRY

ALPHA-TO-ENTER: 0.15   ALPHA-TO-REMOVE: 0.15

Response is Sales on 4 predictors, with N = 15

Step	1	2	3
Constant	135151	126022	125810
AGE	−1974	−1774	−1643
T-Value	−16.18	−14.63	−13.88
P-Value	0.000	0.000	0.000
ENTRY		5846	7222
T-Value		2.82	3.85
P-Value		0.015	0.003
NUMCOMP			−1018
T-Value			−2.31
P-Value			0.042
S	4029	3252	2789
R-Sq	95.27	97.16	98.08
R-Sq(adj)	94.91	96.68	97.56
C-p	15.6	7.0	3.8

Table 10.10 has the MINITAB commands and output for stepwise regression. Note that the subroute terminated at step 3. This is because the statistics package ascertained that only three independent or perditor variable was significant.

In Table 10.10 AGE is the first variable listed; hence, it is the most significant variable. From the first reading for $R^2 = .9527$, AGE gives us 95.27% predictability. The second predictor variable listed (ENTRY) is the second ranked most important independent variable. The second reading for $R^2(.9716)$ is the predictability given by both AGE plus ENTRY. This means that AGE added the difference $(.9716 − .9527 = 0.0189)$ to our predictability. The third predictor variable listed (NUMCOMP) is the third ranked most important independent variable. The third reading for $R^2(.9808)$ is the predictability given by both AGE, ENTRY, and NUMCOMP. This means that NUMCOMP added the difference $(.9808 − .9716 = 0.0092)$ to our predictability. Minitab entered the fourth predictor variable (TFLOW) and found it not to be significant, hence the process ceased.

There are two other approaches to this process called forward and backwards regression. These two processes essentially do the same as stepwise regression. For example the forward regression process would continue to add variables even if they were not proven to be significant to the model. The backwards approach essentially finds the variable ranked last in the model, then proceeds backwards to the first. The command changes for MINITAB for both approaches are given at the end of this chapter.

A Note of Caution

A stepwise program attempts to reveal the effect and relative importance of the predictor variables involved.

An analogy might aid in understanding the difficulty. If you are ill, you may see a physician who may prescribe multiple medications. The independent effect of the medications may be considerably different than their combined effect. Some medications when combined create a toxicity problem that may be deadly. Hence, complex statistical problems can develop in multiple regression models, confusing an analysis of the relative effects of independent variables. In stepwise regression, there is a real possibility of inflating Type I errors. For this reason, forward/backward/stepwise regression analysis is not recommended for beginning students except as an intuitive tool to comprehend the concept of adding or deleting variables to a model.

Adjusting r^2 for Degrees of Freedom

We have learned that adding variables to the multiple regression model cannot reduce SST, but can cause SSE to become smaller or remain the same. Remember that $R^2 = 1 - (\text{SSE/SST})$. Hence, we can continually load the model with independent variables (which probably won't be significant) to create a larger R^2. To counter this problem, we can use an adjusted R^2 formula.

Adjusted R^2 for Lost Degrees of Freedom

$$R^2_{adj} = 1 - (1 - R^2)\left(\frac{n-1}{n-m}\right) \qquad (10.1)$$

where

$R^2 = $ the coefficient of multiple determination

$m = $ the number of coefficients in the regression model

$n = $ sample size

Note: $n > m$ and negative solutions are treated as 0.

Using a numerical equivalent in our model where $Y = f(X_1, X_2, X_3, X_4)$,

$$R^2 = 1 - (1 - 0.982)\left(\frac{15-1}{15-5}\right) = .975$$

 Concept Check 10.G

Stepwise regression attempts to indicate a ranking of the relative importance of the independent variables in a multiple regression model. True or false? If false, explain.

Exercises

10.39 Explain the adjusted r^2 formula.

10.40 Forward regression analysis is a model building approach that evaluates prediction one independent (predictor) variable at a time. Explain.

10.41 For the multiple regression model of Exercise 10.33 [Defects $= f(\#$ of days to complete, $\#$ of employees, surges)], perform a forward regression analysis using MINITAB ($\alpha = .05$).

Cycle	Defects	Number of Days to Complete	Number of Employees	Surges
A	100	2	7	1.5
B	120	3	6	2.1
C	125	2	8	2.1
D	130	4	12	2.0
E	132	2	10	2.5
F	140	5	12	1.8
G	160	7	12	1.9

298

Cycle	Defects	Number of Days to Complete	Number of Employees	Surges
H	162	4	18	2.0
I	165	6	14	2.1
J	180	7	12	2.0
K	190	7	13	2.4
L	200	10	14	2.0

10.42 For the MINITAB file PULSE perform a forward stepwise using pulse2 as the response variable and RAN, SEX, ACTIVITY as the predictor variables.

10.43 For the multiple regression analysis of Exercise 10.34 [Salary $= f$(# of employees, Total assets, Age)], perform a forward regression using MINITAB ($\alpha = .05$).

Firm	Total Salary	Number of Employees	Total Assets	Mean Age
A	2.0	100	50	35
B	2.3	94	60	37
C	2.5	102	90	43
D	3.0	108	100	41
E	3.7	142	120	44
F	5.1	200	125	45
G	6.5	190	130	49
H	8.0	350	225	52
I	8.1	400	140	51
J	8.3	422	180	54
K	8.3	388	190	56
L	8.5	416	200	57
M	8.9	340	250	53
N	9.2	410	240	58
O	9.4	408	240	58

*Note total salary and total assets are in millions of dollars.

10.44 For Exercise 10.43, perform a backwards regression analysis ($\alpha = .05$).

10.45 (Continuation of Exercise 10.35.) A data set is:

Y	X_1	X_2	X_3
1	10	100	17
2	11	95	28
3	12	90	7
4	11	85	19
5	10	80	4
6	9	75	16
7	8	70	29
8	9	65	17
9	10	60	14
10	11	55	31

For the model $Y = f(X_1, X_2, X_3)$, perform a forwards multiple regression analysis ($\alpha = .01$).

10.46 (Continuation of Exercise 10.36.) A university admissions committee is attempting to predict graduate GPA ($Y =$ GGPA) based on the GMAT score (X_1), on undergraduate GPA ($X_2 =$ UGGPA), and on the average number of absences from class at the under graduate level (X_3). Data for twelve randomly selected graduate students are as follows:

Student	Y	X_1	X_2	X_3
1	3.05	560	3.33	15
2	4.00	640	3.79	1
3	3.55	580	3.57	4
4	3.53	480	3.23	3
5	3.58	637	3.92	2
6	3.21	610	3.09	9
7	3.50	430	3.18	3
8	2.80	400	2.48	14
9	3.44	450	3.31	6
10	3.17	525	3.26	7
11	2.46	330	2.56	21

a. For the model $Y = f(X_1, X_2, X_3)$, perform a forwards multiple regression analysis ($\alpha = .05$).

b. For the model $Y = f(X_1, X_2, X_3)$, perform a backwards multiple regression analysis ($\alpha = .05$).

10.8 Multicollinearity

When we work with more than one independent variable, whether we are calculating multiple or partial correlation, a particularly nagging problem occurs when the independent variables themselves are highly correlated to each other. This problem is termed **multicollinearity**. If there were two highly correlated independent variables, it is impossible to factor out or hold constant the influences of one of the two variables. If you have one variable, you have both. Therefore, partial correlation (a condition between Y and a single X variable) is not practical.

Multicollinearity also causes severe problems for multiple regression analysis. One of these problems involves inflated standard errors for the coefficients of the model. A second problem is illogical signs and values for the regression coefficients which tend to approach 0. Sometimes a slope coefficient will be negative, although theoretically it should be positive. Or the absolute value of a regression coefficient will be higher than theory indicates it should be. Also, the regression coefficients sometimes react wildly, or are extremely sensitive to increases or decreases in the number of independent variables or to changes in the data points for a variable.

We will first learn how to detect the general problem, then study the specific relationships giving us problems.

Using MINITAB to obtain Correlation (r) Matrix

Stat > Basic Statistics > correlation
Click independent variables **TFLOW, NUMCOMP, AGE, ENTRY** into variable box
and using MINITAB TO OBTAIN VIF VALUE
STAT > REGRESSION > REGRESSION
PLACE THE RESPONSE AND PREDICTORS IN THEIR APPROPRIATE PLACES
UNDER OPTIONS CLICK ON VARIANCE INFLATION FACTORS

Table 10.11A1&A2 Correlations: TFLOW, NUMCOMP, AGE, ENTRY

A1	TFLOW	NUMCOMP	AGE	A2	*Without P-Values*		
					TFLOW	NUMCOMP	AGE
NUMCOMP	−0.384			NUMCOMP	−0.384		
	0.158						
AGE	−0.926	0.377		AGE	−0.926	0.377	
	0.000	0.166					
ENTRY	0.669	0.019	−0.584	ENTRY	0.669	0.019	−0.584
	0.006	0.946	0.022				
Cell Contents: Pearson correlation				Cell Contents: Pearson correlation			
P-Value							

There are two similar methods for detecting multicollinearity. In the first approach, we run cross-correlations on all of the predictor variables (noting to exclude the response variable). Remember that the coefficient of correlation ranges between −1 to +1. A zero means no association between the two variables. A +1 means a perfect direct relationship and −1 a perfect inverse relationship. The guides usually are absolute values of .9 or greater and P-value $= 0$. We see a value of −0.926 between X_1 (TFLOW) and X_3 (AGE). Hence multicollinearity exists between these two variables. In the second approach, we have Minitab compute Variance Inflation Factors (VIF). In the command sequence be sure to click on VIF under options. Minitab presents the VIF values to the right of the P values (Table 10.11B) to the far right of each predictor variable. Readings between 1–5 indicate no problems with multicollinearity, and readings above 10 represent an extreme problem. We should be very concerned about the reading of 9.131 (TFLOW) as in indication of a problem. There may be some smaller concerns also about a VIF = 7.105 with age.

Table 10.11B   Regression Analysis: SALES versus TFLOW, NUMCOMP, AGE, ENTRY

The regression equation is

SALES = 138315 − 11.6 TFLOW − 1128 NUMCOMP − 1814 AGE + 8125 ENTRY

Predictor	Coef	SE Coef	T	P	VIF
Constant	138315	14750	9.38	0.000	
TFLOW	−11.56	13.13	−0.88	0.399	9.131
NUMCOMP	−1127.7	463.2	−2.43	0.035	1.398
AGE	−1813.7	227.4	−7.98	0.000	7.105
ENTRY	8125	2155	3.77	0.004	2.183

From Table 10.12 we can see the consequences of multicollearity. We see the results of three regressions runs; Sales $= f$(TFLOW); Sales $= f$(AGE); and Sales $= f$(TFLOW, AGE). There are problems with coefficients. They begin to approach zero, and they often change signs. In addition the SE Coefficient increases. This is how the term VIF was instituted. The T-value formula is to divide the coefficient by its own SE Coefficient. With the numerator approaching zero and the denominator getting larger, T will approach zero. In turn the P-value will approach 1. With large P-values we will toss predictor varibles out of the model even though in reality they may be important.

Table 10.12A   Regression Analysis: Sales versus TFLOW

The regression equation is

Sales = 14621 + 95.0 TFLOW

Predictor	Coef	SE Coef	T	P
Constant	14621	6926	2.11	0.055
TFLOW	94.96	11.07	8.58	0.000

Table 10.12B	Regression Analysis: Sales versus AGE			
Sales = 135151 − 1974 AGE				
Predictor	Coef	SE Coef	T	P
Constant	135151	4046	33.40	0.000
AGE	−1973.5	121.9	−16.18	0.000

Table 10.12C	Regression Analysis: Sales versus TFLOW, AGE			
Sales = 119531 + 13.2 TFLOW − 1734 AGE				
Predictor	Coef	SE Coef	T	P
Constant	119531	20186	5.92	0.000
TFLOW	13.18	16.67	0.79	0.445
AGE	−1734.1	327.2	−5.30	0.000

We can see for the predictor variables that T values approach 0 (TFLOW from 8.58 to 0.79; AGE from −16.18 to −5.30). This will result P-Values approaching one where a problem exists (TFLOW from 0.000 to 0.445; AGE from 0.000 to 0.000).

The solution to this problem is to either eliminate one of the predictor variables or to combine them into a new predictor variable by creating a ratio between them. If we were to eliminate either TFLOW or AGE it would be TFLOW because it has a larger P-value (0.455 versus 0.000). We might also consider a new predictor variable, which is the ratio of TFLOW divided by AGE. This would make sense since we want cars to drive past our site but we would want younger people inside (younger buyers eat more fast food than older buyers). Hence

$$X_5 = X_1/X_3 = \text{TFLOW/AGE}$$

We will have Minitab tabulate this new variable for us with the following command sequence.

Calc > Calculator
Type variable name in **Store result in variable** (AGETFLOW).
Click on **Expressions** box.
Click in **AGE**.
Type a / sign.
Click in **TFLOW**.
OK

We then perform a regression analysis with the equation
Sales = f(AGE/TFLOW, NUMCOMP, ENTRY)
We note that only the variable AGETFLOW is a significant predictor. The reason that NUMCOMP and ENTRY is not showing as predictive variables is because we are having a small problem of multicollinearity between the two variables (Table 10.13). Since one of the variables is a binary variable, it would not make sense to combine these two variables into a ratio. We would delete the variable ENTRY from the model because it has a larger P-value (0.301).

Table 10.13	Regression Analysis: SALES versus age/tflow, NUMCOMP, ENTRY					

The regression equation is

SALES $= 99081 - 428700$ age/tflow $- 1101$ NUMCOMP $+ 8670$ ENTRY

Predictor	Coef	SE Coef	T	P	VIF
Constant	99081	3729	26.57	0.000	
age/tflow	−428700	47372	−9.05	0.000	1.899
NUMCOMP	−1100.8	654.8	−1.68	0.121	1.301
ENTRY	8670	2716	3.19	0.009	1.615

$S = 4129.55$ R-Sq $= 9.58\%$ R-Sq(adj) $= 94.6\%$

Analysis of Variance

Source	DF	SS	MS	F	P
Regression	3	4274148663	1424716221	83.55	0.000
Residual Error	11	187584670	17053152		
Total	14	4461733333			

Since our largest VIF value is 1.899, we are no longer plagued with a multicollinear problem.

Indy 500 Problem Revisited

When we first ran our model where the dependent variable was GNP and the independent variable was the winning speed of the Indianapolis 500 motor car race, we were surprised to see an $r^2 = .913$. What caused our problem was that both GNP and Indy 500 speeds (MPH) increase proportionately over time.

There is a strong relationship existing between MPH and the year of the race. With population and inflation growing, nominal GNP will rise over time. If we developed the model: GNP $= f$(Year, MPH), and estimate using MINITAB, the output is:

Table 10.14	Abbreviated Printout of the Data Set of Table 9.10.			

REGRESSION ANALYSIS

The regression equation is

GNP $= -52 + 2.53$ MPH $+ 40.6$ Year

Predictor	Coef	StDev	T	p
Constant	−51.8	934.9	−0.06	0.957
MPH	2.528	7.384	0.34	0.737
Year	40.64	14.38	2.83	0.013

$S = 63.28$ R-Sq $= 94.3\%$ R-Sq(adj) $= 93.6\%$

If we run a correlation on (MPH) and (Year) we obtain a numerical reading of 0.980. Hence both of these variables cannot appear as predictor variables at the same time. Since it does not make sense to combine the variables in this example we would use our p value to tell us to remove MPH from the model.

In summary, concerning the problem of multicollinearity:

Cause: Independent variables themselves are highly correlated.

Detection: Correlations near an absolute value of .9 or above indicate the presence of multicollinearity. To isolate specific relationships, use the Stat > Basic Statistics > Correlate command.

Effect: Regression coefficients and standard errors of the coefficients are altered causing t_{test} values to approach 0 and P-values to approach 1. This means that the null hypothesis ($B_i = 0$) will not be rejected most of the time.

Cure: If two independent variables are highly correlated, attempt to combine the two into a new independent variable, and use that variable on the regression analysis. This assumes that a theoretical basis exists to justify both variables being included in the model. If such a theoretical basis does not exist, or if the combining is not plausible, eliminate the independent variable with the smallest correlation with Y.

Concept Check 10.H

Multicollinearity is caused by a high correlation between Y and one or more of the independent variables in the regression equation. True or false? If false, explain.

Exercises

10.47   Explain multicollinearity in your own words.

10.48   What is the basic cure for multicollinearity?

10.49   Determine if there is a multicollinearity problem in the following model: Defects $= f(\#$ of days to complete, # of employees, surges).

Cycle	Defects	Number of Days to Complete	Number of Employees	Surges
A	100	2	7	1.5
B	120	3	6	2.1
C	125	2	8	2.1
D	130	4	12	2.0
E	132	2	10	2.5
F	140	5	12	1.8
G	160	7	12	1.9
H	162	4	18	2.0
I	165	6	14	2.1
J	180	7	12	2.0
K	190	7	13	2.4
L	200	10	14	2.0

10.50   a. Determine if there is a multicollinearity problem in the following model: Salary $= f(\#$ of employees, total assets, mean age).

b.   If multicollinearity exists, attempt to remove it.

Firm	Total Salary	Number of Employees	Total Assets	Mean Age
A	2.0	100	50	35
B	2.3	94	60	37
C	2.5	102	90	43
D	3.0	108	100	41
E	3.7	142	120	44
F	5.1	200	125	45
G	6.5	190	130	49
H	8.0	350	225	52
I	8.1	400	140	51
J	8.3	422	180	54
K	8.3	388	190	56
L	8.5	416	200	57
M	8.9	340	250	53
N	9.2	410	240	58
O	9.4	408	240	58

304

10.51   A data set is:

Y	X_1	X_2	X_3
8	10	100	20
17	11	95	19
21	12	90	18
36	11	85	17
41	10	80	16
58	9	75	15
71	8	70	14
73	9	65	13
81	10	60	12
93	11	55	11

a.   Have MINITAB determine the linear coefficients for the model $Y = f(X_1, X_2, X_3)$.

b.   Using determine if multicollinearity exists.

10.52   What statistical problems does multicollinearity cause?

10.9   Nonlinear Correlation: The Parabola or Quadratic Equation

We will now turn to nonlinear equations (parabolas) between two variables X and Y. Two variable regression was analyzed in Chapter 9, but the computer solution treats the quadratic equation (second-order or second-degree polynomial) $\hat{Y} = a + bX + cX^2$ as if it were a multiple regression equation such as $\hat{Y} = a + bX_1 + cX_2$, where $X_2 = X^2$.

Figure 10.2 shows examples of nonlinear relationships that frequently are discussed in other business courses. These relationships include a product life cycle curve, learning curve, total cost curve, average variable cost curve, average fixed cost curve, and the production possibility curve. Such relationships cannot be explained adequately by a linear equation.

Figure 10.2   Nonlinear Relationships Commonly Found in Business Curriculum

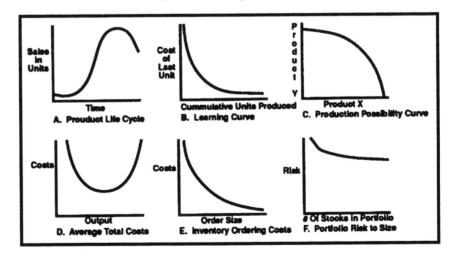

It is computationally burdensome and unnecessary to attempt to solve higher order equations by hand. Using a statistical package such as MINITAB is recommended. As an example, we will solve a small data set just to make you aware of the process. Assume that we are analyzing the relationship between the size of a super market (measured in square feet) and the number of different brands of cereal carried. We believe that as the stores become larger, the number of brands carried increases. This means, as far as B is concerned, we are testing $H_0: B \leq 0$. However, beyond a certain square footage, the stores carry less food items and more of other nonfood items (typical of wholesale discount houses). This refers to an inverse relationship; hence, as far as C is concerned, we are testing $H_0: C \geq 0$. Suppose we collect data from nine different sized supermarkets and record the number of cereals carried (Table 10.15).

Table 10.15 Computing a Second-Degree Polynomial
*Data File on MINITAB CD

Supermarket	Store Square Feet (000)	Number of Cereals Carried
1	5	3
2	10	12
3	20	21
4	30	37
5	40	52
6	50	43
7	60	31
8	70	28
9	80	24

For the parabola $Y = a + bX + cX^2$, the estimated least squares equation is

$$\hat{Y} = -7.286 + 2.1171(X) - 0.022334(X^2): R^2 = 87.0$$

where

$$Y = \text{number of cereals carried}$$

$$X = \text{store's square footage in thousands}$$

If we fitted a linear equation through the data set, the resulting least squares equation is

$$\hat{Y} = 17.4 + 0.259(X): R^2 = 20.5$$

Clearly, the data are better fit by parabola than with a linear equation. Using F_{test}, the model is significant at the 5% level for the polynomial $(.05 \geq .002)$, but not for the linear equation $(.05 < .221)$. In the parabola, both b and c are significant at the 5% level. The significance occurs because $.05 \geq .001/2$ for b and for c. In both instances we are in the tail of rejection for b. The alternate hypothesis is $>$ and the sign of the test's statistic is positive. For c, the alternate hypothesis is $<$ and the test statistic is negative. Note that the residuals for the improper curve fit cause a grouping of negative residuals, followed by a grouping of positive residuals, and, in turn, followed by a grouping of negative residuals (see page 307). Often, the cause for such a grouping of residuals is an improper curve fit.

Stat > Regression > Fitted Line Plot
CEREAL into the Response box.
STSQFT into the Predictors box.
Sequentially click under type of regression model linear, quadratic, cubic

OK

Comparing a Higher Order Equation to Lower Order Equations

Sometimes we may want to compare a higher order equation with that of a lower order to determine if the additional coefficients add any statistical significance to the model. For example, suppose we weren't sure if the parabola's coefficient was significant.

F_{test} to Ascertain If Higher Order Equation is Warranted

$$F_{\text{test}} = \frac{(\text{SSE}_{\text{LowerOrder}} - \text{SSE}_{\text{HigherOrder}})/k}{\text{MSE}_{\text{HigherOrder}}}$$

where

$\text{SSE}_{\text{HigherOrder}} = $ SSE for the higher order model

$\text{SSE}_{\text{LowerOrder}} = $ SSE for the lower order model

$k = $ the # of parameters difference between the two models

$\text{MSE}_{\text{HigherOrder}} = $ Mean Square Error for higher order model

Note: df for MSE $= n - m$

We will now use formula 10.2 to determine if the estimated coefficient c is significant at the 5% level. We will take SSE directly off the MINITAB printouts. Numerator degrees of freedom are $1(k = 1)$ because to go from a linear equation to a parabola we add only one variable (X_2) and one coefficient (c). $\text{MSE}_{\text{HigherOrder}}$ is 3.341. The test statistic is

$$F_{\text{test}} = \frac{(1,460.1 - 239.27)/1}{39.88} = 30.613$$

For "c" to be significantly different from zero $(\alpha = .05)$ the $F_{\text{test}} > F_{\alpha(k,\,n-m)}(5.79)$. Since $F_{\text{test}}(30.613) > F_{.05(1.6)}(5.99)$, we must conclude that the null hypothesis (H_0: $c = 0$) must be rejected. Hence, the parabola or quadratic equation is a proper functional fit.

We could also test the data to see if it were best fit by a cubic function: $Y = a + bX + cX^2 + dX^3$. A cubic equation changes directions twice. We note from the graph that $R^2 = 87.0\%$ for the quadratic equation and 88.7% for the cubic equation. However, from viewing Table 10.16 (supplied by Minitab) we note that only the quadratic equation is significant at the 95% confidence level. We can see from the graph that the cubic equation changes directions only once; hence, d is not significantly different from 0 and dX^3 drops from the equation.

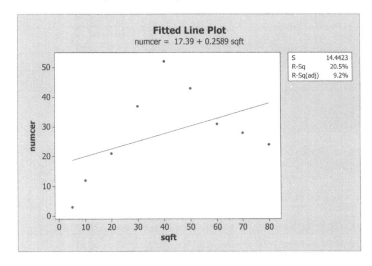

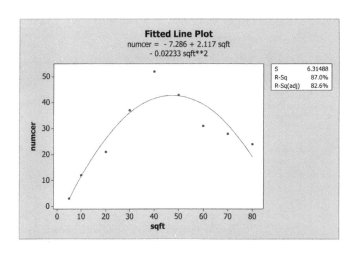

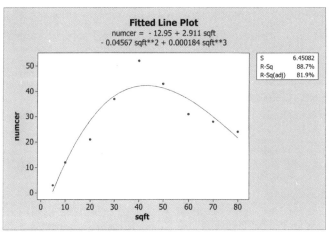

Table 10.16 Evaluating a linear, quadratic, and cubic model for the data in Table 10.15.

Source	DF	SS	F	P
Linear	1	376.83	1.81	0.221
Quadratic	1	1220.79	30.61	0.001
Cubic	1	31.20	0.75	0.426

 Concept Check 10.1

The parabola is handled as a linear trivariate model where $X_2 = X^2$. True or false? If false, explain.

Exercises

10.53 Explain the general shape of a parabola (second-degree polynomial) and state how it differs from a first-degree polynomial (straight line).

10.54　State your individual majors (finance, accounting, etc.) and state one real parabolic (second-degree polynomial) relationship that exists in theory.

10.55　Have MINITAB determine if a linear, quadratic, or cubic equation is the proper fit.

x	y
3	12
7	18
9	21
12	31
17	38
19	44
27	43
31	46
38	41
44	40
50	37
52	36

10.56

x	y
3	7
7	9
9	13
12	17
13	28
15	33
16	36
19	34
24	32
27	31
33	26
37	23
41	20
49	17

Have MINITAB determine if a linear or quadratic equation is the best fit

10.57

x	y
2	8
5	15
10	23
12	26
15	31
19	38
22	43
24	46
28	51
30	55
35	63
36	67
40	72
41	74

Have MINITAB determine if a linear or quadratic equation is the best fit.
a. Use F_{test} to determine if c is significant in comparing the parabola to the linear equation.

10.58

x	y
3	7
7	9
9	13
12	17
13	28
15	33
16	36
19	34
24	32
27	31
33	26
37	23
41	20
49	17
54	16
58	19
64	21
69	29
76	31
81	35
89	40
92	47

a. Fit a linear equation to the data set, give R^2 and p-value.
b. Fit a parabola to the data set, give R^2 and p-value for global and for coefficients b, c.

10.10 There Is No Substitute for Logic or Good Reasoning

Corporate executives often find it difficult to understand that only limited information can be extracted from raw data, and much of that information requires firsthand knowledge of the data. As computer scientists are fond of saying, "garbage in, garbage out." Bad data result in incorrect information. Thus, it is impossible for a statistical consultant hired by an organization to have all of the answers. However, consultants can provide a useful service to organizations by asking the right questions and evoking the correct answers from the organizations that hired them.

Another example of how logic might enter into the evaluation of numerical data is the case of college admissions. One incoming student might have a 3.50 GPA from a local trade school and another a 2.78 GPA from an Ivy League institution. A purely quantitative assessment of applicants might simply select the students with the highest grade point average and reject applicants with grade point averages below some minimum standard. Yet, of these two students, the applicant with the lower GPA would probably have a higher probability of successfully completing graduate school. The person evaluating the data must understand that the two GPA's were probably based on different standards. It might be more difficult to obtain a 2.78 from a top-rated school than to receive a 3.5 from a school not quite so highly rated. A dummy variable might help to account for the differences in standards between schools, and the decision for admission should not be based on the simple model previously described.

Statistics is not meant to supersede logic or reasoning, but rather to formalize the process, and allow for improvements and refinements. When conflicts develop between statistics and logic, it is generally statistics that is misleading,

Often a paradox exists between sound reasoning and statistical inference. In such cases reasoning must take second fiddle to statistics. True or false? If false, explain.

Exercises

10.59 How might a manager help a statistical consultant develop a regression model?

10.60 "Figures never lie," and therefore statistical results should always be trusted. Do you agree? Comment.

10.11 Summary

In Chapters 9 and 10, we discussed the same topic, regression and correlation analysis. However, in this chapter, we extended or generalized the topics in Chapter 9 by adding additional independent variables to the model. In particular, the regression models of Chapter 10 always contained two or more independent variables and were distinct from the single independent variable bivariate models. Since computations become more difficult as the size of the model increases, much of Chapter 10 used MINITAB to perform the statistical analyses.

We used least squares multiple regression equations to estimate the relationship between a dependent variable and a specified set of independent variables. We showed that the standard error of the estimate measures the variability about the regression equation and provides the foundation for statistical inference within regression analysis. We also discussed t_{test} on the significance of the regression coefficients and an F_{test} on the significance of the model. Then we developed $(1 - \alpha) \bullet 100\%$ confidence and prediction intervals based on the regression equation for the mean and individual values of the dependent variables. Finally, we discussed correlation techniques, such as stepwise regression.

 Mini-case 10.1: Estimating Real Estate Values

Suppose you want to forecast the selling price of homes within an area of your local community. The dependent variable in your model is the sales price of a home (Y), not the asking price for the home. Some of the predictor (independent) variables that might influence the price of a home are square footage (X_1), size of the lot (X_2), how close the house is to the better schools, shopping, and public transportation (X_3), and finally amenities that come with the house (swimming pool, central air conditioning, appliances, sewer versus cesspool), the number of baths and bedrooms, the amount of light in the house, and age of the house and appliances (X_4).

The data for fifteen houses sold are given in Table 10.17. To develop this model will involve significant difficulties because so many factors that affect the demand for a particular house. For example, a poor choice of paint color can have a negative effect for prospective buyers when looking at a house, where having fresh bread cooking in the oven can have a positive effect.

    a. Using MINITAB, determine if the model is significant at the 5% level.

    b. Theorize if the independent variables have a direct or inverse relationship to the dependent variable. Then ascertain if they are significant at the 5% level.

    c. Might a serious problem exist concerning multicollinearity?

    d. Perform a forward regression analysis.

    e. Compute confidence and prediction intervals for the entire model, $X_1 = 2400$, $X_2 = .83$, $X_3 = 1$, $X_4 = 1$.

Table 10.17 Data Relating to the Selling Price of Homes in an Area

AMENITIES

Y Sales Price	X_1 Sq. Ft.	X_2 Lot Size (Acres)	X_3 Interior*	X_4 Exterior**
$134	2360	.28	S	E
115	2450	.35	S	P
92	1300	.16	P	E
119	2750	1.00	S	P
93	1590	.16	P	E
76	1310	.20	P	E
90	2200	.25	P	P
66	1400	.26	P	P
210	2000	.41	P	E
57	1200	.31	P	P
168	2000	.28	P	E
188	2120	.22	S	E
194	2310	.28	S	E
66	1490	.31	P	P
241	2600	.80	S	E

Note: sales price in thousands of dollars.

*Internal amenities refer to features of the house. The rating is either Superior ($X_3 = 1$) or Poor ($X_3 = 0$).

**External amenities refer to the environment surrounding the house. The rating is either Excellent ($X_4 = 1$) or Poor ($X_4 = 0$).

Mini-case 10.2: Expanding Operations

A company has a specialty restaurant in each of nine cities, where the cities are of different sizes. Management wants to know if multiple regression analysis will help them select additional cities for expansion. The dependent variable is the average sales revenue per quarter, and the independent variables believed to be important are the number of restaurants in the entire city (X_1), and the population of the entire city (X_2). The company believes the restaurant will draw from the entire city because it is a specialty restaurant. The data for the four specified variables are given in Table 10.18.

Table 10.18 Linear Multiple Regression Model for Restaurant Sales in Nine Cities

City	Y	X_1	X_2
A	17,000	400	400
B	42,000	941	800
C	36,000	875	700
D	24,000	706	1,200
E	98,000	1,317	5,000
F	71,000	923	600
G	56,000	267	200
H	66,000	1,667	1,000
I	99,000	282	1,100

a. Use MINITAB to determine if the model is significant at the 5% level.

b. Would you expect multicollinearity to exist between X_1 and X_2?

c. If you find such multicollinearity, attempt to remove it by combining X_1 and X_2 into a new independent variable X_3 ($X_3 = X_1/X_2$).

312

Listed in Table 10.19 are the ACT and SAT scores for the states.

a. Use MINITAB in a linear regression model to ascertain which of the six independent variables, if any, are significant in predicting either the ACT or SAT scores. Be sure to state if a two-tailed or one-tailed test is involved. Note: For the dummy variable, a pilot program will not have had a chance to take effect; hence, for none or pilot = 0, and yes = 1.

b. Is multicollinearity a problem in the analysis?

Table 10.19   Education Statistics 1998

State	ACT Score	Average Teacher Salary	Pupil/Teacher Ratio	Per Captia Personal Income	1998 H.S Grad. Rate	% of Minorities
Alabama	21.1	32,470	16.4	21,442	78.8	28.1
Alaska	21.3	49,140	17.1	25,675	90.6	28.8
Arizona	21.4	33,208	19.7	23,060	81.9	33.6
Arkansas	20.4	30,987	16.9	20,346	76.8	19.0
Colorado	21.2	36,271	17.9	28,657	89.6	22.3
Idaho	21.5	31,818	17.4	21,081	82.7	10.2
Illinois	21.4	42,339	16.5	28,873	84.2	29.1
Iowa	22.1	33,272	14.9	23,925	87.7	5.5
Kansas	22.1	33,150	14.9	24,981	89.2	13.6
Kentucky	21.7	33,802	16.0	21,506	77.9	8.9
Louisiana	19.5	28,347	15.4	21,346	78.6	36.7
Michigan	21.6	47,769	18.8	25,857	85.4	19.2
Minnesota	22.2	38,276	16.3	27,510	89.4	8.3
Mississippi	18.7	27,662	16.8	18,958	77.3	38.4
Missouri	21.5	33,143	14.9	24,427	82.9	14.1
Montana	21.9	29,958	15.8	20,172	89.1	9.1
Nebraska	21.8	31,768	14.4	24,754	87.7	10.3
Nevada	21.4	40,817	18.5	27,200	89.1	28.7
New Mexico	20.1	29,715	16.6	19,936	79.6	54.8
North Dakota	21.4	27,709	16.1	21,675	84.3	7.5
Ohio	21.4	38,944	16.6	25,134	86.2	14.4
Oklahoma	20.5	30,187	15.3	21,072	84.6	21.1
South Dakota	21.4	26,965	15.3	22,114	86.3	10.7
Tennessee	19.8	34,267	17.1	23,559	76.9	18.8
Utah	20.3	31,310	22.7	21,019	89.3	11.1
Washington	22.6	37,860	20.3	27,961	92.0	17.2
West Virginia	21.6	33,258	14.2	19,362	76.4	4.4
Wisconsin	22.3	38,878	15.4	25,079	88.0	10.6
Wyoming	21.4	31,716	14.2	23,167	90.0	10.0
SAT Scores						
California	1013	42,992	21.5	27,503	80.1	52.2
Connecticut	1019	51,181	13.4	37,598	83.7	19.9
Delaware	994	41,436	16.9	29,814	85.2	24.7
Dist. of Columbia	964	42,424	17.5	37,278	83.8	74.0
Florida	1001	33,885	18.1	25,852	81.9	32.4
Georgia	968	35,679	16.0	25,020	80.0	32.9
Hawaii	996	38,105	17.8	26,137	84.6	75.8
Indiana	997	38,722	17.1	24,219	83.5	11.7
Maine	1005	33,676	13.0	22,952	86.7	2.4
Maryland	1014	41,257	16.9	29,943	84.7	2.4

State	SAT Score	Average Teacher Salary	Pupil/Teacher Ratio	Per Captia Personal Income	1998 H.S Grad. Rate	% of Minorities
Massachusetts	1016	44,101	14.1	32,797	85.6	16.0
New Hampshire	1043	36,029	15.6	29,022	84.0	3.4
New Jersey	1005	49,786	13.9	33,937	86.5	32.0
New York	998	48,000	14.2	31,734	81.5	38.2
North Carolina	982	31,019	16.1	24,036	81.4	26.9
Oregon	1056	41,093	19.9	24,766	58.5	12.3
Pennsylvania	992	47,147	16.8	26,792	84.1	14.1
Rhode Island	996	43,083	14.4	26,797	80.7	13.9
South Carolina	951	32,659	15.3	21,309	78.6	32.8
Texas	995	32,426	15.3	24,957	78.3	45.7
Vermont	1012	36,053	13.1	24,175	86.7	2.9
Virginia	1006	36,116	14.7	27,385	82.6	27.2

Sources: www.Sciway.net for SAT scores; www.aft.org for salaries
National Center for Education Statistics for Pupil/teacher ratios
www.act.org for ACT scores
US Census Bureau for High School Grad. rate and Per Capita Personal Income
Regional Markets (Thomas G. Exter) for Minorities

Mini-Case 10.4: The Heights/Weights of Boys from Birth to 14

Given in Table 10.20 are the average heights and weights of boys from birth to 14 years of age.

a. Using statistical software, run the regression equations: Height = f(Weight). Comment on the results. If R^2 is significant (5% level) venture a guess as to why.

b. Using statistical software, run the regression equations: Height = f(Weight, Age). Comment on the results.

c. Using the regression equations, Height = f(Weight, Age), if your instructor is male, weighs 80kg, and is 40 years old, what height should he be? Explain.

Table 10.20 The Heights/Weights of Boys from Birth to 14

Age	Height(cm)	Weight(kg)
Birth	50.8	3.4
0.5	66.0	7.7
1.0	73.6	9.5
2.0	83.8	11.8
3.0	91.4	14.0
4.0	99.0	15.4
5.0	106.6	17.7
6.0	114.2	20.9
7.0	119.3	23.1
8.0	127.0	25.9
9.0	132.0	28.6
10.0	137.1	31.3
11.0	142.2	34.9
12.0	147.3	37.7
13.0	152.4	41.7
14.0	157.5	48.5

Source: M.A. Krupp and others. Physician's Handbook, Los Altos, CA: Lange Medical Publications, 1983.

Multiple regression model: A model where a dependent (response) variable (Y) is analyzed using information from more than one independent (predictor) variables (X). Since a simple regression model has only one independent variable, a three-variable model would be the simplest multiple regression model.

Origin of the independent variables: The independent variables chosen for a model are determined by the discipline in question. Experts in the field of economics are a good source of information such as the determinants of saving and consumption. Should knowledge about advertising be required for a model, a marketing or consumer behavior expert or text could be consulted.

Standard error of the estimate: The measure of dispersion of the data points about the regression plane assuming normality. Some 68.3% of the observations are located within plus or minus one standard error of the regression function. For two standard errors, the percent is 95.5, and for three the percent is 99.7%.

Coefficient of multiple determination: The ratio of SSR (variation in Y caused by the independent variables within the regression model) to SST (total variation in Y, regardless of the cause).

Dummy or qualitative variables: Sometimes variables fit into an easy classification system where the variable can be classified in either of two groups. For example, a part is either defective or not, you are currently single or not, you are a teen or not. If the question concerns teenagers, a 0 or 1 is placed for respondents who are teens, and if 1 is chosen for teen, the opposite is used for a non-teen (and vice versa). The choice is immaterial, as long as the system is used consistently.

F_{test}: Global test used to determine if the regression model is significant.

t_{test}: Test used to determine if a specific independent variable is significant, If we can conclude that the population (true) regression coefficient for an independent variable equals 0, then the variable is insignificant. Insignificant variables may be removed from the model.

Forward/backward/stepwise multiple regression: A statistical technique in which the independent variables are sequentially added/deleted to the regression model based on a ranking of their importance to the model.

Multicollinearity: Statistical problem that develops when the independent variables are highly correlated in a multiple regression model.

Nonlinear correlation: Often the association existing between variables is nonlinear. Computer programs treat nonlinear correlation as a multiple regression analysis.

315

The Standard Error of the Estimate

$$S_{Y \bullet 12} = \hat{\sigma}_e = \sqrt{\frac{SSE}{n - m}}$$

(9.2)

where

SSE = sum-of-squares due to error = Σe_2^i

n = sample size

m = the number of coefficients in the regression equation; in a linear trivariate
model, $m = 3(a, b_1, b_2)$

Sample Coefficient of Multiple Determination

$$R^2 = 1 - \frac{SSE}{SST} = \frac{SSR}{SST}$$

(9.3)

where

$R_{Y \bullet 12}^2$ = multiple r^2 between Y and both X_1 and X_2

SSE = error sum-of-squares

SSR = regression sum-of-squares

SST = total sum-of-squares

Adjusted R^2 for Lost Degrees of Freedom

$$R_{adj}^2 = 1 - (1 - R^2)\left(\frac{n - 1}{n - m}\right)$$

(10.1)

where

R^2 = the coefficient of multiple determination

m = the number of coefficients in the regression model

n = sample size

Note: $n > m$ and negative solutions are treated as 0.

F_{test} to Ascertain If Higher Order Equation is Warranted

$$F_{\text{test}} = \frac{(\text{SSE}_{\text{LowerOrder}} - \text{SSE}_{\text{HigherOrder}})/k}{\text{MSE}_{\text{HigherOrder}}} \qquad (10.2)$$

where

$\text{SSE}_{\text{HigherOrder}} = \text{SSE}$ for the higher order model

$\text{SSE}_{\text{LowerOrder}} = \text{SSE}$ for the lower order model

$K = $ the # of parameters difference between the two models

$\text{MSE}_{\text{HigherOrder}} = $ Mean Square Error for higher order model

Note: df for $\text{MSE} = n - m$

Review of MINITAB Commands

MINITAB Multiple Regression commands

Stat > Regression > Regression
Double click **Y** into **Response** box.
Double click both **X1** and **X2** into **Predictors** box.
Click on the **Fits** box. (To obtain the estimate Y values)
Click on the **Residuals** box. (To obtain the residuals).
OK

MINITAB Stepwise Regression Sequence

Stat > Regression > Stepwise
Click **SALES** into **Response** box.
Click **TFLOW, NUMCOMP, AGE, ENTRY** into **Predictors** box.
OK twice

MINITAB Nonlinear Analysis

Stat > Regression > Fitted Line Plot
Click **CEREAL** into the **Response** box.
Click **STSQFT** and **STSQFTSQ** into the **Predictors** box.
Click the type of model desired.
OK

End of Chapter Exercises

10.61　How are the regression models of Chapter 9 different from that of Chapter 10?

10.62　a.　Each year an increasing number of small businesses fail. What variables do you think would be likely to determine success or failure?

　　　　b.　Do you think that a business that has been in operation over five years would have a better chance of surviving than one with less than five years of experience?

　　　　c.　Do you think that the industry in which a firm does business has anything to do with failure rates? That is, do certain industries have higher mortality (or success) rates than others?

317

d.   If the answer to part c is yes, provide an example of one industry where the failure rates are high and one where failure rates are low.

10.63   Perform a multiple regression analysis of the SAT scores analysis of Chapter 9 (Table 9.13). The dependent variable is SAT scores, and the two independent variables are teachers' salary (X_1) and student–teacher ratio (X_2).

   a.   Before the computer computations are made do you believe either t value will prove significant?
   b.   Are we involved with one- or two-tailed tests? Be sure to justify your answer.
   c.   Use p-values to determine if X_1 and X_2 are significant at the 5% level.
   d.   Compute confidence intervals about b_1 and b_2.
   e.   For $X_1 = 35,000$, $X_2 = 10.0$, compute the 95% confidence and prediction intervals.

10.64   a.   For the equation $\hat{Y} = 10 + 1X_1, 2X_2 + 4X_3$, determine the predicted value for Y when $X_1 = X_2 = X_3 = 5$.
   b.   Since the coefficient of X_2 is twice that of X_1, is X_2 twice as important as X_1? Explain which of the three independent variables is most important and which is least important.
   c.   If X_2 is a dummy variable, what are the two possible resulting equations?

10.65   a.   For a multiple regression equation with five independent variables and a sample size of 27, the standard error of the estimate is 6.7859. What is the sum of the residuals squared?
   b.   From the information given, is it possible to determine the coefficient of multiple determination?

Appendix A: The Least Squares Assumptions and Residual Analysis

The regression model of this and the previous chapter were estimated using least squares regression models. These models are based on assumptions, which if violated would interfere with the validity of least squares estimates. We attempt an intuitive explanation of these assumptions and their importance, and also to place you on guard to their violations. For the most part, the formal detection and correction procedures are beyond the scope of this text. We list references for those who need a more complete analysis.

10.12 Introduction: The Least Squares Assumptions

Most statistical packages offer advanced procedures for regression analysis. Thus, we include this appendix to help interpret this output. As always, it is easier to explain concepts intuitively with the aid of examples.

10.13 The R-1 Rifle: A Model and Its Assumptions

We use the following example to explain the least squares assumptions. Suppose a rifle with the prototype name, the R-1 rifle (X_i) is being considered by the military. You are asked to give a recommendation on whether the military should contract or not to buy the rifle. Also, assume you have never seen the rifle before. Your decision is based on the firing of 20 rounds at a distant target. You are allowed to set the rifle on a metal tripod stand so that your arms will not be moving to prevent a good shot group. In effect, the position of the rifle is fixed, yet you may tilt it to aim at the bull's-eye (a similar situation can be depicted with a camera).

You squeeze the trigger 20 times. Would you expect to find 1 hole through which 20 bullets passed? Not very likely. Due to variations in the wind conditions, the differences between each bullet, errors in judgment, etc., a small shot group somewhere off the exact target would be expected. The group is off the exact target because each of us looks through a sighting device at a slightly different angle. One person will use the left eye, one the right, one squinting and one with wide open eyes, etc. This variation causes a slightly different trajectory pattern (even though the weapon is on a tripod). Hence, the shot group will land in a different place for each of us. The shot group may land in the fourth quadrant (the Cartesian coordinate system) as shown in Figure 10.3.

Figure 10.3 Shot Group Landing in Fourth Quadrant

An essential property for the rifle is that it can be adjusted for the many ways individuals may look through the sighting device. The weapon has a vertical and horizontal (azimuth) adjustment which will center the shot group as it moves in increments. In our example, assume three vertical (upwards increments) and two horizontal (leftward increments) will center the shot group around the bull's-eye. If we could mathematically describe this centering process (sometimes called "zeroing in" a weapon), we would say the sum of the differences between where the bullet lands (Y_i) and the dead center ($\hat{Y}$) should equal 0, or that the residuals ($e_i = Y_i - \hat{Y}$) must equal to zero ($\Sigma e_i = 0$). Here there are 20 "e" values ($i = 1, \ldots, 20$). The residuals can be defined as either a vertical, horizontal, or diagonal difference between the bullet hole and the dead center of the target. If the sum of the residuals (as defined) could not be made to equal to 0, then the model would not be of maximum value. The violation of this assumption is serious enough to invalidate the model.

One rifle simply represents a sample from a population of R-1 rifles. The military wants all manufactured R-1 rifles to have this property, where $\Sigma e_i = 0$. Also, only 20 shots were fired and it may not be possible to center the rounds exactly, given the sample size. Whereas, if a large number of rounds were fired, it would be possible to center the rounds. In addition, the vertical and horizontal adjustments for most weapons are discrete rather than continuous. Thus, an exact center might not be possible for any one individual, but it should be possible for most individuals. Note that when firing, a bull's-eye hit is not absolutely essential to repel an invader. A hit slightly off target may do as much damage as a direct hit.

A second desired property of the rifle is that the variation in the shot group should be the same for all R-1's under similar conditions. At 100 yards, under identical wind and barometric conditions, etc., each rifle should have the same shot group. In addition, this shot group should contain more individual shots closer to the dead center than farther away from it. In other words, it would be desirable if the shots were normally distributed with the most likely value being a direct hit. Essentially a constant standard deviation of the shot pattern is required at equal distance and conditions. Should the target move from 100 to 200 to 300 yards, the dispersion would increase. However, the increase should be identical for all

319

R-1 rifles and must be within predetermined limits. This assumption is necessary because under emergency conditions people may have to use an R-1 rifle they did not center. Therefore, all R-1 rifles must have identical shot groups. Without this property, a weapon would have limited usefulness for the military. We can express this mathematically as

$$\Sigma e_i^2 = \Sigma e_2^2 = \text{SSE}$$

or simply that the error sum of squares for rifle 1 equals the error sum of squares for rifle 2 (a constant error sum of squares).

A third desired property of the rifle concerns the possible relationship that might exist between successive shots. On some rifles a switch converts a rifle to a machine gun. While in the rifle position a single squeeze on the trigger releases a single projectile, with the switch in the opposite position a single squeeze on the trigger results in the release of multiple projectiles.

In the rifle position, if several shots were squeezed off in succession, would knowledge of where the first round lands help predict where the second will land? Will knowledge of where the first two rounds land help predict where the third lands, etc.? We know the round will land within a certain shot group, and that there is a greater probability it will land closer to the bull's-eye than away from it (normal distribution). However, do we know any other characteristics, such as the quadrant where the round lands? The answer is no, since the shot pattern should be random. The symbolism used to express this phenomena is $\Sigma(e_i e_j) = 0$, when $i \neq j$. The i and j subscripts simply signify that the calculation uses errors from different observations (shots). When a data point is considered, it is the ith point. When the next data point is analyzed, it becomes the ith point, and the point before it is the jth point. The reason for the $i \neq j$ condition is because, if $i = j$, then the sum reverts to Σe_i^2 (the assumption last covered). The $\Sigma(e_i e_j)$ is called a covariance, where the two variables are measured in deviations from a mean. In this instance, the means of both variables are 0, since $\Sigma e = 0$. The $\Sigma(e_i e_j)$ is a measure of cross-variation between two variables as they deviate from their mean. If the covariance equals 0, the predictability (r^2) between the successive data points is 0 and successive data points are independent. This result is because the slope of the regression equation is $\Sigma(e_i e_j)/e_i^2$. If the slope is 0, then $R^2 = 0$ in a two variable model. If the covariance is non-zero, the predictability between the successive data points is non-zero. Independence is required for the R-1 when in the rifle mode.

When the R-1 rifle is in the automatic mode, a single squeezing of the trigger releases multiple projectiles. The purpose of the weapon is to repel a large attacking force. Thus, the weapon is designed to spread a patterned tracing of bullets to act as a repel force. Sometimes every fifth shell is a phosphorus (tracer) shell so that one firing of the automatic weapon provides immediate feedback about the shot pattern. This capability allows for an alternating tracing pattern if necessary. In this instance, $\Sigma(e_i e_j) \neq 0$, when $i \neq j$, and subsequent data points are dependent.

A final property concerns impurities in the rifle barrel. As the trigger is squeezed, the firing pin detonates gun powder in a shell, causing the bullet to proceed down the barrel. Extensive friction develops as the metal bullet passes through the metal barrel. From this, enormous heat can develop. Thus, if the barrel is not made properly, the heat due to friction can cause the opening of the barrel to become egg-shaped rather than circular. As the bullet exits the barrel, centrifugal force makes the bullet exit at an angle (Figure 10.4). Hence, the bullet is forced into the first and third (or second and fourth) quadrants. This deflection indicates a serious design flaw in the weapon. We can mathematically express this flaw as $\Sigma X_i e_i \neq 0$, and the absence of the flaw is $\Sigma X_i e_i = 0$. Again, this relationship is a covariance and if it equals 0, the predictability between X (the R-1 rifle) and e (the deviation between where the bullet lands and the dead center) is 0. If this assumption is violated, estimates from the model will be biased.

Figure 10.4 Shot Group Landing in First and Third Quadrants

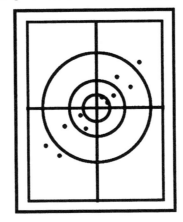

Each violation can occur independently of one another, and any violation can invalidate the model (the R-1 rifle). In all probability each rifle will have some degree of these violations. If the degree of the violation is not extreme, the overall effect on the results will probably be minimal. A shot does not have to land dead center to be effective. In fact, even the assumption that the rifle is mounted on a tripod can be relaxed. If the weapon has to be held this does not eliminate its usefulness. The addition of another factor that creates errors does not limit the design purpose of the R-1 rifle. In fact, some experts claim a greater accuracy when a rifle is freely held than when it is fixed.

Since all of the above possible problems concern the residual values, the evaluation of the assumptions is sometimes called residual analysis. Residual analysis is used to check for violations from model assumptions and provide some insight into methods for dealing with these problems.

 Concept Check 10.K

When we refer to $\Sigma(e_i e_j)$ we are not referring to a literal multiplication between e_i and e_j True or false? If false, explain.

Exercises

10.66   Explain the independence of two variables (X and Y) using the concept of covariance.

10.67   What is the meaning of the expression, $\Sigma(e_i e_j) = 0$?

10.14 The Consumption and Income Model

The R-1 rifle example was used to provide an intuitive understanding of the assumptions of the least squares model and their importance. We will now consider an analysis of a more traditional economic model, that consumption is a function of income. Suppose everyone in your class were asked to record their income and the amount of it they spent last year. Also, suppose the corresponding least squares equation is

$$\hat{Y} = 100 + 0.9(X)$$

where

Y = consumption expenditures for last year

X = income for last year

321

Your class can be regarded as a population of students. If a number of classmates made $10,000, then their average spending would be explained exactly by the regression equation, or $9,100. Moreover, there would be a normal distribution around the mean. If a number of classmates made $20,000, their average spending would be exactly $18,100. Similarly, if a number of classmates made $100,000 last year, their mean spending would be exactly $90,100. Mathematically this is expressed as $E(e_i) = 0$.

Figure 10.5 A Constant Normal Distribution as Income Increases

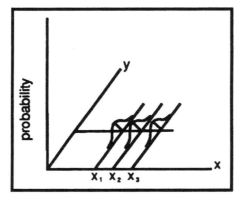

In addition to the fact that the mean spending for each income group is exactly explained be the least squares equation, there is an assumption concerning the dispersions about the means. Figure 10.5 assumes that the standard deviation remains constant as income (X) varies. A standard deviation of $100 means that 68.3% of the observations in the population lie between the following values:

for $X = \$10,000$: $9,000–$9,200
for $X = \$20,000$: $20,000–$20,200
for $X = \$100,000$: $100,000–$100,200

However, there is a logical basis for expecting more variability from the mean level of consumption at higher levels than at lower levels of income. Individuals with relatively low incomes are forced to spend a higher percentage of their income on necessities, and so have little discretionary income. There is ample empirical evidence to support the hypothesis that the variability in consumption increases as income increases. See Figure 10.6. Cases where the variance is constant, as in Figure 10.5, are termed homoscedastic. Nonconstant variances, such as the example in Figure 10.6, are called heteroscedastic. Heteroscedasticity refers to situations where the variability in the error term is not constant with respect to the independent variable. Constant variation in the errors is referred to as homoscedasticity.

Figure 10.6 Heteroscedasticity

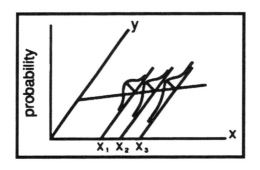

In addition, if you knew the deviation from the mean spending (zero scaling the data) for the first three students, would this help to determine what deviation from the mean spending is for the fourth student? If the answer is no, the data are sequentially independent, if the answer is yes, the data are sequentially dependent. This relationship can be mathematically expressed as $\Sigma(\mu_i \mu_j) = 0$, when $i = j$ for the dependence between the data points and the violation is termed serial or autocorrelation. The symbol u defines a population residual, as opposed to the sample residual e. The u value is the vertical difference between an observed Y value and the true regression equation ($u = Y - A - BX$), while e is the vertical difference between an observed Y value and the estimated regression equation ($e = Y - a - bX$). See Figure 10.7.

Figure 10.7 The Difference Between u and e

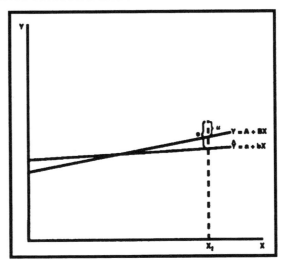

 Concept Check 10.L

With the spending and income model, we would expect heteroscedasticity to occur. True or false? If false, explain.

Exercises

10.68   Explain to what homoscedasticity refers in the spending-income model.

10.69   Explain to what autocorrelation refers in the income-spending model.

10.15 Serial or Autocorrelation

Serial or autocorrelation occurs when there is a sequential dependence between the error terms. Autocorrelation is common in time series data and can even appear in cross-sectional studies as well. A sequential dependence means that a residual in a particular time period will exert influence over errors in subsequent time periods. When this happens, residuals commonly tend to be clumped or grouped together or alternate in a predictable manner. A group of positive residuals will be followed by a group of negative residuals and the pattern repeats itself. Recall that a clumping of residuals can also occur due to incorrect specification of a model. If the model is appropriate, a clumping of residuals may be caused by serial correlation.

323

We will limit our analysis to a residual value related to a residual value in the previous time period. This phenomena is termed first-order autocorrelation. The existing correlation can be positive or negative. We will discuss only positive autocorrelation, since it is more frequently encountered in business applications.

Positive serial correlation is most commonly caused by a cumulative effect of the impact of omitted variables from the regression model on the residuals over time. Using the R-1 rifle model as an example, assume that the shot pattern of an automatic weapon follows that of a sine wave. If you fire too low, you would raise the weapon. This action causes the bullets to rise, probably too high. It would take time before you realized this and took corrective measures by lowering the weapon. See Figure 10.8.

Figure 10.8 Positive Serial Correlation

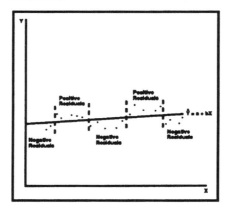

Detection: Durbin–Watson d Statistic

The test for detection of serial correlation is based on the clumping or grouping of positive and negative residuals that is not caused by an incorrectly specified model. If residuals are clumped, then the vertical difference between successive values would be smaller than when the residuals were random (Figures 10.9A and 10.9B). Hence, the key to the detection statistic (developed by J. Durbin and G. S. Watson) is the value of $e_t - e_{t-1}$. For positive autocorrelation, the successive differences would be smaller than that if the residuals were random. Whenever an analysis is made for lagged variables, there is the loss of a paired data set. Thus, the summation can only occur from $t = 2$ to $t = n$. Of course, higher order serial correlation models will lose even more paired observations.

Figure 10.9 Vertical Differences Between Positive, Zero, and Negative Autocorrelation

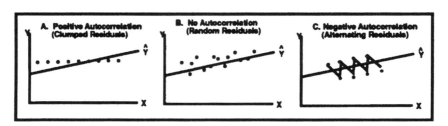

The Durbin–Watson d Statistic

$$d = \frac{\Sigma_{t=2}^{n}(e_t - e_{t-1})^2}{\Sigma_{t=1}^{n} e_t^2} \tag{10.3}$$

where

e_t = the error or residual in time period (observation) t

e_{t-1} = the error or residual in time period (observation) $t-1$

The d statistic has an absolute scale from 0 to 4 ($0 \leq d \leq 4$). If d equals 2, there is no first-order serial correlation in the sample. If $0 \leq d \leq 2$, the presence of positive first-order serial correlation has been detected. Also, if $2 \leq d \leq 4$ the presence of negative first-order serial correlation is indicated. Negative first-order autocorrelation is shown in Figure 10.9C, which reveals that subsequent residual values have opposite signs (rather than the same sign). A negative residual is followed by a positive residual, followed by a negative residual, and so on. If the residuals were random, there should not be any pattern in the signs of the residuals. For positive first-order serial correlation, the successive differences squared would be small. For negative serial first-order correlation, they would be large, and for random residuals, they would be average.

The Durbin–Watson d statistic table provides different test statistics for the number of independent variables within the regression model and for the number of observations. Two limits are given: dl and du. These limits are used to formulate the regions identified in Table 10.21 and the appropriate decision rule. The null hypothesis for the Durbin–Watson test is that there is no autocorrelation in the residuals. The alternative hypothesis is the two-sided alternative that there is autocorrelation in the residuals.

Table 10.21 Range of Durbin–Watson Statistic

Computed d Value	Hypothesis Test
$0 \leq d \leq dl$	Reject Hypothesis: Positive Autocorrelation
$dl \leq\leq du$	Test is Inconclusive
$du \leq d \leq 2$	ISER Hypothesis: No Positive Autocorrelation
$2 \leq d \leq (4 - du)$	ISER Hypothesis: No Negative Autocorrelation
$(4 - du) \leq d \leq (4 - dl)$	Test is Inconclusive
$(4 - dl) \leq d \leq 4$	Reject Hypothesis: Negative Autocorrelation

Computing the d statistic for a specific data set given in Table 10.22 yields $d = .901$. This result indicates that positive first-order serial correlation exists, since $dl = .98$ for $k = 1$ independent variable with $n = 16$.

Auto correlations will not cause a bias problem but rather an efficiency problem. A possible solution would be to determine the actual slope coefficient between the error terms and their previous values. Using the data in Table 10.22 we compute the regression equation and review the residuals. Then using the lag function (Stat>Time Series>Lag), we lag the residuals. We then regress the original residuals (response variable) with the lagged residuals (predictor variable) making sure we turn off the intercept (under options click off **Fit intercept**).

Table 10.22   Computation of the Durbin–Watson Statistic

X	Y	$\hat{Y}$	e_t	e_{t-1}	$e_t - e_{t-1}$	$(e_t - e_{t-1})^2$	e_t^2
1	10.779	9.401	+1.378				1.89888
2	10.890	10.439	+0.451	+1.378	−0.927	0.85933	0.20340
3	10.642	10.477	+0.165	+0.451	−0.286	0.08180	0.02723
4	12.008	12.515	−0.507	+0.165	−0.672	0.45158	0.25705
5	13.416	13.553	−0.137	−0.507	+0.370	0.13690	0.01877
6	14.337	14.591	−0.254	−0.137	−0.117	0.01369	0.06452
7	15.006	15.629	−0.623	−0.254	−0.369	0.13616	0.38813
8	15.520	16.667	−1.147	−0.623	−0.524	0.27458	1.31561
9	17.688	17.705	−0.017	−1.147	+1.130	1.27690	0.00029
10	18.755	18.743	+0.012	−0.017	+0.029	0.00084	0.00014
11	19.355	19.781	−0.426	+0.012	−0.438	0.19184	0.18148
12	20.453	20.819	−0.366	−0.426	+0.060	0.00360	0.13396
13	21.562	21.857	−0.295	−0.366	+0.071	0.00504	0.08703
14	23.092	22.895	+0.197	−0.295	+0.492	0.24206	0.03881
15	23.883	23.933	−0.050	+0.197	−0.247	0.06101	0.00250
16	26.595	24.971	+1.624	−0.050	+1.674	2.80228	2.63738
					Totals	6.53761	7.25516

Thus

$$d = \frac{6.537610}{7.255157} = 0.901$$

Fortunately, MINITAB will compute the d statistic for us.
MINITAB's obtaining of the Durbin–Watson Statistic.

Stat > Regression > Regression
Click **Y** into **Response** box.
Click **X** into **Predictors** box.
Click **Options**.
Click on the box **Durbin–Watson statistic**.
OK twice

Table 10.23A MINITAB's Computation of the Durbin–Watson Statistic

REGRESSION ANALYSIS

The regression equation is
$Y = 8.36 + 1.04X$

Predictor	Coef	SE Coef	T	P
Constant	8.3632	0.3775	22.15	0.000
X	1.03801	0.03904	26.59	0.000

$S = 0.719879$ $R-Sq = 98.1\%$ $R-Sq(adj) = 97.9$

Analysis of Variance

Source	DF	SS	MS	F	P
Regression	1	366.34	366.34	706.91	0.000
Residual Error	14	7.26	0.52		
Total	15	373.60			

Durbin–Watson statistic = 0.901098

When successive error terms are correlated with each other $e_t = \lambda e_{t-1} + u_t$, we have the presence of serial correlation. Using the data set from Table 10.22 and Table 10.23A we see that the DW statistic is 0.901098, which identifies a positive autocorrelation problem. The initial step is to identify the numerical reading for lambda (λ) by regressing the residual on its lagged value (noting to eliminate the Y-intercept). To accomplish this take the residuals (column 4 in Table 10.22) and regress them on their one period lagged component (column 5 in Table 10.22). The Y-Intercept (constant) is eliminated under regression options by clicking off "**Fit intercept**". Lambda equals 0.3722 (Table 10.23B) for our data set.

Table 10.23B MINITAB's Computation of the Durbin–Watson Statistic

The regression equation is

RESI1 = 0.372 C4

15 cases used, 1 cases contain missing values

Predictor	Coef	SE Coef	T	P
Noconstant				
C4	0.3722	0.2701	1.38	0.190

$S = 0.580455$

Analysis of Variance

Source	DF	SS	MS	F	P
Regression	1	0.6399	0.6399	1.90	0.190
Residual Error	14	4.7170	0.3369		
Total	15	5.3569			

Table 10.23C MINITAB's Computation of the Durbin–Watson Statistic

The regression equation is

C8 = 4.66 + 1.13 C7

15 cases used, 1 cases contain missing values

Predictor	Coef	SE Coef	T	P
Constant	4.6556	0.3390	13.73	0.000
C7	1.12822	0.05132	21.98	0.000

$S = 0.539168 \quad R - Sq = 97.4\% \quad R - Sq(adj) = 97.2\%$

Analysis of Variance

Source	DF	SS	MS	F	P
Regression	1	140.47	140.47	483.21	0.000
Residual Error	13	3.78	0.29		
Total	14	144.25			

Durbin–Watson statistic $= 1.73661$

Armed with the numeric value for lambda (λ) we can create new response and predictor variables. They are as follows:

$$Y_1 - \lambda Y_{i-1}$$

$$X_1 - \lambda X_{i-1}$$

Using these lagged variables is termed the **generalized difference or Generalized Least Squares method** of removal. To obtain the numeric values, we first create the lagged components using Stat>Time Series>Lag commands. Next, using calculator we can tabulate the new response and predictor variables. Finally, regress the new response and predictor variables (remembering to click back on the "Fit intercept" command. The results are shown in Table 10.23C. Note that the DW statistic is now 1.73661 and we have eliminated our autocorrelation problem by tilting the regression equation.

A review of the steps is in order in our attempt to detect and remove the serial correlation from the data.

    a. In our original regression equation, have Minitab compute the Durbin-Watson (d) statistic: options box under regression. (d = 0.9011)

    b. Take the printout of residuals and lag them: Stat>Times series>lag

    c. Compute λ using the formula $e_1 = \lambda e_{i-1} = u_1$ ($\lambda = 0.3722$).
       Stat>Regression>Regression options and click off "Fit Intercept".

    d. Use the lag again to find the lagged values of the response and predictor variables.

    e. Under Minitab's Calculator develop the response variable ($Y_1 - \lambda Y_{i-1}$) and a predictor variable ($X_1 - \lambda X_{i-1}$).

    f. Regress the new response and predictor variables. Check the Durbin-Watson (d) test statistic again (d = 1.73661).

 Concept Check 10.M

The d statistic can range from 0–4, with values close to 2 indicating the existence at autocorrelation. True or false? If false, explain.

Exercises

10.70   Explain positive autocorrelation and describe a set of residuals based on its existence.

10.71   Is autocorrelation more likely to be a problem in time series or cross-sectional regression models? Why?

10.72   Explain negative autocorrelation and describe a set of residuals based on its existence.

10.73   If the Durbin–Watson test statistic is 3.2, $n = 20$, $k = 3$, is there positive or negative autocorrelation in the sample?

10.74   a.   View the MINITAB output of Table 10.6 and ascertain if autocorrelation is present at the 5% level.

          b.   Are the data in question time series analysis and of a large enough sample to make inferences?

10.75   Determine if the following data set is autocorrelated at the 5% level.

X	Y	X	Y	X	Y
1	9.62	7	16.94	13	23.96
2	10.69	8	17.60	14	25.27
3	12.85	9	18.87	15	26.36
4	13.13	10	20.71	16	27.09
5	14.11	11	21.65	17	27.42
6	15.76	12	23.12	18	28.68

Another assumption of least squares is that the standard deviation of the residual values remain constant as X increases (termed homoscedasticity). A violation of this assumption occurs wherever $|e|$ is some function of X and is termed heteroscedasticity (see Figure 10.10). Examples of possible functional forms are

$$e^2 = f(X)$$
$$|e| = f(X)$$
$$|e| = a + bX + cX^2$$
$$|e| = a + bX^{-1}$$
$$|e| = a + bX^2$$

Figure 10.10   Absolute Residuals Increasing as X Increases.

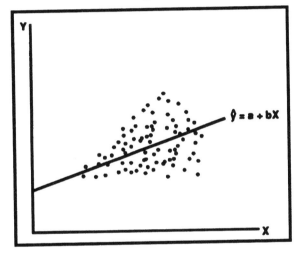

Heteroscedasticity is more likely to be present in cross-sectional data as compared to time series data. This occurs because changes in the dependent and some independent variables will tend over time to be proportional or of equal magnitude. The problem is normally prevalent in budgetary studies. It is always easier for larger firms to deviate from some norm by a greater amount than it is for smaller firms.

The consequences of heteroscedasticity is similar to that of autocorrelation. It will not create a bias problem but rather an efficiency one. With autocorrelation there is some unanimity in the detection process (Durbin-Watson test statistic) although considerable dissent on the correction process. With heteroscedasticity there is no agreement on either the detection, nor the correction process.

The simplest method of detection is to determine if there a relationship between the absolute value of the residual (or the residuals squared) and the predictor variable. If a relationship exists we have a problem.

$$|e| = f(X) \text{ or } e^2 = f(X)$$

329

Let's view Table 10.24 where our response variable is spending and our predictor is income. We can view Figure 10.10 to visualize what might be happening to our residuals. Let's check by having Minitab compute our regression model (Predictor = Income; Response = Spending) and to yield the residuals. Be sure to click on "Graphs", then view the two graphs "Versus Fits" and "Versus Order" (Figure 10.11). We intuitively can detect the residuals becoming larger as the predictor becomes larger.

Table 10.24A Data with a potential heteroscedasticity problem

Income	Spending
35,000	36,510
40,000	41,007
45,000	45,502
50,000	49,992
55,000	54,510
60,000	58,971
65,000	63,517
70,000	67,970
75,000	72,467
80,000	76,957
85,000	81,568
90,000	86,117
95,000	90,350
100,000	95,250
105,000	99,200

Table 10.24B Regression Analysis: Spending versus Income

The regression equation is
spending $= 5036 + 0.899$ income

Predictor	Coef	SE Coef	T	P
Constant	5036.3	107.2	46.96	0.000
income	0.899374	0.001464	614.36	0.000

$S = 122.481$ $R - Sq = 100.0\%$ $R - Sq(adj) = 100.0\%$

Analysis of Variance

Source	DF	SS	MS	F	P
Regression	1	5662118741	5662118741	377433.73	0.000
Residual Error	13	195021	15002		
Total	14	5662313762			

Figure 10.11: The Presence of Heteroscedasticity

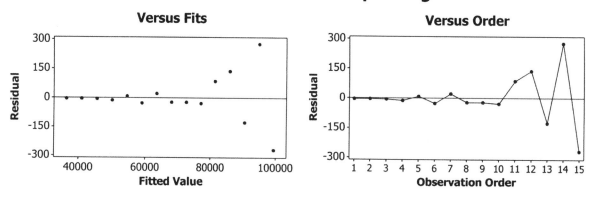

330

The graphs give us the informal approach to detecting heteroscedasticity. For the more formal approach two approaches are utilized. The first is the Park Test, developed by R.E. Park in the journal *Econometrica,* October 1966. The approach is as follows:

a. Obtain the residuals using the least squares equation : Spending = 5036.3 + 0.899374 (Income): (Table 10.24B).

b. Using the log of the squared residuals as the response variable and the log of income as the predictor, have Minitab compute the double log regression equation.

c. See if the P-Value to right of t-test is .05 (95% confidence) or less. If it is we have identified a heteroscedasticity problem. From Table 10.25A we have identified a problem with heteroscedasticity since the P-value to the right of the predictor (log[10] of income squared) = 0.000.

Table 10.25A Testing for Heteroscedasticity: Park Double Log (Base 10) Test
C5 = Log(10) Residual Squares
C6 = Log(10) Income Squares

The regression equation is
C5 = −34.4 + 7.75 C6

Predictor	Coef	SE Coef	T	P
Constant	−34.422	3.596	−9.57	0.000
C6	7.7485	0.7453	10.40	0.000

S = 0.416642   R − Sq =89.3%   R − Sq(adj) =88.4%

Analysis of Variance

Source	DF	SS	MS	F	P
Regression	1	18.761	18.761	108.08	0.000
Residual Error	13	2.257	0.174		
Total	14	21.018			

Table 10.25B Testing for Heteroscedasticity: White Test

The regression equation is
C4 = 105112 − 3.90 income + 0.000034 C7

Predictor	Coef	SE Coef	T	P
Constant	105112	34393	3.06	0.010
income	−3.900	1.045	−3.73	0.003
C7	0.00003371	0.00000739	4.56	0.001

S = 11874.2   R − Sq =81.8%   R − Sq(adj) =78.8%

Analysis of Variance

Source	DF	SS	MS	F	P
Regression	2	7625017138	3812508569	27.04	0.000
Residual Error	12	1691966189	140997182		
Total	14	9316983326			

The second approach is the White test (Halbert White: *Econometrica,* 1980).

a. Obtain the residuals using the least squares equation: Spending = 5036.3 + 0.899374 (Income): (Table 10.24B).

b. Use the residuals squared as the response variable and regress it on all original predictors, all original predictors squared, and the cross product of all predictors times each other (Table 10.25B).

c. The test statistic is **n•R²** (15•.818) = 12.27. It's theorized that the test statistic follows the chi-square distribution (Chapter 13) with a degrees of freedom (df) equal to the number of predictor variables. Since the test statistic (X^2_{test} = 12.27) exceeds the critical value ($X^2_{.05(2)}$ = 5.99147) we reject the null hypothesis the data is homoscedastic. It is heteroscedastic and we have an efficiency problem.

The White test attempts to deal with more different types of heteroscedasticity that may exist. Both tests are based on a similar thought processes.

One possible solution is termed **WEIGHTED LEAST SQUARES**. In essence we have more confidence in the small residuals than in the large values. We always prefer smaller variations than larger ones as we have a better probability of selecting a sample value close to the population value. Since we have more confidence in small residuals we weight them more than large ones.

If we divide our original regression equations by the predictor variable we would have the following solution equation.

$$\frac{Y_i}{X_i} = \frac{a}{X_i} + \frac{bX_i}{X_i} \quad \textbf{or} \quad \frac{Y_i}{X_i} = a\frac{1}{X_i} + b$$

The predictor variable is the inverse of itself and the response variable is the original response variable divided by the original predictor. Note the reversal of the constant and the slope coefficients. These will have to be interchanged in our final Minitab regression run.

Minitab can handle this in two different ways. Our first approach is to regress spending on income being sure that under options, click on weights, then enter income as the weights. These results appear in Table 10.26A. The second method would be to create the new response variable (spending/income) and the predictor (1/income), then regressing the two (Table 10.26B). Note here we must interchange the constant with the slope. Minitab gives us Y = 0.899571 + 5023.02(X), which becomes Y = 5023.02 + 0.899571(X).

Table 10.26A Regression Analysis: Spending versus Income

Weighted analysis using weights in income

The regression equation is
spending = 5055 + 0.899 income

Predictor	Coef	SE Coef	T	P
Constant	5055.5	145.5	34.75	0.000
income	0.899125	0.001833	490.61	0.000

$S = 38587.4 \quad R-Sq = 100.0\% \quad R-Sq(adj) = 100.0\%$

Analysis of Variance

Source	DF	SS	MS	F	P
Regression	1	3.58402E+14	3.58402E+14	240701.19	0.000
Residual Error	13	19356881195	1488990861		
Total	14	3.58421E+14			

Table 10.26B Regression Analysis: C4 versus C3

The regression equation is
spending/income = 0.900 + 5023 (1/income)

Predictor	Coef	SE Coef	T	P
Constant	0.899571	0.000967	930.34	0.000
1/Income	5023.02	57.23	87.77	0.000

$S = 0.00124249$ $R - Sq = 99.8\%$ $R - Sq(adj) = 99.8\%$

Analysis of Variance

Source	DF	SS	MS	F	P
Regression	1	0.011892	0.011892	7703.09	0.000
Residual Error	13	0.000020	0.000002		
Total	14	0.011912			

A review of the steps is in order in our attempt to detect and remove the effects of heteroscedasticity from the data.

Actual problem solving solution: Let's use the data above.

1. Detection: two separate tests.
   a. Regress with Minitab using Income as the predictor. Compute residuals.
   b. Using calculator create an absolute value for e and e*e (e^2).
   c. Park test: Regress using the log of the residuals squared as the response variable and the log of income squared as the predictor variable.
   d. White test: Regress using residuals squared as the response variable and regress it on all original predictors, all original predictors squared, and the cross product of all predictors times each other. The test statistic follows a chi-square distribution whose test statistics equals $n \cdot R^2$

2. Correcting: Two similar solutions using Minitab
   e. First: regress spending = f (Income). Under options see Weights and click in Income. Then regress.
   f. Second: In calculator Create the predictor (1/Income) and new response variable (spending/Income). Regress the two variables and look at residuals again. Note the slope and constant have been reversed. Place the constant and slope back into their original format.

 Concept Check 10.N

Heteroscedasticity involves the residuals (e) having a relationship to X. True or false? If false, explain.

10.76   Explain heteroscedasticity in your own words.

10.77   From a casual observation, do you see any specification problems implied by the following residuals?

X	e	X	e	X	e
1	+0.1	7	+3.1	13	+6.1
2	−0.6	8	−3.6	14	−6.6
3	+1.1	9	+4.1	15	+7.1
4	−1.6	10	−4.6	16	−7.6
5	+2.1	11	+5.1	17	+8.1
6	−2.6	12	−5.6	18	−8.6

10.17 Binary Logistic Regression

Occasionally, we may want to evaluate a response variable that is binary. Such an example would be if someone is applying for a loan to your institution. Either the loan will be approved or it will not. When someone purchases something from your retail outlet, either they will use the store credit, or they will not. Some will use a coupon and others will not.

These types of analyses are made with a different type of regression model. The mathematics and analysis involved is quite complex and beyond the scope of this text. There is an appearance of a multiple regression model in that there is the dependent/response variable and various predictor/independent variables. But the response variable is a binary variable and can only have two values (0 or 1). The computed equation does not yield an expected value for the response variable, but rather an expected probability when its value equals one. The technique uses a maximum likelihood approach.

Let's proceed to use an example involving a world renowned disaster, the sinking of the Titanic. Passengers were divided into three classes, first (337), second (285), and third (721) class. In addition, there were 885 crew members. Ultimately 705 survived and 1523 did not. The average price for the first class passengers in today's value was $2,400, for second class $960, and for third class about $320.

Is it possible that the fact if you lived or died was related to the class ticket that was purchased? Let's sample 26 passengers from our 2,228 passengers and obtain the values in Table 10.27.A.

Table 10.27A   Survival rate from a random sample of the Titanic Passengers

Class	Survived	Perished
1	5	1
2	2	2
3	1	6
Crew	1	8
Total	9	17

The data is entered in to the Minitab spreadsheet. Each passenger is placed in a different row. For the response variable, "1" is entered if the passenger survived and a "0" if they did not. Then under class of passenger, 1st class = 1, 2nd class = 2, 3rd class = 3, and crew = 4. After the data is entered, the following command sequence is utilized:

Stat>Regression>Binary Logistic Regression
place the response variable into the Response in response box
place the passenger class into the model box> OK

Table 10.27B   Binary Logistic Regression: Survive? versus Class

Link Function: Logit

Response Information

Variable	Value	Count	
Survive?	1	9	(Event)
	0	17	
	Total	26	

Logistic Regression Table

Predictor	Coef	SE Coef	Z	P	Odds Ratio	95% Lower	CI Upper
Constant	2.69536	1.29704	2.08	0.038			
Class	–1.32194	0.501439	–2.64	0.008	0.27	0.10	0.71

Log-Likelihood = –11.746

Test that all slopes are zero: G = 10.050, DF = 1, P–Value = 0.002

Table 10.27.B yields part of the complex Minitab output. The null hypothesis (as usual in regression analysis) is that all of the slope coefficients = 0. If we reject the main hypothesis, it means the model has some predictability to it. The test statistic to see if the model is significant or not is the G test statistic, which follows a chi-square distribution with degrees of freedom (df) equal to the number of independent/predictor variables in the model.

We note that G = 10.050 and that P-Value = 0.002. We reject when $\alpha \geq$ P-Value. Hence for all confidence levels between 0 and 99.8 percent, we reject the main hypothesis. We have determined that the model works, that we can predict life or death on the Titanic from knowledge of the class ticket purchased. We now can look at the "Z" value to the right of the predictor "Class" and see Z = –2.64 with a P-Value = 0.008. Again Class is a predictor at the 95% and 99% confidence levels.

The probability is given in the "Odds Ratio". This ratio measures the impact on the odds of a 1 unit increase in X (Y = 1), divided by the odds that (Y = 1) given no change in the value of X. The number 1 stands for those passengers that survived. Since the Odds Ratio = 0.27, a fraction, an inverse relationship is involved. As your class rating decreases by 1 (1 is the first class and 4 is crew) your chances for survival diminish considerably. In reality it declines by almost one fourth.

We must be careful when dealing with a binary response variables. Since there is little definition in the response variable it is difficult to come up with meaningful results. Often such analyses yield contradictory results, and it is often plagued with interpretation problems. This tragedy caused many changes in Maritime law to help prevent some problems in the future. No longer can a ship sail without its full contingent of life boats (capacity for 32, carried 20), and there must be enough life boats to allow all passengers and crew to escape (31.6% escaped; 53.4% could have escaped if all the life boats were filled). Even if the results are evaluated correctly, it may not be possible to extend this to other tragedies. It may not be any safer to be sitting in first class in an airplane than it is in economy class.

We have attempted a cursory review of the assumptions of least squares and their importance. Each assumption is independent of each other. The Durbin–Watson statistic is the most commonly used detection test and appears on most computer print outs. Hence, a greater emphasis was placed on it. Please note the references on this subject matter can be found in econometrics texts in your library.

If the violations of autocorrelation and heteroscedasticity did not seriously alter the outcome of a model, we would say that regression analysis was robust with respect to the violations. This is not the case concerning autocorrelation and heteroscedasticity. With a lack of robustness involved, if these specification errors exist, it will be necessary to correct for them or find alternative techniques.

Review of Important Terms and Concepts

Autocorrelation: Serial or autocorrelation is sequential correlation in the errors or residuals from a regression model.

Heteroscedasticity: Refers to situations where the variability in the error term is not constant with respect to the independent variables. Constant variation in the errors is referred to as homoscedasticity.

Residual analysis: Analysis of least squares residuals to check for violations of model assumptions and provide some insight into methods for dealing with these problems.

Robust: Regression analysis would be robust with respect to autocorrelation and heteroscedasticity if their presence would not seriously alter the outcome of a regression model.

Review of Important Formulas

The Durbin–Watson d Statistic

$$d = \frac{\Sigma_{t=2}^{n}(e_t - e_{t-1})^2}{\Sigma_{t=1}^{n}e_t^2} \tag{10.3}$$

where

$e_t =$ the error or residual in time period (observation) t

$e_{t-1} =$ the error or residual in time period (observation) $t - 1$

Times Series Analysis and Forecasting

Where we have been

> In previous chapters we developed regression models to explain behavior in a Y variable based on one or more independent (or predictor) variables.

Where we are going

> In this chapter, we discuss our ability to analyze the behavior of a single variable as it is measured over a given time frame. We attempt to explain the behavior of our variable not based on independent or predictor variables, but rather from observing the variable's patterns over time. The analysis of a variable over time made from its own historical values is called time series analysis. We will also learn of a technique that projects data ignoring its own past behavior.

11.1 Introduction

When historical data are analyzed and projected forward, the technique is called time series analysis. All projections based on historical data assume past data trends will continue somewhat uniformly into future periods. Otherwise, projections based on past information would be of little value.

Two points must be made before we continue. First, the time periods (months, years, days, minutes, etc.), must be of a constant duration and there should be no missing values when arranged chronologically. For example, we would find it difficult to forecast future fast-class postal rates in the U.S. Table 11.1 contains the price changes from 1963 to the present. Note that although the rate tends to increase in three year intervals, there are inconsistencies. In one year (1981), there were rate increases in both March and November.

Table 11.1   U.S. Postal Services First Class Rate Increases

Year		Rate in Cents
1963		5
1968		6
1971		8
1974		10
1975		13
1978		15
1981	(March)	18
1981	(November)	20
1985		22
1988		25
1991		29
1995		32
1999		33
2001		34
2002		37
2006		39
2007		41
2008		42

Second, the time series must contain observations which are equivalent to one another. If a corporation opened two new branches two years ago, for example, their operating data over the last ten years would be distorted. The last two years of data would represent the sales of three firms, and the first eight data points would represent the sales of one firm. Thus, the ten data points are not consistent in what is being measured.

Hence, when analyzing time series data, the data being analyzed must be of a constant duration when arranged chronologically, and the series must represent equivalent data.

 Concept Check 11.A

In order to work with time series data, the time intervals need not be in constant intervals; hence, missing values are not all that important. True or false? If false, explain.

Exercises

11.1   For time series models to be good predictors of the future, what must you assume about the past and the future?

11.2   For effective time series analysis, why must the time frame not contain missing values and be consistently sequenced?

11.3   "History repeats itself." Comment on this quote and its relevance for time series analysis.

11.4   "What goes around comes around." Comment on this quote and its relevance for time series analysis.

If a company wanted to forecast the economy next year, many variables should be considered. In fact, the list of independent variables (predictor variables) would be almost infinite. To make the problem more manageable, time series analysts often divide the variables into four broad categories, which are based on the time span of the variables.

The first category attempts to combine variables with a long-term influence (secular or trend component). The second category combines the variables that have an intermediate-term influence (cyclical component). The third category combines factors that influence the time series that in the span of one year recur in a periodic manner (seasonal component). Finally, the unpredictable or random elements must be considered (irregular component). Such short-term irregularities can cause major problems for forecasters. Each component will cause a variation within the data set which can be isolated and evaluated.

Irregular Variation

In a sense, each component is what remains after the other three components have been removed, i.e., each component is a residual. Thus, the components can be described in any order. We will review the irregular component first. The irregular variation refers to the short term movements that are random, or unpredictable, in nature. Typical sources of irregular variation include strikes, inclement weather conditions, equipment failure, etc. Since nothing is truly random, virtually everything can be predicted if a large enough data base is available. Strikes frequently are caused by poor, inappropriate, or untimely business decisions. Many scientists believe that even the weather can be accurately predicted, once the complex pattern is understood. However, weather may not repeat itself for 5,000, 50,000, or 500,000 years. Since we only have accurate weather readings for the last fifty years or so, current predictions are plagued with error. If we accept the "big bang" theory of the universe, then even the universe has a finite lifetime that is completely predictable.

Seasonal Variation

Seasonal variation is the within-year variability that is repetitive and regular. For example, a candy manufacturer would probably experience periods of high demand prior to major holidays, such as Valentine's Day, Easter Sunday, Mother's Day, Halloween, and Christmas. Similarly, many holidays also create increased bookings for the travel industry. There will be seasonal variation in your electric bill due to the variability in temperature. Normally, the greater the variation in temperature (high or low) is, the greater the power consumption and subsequent billing are. Many firms experience seasonal variation in sales, and a timing mismatch between production and demand. This variation frequently creates a particular need for cash flow analysis. Some toy manufacturers receive more than 70% of their yearly sales in the month preceding Christmas.

Cyclical Variation

You probably first learned about the business cycle in high school. It is normally drawn as a neat sine wave (Figure 11.1A) consisting of expansion, peak, contraction, and trough. Unfortunately, most business cycles do not follow the neat pattern of sine waves. Some researchers, for example, believe there is a major cycle in the United States every 50 to 60 years, others believe the cycle is 10 to 15 years, and others 3 to 4 years. Some evidence actually justifies all of the hypotheses. If all three hypotheses are correct, there are cycles within cycles within cycles, making cycle theory and analysis very complex (see Figure 11.1B). Although it is important to know that a cycle exists, the cycle may prove difficult to predict. In September 1980, the United States dollar was worth approximately 1.75 Deutsche Marks (West German currency). In February 1983, the dollar rose to approximately 3.5 Deutsche Marks and in mid 1996 it was about 1.40. A cycle was involved, yet few would dare predict the value of the dollar next month.

Figure 11.1 The Business Cycle

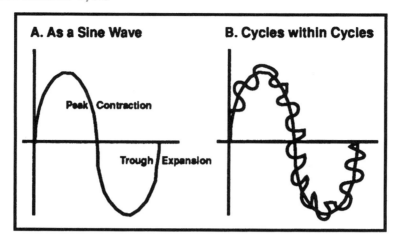

Secular Trend

The secular trend is essentially the residual if we eliminate the irregular, cyclical, and seasonal variation from a time series. The secular trend describes the long-term or general movement of the series over time. In Figure 11.2 three different time series are displayed. The secular trend of the first is positive, the second is 0 (sometimes called a stationary series), and the third is negative. The graphs with positive or negative slopes indicate the existence of a trend.

Figure 11.2 Secular Trends

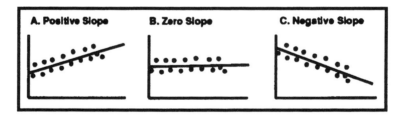

The four components of time series data usually involve different time sequences. The irregular and seasonal components are a year or less in duration, with the cycle and trend components spanning longer time durations. In fact, an analysis of both cycles and trends needs a long enough time span to allow for several complete cycles.

 Concept Check 11.B

The four components of a time series essentially entail equal time periods. True or false? If false, explain.

Exercises

11.5   Is it possible that weather conditions actually follow a discernible pattern? If so, why are we unable to forecast the weather accurately?

11.6   Draw a graph showing a hypothetical time series with a positive secular trend. What factors can account for variation above and below the trend component?

11.7   Of the four components, which do you believe is the easiest to forecast? Which is the most difficult to forecast?

11.8   Why is the irregular component not normally analyzed but considered useful to estimate?

11.3 Theorized Time Series Model

Time series models can be mathematically formulated in a variety of ways. The two most common mathematical representations, however, are the additive and multiplicative time series models. The additive model can be expressed as

Time Series Component Additive Model

$$Y_t = T_t + C_t + S_t + I_t \tag{11.1}$$

where the subscripts refer to time period t and

Y is the time series variable

T is the secular trend

C is the cyclical component

S is the seasonal component

I is the irregular or random component

The multiplicative model is

Time Series Component Multiplicative Model

$$Y_t = T_t \bullet C_t \bullet S_t \bullet I_t \tag{11.2}$$

The additive model is often used when the original time series contains both positive and negative values. The additive model is rarely used in time series analysis due to the inherent assumption that the four components are independent of one another. Most researchers believe a dependence exists between the various components. For example, a positive business cycle prior to Christmas will make the Christmas season more pronounced than it would have been. In other words, the business cycle accentuates the seasonal variation. The more accepted view is that the four components are interrelated; hence, the multiplicative model is more widely used.

 Concept Check 11.C

The additive model of the four time components assumes that they are interdependent with each other. True or false? If false, explain.

11.9   Write the equation for a multiplicative time series model.

11.10   Write the equation for an additive time series model.

11.11   The additive model has been rejected by many statisticians. In your own words, state why this is true.

11.12   What is the fundamental difference between the additive and multiplicative models?

11.4 Obtaining Secular Trend Using Least Squares

Least squares is the primary method used to develop trend equations for a time series. The virtues, logic, and formulas of least squares were discussed in Chapter 9. The main difference between the time series applications and the earlier regression models is that, in the former, the independent variable is time.

The main difference in terms of analysis is that the t_{test} and F_{test} hypothesis tests are no longer valid. This is because an underlying assumption was that the residuals were random and that no sequential dependence existed between successive values (autocorrelation: Section 10.15). This assumption will normally not be true in time series analysis (causing inflated Type I errors); hence, our hypothesis testing and confidence intervals are no longer applicable.

We will enter the average household size (AHS) data into MINITAB and perform a linear forecast for the year 2000. As we saw in Chapter 9, the estimated regression coefficients can be determined by the formula

$$b = \frac{\Sigma XY - n\overline{X}\,\overline{Y}}{\Sigma X^2 - n\overline{X}^2}$$

$$a = \overline{Y} - b\overline{X}$$

(9.1)

If an analyst is working with annual data, the independent variable X refers to the time period, and might take on values such as 1970, 1980, 1990. Since there is nothing inherently magical about the numbering system used for time, it is frequently coded for computational convenience. In fact, historians, and theological researchers admit that an error of four years was made in the prediction of the death of Christ. Hence, this is not the year that the calendar states but rather 2003 + 4. Because it would be cost prohibitive to correct the error, the adjustment is not made. Since the origin of time is arbitrary, there is no reason why time sequences can't be rescaled to ease the computational burdens. The most common coding scheme is to define the first time period as "period 1," the second as "period 2," and so on (Scenario A).

Scale Alteration of the Trend Equation

Even though we will be unable to test hypotheses, we will be able to extrapolate with time series data in order to make future projections. To illustrate the application of a linear least squares trend line, we will use data on the average household size (AHS = total population divided by total number of households) in the United States from 1920 to 2000 for census years, as shown in Table 11.2. Also suppose we want to forecast the household size for 2010.

Table 11.2   Average U.S. Household Size: 1920–2000 in Decades
*Data File on MINITAB CD

Year	X	AHS (Y)			
1920	1	4.34			
1930	2	4.11			
1940	3	3.67			
1950	4	3.37			
1960	5	3.33			
1970	6	3.14			
1980	7	2.76			
1990	8	2.63			
2000	9	2.59	2010	10 = 2.53	

AHS = Average household size is defined as the total population divided by the number of households.

Stat > Time Series > Trend Analysis
Double click AHS into the **Variable** box.
Click on the **Model Type: Linear.**
Click on **Generate forecasts: Number of forecasts.** Type in 1 for one forecast into the future.
OK (Twice)

Figure 11.3 MINITAB Plot of Linear Analysis Plus forecast for the year 2010
             (time period 10)

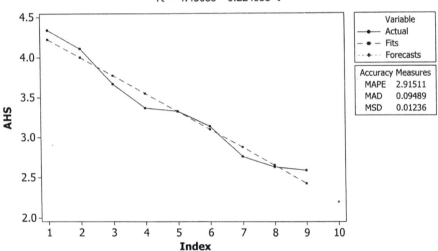

The graph displays the trend equation plus the raw data. The forecast of AHS is given to be 2.2025. Three accuracy measures of fit are given to us by MINITAB. Each of these measures of fit analyzes the difference between the actual data (AHS) and forecasted value (fit) for AHS. The three measures look at the percentage differences, absolute difference, and squared difference. These three measures are the Mean Absolute Percentage Error (MAPE), Mean Absolute Deviation (MAD), and Mean Square Deviation (MSD). MINITAB used the regression commands to obtain the appropriate fit values and resid-

343

uals (differences between AHS and its FITS 1). For MAPE, MINITAB divides FITS by the data for AHS, then if the percent is greater than one we subtract 1, and if less than one we subtract it from 1. For MAD, we average the residuals disregarding their signs. MSD is the same computation as SSE used in Chapters 9 and 10.

 Concept Check 11.D

Time can be rescaled to any base, without altering the forecast, as long as the rescaling is done consistently. True or false? If false, explain.

Exercises

11.13   The data below refer to a retail department store's annual sales in thousands of dollars. Use MINITAB to compute a linear trend equation and forecast for 1995.

Year	Sales	Year	Sales
1980	114	1987	146
1981	120	1988	151
1982	123	1989	158
1983	128	1990	162
1984	134	1991	168
1985	140	1992	173
1986	144	1993	181
		1994	198

11.14   Forecast sales for 1996 using a linear trend and MINITAB for the data set in Exercise 11.13.

11.15   Two companies produce essentially the same product. Develop a linear trend (using MINITAB) for each company and tell when you believe Company A's output will catch Company B's.

Year	Company A	Company B
1989	126	216
1990	149	219
1991	168	228
1992	183	234
1993	199	240
1994	221	249
1995	236	255
1996	254	262

11.16   Take your university's school enrollment over the last 10 years (if available) and forecast for the next year.

11.5 Nonlinear Trend Equations

Second-Degree Polynomial Model (Quadratic Equation)

If a time series falls and then rises, or falls and then levels off, we could not accurately explain the trend using a linear equation. We need a second-degree polynomial (quadratic or parabolic equation) trend equation for forecasting. The basic formula for a parabola is

$$Y = a + bX + cX^2$$

We first introduced the parabola in Section 10.9 where we treated X^2 as a special case of X_2 in a multiple regression analysis.

To illustrate a trend projection using a parabola, we again use our AHS data of Table 11.2. We might have problems visualizing the data to be linear into the future. Before long a negative linear trend will force AHS to get below 1, and then to 0. What we might expect is for the data to decline and level off, or to decline and then to increase. This means we believe the data set to be fit by a quadratic trend model. We utilize MINITAB to yield a quadratic fit for the data set and to make a forecast for the year 2010.

Stat > Time Series > Trend Analysis
Double click AHS into the **Variable** box.
Click on the **Model Type: Quadratic.**
Click on **Generate forecasts: Number of forecasts.** Type in 1 for one forecast into the future.
Click **Options,** then click on **Display Plot.**

Figure 11.4 MINITAB Plot of Quadratic Analysis Plus forecast for the year 2010 (time period 10)

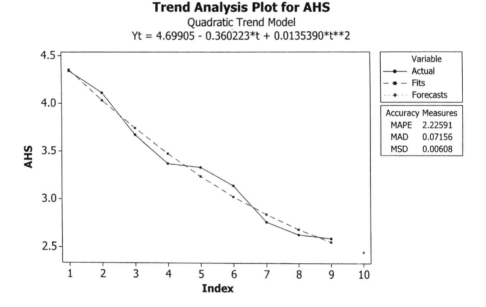

Forecast $t = 10$, $t^{**}2 = 100 = 2.45071$

The forecast given to us by MINITAB for the year 2000 is 2.45071. The numeric values for MAPS, MAD, and MSD are all slightly smaller for the quadratic equation than for the linear equation. However, the determining factor will be what we believe the data to be doing. Average household size will ultimately have to either level off or increase. This means over a longer time period we believe the quadratic equation to be the correct functional form. For the year 2000 the linear approximation may be best but for projections to 2010 and beyond we may have more confidence with the quadratic equation.

345

In business, many time series have a constant increase or decrease with respect to time. However, time series sometimes grow or contract at increasing rates and are more explosive in nature. Such series rise and fall by a constant percentage instead of a constant absolute amount. In high school, you may have been asked if you would be willing to work for 31 consecutive days (1 month) if you were paid $0.01 on the first day, and your salary doubled each day thereafter. Although you would have made only $1.27 after the first week, the total at the end of the 31 days would make you happy to accept the terms of employment ($21,474,837.97 or a daily average salary of $692,736.71). In this example, your daily salary is growing exponentially instead of arithmetically.

The family of exponential equations has its own form. The equation for a first-degree exponential is

$$Y = a \bullet b^X$$

Since exponential equations are more difficult to work with than polynomials, we will convert the exponential equation into its logarithmic form. Taking the logarithm of both sides and using the laws of algorithms, we obtain

---

Log Format for a First-Degree Exponential

$$\log Y = \log a + X \bullet \log b \qquad\qquad (11.3)$$

where

Y = variable to be forecast

X = time variable

$\log a$ = log Y intercept

$\log b$ = log Y/X slope

log = logarithm of variable or constant

Note that after the logarithmic transformation, the first-degree exponential equation is linear. The normal equations for both a first-degree exponential and polynomial are given for your inspection. The only difference is that the word "log" precedes Y, a, and b (not X).

First-Degree Exponential	**First-Degree Polynomial**
$\Sigma \log Y = \log a \bullet n + \log b \Sigma X$	$\Sigma Y = a \bullet n + b\Sigma X$
$\Sigma \log Y = \log a \Sigma X + \log b \Sigma X^2$	$\Sigma XY - a\Sigma X + b\Sigma X^2$

MINITAB will directly compute the solution equation for us, then give us the desired forecasts.

Stat > Time Series > Trend Analysis
Double click AHS into the **Variable** box.
Click on the **Model Type: Exponential growth**.
Click on **Generate forecasts: Number of forecasts**. Type in 1 for one forecast into the future.
Click **Options**, then click on **Display Plot**.

Figure 11.5 Decomposition Fit for Sales

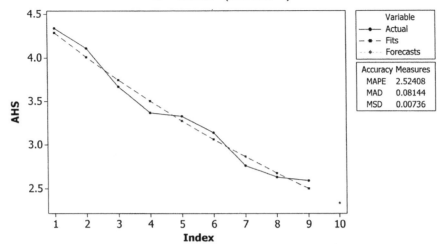

Trend Analysis Plot for AHS
Growth Curve Model
Yt = 4.58803 * (0.934809**t)

Variable
— Actual
– ■ – Fits
···◆··· Forecasts

Accuracy Measures
MAPE 2.52408
MAD   0.08144
MSD   0.00736

  Concept Check 11.E

The normal equations for a first-degree exponential and first-degree polynomial are essentially the same. The only difference is for the first-degree exponential, the word "log" appears before a, b, Y and X. True or false? If false, explain.

Exercises

11.17 The dates below refer to yearly attendance at a regional amusement park in thousands of persons.

a. Compute a parabolic trend equation.
b. Compute an exponential trend equation.
c. Based on your answers in part a and b, forecast attendance for 1997.

Year	Attendance	Year	Attendance	Year	Attendance
1975	513	1985	555	1995	531
1976	520	1986	554	1996	529
1977	527	1987	552		
1978	533	1988	555		
1979	538	1989	553		
1980	543	1990	551		
1981	547	1991	547		
1982	550	1992	541		
1983	553	1993	537		
1984	554	1994	532		

11.18   Which of the following three equations do you feel best approximates the data series (linear, parabolic, or exponential)? Explain.

11.19   Write the general equation for a parabolic trend model.

11.20   Write the general equation for an exponential trend model.

11.21   When is an exponential trend equation most appropriate?

11.22   Write the exponential trend equation obtained from MINITAB in Exercise 11.17 so that it does not contain logarithms.

11.23   A country experienced the following growth rates;

Year	Growth Rates	Year	Growth Rates
1985	9.8%	1990	3.7%
1986	7.3%	1991	2.9%
1987	6.8%	1992	3.4%
1988	6.6%	1993	4.7%
1989	5.3%	1994	4.9%
		1995	5.4%

a.   Does the trend appear to be linear?
b.   Fit a parabolic trend and determine file trend equation.
c.   Using the parabolic trend equation forecast the growth rate for 1996.

11.24   A country experienced the following growth rates;

Year	Growth Rates	Year	Growth Rates
1988	1.8%	1992	5.1%
1989	2.7%	1993	6.8%
1990	3.4%	1994	7.2%
1991	4.8%	1995	8.0%
		1996	9.3%

a.   Just from looking at the data, do they appear to have a linear trend?
b.   If the answer to part a is yes, can this trend continue indefinitely? Explain.
c.   Forecast for 1998 using linear and parabolic models. Compare your answers in terms of that which is more likely.

11.6 A Note of Caution Concerning Trend Projections

We must exercise caution when using trend projections as forecasts for future time periods, because this technique assumes that factors affecting the historical time series will continue in subsequent time periods. For example, suppose you had to punch a time card as you entered this class. This act would provide a monitored recording of your time of arrival. Using these historical times of arrival, a least squares equation could be used to predict your arrival time for future classes. However, suppose that you have been arriving late because your prior class was across campus. Or suppose that you were arriving late because your car was giving you problems and you did not have the cash to repair it. What would future time of arrival projections be if you dropped the class that was across campus, or you received unexpected birthday money to repair your vehicle? The trend equation then would have little value as a forecasting tool.

In most business forecasts, there is limited historical information available for projections. Many applications require trend projections from 10 to 15 periods beyond the last observation. Assume the existence of a cyclical component in the series and that a full cycle lasts 8 years (Figure 11.6). If a 6-year projection were made, there would either be 4 years of above normal data and 2 below or 2 above and 4 below, which would leave a trend equation that is far from the actual level of the series. Hence, any trend equation should encompass what is believed to be at least one complete cycle and hopefully more.

Figure 11.6 Incorrect Estimation of the Duration of a Cycle

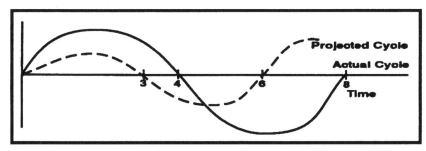

Because the secular trend is primarily desired, and not the shorter term components (cycles, seasonal), it is rare that any function more advanced than the second-degree polynomial or exponential is needed. In fact, the majority of the trends are best explained by the linear approximation, which is easy to use and explain. A quadratic equation (parabola) allows the data to change directions once, a cubic equation twice, and higher order polynomials one less change than their respective orders. However, each higher power places a new curve in the data set, which allows the trend equation to follow the cycle or seasonal patterns. The higher order equations are putting back into the function the very fluctuations that you are trying to remove. Remember that secular trend is what is left after the cyclical, seasonal, and irregular patterns have been removed.

We recommend that a linear trend be used for all data unless there are good theoretical or empirical reasons not to do so. For example, in our average household size data, it is logical to assume that average household size can approach 1, but is unlikely to fall below an average of 1 person per household. Yet, based on the data of Table 11.2, the linear trend equation projects that average household size would drop below one in the year 2061. In this case, a nonlinear equation has a theoretical foundation, but in most examples, no such logic is available. Without strong theoretical rationale to the contrary, it is safer to select the linear equation.

 Concept Check 11.F

A tenth-degree polynomial is generally an appropriate choice for a secular trend equation. True or false? If false, explain.

Exercises

11.25   How many times does a third degree polynomial change directions?

11.26   What are some dangers associated with projecting time series data into the future?

11.27   Define secular trend and explain why a linear trend model is an appealing choice unless there are strong indications of an alternative functional form.

11.28   Suppose you are forecasting average attendance at home games for your college's football team based on a time series model. Assume you find that a positively sloped linear trend equation "fits" best. Do you have any reservations about projections based on this equation? Discuss.

The Use of Moving Averages to Decompose Time Series

So far we have developed the methodology for isolating trend (T) from data that also contain cyclical (C), seasonal (S), and irregular (I) components. We also may want to isolate the seasonal component of the data for business decision purposes. In fact, many firms deseasonalize their data before evaluation. This avoids needless concerns for managers in terms of certain upturns or downturns merely being seasonally normal. The process of deseasonalizing data involves isolating the S and I components, then S, and finally dividing the data series by S, the seasonal norm.

Ratio-to-Moving Average: Isolating the S and I

One common approach to isolating two components (S and I) is to compute a ratio-to-moving-average for the data set. If the data are quarterly, then four quarters constitute a complete year and a full cycle of the seasonal variations. If the data are monthly, then 12 months constitutes a complete year.

The ratio-to-moving-average method provides a measure of seasonal variation by decomposing a time series. The technique computes the ratio of the observed values of the time series to the corresponding seasonal length moving average. The moving average represents the average for a data set for either 12 months or 4 quarters. The moving average consistently adds the next data point while dropping the earliest.

Since seasonal and irregular components are considered short-tern phenomena (a year or less in length), analyzing data in yearly intervals isolates the cycle and secular trend from the shorter term components. Numerous decompositions of time series are possible, such as

---

Various Decompositions for the Multiplicative Model

$$(T \bullet C \bullet S \bullet I)/(T \bullet C) = S \bullet I \qquad (11.4)$$
$$(T \bullet C \bullet S \bullet I)/S = T \bullet C \bullet I \qquad (11.5)$$

where

$$(T \bullet C)/T = C \qquad (11.6)$$
$$(S \bullet I)/S = I \qquad (11.7)$$
$$(T \bullet C \bullet I)/T = C \bullet I \qquad (11.8)$$

T = trend

C = cycle

S = seasonal

I = irregular

We are ultimately interested in the decomposition illustrated with equation 11.5, or the removal of seasonal variation from the data. All of these equations assume the multiplicative (not the additive) relationship between the four components exists.

Equation 11.4, $(T \bullet C \bullet S \bullet I)/(T \bullet C)$, illustrates the ratio-to-moving average method. We will illustrate this technique by analyzing the net quarterly sales for a multinational corporation (Table 11.3). To remove the shorter term components (less than one year), the data are grouped in four quarters (12 months if monthly data). The first four quarters are summed $33.1 (billions) and placed in the center of the four quarters involved. This throws the data off their original time sequence as they now become mid-quarterly data as opposed to quarterly data. The $33.1 sum is placed in between the second and third quarters of 2003. Then the first quarter of 2003 is dropped from the sum ($-$7.8) and the first quarter of 2004 is added ($10.2) to the sum for a net increase of $2.4 ($33.1 + $2.4 = $35.5). Then the second quarter of 2003 is dropped ($-$8.2) and the second quarter of 2004 added ($10.1) for a net increase of $1.9 ($10.1$-$$8.2) and this then increases the previous sum to $37.4 ($35.5 + $1.9). This process is repeated until the data are exhausted. Unfortunately, the technique reduces the number of observations from 24 to 21 (a much greater reduction would occur if monthly data were being used). To obtain the moving average, the moving sum would be divided by 4 (12 if monthly data) because the sum is an aggregation of 4 quarters.

It is customary to avoid shifting the base in such an analysis. If the data began as quarterly data, they usually have to remain quarterly data, and not be converted to mid-quarterly data. Since moving averages based on an even number of observations shifts the timing, then using an even-numbered moving average twice would return it back to the original sequence. Hence, if we find the average of the mid-quarterly data between the second and third quarters of 01 and the third and fourth quarters of 01, the result would be centered at the third quarter of 01. We have returned the time series to a quarterly time sequence, but at the cost of the loss of yet another data point. We call this new column the centered moving average. The column represents the secular trend and cycle components ($T \bullet C$), since the process removed the short-term components.

If we divide the original data (which has all four components) by the centered moving average, the result equals the seasonal and irregular components ($S \bullet I$), since

$$\frac{(T \bullet C \bullet S \bullet I)}{(T \bullet C)} = (S \bullet I) \tag{11.4}$$

Thus, the last column in Table 11.3 represents the combined seasonal and irregular components.

Table 11.3 Quarterly Net Sales for Multinational Corp. 2003–2008 ($000,000,000)
*Data File on MINITAB CD

Year	Qtr.	Net Sales (T • C • S • I)	Sum	Average	Centered Average (T • C)	Sales as a Ratio to Centered Average (S • I)
2003	1st	7.8				
	2nd	8.2				
			33.1	8.275		
	3rd	8.0			8.5750	.93294
			35.5	8.875		
	4th	9.1			9.1125	.99862
			37.4	9.350		
2004	1st	10.2			9.3375	1.09237
			37.3	9.325		
	2nd	10.1			9.3500	1.08021
			37.5	9.375		
	3rd	7.9			9.4625	.83487
	4th	9.3	38.2	9.550	9.7500	.95385
2005	1st	10.9	39.8	9.950	10.1500	1.07389
			41.4	10.350		
	2nd	11.7			10.5750	1.10638
			43.2	10.800		
	3rd	9.5			10.9125	.87056
			44.1	11.025		
	4th	11.1			11.1125	.99888
			44.8	11.200		
2006	1st	11.8			11.2250	1.05122
			45.0	11.250		
	2nd	12.4			11.2875	1.09856
			45.3	11.325		
	3rd	9.7			11.2875	.85936
			45.0	11.250		
	4th	11.4			11.8125	.96508
			49.5	12.375		
2007	1st	11.5			12.3500	.93117
			49.3	12.325		
	2nd	16.9			12.3625	1.36704
			49.6	12.400		
	3rd	9.5			12.4375	.76382
			49.9	12.475		
	4th	11.7			12.0625	.96995
			46.6	11.650		
2008	1st	11.8			12.0000	.98333
			49.4	12.350		
	2nd	13.6			12.6500	1.07510
			51.8	12.950		
	3rd	12.3				
	4th	14.1				

To isolate the seasonal from the irregular component, the sales as a ratio to-centered average data are grouped by the quarter in which they appear, and some measure of central tendency is used to ascertain the norm for each quarter. There is no standard for which measure of central tendency is optimal. Many statisticians use the mean or median. We select the median.

Table 11.4   Recording $S \bullet I$ by Quarter, then Isolating S

Year	1stQtr	2ndQtr	3rdQtr	4thQtr
2003			.93294	.99862
2004	1.09237	1.08021	.83487	.95385
2005	1.07389	1.10638	.87056	.99888
2006	1.05122	1.09856	.85936	.96508
2007	.93117	1.36704	.76382	.96995
2008	.98333	1.07510		
Medians	1.05122	1.09856	0.85936	0.96995

Adjustment coefficient = 4/3.97909 = 1.005255
S = (Adjustment coefficient)(Modified Mean)

S =	1.057	1.104	0.864	0.975

Whether a mean, median, trimmed mean, or other algorithm is used, the sum of the four seasons will not sum exactly to 4. It should sum to 4 because the average is set at 1 per time period. The benchmark or the norm is 1 for any time period, be it a quarter, a month, or a week. Any season that has a median above the norm, say 1.057, means that season (quarter) sales is 5.7% above the norm. Any season below 1, like 0.864, means this season (quarter) sales is 13.6% below the norm. It really wouldn't matter if the data were quarterly, monthly, or weekly. The interpretation would be the same.   To ensure a 4 sum, the data are proportionalized to 4 through an adjustment coefficient. The formula is seen in Table 11.4, and is merely 4 divided by the sum of the medians. The seasonal norm (S) then becomes the median times the adjustment coefficient. Hence, the seasonal norm for the first quarter is 1.057 [(1.05122)(1.005255)].

Once the seasonal norms have been obtained, one last step is necessary in order to deseasonalize the data. We merely divide the original data ($T \bullet C \bullet S \bullet I$) by the seasonal norm ($S$) obtaining deseasonalized data [$(T \bullet C \bullet S \bullet I)/(S) = (T \bullet C \bullet I)$]. Hence, for the first quarter of 2003, the deseasonalized value is 7.379 (7.8/1.057).

Table 11.5   Obtaining Deseasonalized Data $(T \bullet C \bullet S \bullet I)/(S) = (T \bullet C \bullet I)$

Year	Qtr	Net Sales $(T \bullet C \bullet S \bullet I)$	Seasonal Norm (S)	Deseasonalized Data $(T \bullet C \bullet S \bullet I)/(S) = (T \bullet C \bullet I)$
2003	1st	7.8	1.057	7.379
	2nd	8.2	1.104	7.428
	3rd	8.0	0.864	9.259
	4th	9.1	0.975	9.333
2004	1st	10.2	1.057	9.650
	2nd	10.1	1.104	9.149
	3rd	7.9	0.864	9.144
	4th	9.3	0.975	9.538
2005	1st	10.9	1.057	10.312
	2nd	11.7	1.104	10.598
	3rd	9.5	0.864	10.995
	4th	11.1	0.975	11.385
2006	1st	11.8	1.057	11.164
	2nd	12.4	1.104	11.232
	3rd	9.7	0.864	11.227
	4th	11.4	0.975	11.692
2007	1st	11.5	1.057	10.880
	2nd	16.9	1.104	15.308
	3rd	9.5	0.864	10.995
	4th	11.7	0.975	12.000
2008	1st	11.8	1.057	11.164
	2nd	13.6	1.104	12.319
	3rd	12.3	0.864	14.236
	4th	14.1	0.975	14.462

Note that the variation in the deseasonalized series is much less than that of the original data set. This is because seasonal variation, which greatly affects this industry, has been removed.

Deseasonalized data are important to decision makers who want to assess the seasonal performance of an organization or to determine the relative merits of a sales campaign. Suppose that in the second quarter of 2004 the multinational corporation launched a major campaign to sell its automobiles. The original sales data show that the second quarter was the best in terms of revenue, but in a seasonal adjustment, the second quarter was almost the weakest quarter of the year. Thus, we might want to rate the sales campaign as a failure. Conversely, if a major sales campaign was conducted during the third quarter of 2003 (usually our weakest quarter) to make it a strong quarter, we would probably concede that we were successful and we accomplished the desired corporate goals. After deseasonalization, the third quarter was nearly the strongest quarter of 2003.

Now that we have gone through a hand computational analysis we will have MINITAB perform the same computations in much less time plus make forecasts for the following four periods. The command sequence and output is as follows:

Stat > Time series > Decomposition
Double click **Sales** into **Variable** box.
Enter **4** in **Seasonal length** box. (Enter the # of data points that comprise one year)
Model type: click on **Multiplicative**.
Model components: click on **Trend plus seasonal**.
Initial seasonal period is: If quarterly data, if your first data point is for the first quarter leave as 1. If initial data point is for the third quarter change number to 3.
Generate forecasts: **Number of forecasts**: click on **4** if you want forecasts for next year.
Results: **click on Summary table and results table**
OK

Table 11.6   MINITAB Output for Decomposition

Time Series Decomposition for Sales

MULTIPLICATIVE MODEL		SEASONAL INDICES	
Data	*Sales*	*Period*	*Index*
Length	24	1	1.05675
NMissing	0	2	1.10433
FITTED TREND EQUATION		3	0.86387
$Yt = 7.89311 + 0.238048*t$		4	0.97504

Accuracy Measures

MAPE	6.34761
MAD	0.71313
MSD	1.00691

Time	Sales	Trend	Seasonal	Detrend	Deseason	Predict	Error
1	7.8	8.1312	1.05675	0.95927	7.3811	8.5926	−0.79259
2	8.2	8.3692	1.10433	0.97978	7.4253	9.2424	−1.04239
3	8.0	8.6073	0.86387	0.92945	9.2606	7.4356	0.56443
4	9.1	8.8453	0.97504	1.02880	9.3329	8.6246	0.47544
5	10.2	9.0833	1.05675	1.12293	9.6522	9.5988	0.60118
6	10.1	9.3214	1.10433	1.08353	9.1458	10.2939	−0.19392
7	7.9	9.5594	0.86387	0.82641	9.1449	8.2581	−0.35815
8	9.3	9.7975	0.97504	0.94922	9.5380	9.5530	−0.25300
9	10.9	10.0355	1.05675	1.08614	10.3147	10.6050	0.29495
10	11.7	10.2736	1.10433	1.13884	10.5946	11.3455	0.35454
11	9.5	10.5116	0.86387	0.90376	10.9970	9.0807	0.41928
12	11.1	10.7497	0.97504	1.03259	11.3841	10.4814	0.61857
13	11.8	10.9877	1.05675	1.07392	11.1663	11.6113	0.18872
14	12.4	11.2258	1.10433	1.10460	11.2285	12.3970	0.00300
15	9.7	11.4638	0.86387	0.84614	11.2285	9.9033	−0.20330
16	11.4	11.7019	0.97504	0.97420	11.6918	11.4099	−0.00986
17	11.5	11.9399	1.05675	0.96315	10.8824	12.6175	−1.11751
18	16.9	12.1780	1.10433	1.38775	15.3034	13.4485	3.45146
19	9.5	12.4160	0.86387	0.76514	10.9970	10.7259	−1.22587
20	11.7	12.6541	0.97504	0.92460	11.9994	12.3383	−0.63829
21	11.8	12.8921	1.05675	0.91529	11.1663	13.6237	−1.82373
22	13.6	13.1302	1.10433	1.03578	12.3151	14.5001	−0.90008
23	12.3	13.3682	0.86387	0.92009	14.2382	11.5484	0.75155
24	14.1	13.6063	0.97504	1.03629	14.4609	13.2667	0.83328

FORECASTS

ROW	Period	Forecast
1	25	14.4685
2	26	15.3466
3	27	12.2029
4	28	13.9970

We note that we obtain T and S in the first two columns following the raw data. Column five yields the deseasonalized data. We had MINITAB forecast for the four quarters of 2001. MINITAB used the trend equation, then adjusted the data for its seasonality. The computations are:

$Y_t = (8.02971 + 0.225957 * t) S$

for $t = 25$: $Yt = [8.02971 + 0.225957(25)](1.05775) = 14.4685$

for $t = 26$: $Yt = [8.02971 + 0.225957(26)](1.10371) = 15.3466$

for $t = 27$: $Yt = [8.02971 + 0.225957(27)](0.863581) = 12.2029$

for $t = 28$: $Yt = [8.02971 + 0.225957(28)](0.974961) = 13.9970$

MINITAB also gives a series of graphical plots of the components under DECOMP1, DECOMP2, and DECOMP3. These graphs are duplicated in Figure 11.7.

Figure 11.7A   MINITAB Plot of Exponential Growth Analysis Plus forecast for
the year 2010 (time period 10)

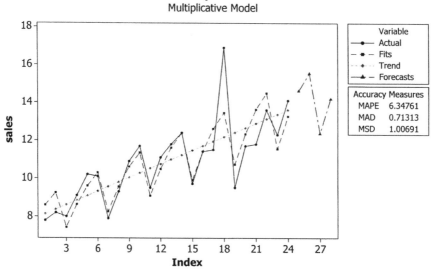

Time Series Decomposition Plot for sales
Multiplicative Model

Forecast $t = 10 = 2.33805$

Exponential growth curve models assume that the data set increases or decreases by a constant percentage. In the short run, for some countries, population growth might be explained by such a model. However, it is unlikely that AHS in the U.S. would follow such a pattern.

Figure 11.7B   Component Analysis for Sales

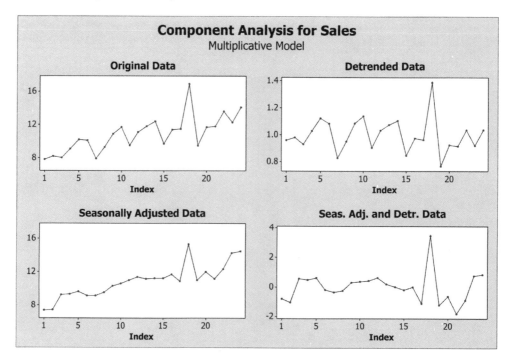

356

Figure 11.7C   Seasonal Analysis for Sales

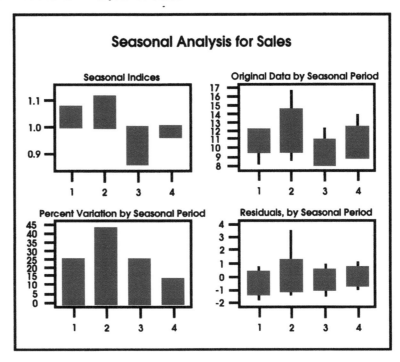

Using Multiple Regression Analysis to Estimate Seasonal Shifts

We can use multiple regression analysis, utilizing dummy variables, to estimate seasonal shifts in a time series. Our multiple regression model is

$$Y_t = a + b_1 X_1 + b_2 X_2 + b_3 X_3 + b_4 X_4$$

where

Y_t = data series

X_1 = quarters

X_2 = Quarter 2: coded 1 = Qtr. 2, otherwise coded 0

X_3 = Quarter 3: coded 1 = Qtr. 3, otherwise coded 0

X_4 = Quarter 4: coded 1 = Qtr. 4, otherwise coded 0

Note that, even though we have 4 quarters, we have one less dummy variable. If we decide to code quarters 2, 3, and 4, our coefficients from these quarters are based or referenced against the 1st quarter. For example if the coefficient of X_2 was 2, this means that, notwithstanding changes due to trend, the second quarter changes the value of the dependent variable by 2 more than quarter 1. If the coefficient for X_2 was 4, notwithstanding changes due to trend, the second quarter changes the value of Y by 4 less than quarter 1.

357

In the coding process, it matters not which quarter is not coded. When all three coded quarters equal 0, the remaining quarter is the uncoded quarter. If we had monthly data, there would be 12 months, but only 11 dummy (binary) variables are necessary.

The least squares model presented is additive rather then multiplicative. It's possible that the seasonal component is not increasing with trend; hence, the seasonal component is additive. We will test this hypothesis by comparing the results of the multiple regression model with our previously discussed multiplicative model and compare the two MSE's. The model with the smallest error sum-of-squares is judged superior.

Table 11.8 yields MINITAB's input and output from the multiple regression model.

Table 11.8A   MINITAB Input for Multiple Regression Model Involving SEASONS as Dummy Variables (Quarters)

	Sales	Time	Quar2	Quar3	Quar4
Case 1	7.8	1	0	0	0
Case 2	8.2	2	1	0	0
Case 3	8.0	3	0	1	0
Case 4	9.1	4	0	0	1
Case 5	10.2	5	0	0	0
Case 6	10.1	6	1	0	0
Case 7	7.9	7	0	1	0
Case 8	9.3	8	0	0	1
Case 9	10.9	9	0	0	0
Case 10	11.7	10	1	0	0
Case 11	9.5	11	0	1	0
Case 12	11.1	12	0	0	1
Case 13	11.8	13	0	0	0
Case 14	12.4	14	1	0	0
Case 15	9.7	15	0	1	0
Case 16	11.4	16	0	0	1
Case 17	11.5	17	0	0	0
Case 18	16.9	18	1	0	0
Case 19	9.5	19	0	1	0
Case 20	11.7	20	0	0	1
Case 21	11.8	21	0	0	0
Case 22	13.6	22	1	0	0
Case 23	12.3	23	0	1	0
Case 24	14.1	24	0	0	1

Table 11.8B   Abbreviated MINITAB Output for Multiple Regression Model Involving Seasons (Quarters)

Stat > Regression > Regression
The regression equation is
Sales = 8.08 + 0.236 time + 1.25 Quar2 − 1.65 Quar3 − 0.257 Quar4

Predictor	Coef	Stdev	T	p
Constant	8.0758	0.5857	13.79	0.000
Time	0.23554	0.03339	7.05	0.000
Quar2	1.2478	0.6461	1.93	0.069
Quar3	−1.6544	0.6487	−2.55	0.020
Quar4	−0.2566	0.6530	−0.39	0.699

S = 1.118   R-sq = 78.0%   R-sq(adj) = 73.4%

ANALYSIS OF VARIANCE

SOURCE	DF	SS	MS	F	p
Regression	4	84.109	21.027	16.84	0.000
Error	19	23.731	1.249		
Total	23	107.840			

We can review the results of our multiple regression equation. Sales are increasing at a rate of 0.236 billion per quarter. Keeping the trend effect separate and apart, sales from the second quarter are 1.2478 billion above the fast quarter, sales from the third quarter are 1.654 billion below the first quarter, and sales from the fourth quarter are 0.2566 billion below the fast quarter.

If we wanted MINITAB to forecast the 1st quarter of 2009 we would enter 25 0 0 0 into the **Prediction intervals for new observations** box. We obtain a forecast of 13.964. Similarly we obtain forecasts for 2nd qtr = 15.448; 3rd qtr = 12.781; and 4th qtr = 14.414.

As to which method is preferred is a matter of controversy. We might compare SSE (23.731) of the regression model to that of MSD of the time series model which we must multiply by the sample size (1.02200)(24) = 24.528. The readings are close with the regression model having a slightly smaller sum of the residuals squared. It would be a toss-up as to which is the best approach.

 Concept Check 11.G

Deseasonalized data will always have less than or equal variation to the original data. True or false? If false, explain.

Exercises

11.29   Explain the logic of using the ratio to moving average technique to obtain a seasonal index. Use a multiplicative model for the discussion.

11.30   What is meant by the decomposition of a time series?

11.31   The quarterly data below are the price charged for a 20-pound turkey. Use MINITAB to find the seasonal norms and deseasonalize this data.

Year-Qtr	Price	Year-Qtr	Price
1990-1	12	1995-1	13
1990-2	10	1995-2	9
1990-3	9	1995-3	8
1990-4	13	1995-4	14
1991-1	14	1996-1	13
1991-2	10	1996-2	10
1991-3	9	1996-3	9
1991-4	15	1996-4	14
1992-1	11	1997-1	15
1992-2	9	1997-2	12
1992-3	8	1997-3	10
1992-4	12	1997-4	16
1993-1	11	1998-1	15
1993-2	10	1998-2	11
1993-3	10	1998-3	9
1993-4	13	1998-4	15
1994-1	15		
1994-2	11		
1994-3	9		
1994-4	14		

11.32   The following are monthly data on occupancy rates for hotels and motels in a particular area (rounded to the nearest percent) for five consecutive years. Use MINITAB to find the seasonal norms and deseasonalize the data.

Month	1994	1995	1996	1997	1998
01	56	51	47	55	62
02	71	67	49	64	71
03	65	61	50	61	67
04	89	82	85	79	81
05	91	89	90	88	87
06	93	91	91	94	89
07	41	51	42	47	39
08	36	31	42	45	39
09	51	47	48	49	56
10	85	77	79	84	81
11	95	91	88	89	92
12	99	98	98	99	99

11.33 The following represents the sales of a company for 20 quarters in millions of dollars. Use MINITAB to find the seasonal norms, then deseasonalize the data. Forecast for 1999-1st quarter.

Year-Qtr	Sales	Year-Qtr	Sales
1994-1	4.2	1997-1	6.0
1994-2	4.3	1997-2	6.1
1994-3	4.6	1997-3	6.4
1994-4	5.1	1997-4	7.5
1995-1	4.8	1998-1	6.8
1995-2	5.0	1998-2	6.9
1995-3	5.0	1998-3	7.6
1995-4	6.2	1998-4	8.5
1996-1	5.4		
1996-2	5.5		
1996-3	5.7		
1996-4	6.9		

a. Use MINITAB and develop a multiple regression model and forecast for 1997-1st quarter.

11.34 The following represents the sales of a company for 20 quarters in millions of dollars.

a. Use MINITAB to find the seasonal norms, then forecast for 1999-1st and 2nd quarter.

Year-Qtr	Sales	Year-Qtr	Sales
1994-1	14	1997-1	41
1994-2	8	1997-2	23
1994-3	9	1997-3	28
1994-4	11	1997-4	29
1995-1	21	1998-1	52
1995-2	13	1998-2	32
1995-3	15	1998-3	33
1995-4	16	1998-4	35
1996-1	29		
1996-2	16		
1996-3	19		
1996-4	22		

b. Use MINITAB and develop a multiple regression model and forecast for 1999-1st and 2nd quarters.

c. Compare the sum-of-squares from the multiple regression model to the sum-of-squares for the seasonal forecasts assuming the multiplicative model.

11.8 Exponential Smoothing

Exponential smoothing is a forecasting technique that has come into widespread use in recent years. This technique is easy to program, use, and has minimum data storage requirements. The method is a pure time series technique that provides forecasts based on a weighted average of all past observations. Thus, while all historical data on a variable are assumed to have some value in forecasting, the weights attached to the observations reflect the greater weight placed on the more recent historical data. The technique processes self-adjusting forecasts that increase or decrease in the opposite direction of earlier errors. An analogy would be if one were driving an automobile on ice and were trying to control the car while in a skid. The steering wheel would be turned opposite to the direction of the spin in order to gain control. Exponential smoothing models correct for forecast errors in much the same way.

A separate process is involved for a stationary data set (single-parameter exponential smoothing) and for a data set in transition (two-parameter exponential smoothing).

Single-Parameter Exponential Smoothing

The single-parameter exponential smoothing technique is designed for data absent of trend. Such a time series is termed stationary and is depicted on a horizontal linear plane ($b = 0$). A weight α is assigned to the most recent data, and the weight must be between 0 and 1 ($0 \le \alpha < 1$). The α weight is, in effect, a smoothing constant. An exponential relationship is involved in the sense that the current data point t is weighted α, the prior data point $t - 1$ is $\alpha(1 - \alpha)$ the prior data point $t - 2$ is weighted $\alpha(1 - \alpha)^2$, $t - 3$ is weighted all $\alpha(1 - \alpha)^3$, and so on.

An alpha value close to 1 means that little emphasis is placed on the older historical data. An alpha reading near 0 means the effect of the older data is less quickly dissipated. For example, if $\alpha = .95$, then for the three data points

$$Y_{t+1} = 0.95Y_t + 0.95(.05)Y_{t-1} + 0.95(.05)^2 Y_{t-2} + 0.95(.05)^3 Y_{t-3}$$
$$Y_{t+1} = (0.95) + (0.0475) + (0.002375) + (0.00011875)$$

However, if $\alpha = .05$, then

$$Y_{t+1} = 0.05Y_t + 0.05(.95)Y_{t-1} + 0.05(.95)^2 Y_{t-2} + 0.05(.95)^3 Y_{t-3}$$
$$Y_{t+1} = (0.05) + (0.0475) + (0.045125) + (.04286875)$$

and the effect of past data is removed slowly and older data points have only slightly lower weights than recent data points.

The actual calculations are quite simple once a numerical value for a has been determined. However, the computations are burdensome; hence, the use of a computer is recommended. A MINITAB printout is given in Table 11.9 using $\alpha = .290964$. The data represent the quarterly series of net sales for our multinational corporation. MINITAB computes the initial smoothed value by backcasting. If a weight is specified, MINITAB uses the average of the first six observations for the initial smoothed value.

MINITAB will also graph the single exponential smoothing approach for us. The command sequence is:

Stat > Time Series > Single Exp Smoothing
Click in **Sales** into **Variables** box.
Click on **Weight to Use in Smoothing** as **Optimize**.
Click on **Generate Forecasts** and enter 1 in **Number of forecasts**.
Click on **Title** and enter **Sales of Multinational company**.
Click on **RESULTS Summary tables and results table**.
OK twice.

ROW	Time	Sales	Smooth	Predict	Error
				Table 11.9 One-Parameter Exponential Smoothing Results from MINITAB. Alpha = 0.290964	
1	1	7.8	8.3650	8.5969	−0.79691
2	2	8.2	8.3170	8.3650	−0.16504
3	3	8.0	8.2248	8.3170	−0.31722
4	4	9.1	8.4794	8.2248	0.87522
5	5	10.2	8.9801	8.4794	1.72056
6	6	10.1	9.3059	8.9801	1.11994
7	7	7.9	8.8968	9.3059	−1.40592
8	8	9.3	9.0142	8.8968	0.40315
9	9	10.9	9.5629	9.0142	1.88585
10	10	11.7	10.1847	9.5629	2.13713
11	11	9.5	9.9855	10.1847	−0.68470
12	12	11.1	10.3098	9.9855	1.11453
13	13	11.8	10.7434	10.3098	1.49024
14	14	12.4	11.2254	10.7434	1.65663
15	15	9.7	10.7816	11.2254	−1.52539
16	16	11.4	10.9615	10.7816	0.61845
17	17	11.5	11.1182	10.9615	0.53850
18	18	16.9	12.8005	11.1182	5.78182
19	19	9.5	11.8402	12.8005	−3.30049
20	20	11.7	11.7994	11.8402	−0.14016
21	21	11.8	11.7996	11.7994	0.00062
22	22	13.6	12.3234	11.7996	1.80044
23	23	12.3	12.3166	12.3234	−0.02342
24	24	14.1	12.8355	12.3166	1.78339

ROW	Period	Forecast	Lower	Upper
1	25	12.8355	9.64178	16.0292

Figure 11.8 MINITAB Plot Using the Single Exponential Smoothing Approach

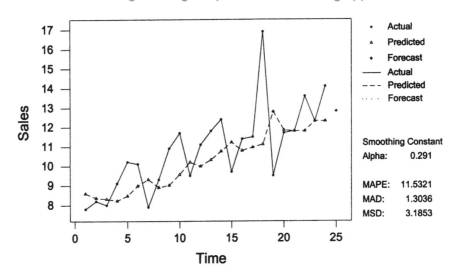

363

The computational equation is

Single-Parameter Exponential Smoothing Equation

$$F_{t+1} = \alpha Y_t + (1 - \alpha) F_t \tag{11.9}$$

where

F_{t+1} = forecast or predicted value of Y in time period, $t + 1$

α = smoothing constant

Y_t = observed value of Y in time period t

For example, substituting the numerical equivalents (Y_2 and F_2) to forecast or predict for period 3 (F_3) yields

$$F_3 = (0.291)8.2 + (0.709)8.365 = 8.3170$$

For period 25, we obtain:

$$F_{25} = (0.291)14.1 + (0.709)12.3166 = 12.8355$$

The process repeats itself in a consistent fashion. Thus, once the correct smoothing constant has been determined, the process is quite mechanical.

One difficulty with exponential smoothing is the need to determine the optimal smoothing constant. Unfortunately, there is no optimizing formula that can be used. Without such a formula an iterative, or trial-and-error process is required. That is, the errors must be computed and aggregated for each and every possible value of α. It is essential that the concept of an "optimum" α value is defined so that alternatives can be consistently compared. Since it is possible for the sum of the errors to equal 0, it is common to square the residuals. The optimum criterion is to minimize the mean of the deviations squared (MSD) which MINITAB does for us upon command.

Two-Parameter Exponential Smoothing

When a trend is present in a time series, the single-parameter technique will yield a constantly growing error. This result is because the weight applied to historical data, which is less than the recent data for an increasing trend (or more than the current data for a decreasing trend), will cause forecasts to continually lag behind the actual data. Smoothing techniques are available to incorporate the trend into a forecast. These techniques, however, require additional parameters. Two-parameter exponential smoothing is appropriate if the series contains a linear trend. One weight (α_1) will smooth the data, while the second weight (γ_1) smooths the existing trend. Three equations are required, one to smooth the data, one to smooth the trend, and one to forecast.

As was the case for single-parameter exponential smoothing, there is no formula that can identify the optimum weight values. Therefore, a trial-and-error process using a computer is generally required. Fortunately, MINITAB will allow us to yield only the optimum weights. If we apply the two-parameter technique to the multinational's sales, our results would be $\alpha = 0.264067$ and $\gamma = 0.126614$ with a forecast for the first quarter of 2003 to be 13.0472.

The optimum weights selected by MINITAB are $\alpha = 0.264$ and $\gamma = 0.127$. The command sequence from MINITAB is:

Stat > Time Series > Double Exp Smoothing
Click in **Sales** into **Variables** box.
Click on **Optimal ARIMA**.
Click on **Generate Forecasts** and enter **1** in **Number of forecasts**.
Click on **Results > Summary tables and results table**.
OK twice.

Figure 11.9 MINITAB Plot Using the Double Exponential Smoothing Approach

Double Exponential Smoothing for Sales

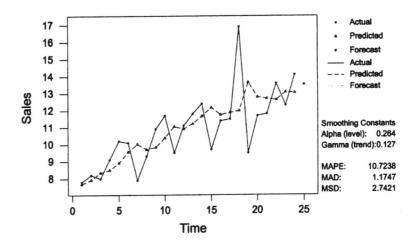

 Concept Check 11.H

If there is a linear trend in a time series, a single-parameter exponential smoothing procedure should be used for forecasting. True of false? If false, explain.

11.35　The quarterly data below are the prices charged for a 20-pound turkey.

Year-Qtr	Price	Year-Qtr	Price
1990-1	12	1995-1	13
1990-2	10	1995-2	9
1990-3	9	1995-3	8
1990-4	13	1995-4	14
1991-1	14	1996-1	13
1991-2	10	1996-2	10
1991-3	9	1996-3	9
1991-4	15	1996-4	14
1992-1	11	1997-1	15
1992-2	9	1997-2	12
1992-3	8	1997-3	10
1992-4	12	1997-4	16
1993-1	11	1998-1	15
1993-2	10	1998-2	11
1993-3	10	1998-3	9
1993-4	13	1998-4	15
1994-1	15		
1994-2	11		
1994-3	9		
1994-4	14		

Use MINITAB to determine alpha and forecast for the next time period using the single parameter technique.

11.36　The following are monthly data on occupancy rates for hotels and motels in a particular area (rounded to the nearest percent) for five consecutive years.

Month	1994	1995	1996	1997	1998
01	56	51	47	55	62
02	71	67	49	64	71
03	65	61	50	61	67
04	89	82	85	79	81
05	91	89	90	88	87
06	93	91	91	94	89
07	41	51	42	47	39
08	36	31	42	45	39
09	51	47	48	49	56
10	85	77	79	84	81
11	95	91	88	89	92
12	99	98	98	99	99

Use MINITAB to determine alpha and forecast for the next time period using the single parameter technique.

11.37 The following data represents the sales of a company for 20 quarters in millions of dollars.

Year-Qtr	Sales	Year-Qtr	Sales
1994-1	4.2	1997-1	6.0
1994-2	4.3	1997-2	6.1
1994-3	4.6	1997-3	6.4
1994-4	5.1	1997-4	7.5
1995-1	4.8	1998-1	6.8
1995-2	5.0	1998-2	6.9
1995-3	5.0	1998-3	7.6
1995-4	6.2	1998-4	8.5
1996-1	5.4		
1996-2	5.5		
1996-3	5.7		
1996-4	6.9		

Use MINITAB to determine alpha and forecast for the next time period using the single parameter technique.

11.38 The following data represents the sales of a company for 20 quarters in millions of dollars.

Year-Qtr	Sales	Year-Qtr	Sales
1994-1	14	1997-1	41
1994-2	8	1997-2	23
1994-3	9	1997-3	28
1994-4	11	1997-4	29
1995-1	21	1998-1	52
1995-2	13	1998-2	32
1995-3	15	1998-3	33
1995-4	16	1998-4	35
1996-1	29		
1996-2	16		
1996-3	19		
1996-4	22		

Use MINITAB to determine alpha and forecast for the next time period using the single parameter technique.

11.39 a. Exercise 11.37 appears to have a strong trend existing. Using MINITAB, find the optimal α and γ and forecast for the next time period.

b. Do the single or dual parameter techniques yield smaller errors?

11.40 a. Exercise 11.38 appears to have a strong trend existing. Using MINITAB, find the optimal α_1 and γ_2 and forecast for the next time period.

b. Do the single or dual parameter techniques yield smaller errors?

11.41 Explain why the single-parameter exponential smoothing technique would be inappropriate in forecasting the consumer price index.

11.42 Would the single- or two-parameter exponential smoothing technique be more appropriate in forecasting real (not nominal) Gross National Product (GNP)?

Suppose the data in Table 11.10 represent your annual car insurance premiums for the last eight years. The table shows that an increasing or upward trend exists. Many economists feel that there is downward rigidity in pricing and wages. This means prices are flexible upward to meet supply and demand scenarios, but not downward. If this is true, then this period's insurance premiums are dependent on past period rates.

Table 11.10 Student's Car Insurance Premiums: 2001–2008

Year	Insurance Premium
2001	$427.00
2002	516.00
2003	687.00
2004	867.00
2005	1,015.00
2006	1,486.00
2007	1,717.00
2008	2,174.00

Simple Autoregressive Model

If we believe that the current insurance premiums depend on past period premiums, we have a simple autoregressive model. Autoregression simply means that a time series variable, Y_t, is being regressed as a function of its own lagged values, such as

Y_{t-1} or Y_{t-2}.

Thus, an example of a linear autoregressive model is

First-Order Autoregressive Model

$$Y = a + bY_{t-1} \qquad (11.10)$$

where

Y_t = observed value of Y in time period t

Y_{t-1} = observed value of Y in time period $t - 1$

Essentially, we have a simple regression model (Chapter 9) in which the independent variable is merely a lagged value of the dependent variable. If the lag is one time period, it is called a first-order lag. If the lag is two time periods, it is termed a second order lag. Note that each order of lag effectively reduces the sample size as shown in Table 11.11. This reduction occurs because regression analysis requires paired (or equal numbers of) observations for the dependent and independent variables.

Table 11.11 First- and Second-Order Autoregressive Series

FIRST ORDER LAG (n = 7)			SECOND-ORDER LAG (n = 6)	
Year	Y_t	$(Y_t - 1)$	Y_t	(Y_{t-2})
2002	516	427		
2003	687	516	687	427
2004	867	687	867	516
2005	1,015	867	1,015	687
2006	1,486	1,015	1,486	867
2007	1,717	1,486	1,717	1,015
2008	2,174	1,717	2,174	1,486

The least squares estimates for the first-order equation is

$$Y_t = 40.9 + 1.2176(Y_{t-1})$$

with $R^2 = 96.7\%$ and $t_{\text{test}} = 12.04$ for the slope coefficient, which makes the slope significant. For the second-order least squares equation, the result is

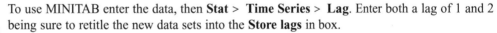

Second-Order Autoregressive Model

$$Y_t = a + b(Y_{t-2}) \tag{11.11}$$

where

$Y_t =$ observed value of Y in time period t

$Y_{t-2} =$ observed value of Y in time period $t - 2$

with $a = 119.8$, $b = +1.4461$, and $R^2 = 96.9\%$ and $t_{\text{test}} = 11.12$ (for the slope coefficient) which also makes the slope significant.

 To use MINITAB enter the data, then **Stat** > **Time Series** > **Lag**. Enter both a lag of 1 and 2 being sure to retitle the new data sets into the **Store lags** in box.
　　　　Use simple regression for the first order model, using $X = 2174$, and obtain a forecast for 2009 to be 2687.9. We again use simple linear regression where X is Y lagged 2, enter $X = 2174$ and obtain a forecast of 3263.5. With such a small sample size it would be difficult to evaluate the difference between the results. If unsure the most basic model is preferred over an advanced model.

✔ Concept Check 11.1

In a second-order autoregressive model, the independent variable is simply the value of the dependent variable two time periods before. True or false? If false, explain.

Exercises

11.43　What is meant by an autoregressive time series model?

11.44　Write the equations for a first- and second-order autoregressive models.

11.45   The data below refer to yearly attendance at a regional amusement park in thousands of persons. Estimate a first-order autoregressive model. Then forecast sales for the next period (one period ahead).

Year	Attendance	Year	Attendance
1977	513	1988	557
1978	520	1989	558
1979	527	1990	562
1980	533	1991	566
1981	538	1992	567
1982	543	1993	570
1983	547	1994	573
1984	550	1995	576
1985	553	1996	579
1986	554	1997	582
1987	555	1998	587

11.46   For the time series in Exercise 11.45, estimate a second-order autoregressive model. Then forecast sales for the next two periods (one and two periods ahead). Do you feel more comfortable with the equation with a one or two period lag?

11.47   The following data reflect the profits in thousands of dollars for a single proprietorship.

Year	Profit	Year	Profit
1988	36	1994	67
1989	42	1995	73
1990	47	1996	77
1991	53	1997	83
1992	58	1998	90
1993	62		

Determine the first-order autoregressive equation.

11.48   In Exercise 11.47, determine the second-order autoregressive equation. Which equation is preferred?

11.10 The Delphi (Qualitative) Approach to Forecasting

All of the forecasting approaches we have discussed are quantitative in nature. The techniques rely on a specific analytical approach to analyze and make projections about data bases. Qualitative approaches to forecasting (not based on numbers from continuous data sets) are available that we can use. One of the most commonly used qualitative techniques is the Delphi method. The Delphi technique is one where a series of questionnaires are completed and evaluated in order to determine an optimum course of action (or reaction) by consensus of a group of experts.

The Delphi method is primarily used when historical data can't be used to interpret future courses of events. Instead a series of questionnaires is used. For example, assume we are on the staff of General George C. Patton during the latter stage of World War II (Winter 1944). Germany is clearly losing the battle on all fronts. The Soviet forces are advancing from the east and the Allies from the west. The German army is quickly giving ground and the end of the war in the European theater is imminent.

Patton believes that a proud and determined German army will not simply roll over and instead will launch a major counteroffensive. This is in light of the fact that historically the German nation has never launched such a counteroffensive before under these conditions. Hence, historical information will not prove fruitful. So he calls his staff together and says that he believes that the German commanders still think they have a chance ultimately to win the war, but they must turn things around quickly so that their heavy water experiments (a prelude to the atomic bomb) can continue and the ultimate weapon can be made. The staff members are asked to place themselves in the role of the German commanders and ask themselves what they would do in their place. The staff members might be given a questionnaire and asked to write any scenario they can conceive, no matter how bizarre. What is desired is originality; no one will laugh at any unusual scenarios. The scenarios should be obtained by written questionnaire, because if the results were given orally in a group, the senior officer would probably dominate and originality would have been minimized. In fact, in many applications of the Delphi technique, the respondents will not even know each other and will be physically separated from each other in their daily operations.

After the questionnaires are returned, they are tabulated and used to develop a second questionnaire. The goal is to approach a group consensus. On the second questionnaire, the respondents are asked to reconsider their initial scenarios based on the aggregate findings to date. As the process continues the group approaches a single or multiple consensus.

For example, in our example, one staff member might believe that the enemy will devise a major counteroffensive. Another member might hypothesize that the enemy will pull back to that area where the heavy water research is occurring and defend it with all their reserves. Yet another member might believe that an early capitulation will result.

On the second questionnaire, new thought processes will develop. If there is an early capitulation by the Germans, there will be no negative consequences for not planning for a counterattack. The first and second scenarios seem more likely. With the second scenario, the enemy will be concentrated in a small geographic area, and with total air control, bombing will prove even more effective.

The optimum scenario for the enemy would be to mass a major counteroffensive. Since the German army never before massed a counteroffensive in the modern history of warfare, historical information would not prove useful. In fact, the German commanders counted on this fact to ensure that the offensive would take the Allied army by complete surprise.

After the consensus was reached on a counteroffensive, the same Delphi method could be used to determine the optimum location for the counteroffensive and the optimum time for it to occur. Once the location and time were determined by consensus, a plan would be developed to thwart the counteroffensive. Although this analysis was hypothetical, some historians believe that General Patton actually set this plan in motion (minus the questionnaires) and was the only field commander to have a completed plan to stop the "Battle of the Bulge" counteroffensive, which began on December 16, 1944. Military and business decision-makers must be prepared for the unexpected if they are to survive and prosper. Strategic planning is an important part of business planning, and the Delphi method can be an important tool in overcoming such events as strikes, shortages of resources, and new developments by competitors.

 Concept Check 11.J

The Delphi method is a quantitative model for forecasting. True or false? If false, explain.

Exercises

11.49   Form a group with three fellow students and try to predict if a pop quiz will be given next week in this class. Then try to determine which day and what subject matter. Write down what you believe are the answers, then pass a copy to each of the other three students. See if a consensus can be developed.

11.50   Assume you are the president of a company that has an exact production schedule that must be followed. If one of your suppliers fails to deliver on time, it would not be possible to make your production schedules. Explain how the Delphi method could be used to alleviate the problem.

Time series analysis was introduced in this chapter. We saw that while time series analysis provides descriptive information that we can use in decision-making, its primary purpose is in forecasting. First we discussed the decomposition of a time series into its component parts. Then we saw how to analyze secular trend, seasonality, and cyclical variation. We used autoregressive models and developed linear, quadratic, and exponential trend models. The chapter ended with a description of time series forecasting techniques that did not rely on historical data.

Mini-case 11.1: Bidding for the 2016 Olympic Games

The following represents TV's summer Olympic winning bids to obtain the rights to video coverage.

a. If we are to project the data forward in time does it matter that the time sequence is every four years and not every year?
b. Is it important that the U.S. pulled out of the 1980 summer Olympics, and hence only minimum fees were actually paid?
c. Determine the least squares linear trend and predict the winning bid for the 2012 summer Olympic games.
d. Determine the least squares second degree polynomial (parabolic) trend equation and predict the winning bid for the 2008 summer Olympic games.
e. Determine the least squares first degree exponential equation and predict the winning bid for the 2012 Olympic games.
f. Which forecast do you feel most comfortable with? Explain.
g. How is it that TV networks can bid so much more now than they were able in earlier years?
h. Is the limited sample size a factor in prediction?

Table 11.12 Network Winning Bids for the Summer Olympics*

Year	Summer Olympic Site	Network	Winning Bid (Millions)
1968	Mexico City, Mexico	ABC	6.0
1972	Munich, West Germany	ABC	10.0
1976	Montreal, Canada	ABC	25.0
1980	Moscow, U.S.S.R.	NBC	87.0
1984	Los Angeles, U.S.A.	ABC	91.5
1988	Seoul, Korea	NBC	300.0
1992	Barcelona, Spain	NBC	401.0
1996	Atlanta, U.S.A.	NBC	456.0
2000	Sidney, Australia	NBC	705.0
2004	Athens, Greece	NBC	793.0
2008	Beijing, China	NBC	894.0
2012	London, England	NBC	1,180.0

*2 Billion was paid for the rights to the 2010 Winter Olympics (Vancouver) and the 2012 Summer Olympics

Most business decisions must be made based on a limited data base. Yet sometimes a complete data series over a long term period of time is available. One such data base is the population of the United States from 1790 to 1990, which is shown in Table 11.13.

a. Is the data series distorted by the fact that the actual geographical territories of the United States have increased over this 200 year time span?

b. Do you believe that major confrontations such as wars seriously affect the population data?

c. Only in one year did the population actually decline. Which year was it and why do you believe it declined that year?

d. Use Census years (decades) only, from 1790 to 1990, and forecast the United States population for the year 2000 using linear and parabolic (quadratic) least squares estimates. Note the U.S. Census forecasts the 2000 population to be 267,987,000. Which of the two models do you feel best represents the data series? Which yields the most accurate estimate for 1990? Is the model with the most accurate forecast for 1990 necessarily the best fit equation?

e. Use the years 1975 to 1988 to forecast for the year 1990 using both a linear and parabolic (quadratic) equation. Are the forecasts accurate?

f. For the census years, determine the exponential trend equation (1790 to 1990), and use the equation to forecast for the year 2000. Based on the results, do you believe that the data justify such an equation?

g. Even if a particular function seems to represent the trend for the series, will this always be true? What would seem inevitable for the future? Are there similar patterns existing in other countries throughout the world now?

Table 11.13 U.S. Population from 1790–2000 (000's)

Year	Pop.	Year	Pop.	Year	Pop.	Year	Pop.
1790	3,929	1843	18,957	1896	70,885	1948	146,631
1791	4,056	1844	19,569	1897	72,189	1949	149,188
1792	4,194	1845	20,182	1898	73,494	1950	151,684
1793	4,332	1846	20,794	1899	74,799	1951	154,287
1794	4,469	1847	21,406	1900	76,094	1952	156,954
1795	4,607	1848	22,018	1901	77,584	1953	159,565
1796	4,745	1849	22,631	1902	79,163	1954	162,391
1797	4,883	1850	23,261	1903	80,632	1955	165,275
1798	5,021	1851	24,086	1904	82,166	1956	168,221
1799	5,159	1852	24,911	1905	83,822	1957	171,274
1800	5,297	1853	25,736	1906	85,450	1958	174,141
1801	5,486	1854	26,561	1907	87,008	1959	177,830
1802	5,679	1855	27,386	1908	88,710	1960	180,671
1803	5,872	1856	28,212	1909	90,490	1961	183,691
1804	6,065	1857	29,037	1910	92,407	1962	186,538
1805	6,258	1858	29,862	1911	93,863	1963	189,242
1806	6,451	1859	30,687	1912	95,335	1964	191,889
1807	6,644	1860	31,513	1913	97,225	1965	194,303
1808	6,838	1861	32,351	1914	99,111	1966	196,560
1809	7,031	1862	33,188	1915	100,546	1967	198,712
1810	7,224	1863	34,026	1916	101,961	1968	200,706
1811	7,460	1864	34,863	1917	103,268	1969	202,677
1812	7,700	1865	35,701	1918	103,208	1970	205,052
1813	7,939	1866	36,538	1919	104,514	1971	207,661
1814	8,179	1867	37,376	1920	106,461	1972	209,896
1815	8,419	1868	38,213	1921	108,538	1973	211,909
1816	8,659	1869	39,051	1922	110,049	1974	213,854
1817	8,899	1870	39,905	1923	111,947	1975	215,973
1818	9,139	1871	40,938	1924	114,109	1976	218,035
1819	9,379	1872	41,972	1925	115,829	1977	220,239
1820	9,618	1873	43,006	1926	117,397	1978	222,585
1821	9,939	1874	44,040	1927	119,035	1979	225,055
1822	10,268	1875	45,073	1928	120,509	1980	227,757
1823	10,596	1876	46,107	1929	121,767	1981	230,138
1824	10,924	1877	47,141	1930	123,188	1982	232,520
1825	11,252	1878	48,174	1931	124,149	1983	234,799
1826	11,580	1879	49,208	1932	124,949	1984	237,001
1827	11,909	1880	50,262	1933	125,690	1985	239,283
1828	12,237	1881	51,542	1934	126,485	1986	241,613
1829	12,565	1882	52,821	1935	127,362	1987	243,915
1830	12,901	1883	54,100	1936	128,181	1988	246,113
1831	13,321	1884	55,379	1937	128,961	1989	248,300
1832	13,742	1885	56,658	1938	129,969	1990	249,907
1833	14,162	1886	57,938	1939	131,028	1991	252,618
1834	14,582	1887	59,217	1940	132,122	1992	255,391
1835	15,003	1888	60,496	1941	133,402	1993	258,132
1836	15,423	1889	61,775	1942	134,860	1994	260,682
1837	15,843	1890	63,056	1943	136,739	1995	263,168
1838	16,264	1891	64,361	1944	138,397	1996	265,557
1839	16,684	1892	65,666	1945	139,928	1997	267,645
1840	17,120	1893	66,970	1946	141,389	1998	270,330
1841	17,733	1894	68,275	1947	144,126	1999	273,216
1842	18,345	1895	69,580			2000	277,618

Mini-case 11.3: Corruption During a U.S. Presidency

Historians believe the most corruption during a U.S. Presidency occurred under U. Grant (1869–77), W. Harding (1921–3), and R. Nixon (1969–74). All three presidents were Republican, and they occurred roughly in 50 year intervals. Does this mean corruption will occur under a Republican presidency in 2020?

Mini-case 11.4: An Analysis of General Motors

The following are the net sales ($000,000,000's) for the General Motors Corporation from 1982–2001.

Table 11.14 General Motors Sales
      *Data File on MINITAB CD

Year	Qtr	Sales	Year	Qtr	Sales	Year	Qtr	Sales	Year	Qtr	Sales
1982	1	14.7	1989	1	33.3	1996	1	39.2	2003	1	49.4
	2	17.1		2	33.6		2	44.8		2	48.3
	3	14.3		3	28.8		3	39.1		3	45.9
	4	13.9		4	31.4		4	40.9		4	49.1
1983	1	16.7	1990	1	30.1	1997	1	42.3	2004	1	47.8
	2	19.4		2	33.9		2	45.1		2	49.1
	3	17.6		3	30.8		3	41.9		3	44.9
	4	20.8		4	29.9		4	47.2		4	51.9
1984	1	22.9	1991	1	29.2	1998	1	41.6	2005	1	45.8
	2	21.6		2	31.3		2	38.9		2	48.5
	3	18.5		3	28.9		3	34.4		3	47.2
	4	20.9		4	33.6		4	46.4		4	51.2
1985	1	24.2	1992	1	32.0	1999	1	42.4	2006	1	52.2
	2	25.1		2	35.2		2	45.1		2	54.4
	3	22.5		3	29.4		3	42.8		3	48.8
	4	24.6		4	35.8		4	46.3		4	51.2
1986	1	26.8	1993	1	35.0	2000	1	46.9	2007	1	43.4
	2	27.6		2	36.7		2	48.7		2	45.9
	3	22.8		3	32.4		3	42.7		3	43.1
	4	25.5		4	34.1		4	45.1		4	46.7
1987	1	29.3	1994	1	37.5	2001	1	42.6	2008	1	42.7
	2	29.9		2	40.4		2	46.1		2	
	3	26.0		3	34.5		3	42.5		3	
	4	29.1		4	42.6		4	46.0		4	
1988	1	29.8	1995	1	43.3	2002	1	46.2	2009	1	
	2	33.2		2	44.1		2	48.3		2	
	3	28.2		3	37.5		3	43.6		3	
	4	32.4		4	43.9		4	48.7		4	

Update the data set: www.GM.com; ... invest. Then guess at what you believe GM's strongest and weakest quarters are. Subjectively forecast sales for the next quarter. Finally do exercises 11.69–71.

Table 11.15 National Basketball Association Average Attendance for 82 Regular-Game Season
*Data File on MINITAB CD

Season	Average	Season	Average	Season	Average	Season	Average
68–69	6,484	80–81	10,021	92–93	16,060	04–05	17,314
69–70	7,563	81–82	10,567	93–94	16,246	05–06	17,558
70–71	7,648	82–83	10,220	94–95	16,727	06–07	17,757
71–72	8,061	83–84	10,620	95–96	17,252	07–08	17,393
72–73	8,396	84–85	11,141	96–97	17,077	08–09	
73–74	8,479	85–86	11,893	97–98	17,135		
74–75	9,339	86–87	12,795	98–99	16,738		
75–76	10,179	87–88	13,419	99–00	16,870		
76–77	10,974	88–89	13,419	00–01	16,778		
77–78	10,974	89–90	15,690	01–02	16,959		
78–79	10,822	90–91	15,245	02–03	16,887		
79–80	11,017	91–92	15,689	03–04	17,059		

If necessary update file; www.NBA.COM. Forecast the average NBA attendance for the next season using a linear equation, a parabola, and an exponential equation. Which forecast do you feel most comfortable with (explain your answer)?

Review of Important Terms and Concepts

Consistent Time Intervals: In order to analyze time series data each interval must have the same duration and when arranged in chronological order, there should be no missing values.

Four Components of Time Series Models: The classical time series model hypothesizes four components in time series.

Irregular Component: Short-term variation that is random and can not be modeled mathematically.

Seasonal Component: Short-term variation that has a within-year pattern which may be constant or reflect a trend.

Cyclical Component: Periodic (wave like) between-year variability that consists of expansion, peak, contraction, and trough. Unfortunately, recurring cycles are not usually of equal amplitude or duration.

Secular Trend: Long-term variation that remains after the first three components have been removed.

Decomposition of Time Series Data: Time series data can be decomposed into the four components that comprise it.

Additive Time Series Model: Assumes that the four components of time series are independent, and so they can be expressed as $(I + S + C + T)$.

Multiplicative Time Series Model: Assumes that the four components are interrelated, and so they can be expressed as $(I \cdot S \cdot C \cdot T)$.

Forms of Least Squares Trends: The technique of least squares is often used to develop trend equations for time series data. The forms of the trend equations are usually linear, parabolic (quadratic), or exponential.

Linear Equation: $Y = a + bX$, where X is time. A linear time series typically increases or decreases by some constant amount (unless $b = 0$).

Parabolic (Quadratic) Equation: $Y = a + bX + cX2$, where X represents time. A parabolic (quadratic) time series typically either changes direction or eventually levels out.

Exponential Equation: $Y = a \cdot bX$, where X represents time. An exponential time series typically increases or decreases by a constant percentage.

Scaling Of a Time Series: Time is divided into constant intervals, such that when arranged in chronological order, there are no missing values. It does not matter what time frame is used, as long as the scale is consistently used.

Extrapolation of Time Series: Assumes that the factors which influenced the series in the past will also be in place in the future. Thus, extreme care must be used when using trend models to make forecasts of time series.

A Note of Caution: Before determining which forecasting approach to use, it is important to understand the series involved and the forces that shape it.

Single-Parameter Exponential Smoothing: A forecasting procedure that weights recent data more than past data. Single-parameter exponential smoothing is only appropriate if there is no trend in the data. A weight (alpha) is selected to minimize forecast error. Frequently, the goal is to select an alpha that will minimize the mean square error (MSE). The weight is the smoothing constant and the process is recursive, once the optimal alpha is selected.

MSE, the Determinant of the Optimal Weights: MSE is a measure of forecast accuracy and is often used to determine the optimum weights in an exponential smoothing model.

Two-Parameter Exponential Smoothing: An exponential smoothing process that adjusts for linear trend. There are two weights ($a1$ and $a2$) involved, one to smooth the data and the other to smooth the trend.

Simple Autoregressive Model: The model regresses Y_t on its previous lagged values. If a first-order relationship exists, the independent variable is Y_{t-1}. If a second order relationship exists, the independent variable is Y_{t-2}. There is a direct relationship between successive data points within the time series that can be used to predict subsequent data points.

The Delphi Method: A method that uses expert opinion in an iterative process. It frequently uses questionnaires in a repeated process to arrive at an optimal forecast. It is important in strategic planning.

Time Series Component Additive Model

$$Y_t = T_t + C_t + S_t + I_t \qquad (11.1)$$

where the subscripts refer to time period t and

Y is the time series variable

T is the secular trend

C is the cyclical component

S is the seasonal component

I is the irregular or random component

Time Series Component Multiplicative Model

$$Y_t = T_t \bullet C_t \bullet S_t \bullet I_t \qquad (11.2)$$

Log Format for a First-Degree Exponential

$$\log Y = \log a + X \bullet \log b \qquad (11.3)$$

where

$Y =$ variable to be forecast

$X =$ time variable

$\log a = \log Y$ intercept

$\log b = \log Y / X$ slope

$\log =$ algorithm of variable or constant

Various Decompositions for the Multiplicative Model

$$(T \bullet C \bullet S \bullet I)/(T \bullet C) = S \bullet I \qquad (11.4)$$

$$(T \bullet C \bullet S \bullet I)S = T \bullet C \bullet I \qquad (11.5)$$

$$(T \bullet C)/T = C \qquad (11.6)$$

$$(S \bullet I)/S = I \qquad (11.7)$$

$$(T \bullet C \bullet I)/(T = C \bullet I) = I \qquad (11.8)$$

where

$T = $ trend

$C = $ cycle

$S = $ seasonal

$I = $ irregular

Single-Parameter Exponential Smoothing Equation

$$F_{t+1} = \alpha Y_t + (1 - \alpha)F_t \qquad (11.9)$$

where

$F_{t+1} = $ forecast or predict value of Y in time period, $t + 1$

$\alpha = $ smoothing constant

$Y_t = $ observed value of Y in time period t

Two-Parameter Exponential Smoothing Equations

$$F_{t+1} = SD_t + ST_t$$

$$SD_t = \alpha \bullet Y_t(1 - \alpha)(SD_{t-1} + ST_{t-1}) = \alpha \bullet Y_t + (1 - \alpha)F_t$$

$$ST_1 = \gamma \bullet (SD_t - SD_{t-1}) + (1 - \gamma)ST_{t-1}$$

where

$SD_t = $ smoothed data in time period t

$S_t = $ smoothed trend in time period t

$F_{t+1} = $ forecast value of Y in time period $t + 1$

$\alpha = $ smoothing constant

$\gamma = $ trend smoothing constant

$Y_t = $ observed value of Y in time period t

First-Order Autoregressive Model

$$Y_t = a + bY_{t-1} \qquad\qquad (11.10)$$

where

Y_t = observed value of Y in time period t

Y_{t-1} = observed value of Y in time period $t - 1$

Second-Order Autoregressive Model

$$Y_t = a + b(Y_{t-2}) \qquad\qquad (11.11)$$

where

Y_t = observed value of Y in time period t

Y_{t-2} = observed value of Y in time period $t - 2$

Review of MINITAB Commands

Using MINITAB to obtain Forecasts.

Stat > Time Series > Trend Analysis
Double click AHS into the **Variable** box.
Click on the **Model Type: Linear/Quadratic/Exponential growth**.
Click on **Generate forecasts**: **Number of forecasts**. Type in 1 for one forecast into the future.
Click **Options**, then click on **Display Plot**.

MINITAB's decomposing of time series sequence.

Stat > Time series > Decomposition
Double click **Sales** into **Variable box**.
Enter 4 in **Seasonal length** box. (enter the # of data points that comprise one year)
Model type: click on **Multiplicative**
Model components: click on **Trend plus seasonal**.
Generate forecasts: Number of forecasts: click on 4 if you want forecasts for next year.
Options:
Display plot and Summary table and results table.

MINITAB's exponential smoothing sequence.

Stat > Time Series > Single Exp Smoothing
Double click Sales into **Variable** box.
Click to optimize alpha.
Click on **Generated Forecasts**: enter 1 into **Number of forecasts**. (note, we may forecast only for one time period in advance).
Click **Options, then Summary Table and results tables.**

11.51   National Association of Home Builders data show that United States homeowners represented as a percentage of United States households is as follows:

Year	Overall Percent
1982	64.7
1983	64.7
1984	64.4
1985	63.9
1986	63.8
1987	64.0

a.   Use a least squares linear equation to forecast the percent in 1988.
b.   Does a trend appear to exist within the data?
c.   If there were a trend in the data, would it be important for government policy makers to be aware of it? Explain.

11.52   The following data represents the drug removals (in pounds) from the domestic market by the Drug Enforcement Administration (DEA) for cocaine from 1990 to 1998.

Cocaine Removal from Domestic Market Made by DEA, FBI, US Customs Services, and US Border Patrol (in Pounds)

Year	Cocaine
1990	235,891
1991	246,318
1992	304,086
1993	244,315
1994	309,928
1995	233,447
1996	254,437
1997	253,536
1998	263,988

Source: Drug Enforcement Administration

11.53   The following represents the estimated average illegal market retail price of heroin per gram.

Year	Price of Heroin (per gram)
1976	$1,400
1977	1,590
1978	2,190
1979	2,290
1980	2,200
1981	2,340
1982	2,130
1983	2,150
1984	2,370
1985	2,300
1986	2,120

a.   From a visual observation, do you think a linear approximation is required or does a non-linear relationship exist? Explain.
b.   Forecast the price in 1987 using both a linear and parabolic equation.

11.54   Why is it so difficult to predict the value of a particular currency when there are so much data available concerning that currency?

11.55   If you were given the daily stock prices for a company for the last ten years, do you believe that a time series projection will aid in predicting the price of the stock in the near future? Explain.

11.56   Our television network is considering bidding on the next winter Olympic games. State how the Delphi technique might be used first to determine if we indeed wish to place a bid.

11.57   Explain why it is simpler to project over time the movement of an object in space than to project most business or economic data.

11.58   The following data set represents the projected production of orange juice in Florida and Brazil.

Season	Florida	Brazil
1989–90	916	1,165
1990–91	972	1,189
1991–92	1,031	1,227
1992–93	1,089	1,269
1993–94	1,144	1,291
1994–95	1,192	1,310
1995–96	1,235	1,321
1996–97	1,275	1,322
1997–98	1,312	1,321
1998–99	1,344	1,320

Source: Florida Citrus Department/*The Orlando Sentinel.* All data in millions of gallons.

a.   From observation, determine if the data set are best represented by a linear equation, a parabola, or a first-degree exponential.
b.   Use MINITAB to determine the equation chosen in "a" and forecast for 1999–2000.

11.59   The following information was supplied by the XYZ Co.

Year	Revenue	Profit
1994	$1,500	$97.8
1995	1,700	173.5
1996	2,200	247.3
1997	2,900	444.7
1998	3,400	522.0

Revenue and profits in millions of dollars.

a.   Forecast revenue and profits for 1999 using a linear approximation.
b.   Is the sample size adequate to make such a forecast?
c.   What are some of the problems with trying to project revenues and profits in advance? Can you indicate some of the factors on which such a forecast might depend?

11.60 Revenues for Company X ($000's) are as follows:

Year	Revenues
1988	$106.9
1989	129.3
1990	136.8
1991	149.2
1992	159.5
1993	163.1
1994	158.1
1995	152.6
1996	147.1
1997	143.7
1998	136.8

a. Using MINITAB and a linear and quadratic equation, forecast for 1999.
b. Have MINITAB compute the residual values for each equation. Comment on the residuals for the linear equation.
c. Which of the two equations would seem to be the "best-fit"?

11.61 A pharmaceutical company develops a new strain of bacteria. The growth of the bacteria is recorded for several days with the following results:

Day	Bacteria Count	Day	Bacteria Count
1	1.0	8	2,089.6
2	3.2	9	6,665.8
3	9.1	10	20,330.6
4	27.8	11	58,348.8
5	86.6	12	180,881.2
6	250.3	13	539,026.0
7	735.8		

a. Determine the least squares equations $Y = a + bX$ and $Y = a \cdot bX$ that best fit the data.
b. If you plotted the exponential equation on semilog paper, what would you expect to find?
c. Forecast the bacteria count on day 14 using the linear and exponential equations. Comment on the results.

11.62 A company is producing a flowering plant that it sells for holidays and birthdays. The research scientist notices that the plant develops a new shoot from its root every 10 days. These shoots can be used to make new plants. Write the equation and state how many new plants the company can have at the end of 50 days.

11.63 A golf course has recorded its quarterly customers for 5 years with the following results:

	1st Qtr	2nd Qtr	3rd Qtr	4th Qtr
1994	2520	4714	6819	3692
1995	2671	4658	7102	3219
1996	2819	4612	6967	3591
1997	3116	4538	7019	3457
1998	3276	4498	6799	3698

a. Have MINITAB isolate S, then obtain the deseasonalized and trend data.
b. Have MINITAB perform a multiple regression model including the independent variables time as measured in quarters, and 3 of the 4 seasons involved. Comment on the results.

11.64 A golf course has recorded its monthly customers for 5 years with the following results:

	1993	1994	1995	1996	1997
Jan.	840	870	830	860	830
Feb.	670	680	640	710	680
March	1080	1090	1020	1040	1090
April	1230	1190	1090	1210	1160
May	1510	1540	1590	1620	1660
June	1830	1810	1790	1840	1820
July	2260	2290	2210	2250	2280
Aug.	1830	1800	1860	1790	1820
Sept.	1470	1490	1410	1510	1460
Oct.	1080	1010	1100	1060	1040
Nov.	930	900	860	840	800
Dec.	800	810	770	830	790

a. Have MINITAB isolate S.
b. Have MINITAB deseasonalize the data set.

11.65 a. Using the data set of Exercise 11.63, determine the optimal alpha value for a single-parameter exponential smoothing technique.

b. Using the same data set, determine the optimum weights for a two parameter exponential smoothing technique.

11.66 a. Using the data set of Exercise 11.64, determine the optimal alpha value for a single-parameter exponential smoothing technique.

b. Using the same data set, determine the optimum weights for a two parameter exponential smoothing technique.

11.67 The following represents sales for the X Corporation.

Year	Sales (000's)	Year	Sale (000's)
1988	2	1994	31
1989	7	1995	37
1990	13	1996	41
1991	17	1997	46
1992	22	1998	50
1993	26		

a. Determine the regression equation where Y = sales in period t, and X = sales in period $t - 1$.
b. Determine the regression equation where Y = sales in period t and X = sales in period $t - 2$.
c. Using a visual observation of the residuals (obtained from MINITAB), determine the best of "a" and "b."

11.68 Take a serious problem currently facing the political leader of your country. How might the Delphi method be used to solve, or partially solve, the problem?

11.69 Update the data file in Mini-case 11.4.

a. Use MINITAB to obtain the seasonal norms and then deseasonalize the data set.
b. Use MINITAB to transform the data to deseasonalize it.

384

11.70 a. Using the data set in Mini-case 11.4, determine the optimum alpha weight (one-parameter exponential smoothing) using MINITAB.

b. Explain why the optimum alpha weight was where it was. Forecast for the next quarter.

11.71 For the data set in Mini-case 11.4, determine which of the optimum weights for the two-parameter exponential smoothing technique.

Index Numbers

Where we have been:

So far we have not been concerned with the general topic of an index.

Where we are going:

We will not discuss the importance of index numbers and how the information they yield can be utilized in decision making. Many indices that affect us are not termed as such. An example is our grade in this course which is likely a composite of examination grades, homework, attendance, and computer assignments. This and many other indices are important to us and their value affects the way we live.

12.1   Introduction

We will begin our analysis of index numbers by reviewing some indices we face in our daily activities. Then we will give some intuitive insight into the development of an index. Finally, we will discuss the Consumer Price Index (CPI) and learn to utilize its findings in terms of converting money values into real or constant purchasing power.

12.2   Examples of Everyday Indices

Our lives are very much tied to indices that have been developed to measure various factors. We measure how uncomfortable we are by what is termed the wind chill factor. The temperature is not sufficient to ascertain how a cold temperature may penetrate our bodies. Hence, we combine the heterogeneous factors of temperature and wind velocity into an index. If we compare different temperature readings we are comparing relative values of a single variable which is not considered an index. When the wind factor enters the net result, an index is formed combining two elements—temperature and wind velocity.

Most employees undergo evaluations, usually yearly. Such evaluations are weighted measures of other indices. For example, we may be evaluated on such factors as cooperativeness, initiative, being a team player, leadership, performance, etc. Usually arbitrary scales are used, such as 0 to 10, and an administrator assigns a numeric rating depending how he or she believes an employee rates on a particular factor. Then a weighting of multiple factors (an index) establishes an employee's performance at the company for the past year. Since a great deal of subjectivity is involved, there is sometimes a lack of consistency in applying the technique. In addition, personal bias can cause a distortion in an employee's evaluation. Our careers are very much affected by such an index. It is unfortunate that many employees spend more time in considering how to achieve the highest possible evaluation than on performing their duties. Hence, many employees will engage in activities which will result in vitae entries which, in turn, will score points on their evaluation. Corporations normally don't term their evaluations as indices, yet this is what they are.

In football, we have the *New York Times* that is used to evaluate individual teams. Wall Street indices record the buying activity of the New York Stock Exchange. The Richter scale (a logarithmic scale) is used to measure the energy released at the epicenter of an earthquake. The Consumer Price Index allows a comparison of our purchasing power over time, and there is an index of leading economic indicators which attempts to predict turning points in economic activity. Whether you get into a business graduate school or not usually depends on how you perform on an index involving your undergraduate grade point average and your score on the GMAT (Graduate Management Admission Test).

When an athlete competes in a decathlon or heptathlon, he or she is competing against an index. You receive so many points for running so fast and jumping so far. Competition is against the index and not against fellow athletes. A competitor can beat you in more events than you beat him or her, yet it's still possible for you to win the decathlon. This was the case in the 1960 Olympic decathlon when Rafer Johnson defeated Yang Chuan-Kwang, even though Mr. Johnson lost 7 of the 10 events to Mr. Yang.

In finance classes we evaluate profits-to-sales or profits-to-assets ratios. We compare inventory and employee turnover ratios or indices between firms over time. With the use of these comparisons, we can determine performance or lack thereof.

Some of these indices are more clearly defined than others, yet all have a great deal of subjectivity involved. Normally, the index has no value by itself, but has value when compared over time or when compared to other individuals, firms, or events of a similar nature, or those who computed their index by similar methodologies.

 Concept Check 12.A

The temperature reading on the Fahrenheit scale is an example of an index. True or false? If false, explain.

Exercises

12.1   Explain how the heptathlon is an index and, if one is to win, it is a competition against the index and not against fellow athletes.

12.2   State two indices, not previously mentioned, of which you are aware.

12.3 Designing a Special Purpose Index

In many cases we may wish to design a special purpose index to measure some phenomenon at work over time. When designing such an index, we will want to know if the variables or factors affecting it do so in a direct or inverse relationship. Say that variable Y directly affects our index (called W) and variable Z affects it inversely. Then the formula for the index would be

$$W = \frac{Y \text{ (directly related to } W)}{Z \text{ (inversely related to } W)}$$

If the effect of one of the variables dissipates as its value becomes larger, then the index should involve its square root. Suppose we believe this to be true about the variable Z. Then

$$W = \frac{Y}{\sqrt{Z}}$$

If one variable's effect increases as its value becomes larger, consider squaring it. Suppose we believe this to be true about variable Y. Then

$$W = \frac{Y^2}{\sqrt{Z}}$$

Suppose that two variables are directly related (Y and X) to W, yet are measured on different scales. Such is the case if the admittance of graduate students is based on undergraduate GPA and score on GMAT exams. One variable has a 0–4 scale, and the other 200–800 scale. To weight the two variables approximately equal, just divide the mean score of the larger (500) by the mean score of the smaller (2.0, then use this as a multiplier in the formula. Hence

$$W = Y + 250X$$

If $W = Y + X$, it means that the factors Y and X are independent of each other. If a dependence between the two exists then a multiplication is in order, hence,

$$W = Y \bullet X$$

and if the weighting were still desired,

$$W = Y \bullet 250X$$

Remember that all indices are merely relative measures and should be monitored for inconsistencies and inaccuracies. Problems in the use of an index should provide some insight into ways to redesign and improve it.

 Concept Check 12.B

Formula $W = Y/X$ indicates that W is inversely related to Y and directly related to X. True or false? If false, explain.

Exercises

12.3   Develop a general formula for an index which is directly related to A and B, but inversely related to C.

12.4   In exercise 12.3, it is believed that A should be weighted 3 times that of B. What might the formula be?

12.5   In exercise 12.3, it is believed that the impact of C dissipates as C becomes larger. What might the formula look like?

12.6   In exercise 12.3, it is believed that the impact of B greatly increases as B increases. What might the new index be?

Probably the most closely followed indices throughout the world are the Consumer Price Index (CPI) of individual countries. Consumer Price Indices are usually weighted by the amount of average expenditures made on each product or service. We now begin to develop indices which will evaluate this important concept.

Price Relatives

Suppose we have observed the price of a food staple over a 6 year time span and its price has risen from $3 to $11. To monitor the prices over the 6 years, it is necessary to select a base year. The base year is the year to which all years will be compared. It is the standard. As such, great care must be taken not to select an abnormal year as the designated base. Let's say that we believe 2004 is to be the base (written as 2004 = 100). The actual price for the base period is symbolically designated as P_o The price in the year being evaluated is called the price in the given period and symbolically designated as P_n. We compare the price in a given period to the price in a base period, then multiply by 100 to place the answer in a percentage format. The formula is

A Simple Price Relative

$$P = \frac{P_n}{P_o}(100) \qquad\qquad (12.1)$$

where

P_n = the price in a given or selected year

P_o = the price in a base or reference year

We are merely comparing a price in a given year to that of a selected base year. This result is actually not an index, but rather a price relative because we are comparing relative prices. The word index is generally reserved for the combination or aggregation of more than one variable or factor. The actual computational process is quite simple and is given in Table 12.1. Note in 2004 we are dividing the price of product A by itself; hence, a 100 reading is inevitable. The statement that 2004 = 100.0 signifies that 2004 is the base or reference period. The value for P in 2005 $[(P_{2003}/P_{2002}) \cdot 100]$ indicates that the price of product A has increased by 50% from the base period. Any year may be selected as the base; hence, the actual results can differ, yet the format is always the same.

Table 12.1   Price Relatives for Product A (a food staple): 2004 = 100

Year	Price of Product A	Price Relative = $(P_n/P_o) \cdot 100$
2003	$3	($3/$4)·100 = 75.00
2004	$4	($4/$4)· 100 = 100.0
2005	$6	($6/$4)·100 = 150.0
2006	$7	($7/$4)·100 = 175.0
2007	$10	($10/$4)·100 = 250.0
2008	$11	($11/$4)·100 = 275.0

Of course, a price index should encompass more than a single product. We will now add two products to our food staple, a transportation item (product B) and a housing item (product C). We sum the prices for the 3 products and compare the relative prices using 2004 as the base designate. The formula is

An Aggregate Unweighted Price Index

$$P = \frac{\Sigma P_n}{\Sigma P_o}(100) \qquad\qquad (12.2)$$

where

$$P_n = \text{the price in a given or selected year}$$

$$P_o = \text{the price in a base or reference year}$$

The computations for the index are made in Table 12.2. The prices for the three products in 2005 have increased by 20.4% since 2004.

Table 12.2   An Unweighted Price Index: 2004 = 100

Year	*Products* A	B	C	A+B+C	*Unweighted Price Index*
2003	$3	$1	$200	$204	(204/216) • 100 = 94.4%
2004	4	2	210	216	(216/216) • 100 = 100.0
2005	6	4	250	260	(260/216) • 100 = 120.4
2006	7	5	280	292	(292/216) • 100 = 135.2
2007	10	6	320	336	(336/216) • 100 = 155.6
2008	11	8	350	369	(369/216) • 100 = 170.8

Note that the results of Table 12.2 lead to meaningless conclusions, since our 3 products are measured in different scales or measurement units. Food prices could be measured in dollars per gallon, per pound, per loaf, etc. Transportation prices can be measured in terms of dollars per gallon or depreciation per mile. Housing prices could be in terms of dollars per unit or square feet. Hence, the aggregation of unlike quantities leads to meaningless results unless the data is normalized in some way. Such normalization process occurs if a weighted index is used. Hence, most Consumer Price Indexes are weighted indexes.

 Concept Check 12.C

An unweighted index will be meaningless if the units of measurement differ between the items being evaluated. True or false? If false, explain.

Exercises

12.7   The following data represent prices for 3 food items:

	A	B	C
1999	$1	$2	$3
2000	3	3	4
2001	7	4	6
2002	10	5	8

a.   Develop a price relative for product A using 1999 = 100.

b. Develop price relatives for products B and C using 1999 = 100.

c. Develop a price relative for product A using 2001 = 100.

d. Compare your answers to parts 12.7a and 12.7c.

12.8   a. For Exercise 12.7, develop an Aggregate Unweighted Price Index (1999 = 100).

     b. For Exercise 12.7, develop an Aggregate Unweighted Price Index (2001 = 100).

12.9   The following data represent prices for 4 food items:

	A	B	C	D
1999	$1	$2	$3	$4
2000	3	3	4	8
2001	7	4	6	10
2002	10	5	8	16

    a. Develop a price relative for product D using 1999 = 100.

    b. Develop a price relative for product D using 2001 = 100.

12.10   For Exercise 12.9, develop an Aggregate Unweighted Price Index (1999 = 100).

12.11   For the following data represent prices for 5 food items

	A	B	C	D	E
1999	$0.20	$0.50	$0.60	$1.00	$5.00
2000	0.30	0.75	0.80	1.80	7.00
2001	0.50	1.10	0.80	2.20	15.00
2002	0.80	1.50	0.70	2.50	25.00

    a. Develop a practice relative for all 5 products using 1999 = 100.

    b. Develop a price relative for all 5 products using 2001 = 100.

12.12   a. For Exercise 12.11, develop an Aggregate Unweighted Price Index (1999 = 100).

    b. Are all 5 products equally weighted?

    c. Do all 5 products have the same quantitative effect on the index?

    d. If the 5 products were to be weighted, can you determine at least 2 criteria that should be used to do the actual weighting?

12.5 Weighted Indices

To normalize the three products which are measured on different scales, we will develop a weighted index. The method used to normalize the products is to equate them in terms of the consumer expenditures on each. Expenditures involve both price and quantity. Hence, we would have to survey our households to find the average quantities of the 3 products consumed in a specified time period. Such a survey, if constructed on a national scale, would be extremely expensive. Hence, quantity estimates tend to remain fixed over short time periods.

Laspeyres Weights

The most common method of weighting was developed by Etienne Laspeyres two centuries ago. The Laspeyres method requires quantities only for a single selected (base: Q_o) year. Since advanced survey techniques (that are quite costly) are needed to obtain the quantities, this technique is particularly attractive. Once the average quantities consumed per period of time are found, they are multiplied by the current period prices to obtain an estimate of consumer expenditures.

The solution involves the yearly expenditures in purchasing a fixed basket of goods. The basket involved in 2003 (the designated base) costs $330 (Table 12.3). The same basket costs $390 in 2004 and

$530 in 2005. We then divide the price of the consumer basket in each year by the cost in the designated base year. The formula is

A Laspeyres Weighted Index

$$\text{Laspeyres Weight} = \frac{\Sigma P_n \bullet Q_o}{\Sigma P_o \bullet Q_o}(100) \qquad (12.3)$$

where

P_n = the price in a given or selected year

P_o = the price in a base or reference year

Q_o = the quantity in a base or reference year

Table 12.3 A Laspeyres Weighted Index: 2003 = 100

Year	Product A			Product B			Product C			$\dfrac{\Sigma P_n \bullet Q_o}{\Sigma P_o \bullet Q_o}$	Index
	P	Q	P•Q	P	Q	P•Q	P	Q	P•Q		
2003	$3	• 40	= $120	$1	• 10	= $10	$200	• 1	= $200	$330/330 =	100.0%
2004	4	• 40	= 160	2	• 10	= 20	210	• 1	= 210	390/330 =	118.2
2005	6	• 40	= 240	4	• 10	= 40	250	• 1	= 250	530/330 =	160.6
2006	7	• 40	= 280	5	• 10	= 50	280	• 1	= 280	610/330 =	184.9
2007	10	• 40	= 400	6	• 10	= 60	320	• 1	= 320	780/330 =	236.4
2008	11	• 40	= 440	8	• 10	= 80	350	• 1	= 350	870/330 =	263.6

A strict interpretation of the Laspeyres index requires that the base period used to find the quantities also be used as the base for the price index. If we surveyed in 2003 to estimate quantities, the base for the price index must be that of 2003. To determine the index value for 2005, we divide the price of our consumer basket in 2005 ($530) by the price of the basket in our 2003 base ($330). The solution is 160.6; hence, the consumer basket increased by 60.6% between 2003 and 2005.

The effect of the Laspeyres weight in this example is that the food item is weighted 36%, the transportation item 3%, and housing 61% (see Table 12.4). In the base period, these represent the average percentages consumed of our expenditures for each product or service in our example.

Table 12.4 The Weights Assigned to Each Product: 2003 = 100

	P Q P • Q	Item Weights
Food Item	$3 • 40 = $120	120/330 = 36.364%
Transportation Item	1 • 10 = 10	10/330 = 3.030%
Housing Item	200 • 1 = 200	200/330 = 60.606%
	Σ = 330	

A hybrid of the Laspeyres index (called a general fixed base index) is to allow the survey year used to obtain the quantities to differ from the base selected for the price index. For example, even though our quantities were established in 2003, we can still select 2004 as the designated base. The new weights using the 2004 prices are given in Table 12.5. To obtain the index we would divide the price of our consumer baskets for a given year by the price of the consumer basket in 2004. The value for the index in 2005 would be 135.90 [($530/$390)•100].

Table 12.5   The Weights Assigned for Each Product: 2004 =100

Food Item	$4 • 40 = $160	160/390 = 41.026%
Transportation Item	2 • 10 = 20	20/390 = 5.128%
Housing Item	210 • 1 = 210	210/390 = 53.846%
	Σ = 390	

In the selection of the base year, it is important not to select data that are an aberration from the norm. Unfortunately, what is a norm (or typical period) for one time period may be abnormal for another. For this reason, sometimes, in the development of a general fixed base index, rather than selecting a single time period as the base, we average more than one time period. This is done to lessen the effect of an extreme data point which may have inadvertently been selected as the base designate. Unfortunately, in many instances, all of the periods surrounding an unusual year may also be distorted. An example happened when the price of gold soared to $840 per ounce, way above its normal value. This would create a problem even with an average base period.

In computing such an index, the given data for any year are divided by the average value of the designated base. The current base of the U.S. CPI is a 36 month average (1982–84 = 100). One month, or possibly even twelve months, may be too short a time span to which to compare all other months.

Paasche Weights

An alternative way to weight our consumer basket is to use an index with a moving base. In this case, we conduct our survey in the most recent year, and use that year as our designated base. The technique generates what is termed a Paasche index and the formula is

A Paasche Weighted Index

$$\text{Paasche Index} = \frac{\Sigma P_n • Q_n}{\Sigma P_o • Q_n}(100) \qquad (12.4)$$

where

P_n = the price in a given or selected year

P_o = the price in a base or reference year

Q_n = the quantity in a given or selected year

Let us assume that the survey is completed in every year and the quantity figures are listed in Table 12.6. For the numerator, we would multiply current prices times current quantities consumed. For the denominator, we multiply current quantities times the price in the selected base year. If the base year for prices is 2003, the Paasche Index values are given in Table 12.6.

394

Table 12.6 A Paasche Weighted Index: 2003 = 100

Year	Product A P Q P•Q	Product B P Q P•Q	Product C P Q P•Q	$\Sigma P_n \cdot Q_n$
2003	$3•40 = $120	$1•10 = $10	$200•1 = $200	$330
2004	4•42 = 168	2•11 = 22	210•1 = 210	400
2005	6•43 = 258	4•11 = 44	250•1 = 250	552
2006	7•45 = 315	5•12 = 60	280•2 = 560	935
2007	10•47 = 470	6•11 = 66	320•2 = 640	1176
2008	11•50 = 550	8•11 = 88	350•2 = 700	1338

Year	Product A P Q P•Q	Product B P Q P•Q	Product C P Q P•Q	$\Sigma P_0 \cdot Q_n$
2003	$3•40 = $120	$1•10 = $10	$200•1 = $200	$330
2004	3•42 = 126	1•11 = 11	200•1 = 200	337
2005	3•43 = 129	1•11 = 11	200•1 = 200	340
2006	3•45 = 135	1•12 = 12	200•2 = 400	547
2007	3•47 = 141	1•11 = 11	200•2 = 400	552
2008	3•50 = 150	1•11 = 11	200•2 = 400	561

Year	$[(\Sigma P_n \cdot Q_n)/(\Sigma P_0 \cdot Q_n)](100)$	=	Paasche Index
2003	$330/$330	=	100.0%
2004	400/337	=	118.7
2005	552/340	=	162.4
2006	935/547	=	170.9
2007	1176/552	=	213.0
2008	1338/561	=	238.5

The obvious advantage to the Paasche weight is that very current information is being used. Sometimes spending habits change over time and this would be missed by the Laspeyres method. The overwhelming disadvantage is that a new study would have to be conducted yearly. In the case of a consumer price index, the costs of obtaining accurate quantities would be prohibitive. It is also difficult to interpret changes in the index as changes are not solely due to price changes, but can also be caused by changes in consumer behavior.

Another index that requires quantities in every year is the Value Index. Its formula is

---

A Value Index

$$\text{Value Index} = \frac{\Sigma P_n \bullet Q_n}{\Sigma P_o \bullet Q_o}(100) \tag{12.5}$$

where

$P_n =$ the price in a given or selected year

$P_o =$ the price in a base or reference year

$Q_n =$ the quantity in a given or selected year

$Q_o =$ the quantity in a base or reference year

The value index uses the numerator for the Paasch Index with a designated base. Using the data from Table 12.6, the solution to the value index is (see Table 12.7) as follows:

Table 12.7   A Value Index: 2003 = 100

Year	$[(\Sigma P_n \bullet Q_n)/(\Sigma P_o \bullet Q_o)](\mathbf{100})$	=	Value Index
2003	$330/$330	=	100.0%
2004	400/330	=	121.2
2005	552/330	=	167.3
2006	935/330	=	283.3
2007	1176/330	=	356.4
2008	1338/330	=	405.5

Fisher's Ideal Index

An index designed to overcome the shortcomings of both the Laspeyres and Paasche indices is Fisher's Ideal Index. The Laspeyres index can have an upward bias to it if increased prices result in reduced quantities purchased (quantities are constant in index). Hence, an overestimation of the price in the consumer basket will occur using earlier base quantities. The Paasche index will work in the opposite direction to a possible reduction in price as quantities increase. However, a solution might be to take the geometric mean (Formula 2.2, Section 2.5) of both the Laspeyres and Paasche indices.

Fisher's Ideal Index

$$\text{Fishers Ideal Index} = \sqrt{(\text{Laspeyres Index})(\text{Paasche Index})} \tag{12.6}$$

The computational process is shown in Table 12.8. The Ideal Index is the square root of the product of the Laspeyres and Paasche indices. Since the geometric mean is a measure of central tendency, the resultant index must have a value between the Laspeyres and Paasche index. The geometric mean was selected because it deals best with percentage versus absolute changes. Percentage change is the hallmark of index numbers in general. Unfortunately, Fisher's Ideal Index still requires quantities in each year, making it unaffordable for a consumer price index.

Table 12.8 Fisher's Ideal Index: 2003 = 100

Year	Laspeyres Index	Paasche Index	Fisher's Ideal Index
2003	100.0%	100.0%	100.0% ($\sqrt{100.0 \bullet 100.0}$)
2004	118.2	118.7	118.4 ($\sqrt{118.2 \bullet 118.7}$)
2005	160.6	162.4	161.5 ($\sqrt{160.6 \bullet 162.4}$)
2006	184.9	170.9	177.8 ($\sqrt{184.9 \bullet 190.9}$)
2007	236.4	212.0	224.4 ($\sqrt{236.4 \bullet 213.0}$)
2008	263.6	238.5	250.7 ($\sqrt{263.6 \bullet 238.5}$)

 Concept Check 12.D

If we had price data for the last 5 years, and quantity data for only the most recent year, we would be able to compute a Paasche Index. True or false? If false, explain.

Exercises

12.13   The following data represents prices and quantities consumed for 3 food items. The quantities listed represent 3 different scales (pounds, quarts, and dozens).

		A		B		C	
	P	Q	P	Q	P	Q
1999	$1	12	$2	1	$3	4
2000	3	11	3	2	4	7
2001	7	6	4	3	6	10
2002	10	5	5	4	8	12

   a.   Compute a Laspeyres weighted index: 1999 = 100.
   b.   Compare your answers with Exercise 12.8a, where we developed an Aggregate Unweighted Price Index (1999 = 100).
   c.   Which do you believe to be the superior index? Explain.

12.14   a.   For the data in Exercise 12.13, compute a Paasche weighted index (1999 = 100).
   b.   How do the Paasche and Laspeyres weighted indices weight the 3 products differently?

12.15   a.   For the data in Exercise 12.13, compute a Value Index (1999 = 100).
   b.   How does the Value index differ from that of the Paasche base?

12.16   a.   Compute a general fixed base index using quantities obtained in 2001 (1999 = 100).
   b.   We have computed a Laspeyres index (Exercise 12.13a) and a Paasche index (Exercise 12.14a); now compute Fisher's Ideal Index for the same years.

12.17   The following information represents prices and quantities consumed for 4 food items.

		A		B		C		D	
	P	Q	P	Q	P	Q	P	Q
1999	$1	17	$2	10	$3	1	$4	7
2000	3	24	3	9	4	2	8	5
2001	7	34	4	7	6	5	10	4
2002	10	40	5	5	8	12	16	4

   a.   Compute a Laspeyres weighted index: 1999 = 100.
   b.   Compare your answers to a with Exercise 12.10, where we developed an Aggregate Unweighted Price Index (1999 = 100).
   c.   Which do you believe to be the superior index? Explain.

12.18   a.   For the data in Exercise 12.17, compute a Paasche Weighted Index (1999 = 100).
        b.   How do the Paasche and Laspeyres Weighted Indices weight the 3 products differently?

12.19   a.   For the data in Exercise 12.17, compute a Value Index (1999 = 100).
        b.   How does the Value Index differ from that of the Paasche base?

12.20   a.   Compute a general fixed base index using quantities obtained in 2000 (1999 = 100).
        b.   We have computed a Laspeyres Index (Exercise 12.17a) and a Paasche Index (Exercise 12.18a); now compute Fisher's Ideal Index for the same years.

12.21   The following represents prices and quantities consumed for 5 food items:

	A		B		C		D		E	
	P	Q	P	Q	P	Q	P	Q	P	Q
1999	$0.20	22	$0.50	10	$0.60	1	$1.00	7	$5.00	15
2000	0.30	28	0.75	14	0.80	4	1.80	6	7.00	18
2001	0.50	44	1.10	16	0.80	6	2.20	4	15.00	20
2002	0.80	54	1.50	20	0.70	8	2.50	3	25.00	25

Compute a Laspeyres Weighted Index: 1999 = 100.

12.22   For the data in Exercise 12.21, compute a Paasche Weighted Index (1999 = 100).

12.23   a.   For the data in Exercise 12.21, compute a Value Index (1999 = 100).
        b.   How does the Value Index differ from that of the Paasche base?

12.24   a.   Compute a general fixed base index using quantities obtained in 2001 (1999 = 100).
        b.   We have computed Laspeyres Index (Exercise 12.21a) and a Paasche Index (Exercise 12.22a); now compute Fisher's Ideal Index for the same years.

12.6   Using the Consumer Price Index

In economic and business analyses, we always want to place dollar values in terms of constant purchasing power. Money has no intrinsic value. For example, in Unites States currency, there is little demand for dirty, folded, green and white pictures of George Washington or Abraham Lincoln. However, there are some exceptions. We can find businesses that display the first dollar they received. In this case, the currency does have intrinsic value. However, most of the time, the only value of one and five dollar bills is in the goods and services we can purchase with them. This value is termed the real value or purchasing power of money. The formula used to ascertain the real value of money is

Determining the Real Value or Purchasing Power of Money

$$\text{Real Value} = \frac{\text{Money Value}}{\dfrac{\text{CPI}}{100}} \qquad (12.7)$$

where

$$\text{CPI} = \text{the consumer price index}$$

Let's assume that the Laspeyres weighted index computed earlier (2003 = 100) is our consumer price index, but with a 2004 base. We will record our yearly money income from 2003 to 2008 (see Table 12.9). Our income increases from $28,900 in 2004 to $47,000 in 2008. This represents an increase in money income of 62.63% [($47,000 − $28,900)/$28,900]. However, if inflation has risen by a rate greater than 62.63%, our real purchasing power will have dropped.

398

Table 12.9　Converting Money Income to Real Income

Year	Money Income	CPI/100*	CPI:2001 = 100	Real Income
2003	$28,900	0.8462	0.8462/0.8462 = 1.0000	$28,900.00
2004	30,200	1.0000	1.0000/0.8462 = 1.1818	25,555.24
2005	34,000	1.3590	1.3590/0.8462 = 1.6060	21,170.57
2006	39,000	1.5641	1.5641//0.8462 = 1.8484	21,099.55
2007	43,000	2.0000	2.0000/0.8462 = 2.3635	18,193.20
2008	47,000	2.2308	2.2308/0.8462 = 2.6363	17,828.31

*2004 = 100

Shifting the Base of an Index

Note that we have taken the CPI out of its percentage format by dividing by 100. If we began employment in 2003, it may be convenient to shift the base of the CPI to that year. If 2003 were the base, it must have a numeric reading of 1.00. The only way to accomplish this is to divide the CPI in 2003 (2004 = 100) by itself. This yields a CPI based in 2003 (See Table 12.9). To change the base to any year, simply divide the index in every year by the year you want to be the designated base.

There are many reasons to shift the base of an index. If we are comparing indices from different countries, they will probably have different bases. Hence, it would be advantageous to shift the base of one country's index to make comparisons simpler.

Computing Real Incomes

Once the CPI base has been converted to 2003, we merely implement formula 12.5. For example, the real income for 2004 is $25,555.24 ($30,200/1.1818). The real income for 2008 is $17,828.31 ($47,000/2.6363). Even though money income increased by 62.63%, the inflation rate increased by 163.63%, reducing real income or purchasing power by 38.31% [($28,900–$17,828.31)/$28,900]. This reduction in real income could be magnified by the fact that our duties and responsibilities with our employer may have increased substantially over the six year period.

An Escalator Clause

Everyone knows that an escalator clause is designed to keep wages in pace with inflation. Yet few can make the necessary computations to determine the actual payments needed. What an escalator clause states is that the real purchasing power of money must remain constant, and that money wages must be adjusted to ensure this. Formula 12.7 can be modified to achieve Formula 12.8.

Adjusting Money Wages to Maintain a Constant Purchasing Power

$$\text{Money Wages} = \text{Real Wage} \bullet \text{CPI} \qquad (12.8)$$

where

$$\text{CPI} = \text{the consumer price index}$$

Since we started our employment in 2003 with a yearly income of $28,900, an escalator clause requires that our real income be maintained at this value. Utilizing Formula 12.8, we would have to receive $76,189.07 in 2008 to make us equally well off as when we made $28,900 in 2003 (Table 12.10).

Table 12.10 Converting a Constant Real Income into Money Income

Year	Real Income	CPI:2001 = 100	Money Income
2003	$28,900	1.0000	$28,900.00 = (28,900•1.0000)
2004	28,900	1.1818	34,154.02 = (28,900•1.1818)
2005	28,900	1.6060	46,413.40 = (28,900•1.6060)
2006	28,900	1.8484	53,418.76 = (28,900•1.8484)
2007	28,900	2.3635	68,305.15 = (28,900•2.3635)
2008	28,900	2.6363	76,189.07 = (28,900•2.6363)

 Concept Check 12.E

An escalator clause ensures that real wages will remain constant over a period of time. True or false? If false, explain.

Exercises

12.25 The consumer price index for a particular nation is

Year	CPI
1998	100.0
1999	112.6
2000	126.8
2001	135.9
2002	147.8

What has happened to the real purchasing power of the country's currency from 1998 to 2002?

12.26 The consumer price index for a particular nation is (1990 = 100)

Year	CPI
1998	169.2
1999	189.8
2000	216.8
2001	256.9
2002	310.1

a. Shift the base of the index so that 1998 = 100.
b. Trace the purchasing power of this currency from 1998 to 2002.

12.27 The consumer price index for a particular nation and the median money income for all adults is

Year	CPI	Money Wage
1998	100.0	$24,987
1999	126.6	28,910
2000	148.8	31,899
2001	159.9	32,410
2002	187.1	32,800

a. What has happened to the real purchasing power from 1998 to 2002?
b. Determine the money wage necessary to keep this individual exactly at pace with inflation.

12.28 The consumer price index for a particular nation and the median money income for all adults is

Year	CPI	Money Wage
1998	100.0	$24,987
1999	156.6	28,910
2000	188.8	31,899
2001	219.3	32,410
2002	287.1	32,800

    a.   What has happened to the real purchasing power from 1998 to 2002?

    b.   Determine the money wage necessary to keep this individual exactly at pace with inflation.

12.29 In your own words state what a consumer price index is and what it measures.

12.30 The consumer price index for two nations is (Country A: 1984 = 100 and Country B: 1996 = 100)

Year	Country A	Country B
1998	169.2	67.9
1999	189.8	84.3
2000	216.8	100.0
2001	256.9	129.6
2002	310.1	146.9

    a.   Shift country A's CPI to 1998.

    b.   Which of the two countries has a higher inflation rate?

12.31 Some political leaders fear that escalator clauses add to the inflation problem. Explain.

12.32 In your own words explain the escalator clause that appears in many labor contracts.

12.7 Summary

Our lives are very much affected by the information that indices provide. We have stressed the consumer price index and how it allows us to ascertain if raises in salary represent real increases in wages, or just monetary increases. Other examples of indices that are commonly encountered are employee evaluations and the wind chill factor. Many companies develop their own indices to measure an aspect of performance of the company over time. Indices can be extremely helpful in monitoring such performance.

Mini-case 12.1: Quality of Life Index

We are interested in developing an index to measure our quality of life (QOL Index). Sometimes the number of consumer durables we possess (note, not necessarily own) is used as the measure of our success. Yet it is possible to be quite dissatisfied having all the amenities of life. The question to be answered is "What variables should be considered in developing a QOL index?"

Attempts at developing a QOL index have been made by the U.S. Census Bureau, by former President Jimmy Carter (a misery index), by Public Opinion's Gross National Spirit Index, and by *USA Today's* Life Quality Index. The latter index uses five sub-indices. These 5 consider

- job satisfaction
- health
- marriage and the family
- environment and personal safety
- social life

Each of these 5 variables was further stratified into 2 to 5 strata yielding 17 factors indicated by 5 variables that make up a single index (Life Quality Index).

    a. Comment on the selection of the five variables.

    b. Should additional variables be considered?

    c. Most of the results come from asking a sample of approximately 1,500 to rank certain criteria. Should any nationally available statistics, like infant mortality rates and education dropout rates, be considered?

    d. If a QOL index can be tabulated and published every year, would the results be meaningful? Explain.

Mini-case 12.2: Qualifications for University Acceptance

Many universities use an index to ascertain your qualifications to enter their programs. This index usually weights two variables approximately equally. These variables are your grade point average and score on a national standardized test.

    a. Can you state some problems that might be encountered in using these two variables?

    b. Can you state other factors that you deem important that should be considered? Be sure to develop a way of measuring these variables.

Mini-case 12.3: The U.S. Consumer Price Index

The CPI, which is published by the Bureau of Labor Statistics (BLS), represents an average market basket of 100,000 expenditures from seven strata. Surveys are conducted on over 8,300 households and 21,000 retail establishments which are used in the monthly reports. Very costly surveys are also used to obtain the average quantities consumed by households across the country. This survey is so costly that considerable time passes before a new survey is taken. The weights currently used were obtained in 1982–83. Many electronic items that were not included in the original weights are included in the updated figures (like personal computers). Note the changes that occurred from the decade before

	1972–73 Weights	1982–83 Weights
Housing	37.8%	42.6%
Transportation	21.6	18.7
Food & beverages	20.1	17.8
Apparel & upkeep	5.2	6.5
Medical care	6.1	4.8
Entertainment	4.2	4.4
Other goods & services	5.1	5.1

Over the decade between the change of weights, a greater percentage of the population was residing in its own household. In addition, these households had more amenities than previously (central air conditioning, more bathrooms, etc.). Since the median age is becoming older, it is difficult to understand the drop in medical care.

Based on your intuition, do you believe any of these weights would have changed since 1982–83?

Please note that, even though the weights are derived from the 1982–83 period, the current price base for the CPI is 1982–1984. Hence, the CPI, for the first time in recent history, is essentially a Laspeyres based index.

Mini-case 12.4: The German Hyperinflation 1914 to 1923

Year	Price Level
1914	100.0
1915	105.3
1916	152.5
1917	178.8
1918	216.8
1919	416.2
1920	1,488.3
1921	2,296.0
1922	147,480.0
1923	126,160,000,000,000.0

a. Determine the value of the Deutsche mark from 1914 to 1923.
b. Is it now easier to understand how a radical political party can gain control over a nation?

 Mini-case 12.5: The Intelligence Quotient (IQ)

The Webster's New Universal Unabridged Dictionary defines intelligence as (a) the ability to learn or understand from experience; to acquire and retain knowledge; mental ability; (b) the ability to respond quickly and successfully to a new situation; use of the faculty of reason in solving problems, directing conduct, etc. effectively; (c) in psychology, measured success in using these abilities to perform certain tasks. From (c) we develop an IQ index that purports to measure intelligence.

a. How many variables do you think might be involved with the concept of intelligence?
b. From the above definition of intelligence, do you think it is possible to quantify the variables, accurately measure them, and develop an index of intelligence?

Review of Important Terms and Concepts

A special purpose index: An index developed to fulfill a special purpose or need.

Price relatives: A comparison of a price in a given or selected year to that of a price in a base or reference year.

An aggregate unweighted price index: A comparison of the summation of the prices in a given or selected year to that of the summation of the prices in a base or reference year.

A Laspeyres weighted index: A weighted process utilizing quantities and consumer expenditures in an early year of a data set.

A Paasche weighted index: A weighting process utilizing quantities and consumer expenditures in the latest year of a data set. The technique requires new weights after the expiration of each time period.

A Value index: A weighting process utilizing a ratio of consumer expenditures in a given period to consumer expenditures in a base period. Like the Paasche method, new weights are needed at the expiration of each time period.

Fisher's Ideal Index: The geometric mean of the Laspeyres and Paasche Indices. It attempts to reduce a possible upwards bias of the Laspeyres index with the possible downwards bias of the Paasche index.

The real value or purchasing power of money: Money values are converted into a constant purchasing power by dividing by the consumer price index.

Escalator clause: A component of contracts that provides an adjustment to money income to account for inflation.

Review of Important Formulas

A Simple Price Relative

$$P = \frac{P_n}{P_o}(100) \tag{12.1}$$

where

P_n = the price in a given or selected year

P_o = the price in a base or reference year

An Aggregate Unweighted Price Index

$$P = \frac{\Sigma P_n}{\Sigma P_o}(100) \tag{12.2}$$

where

P_n = the price in a given or selected year

P_o = the price in a base or reference year

A Laspeyres Weighted Index

$$\text{Laspeyres Weight} = \frac{\Sigma P_n \bullet Q_o}{\Sigma P_o \bullet Q_o}(100) \tag{12.3}$$

where

P_n = the price in a given or selected year

P_o = the price in a base or reference year

Q_o = the quantity in a base or reference year

A Paasche Weighted Index

$$\text{Paasche Index} = \frac{\Sigma P_n \bullet Q_n}{\Sigma P_o \bullet Q_n}(100) \qquad (12.4)$$

where

P_n = the price in a given or selected year

P_o = the price in a base or reference year

Q_n = the quantity in a given or selected year

A Value Index

$$\text{Value Index} = \frac{\Sigma P_n \bullet Q_n}{\Sigma P_o \bullet Q_o}(100) \qquad (12.5)$$

where

P_n = the price in a given or selected year

P_o = the price in a base or reference year

Q_n = the quantity in a given or selected year

Q_o = the quantity in a base or reference year

Fisher's Ideal Index

$$\text{Fishers Ideal Index} = \sqrt{(\text{Laspeyres Index})(\text{Paasche Index})} \qquad (12.6)$$

Determining the Real Value or Purchasing Power of Money

$$\text{Real Value} = \frac{\text{Money Value}}{\dfrac{\text{CPI}}{100}} \qquad (12.7)$$

where

CPI = the consumer price index

Adjusting Money Wages to Maintain a Constant Purchasing Power

$$\text{Money Wages} = \text{Real Wage} \bullet \text{CPI} \qquad (12.8)$$

where

CPI = the consumer price index

12.33 If you were to develop an index of your overall quality of life, list 3 variables or factors that you would want considered.

12.34 The following data represent prices and average quantities consumed for 3 consumer items.

	A		B		C	
	P	Q	P	Q	P	Q
1999	$2	12	$2	2	$2	4
2000	4	14	3	6	4	7
2001	8	9	4	7	9	10
2002	14	3	5	9	14	9

a. Compute the price relatives for product A (1999 = 100).
b. Compute an unweighted aggregate index for all products (1999 = 100).
c. Compute a Laspeyres Weighted Index (1999= 100).
d. Compute a Paasche Weighted Index (1999 = 100).
e. Compute a Value Index (1999 = 100).
f. Compute a Fisher's Ideal Index.
g. Compute a general fixed based index using 2000 quantities (1999 = 100).

12.35 Using the answer obtained in exercise 12.34c as the Consumer Price Index, determine the value of the country's currency from 1999 to 2002.

12.36 The following data represent prices and quantities consumed for 4 food items.

	A		B		C		D	
	P	Q	P	Q	P	Q	P	Q
1999	$2	20	$2	10	$3	4	$4	20
2000	5	24	3	15	7	5	8	15
2001	9	44	4	19	12	5	10	14
2002	20	36	5	15	15	4	16	10

a. Compute the price relatives for product A (1999 = 100).
b. Compute an unweighted aggregate index for all products (1999 = 100).
c. Compute a Laspeyres Weighted Index (1999 = 100).
d. Compute a Paasche Weighted Index (1999 = 100).
e. Compute a Value Index (1999 = 100).
f. Compute a Fisher's Ideal Index.
g. Compute a general fixed based index using 2000 quantities (1999 = 100).
Compare the weights used on the different indices.

12.37 Using the answer obtained in exercise 12.36d as the Consumer Price Index, determine the value of the country's currency from 1999 to 2002.

12.38 The consumer price index for a particular nation and the median money income for all adults is

Year	CPI	Money Wage
1998	100.0	$15,987
1999	160.6	17,972
2000	198.2	21,001
2001	235.9	22,410
2002	302.1	25,876

a. What has happened to the real purchasing power from 1998 to 2002?
b. Determine the money wage necessary to keep this individual exactly at pace with inflation.

12.39   The consumer price index for three nations is

CONSUMER PRICE INDEX

Year	Country A	Country B	Country C
1998	158.2	100.0	796.9
1999	181.8	126.9	803.2
2000	206.3	147.6	807.8
2001	237.4	155.3	820.6
2002	249.4	176.2	829.5

a.   Shift country A's and country C's CPI to a 1998 base.
b.   Determine the value of each country's currency from 1998 to 2002.
c.   Which of the three countries has experienced the greatest loss in purchasing power?

12.40   For the data in exercise 12.39 (assuming in 1998 the median income for all three nations was 10,000, whatever the denomination of currency), determine the money value of wages needed to keep each at pace with inflation.

Chi-square Analysis

Where we have been

We have dealt with hypothesis testing in great depth to this point. However, we have not dealt with hypothesis testing as it relates to observed frequencies.

Where we are going

We return to hypothesis testing and develop a technique of testing the independence of data. The analysis involves two variables which are stratified by rows and columns, called contingency tables. The hypothesis test compares observed and expected frequencies. The expected frequencies are based on the null hypothesis that the data contained within the rows and columns are independent of each other. If the null hypothesis is rejected, an apparent dependence between the rows and columns exists. We then proceed to use the chi-square technique to ascertain if a given data set can be explained by a particular distribution.

13.1   Introduction

In many business applications of hypothesis testing we want to know if differences exist between different groups of data. Do teenagers' purchasing habits differ from those of pre-teens or older adults? Do more males watch sporting events on TV than females? Do college students taking this course have shorter finger nails and tend to be more neurotic than those not taking it? The answers to questions of this type can be used by marketing professionals to find the correct marketing niche for their products.

In this chapter we utilize a hypothesis testing technique known as chi-square. The technique allows two variables, segregated into groups or strata, to be tabulated to ascertain if a relationship exists between them. For example, do consumers in different geographic regions differ in terms of their preferences for soft drink beverages? The answer to such a question allows marketing professionals to segment the market for maximum profitability. The chi-square technique allows us to evaluate some of these questions.

Because the chi-square methodology does not require very stringent assumptions, it is called a non-parametric technique. In Chapter 14 we will cover other such techniques.

The chi-square analysis compares two variables which have been stratified in the form of a cross tabulation. The main or null hypothesis states that the two variables, which are spread in rows and columns, are independent of each other. The basis of the hypothesis test is to establish frequencies based on the null hypothesis and compare these frequencies with those observed from sampling. As with the use of many statistical techniques, chi-square tests are best explained and developed through the use of an example.

Suppose that we own a soft drink company and must produce one of two soft drink beverages. The first beverage (#1) tastes sweet and the other tastes dry (#2). To determine which one to produce and market, we hire a market research firm to do a taste test in the U.S. and in Europe. The taste test requires consumers to drink small volumes of the two beverages, and then state their preference. The consumers will not know which container contains beverage #1 or #2. The test is being conducted in the Northeast, Midwest, South, West, and in a randomly selected city in Europe. If a preference exists for one of the beverages, we will produce that product. If no preference exists, we will choose the sweet beverage (#1), because it is less expensive to produce. If preferences vary for the different areas, we may produce the two drinks on a regional basis.

The null hypothesis is that the proportion that favor either beverage in the five geographical regions is the same:

H_0: $P_A = P_B = P_C = P_D = P_E$

The alternative hypothesis is that the proportion that favors either beverage is different in at least one region, or that they are not equal.

H_A: At least one region is different.

Most applications involve a qualifying question to make the results more meaningful. In our example, we ask each individual to sample two beverages and select his or her favorite. To select a favorite means that the respondents are able to differentiate between the two beverages; otherwise, they could not possibly have a preference. If respondents could not differentiate between the beverages, their choice would not be consistently selected. The second time the test was administered, the respondent might select the other beverage. Since many of the individuals taking the test might not be able to differentiate between the two beverages, we must test for this possibility. Three beverage containers are placed in front of each respondent. Two of the containers contain the same beverage and the third contains the other beverage (either two contain beverage #1 and one contains #2, or two contain #2 and one contains #1). Each respondent is asked to taste the beverage in all three containers, and then identify which two are the same. If that question is answered correctly (a respondent can correctly differentiate between the two drinks), then the individual is asked for his or her preference. Any individual who can't differentiate between the two drinks, would be disqualified from the survey.

Thus, the former advertising campaign called the "Pepsi Challenge" is only valid if the individuals who preferred Pepsi to Coke could actually differentiate between the two. You can test people's ability to differentiate between beverages yourself by selecting several different brands of coffee or soft drinks for testing. The brands should vary from expensive to inexpensive. For each individual, place one brand of coffee in two cups and another brand of coffee in a third cup. If they can identify the two cups that contain the same coffee, ask for their preference. Using a series of rounds, the optimum coffee can be determined for each person participating in the test.

Let us return to the soft drink company example. Assume the survey is complete. Table 13.1 shows that approximately an equal number of respondents preferred the two beverages. Note, however, that the results between the regions appear to differ. We must test to determine if the differences among the regions are caused by sampling variation (chance occurrence) or distinct regional preferences.

Table 13.1 Survey Response for the Two Beverages in Five Regions
*Data File on MINITAB CD

| | REGIONS | | | | | |
	Northeast	Midwest	South	West	Europe	Total
Beverage #1	67	58	61	79	45	310
Beverage #2	47	51	57	69	76	300
Total	114	109	118	148	121	610

In Table 13.1, the columns and rows represent different bases for classification, or different variables. Such tables are called contingency tables. In our problem, there are two rows (horizontal readings), which classify the data as either a sweet beverage (#1) or a dry beverage (#2). The columns (vertical readings) classify the data by the different geographical regions. Table 13.1 is called a 2×5 contingency table because it has two rows and five columns. In standard matrix notation, rows are always listed before columns. Note that row and column totals are not included. Hence, Table 13.1 is **not** a 3×6 contingency table.

Expected frequencies (f_e)

The expected frequencies (f_e) are what we would expect if there were no regional preference for the two beverages. For example, approximately 51% (310/610) of the grand total of respondents favored the sweet beverage (#1) and 49% (300/610) favored the dry beverage (#2). If the null hypothesis is correct (there is no regional preference for the two beverages), we should find the same 51%/49% split for each geographic region.

We must now compute the frequencies that would be expected if H_0 were correct. The computational process is simple, the formula used to develop the expected frequencies is

Cell Expected Frequency f_e

$$f_e = \frac{(\text{row total})(\text{column total})}{n}$$

(13.1)

Table 13.2 reveals the computational process used to compute the f_e values. For beverage #1 (the sweet beverage), in the Northeast, we multiply the row and column totals (310•114) and divide by the overall sample size (310•114/610 = 57.9394). The remaining computations for f_e are listed for your inspection.

Table 13.2 Computation of Expected Frequencies (f_e) for the Beverage Problem

(r,c)	Row	Column	f_e
1,1	Beverage #1:	Northeast	310 • 114/610 = 57.9344
1,2	Beverage #1:	Midwest	310 • 109/610 = 55.3934
1,3	Beverage #1:	South	310 • 118/610 = 59.9672
1,4	Beverage #1:	West	310 • 148/610 = 75.2131
1,5	Beverage #1:	Europe	310 • 121/610 = 61.4918
2,1	Beverage #2:	Northeast	300 • 114/610 = 56.0655
2,2	Beverage #2:	Midwest	300 • 109/610 = 53.6066
2,3	Beverage #2:	South	300 • 118/610 = 58.0328
2,4	Beverage #2:	West	300 • 148/610 = 72.7869
2,5	Beverage #2:	Europe	300 • 121/610 = 59.5082

Our test statistic is based on the premise that if H_0 is correct, the differences between f_o and f_e will be small. Large difference between f_o and f_e will lead us to reject H_0. The actual test statistic concerning the comparison between f_o and f_e is called the chi-square statistic. The formula

---

The Chi-Square Test Statistic

$$\chi^2_{\text{test}} = \sum \frac{(f_o - f_e)^2}{f_e}$$

(13.2)

where

$$f_o = \text{the observed frequency}$$
$$f_e = \text{the expected frequency}$$

Since the chi-square value uses squared differences, negative values are impossible. The smaller the numerical value of chi-square (the closer it comes to 0), the smaller the difference between the observed and the expected values. The larger is the value of chi-square, the greater is the difference between f_o and f_e. If we compute the numerical value for chi-square for the beverage problem, we obtain 12.5512, which is tabulated in Table 13.3. With two rows and five columns, there are ten (2×5) differences to be squared, where each squared difference is divided by f_e, and then summed. We divide by f_e (and not by f_o) because the chi-square distribution is based on f_e. This choice is fortunate, because in some real-world situations f_o can be an empty cell or equal 0 and division by 0 is undefined.

Table 13.3 Computation of χ^2 (Chi-square) Test Statistic for the Beverage Problem Using f_o and f_e

(r, C)	f_o	f_e	$f_o - f_e$	$(f_o - f_e)^2$	$(f_o - f_e)^2 / f_e$
(1,1)	67	57.9344	+9.0656	82.185103	1.4185850
(1,2)	58	55.3934	+2.6066	6.794364	0.1226566
(1,3)	61	59.9672	+1.0328	1.066676	0.0177877
(1,4)	79	75.2131	+3.7869	14.340612	0.1906664
(1,5)	45	61.4918	−16.4918	271.979470	4.4230207
(2,1)	47	56.0655	−9.0656	82.185103	1.4658766
(2,2)	51	53.6066	−2.6066	6.794364	0.1267449
(2,3)	57	58.0328	−1.0328	1.066676	0.0183806
(2,4)	69	72.7869	−3.7869	13.340612	0.1970219
(2,5)	76	59.5082	+16.4918	271.979470	4.5704537
				$\chi^2_{\text{test}} =$	12.551194

The Chi-Square Distribution

The chi-square distribution is the sampling distribution which exists if a number of samples were taken from a normally distributed population. Each value of the random variable is converted to its z equivalent, and then squared and summed. If this process were repeated for each sample size, we would obtain the chi-square distribution. There is a different chi-square distribution for each degree of freedom, which is also true for the t distribution. Figure 13.1 shows four chi-square distributions with different degrees of freedom. The distribution becomes more symmetrical or bell shaped as the degrees of freedom increase. For large degrees of freedom, we can approximate the chi-square distribution with the normal distribution. The chi-square table has a maximum of 30 degrees of freedom. Above this value, the normal distribution would be used to approximate the chi-square distribution.

Figure 13.1 Chi-Square Distributions with Different Degrees of Freedom

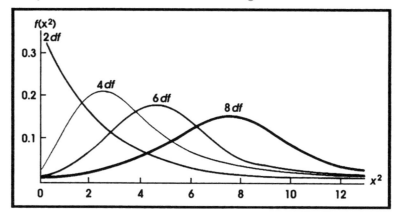

Since the chi-square distribution approximates a normal distribution as the degrees of freedom increase, the total area under the curve is 1.0. The number of possible chi-square distributions is large. Thus, as a convenience, we limit the number of chi-square distributions in Appendix A, Table 6 to the more commonly used levels of significance (a). Hence, the subscripts for various chi-square table readings list the desired significance level (confidence level $= 1.0 - \alpha$) and sometimes the degrees of freedom inside parentheses. For example, it's common to see the chi-square table reading for 5% level of significance (95% confidence level) using four degrees of freedom written as $\chi^2_{.05(4)}$. The corresponding chi-square table reading is 9.488, or $\chi^2_{.05(4)} = 9.488$. Note that the chi-square statistic involves a one tailed test, which is appropriate for our analysis since the tabulated chi-square value can't be negative.

Determining the Degrees of Freedom

The basic formula used to determine the degrees of freedom for a test of independence is

Formula for the Degrees of Freedom in a χ^2 Contingency Table

$$df = (r - 1)(c - 1) \tag{13.3}$$

where

$r =$ the number of rows

$c =$ the number of columns

In our soft drink example, two rows represent the sweet and dry soft drinks, and five columns represent the five geographic regions. Hence, the number of degrees of freedom is

$$df = (2 - 1)(5 - 1) = (1)(4) = 4$$

The determination of the degrees of freedom is based on the following logic. In the soft drink problem, the total sample size is known to be 610, and the row and column totals are known. Hence, when row one is analyzed (the sweet beverage), its number of respondents (or frequency) is a random variable. Once this number is known, the frequency in row two (the dry beverage) is fixed. When analyzing the columns (geographical regions), the first four columns may vary. Once their numbers are known, the frequency in column five is fixed (because the total is known). Remember that the sums off f_o and f_e must be equal. The number of degrees of freedom for several examples are given in Table 13.4.

413

Table 13.4 Determining Degrees of Freedom in Five Examples

Example	# of rows (r)	# of columns (c)	(r − 1)	(c − 1)	df
A	2	8	1	7	7
B	8	2	7	1	7
C	4	6	3	5	15
D	3	3	2	2	4
E	10	3	9	2	18

Testing the Null Hypothesis with the Chi-square Statistic

We are finally ready to test the null hypothesis that there are no regional preferences of sweet/dry soft drinks. The alternate hypothesis is that there is at least one regional preference. The degrees of freedom are 4 because

$$df = (r − 1)(c − 1); \; (1 \bullet 4) = 4$$

Using a 95% confidence level, the appropriate critical value is $\chi^2_{.05(4)} = 9.488$. Thus, with 4 degrees of freedom (df), the area to the right of the chi-square value of 9.488 contains 5% of the area under the curve. The ISER H_0 region goes from the left tail to the critical value of 9.488, and the rejection area (shaded on figure 13.2) extends to the right of the critical value.

The decision rule is to reject the null hypothesis whenever $\chi^2_{\text{test}} > \chi^2_{\alpha(df)}$. Since our chi-square computed value of 12.5512 (Table 13.3) exceeds the 9.488 table reading, we must reject the null hypothesis of no regional differences. The regional differences in the sample are greater than what could reasonably have been caused by chance variation. Table 13.1 shows that the randomly selected European city does appear to prefer the dry beverage taste. We should not be alarmed by this result; Europeans typically consume much less sugar in their foods and beverages than Americans. Thus, our firm might consider producing the dry beverage overseas and the sweet beverage in the United States.

Figure 13.2 ISER and Rejection Regions of the Chi-Square

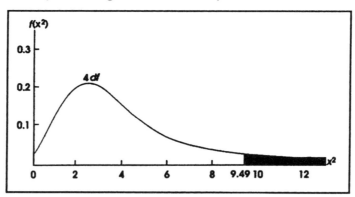

Two Requirements for Using Chi-Square Analysis

We must keep in mind two points when we use the chi-square test. First, the chi-square analysis must be based on frequencies and not proportions or percentages. We can't compute a squared difference between the observed and expected proportions, and divide by the expected proportion, and then be able to reject the null hypothesis because the computed chi-square reading would be too small.

The second condition or requirement is that each row/column component (sometimes referred to as a cell) for f_e must have some minimum required frequency. Most authors use 5 as the minimum value for any f_e value. If f_e is less than 5 for any cell, then the data must be regrouped or certain groups added/deleted to ensure a minimum size of 5. Such a regrouping will reduce the number of degrees of freedom for the problem, causing a larger $\chi^2_{\alpha(df)}$ value, which makes it a little more difficult to reject the null hypothesis.

To Use the Chi-square Test of Independence:

1. Convert the proportions (percents) into frequencies.
2. Be sure that each cell has an expected frequency greater than or equal to 5 ($f_e \geq 5$).

Computer Application

The MINITAB can be used to perform tests of independence for 2 qualitative variables. Enter the data as it appears in Table 13.1 with 5 columns (labeled NE, MW, S, W, E) and 2 rows.

The output provides the contingency table (TABLE OF FREQUENCIES), the chi-square test statistic (VALUE), and the degrees of freedom (DF). The more the expected frequencies, which are generated based on the assumption of independence, differ from the observed frequencies, the larger is the chi-square statistic. Thus, rejection of the null hypothesis of independence depends on the test statistic being sufficiently large (rejection region in the upper tail), MINITAB provides us with the area under the relevant chi-square distribution (in our example, that with 4 degrees of freedom) to the right of the test statistic. MINITAB (using the calculator function) will yield us the appropriate p-value table 0.0137. In this case, MINITAB tells us that the area to the right of 12.551 (VALUE) is .0137 (PROB). Thus, if our level of significance is 5 percent, we would reject the null hypothesis of independence between beverage type and region (.05 ≥ .0137). However, note that at a 1 percent level of significance, we could not reject the null hypothesis (.01 < .0137). Our rejection rule concerning our P-value is the same as encountered in earlier chapters. We will reject H_0 whenever $\alpha \geq P$-value. In effect the P-value is the smallest α at which H_0 will be rejected.

Using MINITAB to conduct a Test of Independence

Stat > Tables > Chisquare Test
Enter the columns NE NW S W and E into the **Columns containing the table** box.
OK

Table 13.5   Using MINITAB to Conduct a Chi-Square Test of Independence

Expected counts are printed below observed counts

		NE	MW	S	W	E	Total
	1	67	58	61	79	45	310
		57.93	55.39	59.97	75.21	61.49	
	2	47	51	57	69	76	300
		56.07	53.61	58.03	72.79	59.51	
Total		114	109	118	148	121	610
ChiSq =		1.419	+0.123	+0.018	+0.191	+4.423	
		1.466	+0.127	+0.018	+0.197	+4.570	

Chi-Sq = 12.551, $df = 4$, P-Value = 0.014

A Special Adjustment for $df = 1$

In some problems, the contingency table contains only two rows and two columns. For example, in the past, the Equal Employment Opportunity Commission (EEOC) used 2×2 tables to determine if a company discriminates against sex, age, race, etc. Suppose a company has interviewed 1300 people for

50 positions as server in a restaurant. Of the 1300 individuals interviewed, 200 were male and 1100 were female. The company hired 1 male and 49 females. EEOC could develop a contingency table based on two rows for the condition of employment (hired or not hired) and two columns representing the two sexes (male and female). Hence in terms of the respective rows and columns, row 1 = hired, row 2 = not hired, column 1 = male and column 2 = female. Thus, a row/column combination of (1,2) would be females hired, and (2,1) would be males not hired. Table 13.6 yields the appropriate analysis to test the following hypotheses:

H_0 = The company is not a sex discriminator.

H_A = The company is a sex discriminator.

Table 13.6   Computation of f_e and Chi-square for EEOC Problem

Proportion of male applicants	=	200/1300	=	.15385
Proportion of female applicants	=	1100/1300	=	.84615

EEOC null hypothesis: If 15.39% of the applicants are male, then 15.39% of those hired should be males. Hence:

Males that should be hired	=	50 • 200/1300	=	7.6923
Males that should not be hired	=	1250 • 200/1300	=	192.3077
Females that should be hired	=	50 • 1100/1300	=	42.3077
Females that should not be hired	=	1250 • 1100/1300	=	1057.6923

(r, c)	f_o	f_e	$f_o - f_e$	$(f_o - f_e)^2$	$(f_o - f_e)^2/f_e$
1,1	1.0	7.6923	−6.6923	44.786879	5.8223001
2,1	199.0	192.3077	+6.6923	44.786879	0.2328918
1,2	49.0	42.3077	+6.6923	44.786879	1.0585988
2,2	1,051.0	1,057.6923	−6.6923	44.786879	0.0423440
				$\chi^2 =$	7.1561347

The appropriate degrees of freedom are
$$df = (r - 1)(c - 1) = (2 - 1) = (1)(1) = 1$$

The appropriate chi-square critical value is $\chi^2_{.05(1)} = 3.841$. Hence, the null hypothesis that there is no relationship between the columns and rows is rejected. The null hypothesis is, in effect, the statement that the company is not a sex discriminator. Rejecting the null hypothesis implies that the company does discriminate on the basis of sex in this particular job category (server).

Some statisticians believed that in a 2×2 contingency table the computed chi-square value will be biased in favor of rejecting the null hypothesis. To adjust for this, some authors recommend a correction process whenever the number of degrees of freedom equals 1. The Yates' correction subtracts .5 from the absolute differences between f_o and f_e. The formula is

Chi-square Test Statistic with Yates' Correction Factor for $df = 1$

$$\chi^2_{Y\text{-test}} = \Sigma \frac{(|f_o - f_e| - .5)^2}{f_e} \tag{13.4}$$

where

f_o = the observed frequency

f_e = the expected frequency

In our example, the chi-square computation is 6.127 (Table 13.7). The chi-square critical value remains unchanged at $\chi^2_{.05(t)} = 3.841$. Thus, the hypothesis that the company was not a sex discriminator would be rejected. However, if a 99% confidence level were desired, the Yates' correction process would cause the null hypothesis to move from the rejection to the ISER region (Figure 13.3). Using this method could help the company avoid significant litigation and possible penalty costs. The appropriate critical value for the chi-square statistic is $\chi^2_{.01(1)} = 6.635$.

Table 13.7   Chi-Square Computations Using Yates' Correction Factor

(r, c)	f_o	f_e	$\|f_o - f_e\| - .5$	$(\|f_o - f_e\| - .5)^2$	$(\|f_o - f_e\| - .5)^2/f_e$
1,1	1.0	7.6923	6.1923	38.344579	4.9848003
1,2	199.0	192.3077	6.1923	38.344579	0.1993918
2,1	49.0	42.3077	6.1923	38.344579	0.9063263
2,2	1,051.0	1,057.6923	6.1923	38.344579	0.0362531
				$\chi^2_{Y\text{-test}} =$	6.1267715

Figure 13.3 Chi-Square Test With and Without the Yates' Correction Process $(\alpha = .01)$.

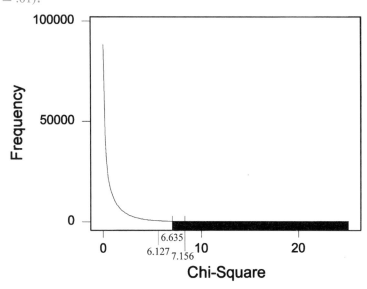

Contingency Tables Where r and $c \geq 3$

So far we have compared two factors (or variables), such as sex (male and female), condition of employment (hired and not hired), and beverage preference (sweet and dry beverage). Computing the expected frequencies is relatively simple when at least one variable has only two strata involved. The question arises as to what happens when both the number of rows and columns exceeds 2.

Fortunately, there are no changes in procedures or formulas when the number of rows and columns exceeds 2. Computing the expected frequencies when both variables contain more than 2 is simply more lengthy. Let's illustrate with an expansion of the beverage example. Assume, after the respondents are screened to ensure they can differentiate between the beverages, they are given an additional choice: no preference. Table 13.8 has the results from the survey yielding the appropriate f_o values. Note that we now have a 3 × 5 contingency table (3 rows and 5 columns).

Table 13.8   Adding Another Dimension to the Beverage Problem
*Data File on MINITAB CD

	REGIONS					
Preference	Northeast	Midwest	South	West	Europe	Total
Beverage #1	60	41	59	71	42	273
Beverage #2	38	43	54	63	76	274
No Preference	16	25	5	14	3	63
Total	114	109	118	148	121	610

Our null hypothesis is that there is no relationship between the rows and columns. That is, there is no relationship between beverage preference or indifference and the geographical regions involved. A 3×5 matrix of the data contains 15 cells from which the f_e values must be computed. To determine the expected frequency, we simply utilize formula 13.1. As an example, for cell (1,1), we multiply the row and column totals (273 • 114) and divide by n (273 • 114/610 = 51.0197). The remaining values for f_e are for your review in Table 13.9.

Table 13.9   The f_e Values for the Revised Beverage Problem

(r, c)		Row • Column/n		f_e
1,1	Beverage #1: Northeast	273 • 114/610	=	51.0197
1,2	Beverage #1: Midwest	273 • 109/610	=	48.7820
1,3	Beverage #1: South	273 • 118/610	=	52.8098
1,4	Beverage #1: West	273 • 148/610	=	66.2361
1,5	Beverage #1: Europe	273 • 121/610	=	54.1525
2,1	Beverage #2: Northeast	274 • 114/610	=	51.2066
2,2	Beverage #2: Midwest	274 • 109/610	=	48.9607
2,3	Beverage #2: South	274 • 118/610	=	53.0033
2,4	Beverage #2: West	274 • 148/610	=	66.4787
2,5	Beverage #2: Europe	274 • 121/610	=	54.3508
3,1	Beverage #2: Northeast	63 • 114/610	=	11.7738
3,2	Beverage #2: Midwest	63 • 109/610	=	11.2574
3,3	Beverage #2: South	63 • 118/610	=	12.1869
3,4	Beverage #2: West	63 • 148/610	=	15.2852
3,5	Beverage #2: Europe	63 • 121/610	=	12.4967

We then substitute the appropriate f_o and f_e values into equation 13.2, which yields a chi-square value of 49.43012 (Table 13.10). The appropriate critical value $\chi^2_{.05(8)} = 15.507$, which means we must reject the null hypothesis ($\chi^2_{\text{test}} > \chi^2_{\alpha(df)}$) that there is no relationship between taste preference or indifference and geographical region. Favoring the alternate hypothesis implies that there is a dependence between taste preference or indifference and the geographic regions involved.

Table 13.10 Computing the Chi-square Statistic

(r, c)	f_0	f_e	$f_0 - f_e$	$(f_0 - f_e)^2$	$(f_0 - f_e)^2/f_e$
1,1	60	51.0197	+8.9803	80.64579	1.58068
1,2	41	48.7820	−7.7820	60.55952	1.24143
1,3	59	52.8098	+6.1902	38.31858	0.72560
1,4	71	66.2361	+4.7639	22.69474	0.34263
1,5	42	54.1525	−12.1525	147.68326	2.72717
2,1	38	51.2066	−13.2066	174.41428	3.40609
2,2	43	48.9607	−5.9607	35.52994	0.72568
2,3	54	53.0033	+0.9967	0.99341	0.01874
2,4	63	66.4787	−3.4787	12.10135	0.18203
2,5	76	54.3508	+21.6492	468.68786	8.62338
3,1	16	11.7738	+4.2262	17.86077	1.51699
3,2	25	11.2574	+13.7426	188.85905	16.77644
3,3	5	12.1869	−7.1869	51.65153	4.23828
3,4	14	15.2852	−1.2852	1.65174	0.10806
3,5	3	12.4967	−9.4967	90.18772	7.21692

$$\chi^2_{\text{test}} = 49.43012$$

MINITAB Output

The MINITAB commands and output for the chi-square test statistic remain unchanged. Note that there are simply 15 cells in the expanded beverage example compared to the 10 cells of the original version of the problem. Since the p-value $= 0$, the chi-square test statistic is significant at any reasonable level.

Remember that the size of the test statistic is based on the magnitude of the differences between observed and expected frequencies (based on the assumption of independence). Thus, the larger the test statistic, the less likely are the two qualitative variables (beverage preference and region) to be independent. In this case the test statistic is sufficiently large to lead to a rejection of the null hypothesis that the two are independent. Enter the raw data as it appears in Table 13.8 with 5 columns and 3 rows.

Using MINITAB to conduct a Test of Independence

Stat > Tables > Chisquare Test
Enter the columns NE NW S W and E into the **Columns containing the table** box.
OK

Table 13.11 Using MINITAB to Conduct a Chi-square Test of Independence

	NE	MW	S	W	E	Total
1	60	41	59	71	42	273
	51.02	48.78	52.81	66.24	54.15	
2	38	43	54	63	76	274
	51.21	48.96	53.00	66.48	54.35	
3	16	25	5	14	3	63
	11.77	11.26	12.19	15.29	12.50	
Total	114	109	118	148	121	610

ChiSq = 1.581 + 1.241 + 0.726 + 0.343 + 2.727 +
3.406 + 0.726 + 0.019 + 0.182 + 8.623 +
1.517 + 16.777 + 4.238 + 0.108 + 7.217 =
Chi-Sq = 49.430, $df = 8$, P-Value = 0.000

419

A Review of the Procedures in Using a Chi-square Analysis

1.   Formulate the null and alternate hypotheses, and determine the significance value.

2.   Obtain the observed frequencies. In real-world problems, this might require some survey research. Typically, students are provided with survey data, and so f_0 is available.

3.   Compute the expected frequencies based on the null hypothesis. The null hypothesis states that there is no relationship between the rows and columns of data, that they are, in effect, independent. If the overall percentage of the respondents favor the sweet beverage, then the sweet/dry beverage proportion must hold for all regions allowing for chance variations. Be sure to convert the expected proportions to expected frequencies. We can obtain f_e by utilizing formula 13.1.

4.   Compare f_0 and f_e as shown in Table 13.3 and compute the chi-square test statistic (formula 13.2). If any cells are less than 5, certain columns or groups must be added together.

5.   Determine the appropriate degrees of freedom (formula 13.3) and find the appropriate critical value for chi-square at the significance level determined in step 1. If $df = 1$, use $\chi^2_{Y\text{-test}}$ in place of χ^2_{test}.

6.   If $\chi^2_{test} > \chi^2_{\alpha(df)}$ (or if $\chi^2_{\alpha(df)} \geq \chi^2_{test}$), then reject the null hypothesis that there is no difference between the rows and the columns, and favor the alternative hypothesis that at least one of the groupings is different.

7.   Using p-values: If $\alpha \geq p$-value, reject H_0.

 Concept Check 13.A

The null hypothesis in a chi-square analysis is that a relationship exists between the rows and columns of the data set. True or false? If false, explain.

Exercises

13.1   An automobile manufacturer wants to know if there are any car color preferences between males and females. A survey provided the following results:

Automobile Color

Sex	White	Red	Blue	Green	Grey	n
Male	87	29	47	16	56	235
Female	44	97	81	22	21	265
n	131	126	128	38	77	500

a.   What are the null and alternative hypotheses (H_0 and H_A)? From a casual observation of the data, do you believe the null hypothesis is correct?

b.   What is the f_e value for females wanting blue cars?

c.   What is the f_0 value for males wanting white cars?

d.   Determine the appropriate degrees of freedom.

e.   Compute the chi-square test statistic (χ^2_{test}).

f.   Is the null hypothesis supported at the 5% and 1% levels of significance?

g.   If you were the CEO, what information is being given to you that you might use to increase future sales?

13.2 The professor of a business statistics class wants to know if these are any differences in performance between freshmen, sophomores, juniors, and seniors. The professor recorded the following data:

GRADES

Year in college	A	B	C	D	F
1st & 2nd	9	22	63	30	17
3rd & 4th	6	40	71	8	2

a. The professor believes that there is no relationship between the year in school and performance as measured by final grade. Is this true at 5% level?

b. Comment on how the results may be useful to the professor in terms of improving performance.

13.3 The director of personnel at a real estate company wants to establish if her company is discriminating against individuals aged 55 and over, who are applying for positions. She obtained the following results from the computer data bank:

Age	Employed	Not-Employed
18–54	46	412
55+	3	71

a. What is the usual null hypothesis (H_0)?

b. At the 90% confidence level (10% significance level), is the hypothesis rejected?

c. Recompute the problem using the Yates' correction factor. Do you reject the null hypothesis?

d. Comment on how the results may be useful to you as the personnel director to ensure against age discrimination.

13.4 A researcher believes that frogs jump greater distances than toads. The researcher developed a jumping contest for frogs and toads. The following table shows the frequency of jumping times for the frogs and toads:

Species	0–4.9 ft.	5–9.9 ft.	10–14.9 ft.	15+ ft.
Frogs	34	41	22	12
Toads	28	21	14	7

a. Based on the 5% level of significance, do frogs jump higher than toads?

b. Can you think of any practical business use for this information other than winning a wager?

13.5 The manager of a tennis club wants to determine if there is any relationship between the sex of the members and the hours the club is open. The manager records the number of males and females playing in certain time intervals.

Sex	10 to 1 pm	1+ to 4 pm	4+ to 7 pm	7+ to 10 pm
Female	78	91	38	17
Male	16	20	56	118

a. Based on the 5% level of significance, is there a relationship between sex and the hours the club is open?

b. If a relationship exists, could you give a reason for it?

13.6 A small company wishes to determine if any relationship exists between its sales volume categorized into business or home sales (in percent) and the quarter of the year. The company tabulates the sales percentage as:

Quarter	1st	2nd	3rd	4th
Business Sales	72	84	43	39
Home Sales	28	16	57	61

a. Based on the 1% level of significance, is there a relationship between business or home sales percent and the quarter of the year?

b. If a relationship exists, could you give a reason for it?

c. Should the Yates' correction factor be used?

13.7 A small repair garage wants to know if there is a relationship between repairing domestic and foreign cars and the average bill for the repairs. The appropriate number in each category is recorded as follows:

Auto	0 to $99	$100 to $199	$200 to $299	$300 to +
Foreign	50	60	80	200
Domestic	160	180	140	190

a. Based on the 5% level of significance, is there a relationship between foreign and domestic autos and the average repair bill?

b. Based on the 1% level of significance, is there a relationship between foreign and domestic autos and the average repair bill?

13.8 A new car dealership wants to know if there is a relationship between repairing new cars costing more or less than $15,000 and the average number of vehicle complaints. The manufacturer does not wish for the number of complaints on new cars to exceed 5. The dealership checks its records and finds:

Auto	Complaints $\leq$ 5	Complaints $>$ 5
Cost $>$ $15,000	679	256
Cost $\leq$ $15,000	201	105

a. Based on the 5% level of significance, is there a relationship between the cost of the car and the number of complaints?

b. Use Yates' correction factor to determine if there is a relationship.

13.9 A utility company wants to know if there is a difference in older customers paying their bill on time. The accountant checks the payment record and finds:

Age	Payment on time	0 to 5 days late	5+ days late
Under 55	3,891	256	285
$\geq$55	617	31	51

a. Based on the 1% level of significance, is there a relationship between age and time of payment tardiness?

b. Is the Yates' correction factor relevant?

13.10 A large computer firm wishes to know if certain professions utilize their computers differently. The company reviews its records with the following findings in terms of weekly usage:

	$\leq$ 1 hour of utilization	$>$1 hour of utilization
Engineers	28	718
Auto Mechanics	1617	19
Chemists	14	112
Gardeners	12	219
Teachers	98	47
Physicians	19	310
Attorneys	43	416

a. Based on the 5% level of significance, is there a relationship between careers and computer utilization?

b. Would you expect that a relationship would exist? Explain.

c. How might the computer firm utilize such information in relation to marketing?

13.11   A beer producer wishes to know if certain professions consume their products. The company reviews the results of a survey in terms of 12 ounce cans consumed per week and finds:

	0 or 1 can per week	>1 can per week
Engineers	40	134
Auto Mechanics	77	259
Teachers	53	172
Physicians	9	31
Attorneys	19	84

a.   Based on the 5% level of significance, is there a relationship between consumption and careers?

b.   How might the beer company utilize such information in relation to marketing?

13.12   A newspaper wishes to analyze their morning delivery complaints. An executive feels that most of the complaints come from households where one adult member does not work. Survey results reveal:

	HOUSEHOLDS	
	All Adults Work	At least one adult does not work
Complaints	57	83
No Complaints	318	410

a.   Based on the 1% level of significance (not using the correction factor), is the executive's hypothesis correct?

b.   Recompute using the Yates' correction factor.

13.13   The military is testing three different air-to-air missiles used to terminate incoming aircraft. The officer in charge has recorded the following information:

	AIR-TO-AIR MISSILES			
Destructions	A	B	C	n
Full Kills	16	19	31	66
Partial Hits	15	15	19	49
Miss	7	6	5	18
n	38	40	55	133

a.   What is the normal null hypothesis (H_0) that is established in using the chi-square statistic?

b.   What is f_e for missile C and full kills?

c.   What is the appropriate number of degrees of freedom?

d.   Would Yates' correction factor be applicable?

e.   Compute the chi-square test statistic (χ^2_{test}).

f.   At the 10% significance level, is the null hypothesis correct?

g.   Comment on how you might utilize the results of this analysis.

13.14   A company that makes perfume is testing three different perfumes on women with different metabolic rates. The marketing manager fears that women with higher metabolic rates might react negatively to perfumes with sweeter fragrance. The test results are:

	HIGH—METABOLIC RATES—LOW			
Perfumes	A	B	C	D
A: Very Sweet	12	16	9	18
B: Somewhat Sweet	19	20	17	15
C: Non-sweet	17	14	15	10

a. The null hypothesis states that there is no relationship between metabolic rates and the sweetness of the perfume. At the 5% level of significance, is the test statistic significantly different from the critical value obtained from the table?

b. What is the appropriate number of degrees of freedom?

c. What policy might the marketing manager establish based on the results?

13.15 Critics are asked to rank (according to acting ability as defined by the profession) 100 different actresses, from the different continents, on a scale from 1 to 5 (with 5 being the best). The actresses come from Europe, Asia, and North America. The results are as follows:

	RANKINGS				
	1	*2*	*3*	*4*	*5*
Europe	5	10	15	35	35
Asia	25	20	20	25	10
North America	20	20	20	20	20

a. Is the continent of birth related to the above rankings, based on a 95% confidence level ($100\% - 95\% = 5\%$ significance level)?

b. Does a rejection of the null hypothesis indicate discrimination is taking place?

c. If discrimination is taking place, is it possible its derivative is acting ability and not continent of origin?

13.16 Suppose three different sales approaches are being used in four industries. Assume an identical product is being sold at the same price and that an equal effort is used in each case. The date represent the sales in units of 1,000 and are:

	SALES APPROACH		
Industrial classification	*A*	*B*	*C*
The banking sector	56	75	43
The insurance sector	26	37	22
The agricultural sector	12	15	10
The heavy industry sector	59	101	90

a. Based on the 1% level of significance, are the three sales approaches equally effective?

b. Comment on how you might utilize this information to increase your overall sales.

c. Comment on how you might utilize the results if you were considering expanding into another market.

13.17 A new car dealership wants to know if there is a relationship between new car costs and the average number of vehicle complaints. The dealership checks its records and finds:

	NUMBER OF COMPLAINTS		
Auto	*≤5*	*6 to ≤10*	*≥11*
Cost > $30,001	679	946	718
Cost $15,001 to ≤$30,000	856	765	810
Costs ≤$15,000	1021	954	1010

Based on the 5% level of significance, is there a relationship between the cost of the car and the number of complaints?

13.18 Suppose four different sales approaches are being used in four industries. Assume an identical product is being sold at the same price and that an equal effort is used in each case. The data represent the sales in units of 1,000 and is:

		SALES APPROACH		
Industrial classification	A	B	C	D
The banking sector	41	56	75	43
The insurance sector	68	26	37	22
The agricultural sector	25	12	15	10
The heavy industry sector	100	89	101	90

Based on the 5% level of significance, are the four sales approaches equally effective?

13.19 A discount store wishes to determine if there is a relationship existing between the number of customers who purchase from four of their departments and the zip code from which the customer comes. The retail store records the following information from a day's activities.

			ZIP CODES		
Departments	32801	32802	32803	32804	32805
Jewelry	89	21	42	39	7
Sports	56	19	24	29	4
Clothing	187	98	110	65	26
Hardware	41	15	20	30	5

a. Using the 5% level of significance, is there a relationship between the number of customers at the various departments and the zip codes?
b. Why would a retail store's manager want to know from what zip code its customer base originates?

13.20 A market research firm asks consumers in four geographic areas how they evaluated a product that was mailed to them for trial use. The number of respondents is recorded as follows:

Evaluation	Market A	Market B	Market C	Market D
Excellent	12	28	18	20
Good	38	49	22	26
Fair	42	45	19	30
Poor	10	8	12	18

a. Using the 5% level of significance, is there a relationship between the geographic areas and the evaluation given?
b. Would the Yates' correction factor be appropriate here?

13.21 A utility company wants to know if there is a difference in how different aged customers pay their bills on time. The accountant checks the payment record and finds:

Age	Payment on time	0 to 5 days late	5+ days late
20–40	105	8	12
41–60	260	18	55
60+	92	8	12

Based on the 5% level of significance, is there a relationship between age and payment tardiness?

13.22 A large computer firm wishes to know if certain professions utilize their computers differently. The company reviews its records with the following findings in terms of weekly usage:

HOURLY UTILIZATION

	≤1 hour	1 to 3 hours	>3 hours
Engineers	16	31	110
Auto Mechanics	219	9	4
Chemists	14	22	112
Gardeners	119	12	14
Teachers	98	23	23
Physicians	19	5	5
Attorneys	43	21	8

a. Based on the 5% level of significance, is there a relationship between careers and computer utilization?

b. How might the computer firm utilize such information in relation to marketing?

13.23 A financial firm's executive believes that those customers that drive conservative colored cars buy conservative (less risk) stock. The executive performs a survey of accounts and finds:

RISK OF STOCK

Colors	low risk	medium risk	high risk
grey	21	31	36
blue	29	34	26
red	38	27	21
chartreuse	45	21	18

At the 5% level, test the hypothesis that car color and risk of stock are unrelated.

13.24 A basketball coach thinks he gets the same scoring from his center, forwards, and guards regardless of the opponent. He has his assistant compile the scoring record against the 4 teams in his division. The record is:

	Center	Forwards	Guards
Team A	21	41	59
Team B	25	38	66
Team C	17	44	61
Team D	20	45	56

At the 1% level, is the coach correct?

13.3 Summary

In this chapter we discussed the chi-square statistic. We used the chi-square distribution to test the independence or dependence between various strata of two variables. This is of particular interest to marketing specialists who are trying to find a market niche for their products and services. The technique involved the comparison of an observed and expected frequency. The critical question is whether the difference between f_o and f_e is attributable to sampling error or not. If it is, we have ISER for the null hypothesis. However, if the difference between f_o and f_e is too great to be explained by sampling error alone, we reject the null hypothesis. A rejection of the null hypothesis implies at least one of the strata proportions is different from the rest.

Mini-case 13.1: The Personnel Department's Screening Exam

A company screens initial applicants using a test developed by the personnel department. Records have been kept, with 43 of the 96 minority applicants and 105 of the 314 non-minority applicants failing the test. Company executives fear the test discriminates against minorities.

    a.   Using the chi-square test statistic at the 5% level, does the test discriminate against minorities?

    b.   Using the Yates' correction factor, compute the chi-square test statistic.

    c.   Do the results from a and b differ? Explain.

Mini-case 13.2: Home Court Advantage

A basketball team coach believes the home court advantage to be significant, but has never statistically performed any analysis. The coach records the games won and lost at home, away from home, and on neutral grounds where neither team was home (as is the case in tournament play).

	Won	Lost
At Home	19	6
Away	16	9
Neutral	7	3

    a.   Does the Yates' correction factor have to be invoked?

    b.   At the 5% level, does the home court advantage exist?

Review of Important Terms and Concepts

Contingency table: A table set up to compare hypotheses concerning the headings in the rows and the columns. A contingency table with 4 rows and 5 columns is called a 4 by 5 contingency table.

Observed frequency (f_o)**:** Frequencies observed from sample information. Such frequencies are usually given in problems which students must work.

Expected frequency (f_e)**:** The null hypothesis for chi-square problem is that there is no relationship between the rows and columns of data. The expected frequencies are the frequencies which would be expected if the null hypothesis were correct.

Chi-square test statistic: A test statistic that compares observed and expected frequencies to determine if a relationship exists between them. Variables that the researcher wishes to evaluate are placed in the columns and rows of the contingency table. The chi-square test statistic can also be used to determine whether or not a data set approximates a particular distribution. In such cases, the test is called a goodness-of-fit test.

Yates' correction factor: A correction process that adjusts the chi-square test statistic when there is a single degree of freedom.

Non-parametric technique: Using test statistics that do not involve stringent assumptions concerning the parent population.

Cell Expected Frequency f_e

$$f_e = \frac{(\text{row total})(\text{column total})}{n} \qquad (13.1)$$

The Chi-Square Test Statistic

$$\chi^2_{\text{test}} = \sum \frac{(f_o - f_e)^2}{f_e} \qquad (13.2)$$

where

f_o = the observed frequency

f_e = the expected frequency

Formula for the Degrees of Freedom in a χ^2 Contingency Table

$$df = (r - 1)(c - 1) \qquad (13.3)$$

where

r = the number of rows

c = the number of columns

Chi-square Test Statistic with Yates' Correction Factor for $df = 1$

$$\chi^2_{Y\text{-test}} = \sum \frac{(|f_o - f_e| - .5)^2}{f_e} \qquad (13.4)$$

where

f_o = the observed frequency

f_e = the expected frequency

Review of MINITAB Commands

MINITAB sequence to obtain Chisquare test statistic.
Stat > Tables > Chi-square Test
Enter the columns C1, C2, C3, C4, etc. into the **Columns containing the table** box.
OK

13.25   A company that sells artificial Christmas trees believes there may be a relationship between the consumer's age and the color of the Christmas tree purchased. The company plans to use the chi-square test to test its hypothesis. The following table shows the results of a survey of the number of Christmas trees purchased by age groups:

	RESPONDENTS			
Color Tree	18–30	31–44	45–59	60+
Green	24	76	99	110
White	27	61	27	100

   a.   Using a chi-square analysis, what is the value for f_e (expected frequency) for white Christmas trees in the 31 to 44 age group?
   b.   Determine the number of degrees of freedom.
   c.   Using a 5% level of significance, is there a relationship between age and the preferred color of a Christmas tree?

13.26   For exercise 13.25, add a third Christmas tree that is colored mauve. Assume the sample sizes for the green and white Christmas trees remain the same. The results of the mauve tree survey is 18–30: 12; 31–44: 10; 45–59: 15; 60+: 47.

   a.   Using the chi-square analysis, what is the value for f_e (expected frequency) for white Christmas trees in the 31 to 44 age group?
   b.   Determine the number of degrees of freedom.
   c.   Using a 5% level of significance, is there a relationship between age and the preferred color of a Christmas tree?

13.27   In a city with a private and a public university there is a disagreement over who has the smarter students. The two presidents have obtained information on the standardized test scores of seniors and the number who made certain scores. They are as follows;

University	200–499	500–799	800–1099	1100+
Public	37	89	141	123
Private	17	48	91	66

   a.   Using a chi-square analysis, is there a difference in performance between the two schools (based on a 1% level of significance)?
   b.   Explain how it may be possible for students in either university to do better than the other.

13.28   Four universities are located within a city. The faculty of each school believes that they have the best university. The mayor of the city believes there are four equally, but superior universities, in the city. The following table shows standardized test results:

University	200–499	500–799	800–1099	1100+
A	16	76	100	75
B	9	56	71	43
C	41	103	189	110
D	22	51	84	69

Using a chi-square analysis, is the hypothesis of the mayor correct at the 5% level of significance?

13.29   An electronic products retailer believes that customers have no preference between four different brands of televisions. The retailer establishes identical prices on the four brands and observes the choices of 200 customers. Based on the data provided, test the retailer's hypothesis at the 5 percent level.

NUMBER OF CONSUMERS PREFERRING BRAND

A	B	C	D
42	30	68	60

13.30   An automobile insurer believes that the size of the automobile is related to the severity of personal injuries in accidents. To evaluate this hypothesis, accident records were examined and categorized according to the severity of the personal injuries to policyholders and the size of their car. Test independence between the two qualitative variables at a 1 percent significance level based on the records shown.

		SIZE OF CAR		
		Small	Medium	Large
Severity of	Low	10	30	80
Injuries	Moderate	40	40	20
	High	50	20	10

13.31   Explain in your own words how the expected frequencies are generated for a normally distributed goodness of fit test.

Nonparametric Statistics

Where we have been

In earlier chapters we covered hypothesis testing based on samples drawn from some population. In all previous cases we assumed we knew something about the population from which the sample was drawn.

Where we are going

However, frequently such information is unavailable. Hence, statisticians have developed alternative inferential techniques that do not require such stringent assumptions concerning the parent population. These statistical techniques and procedures are termed nonparametric techniques and in many cases are the formalization of simple rules of logic. In fact, students normally find these techniques less cumbersome and easier to learn than the more formal hypothesis testing techniques previously covered.

14.1 Introduction

We will now present a series of nonparametric tests which can be used to test various hypotheses. Some of these tests will appear extremely simple, because the logic is intuitively obvious. However, it is their simplicity that has led to such widespread use by practitioners in the business community. Moreover, the simpler approaches sometimes provide understanding not provided by more advanced techniques.

Nonparametric techniques require minimum, or in some cases no, assumptions concerning the parent populations. Since parent populations are explained by their respective parameters (such as a mean and standard deviation), nonparametric methods are often termed distribution-free statistics. Many statisticians differentiate between distribution free and nonparametric statistics. To simplify the discussion, however, we group them together in this chapter. Some of the tests will depend on ranked data, while others use frequency differences, or groupings of the data.

It is often convenient at this point to review the different measurement scales that can be utilized. The first is the nominal scale where we merely attempt to differentiate one object from another. Football players wear numbers which have no meaning except to differentiate between players or players' general positions. However, if one player's number is twice that of another, it does not follow that they are twice as good, or even just better at what they do. If we could say that the player with the higher number was better (according to some specified characteristic) than another, we would be involved with an ordinal scale. If the superiority difference between players with the numbers 15 and 10 on their uniforms is the same as the superiority difference between players with the numbers 50 and 45 on their uniforms, we are involved with an interval scale. Finally, if the player with the number 44 was twice as good as the player with a 22 on his or her jersey, we would be involved with a ratio scale.

Most of the data analyzed to this point in the text was based on the interval scale. In this chapter we will concentrate on data measured on ordinal and nominal scales. In many of our nonparametric tests we will be involved in taking a data base and converting it to its rank (ordinal scale).

For example, suppose we asked four students who saw a particular movie to rate it from 0–10. Suppose the four ratings (listed in order of ascending magnitude) were 4, 8, 9, and 10. The actual number assigned is quite arbitrary and imprecise. The number itself has little meaning except in terms of its relative position. Hence, we convert the numbers into their relative ranks. Ranking the numbers from low to high yields a rank of 1 to the number 4, the rank of 2 to the number 8, the rank of 3 to the number 9, and the number 10 is rank 4. We are really not able to say that the individual who assigned an 8 liked the movie twice as much as the individual who assigned the 4. We can say that looking at all four students the number 4 is the lowest number in the data set (rank 1) and the number 8 is the second lowest number (rank 2). We will learn to make and test hypotheses concerning such ranks.

In this chapter, we will also take data and categorize it into two groups. They will simply be part of one group or another. We will analyze a particular property of the data set; hence, we will be involved with a nominal scale.

14.2 The Sign Test

Before we begin our analysis it will be useful to review the rules of hypothesis testing involved. Most of our analyses will be comparing two or more columns of data. When making comparisons between two columns of data we may be involved with a one- or two-tailed test. For a two-tailed test, the null hypothesis states that whatever statistic we are comparing (mean, median, standard deviation, etc.) are statistically the same in both columns. For a one-tailed test, we are stating that one of the column statistics is either greater than or less than the other. This establishes the alternate hypothesis. To determine if a greater than or less than arrow is appropriate we simply need to understand which data set is in which column, and whether the largest or the smallest statistic is optimum.

When dealing with more than two columns of data we normally are involved with a two-tailed test. The null hypothesis states that the statistic being analyzed is statistically the same between all the columns of data. The alternate hypothesis states that at least one of the column statistics differs from the rest.

Another basis for determining if we are involved with a one- or two-tailed test involves what the researcher believes to be true. A consumer advocate group might believe that there is on average less than 355 ml in the beverage cans. This establishes the alternative hypothesis as H_A: $\mu < 355$ ml; hence, H_0: $\mu \geq 355$ ml. The statement we are attempting to prove, based on survey information, makes this a one-tailed test.

After reviewing one- and two-tailed tests, we will now return to nonparametric tests. The first of these tests to be analyzed, which is possibly the simplest, is the sign test. The sign test is applied to paired data, where one group is compared to another to determine if a difference exists from a statistical viewpoint. We will introduce the sign test with an example concerning the judging of a sporting event.

There have been many disputed decisions in prize fighting, both at the amateur and professional level. Suppose we want to use 21 scorekeepers (judges) for a boxing match, instead of the normal 3. An odd number is normally chosen to minimize ties (usually a split decision involves two judges thinking one fighter won while the remaining judge chooses the other), which are still possible, but less probable. The standard 10-point must system is to be assumed. This system requires that each scorekeeper give 10 points to the winner of a round (3-minute time intervals or rounds). Then a subjective lower number is given to the loser of the round. If the round was close, a scorekeeper might give the loser 9 points. If the round was rather one-sided, involving knock downs, then the loser might receive only 6–8 points. If the round was a draw, then 10 points would be given to each fighter. Each scorekeeper sums each boxer's point totals for all rounds and the boxer with the greatest total is considered the winner by that scorekeeper. The boxer who is considered the winner by the majority of scorekeepers is declared the winner of the match.

Suppose a championship match has just been completed and the scorecards for the 21 judges has been turned in for evaluation (Table 14.1). Twelve of the judges believe fighter B has won (12 negative signs, $\hat{q} = 12/20 = .6$), eight believe fighter A won (8 positive signs, $\hat{p} = 8/20 = .4$), and one believes the contest was a draw. Note that $\hat{p}$ equals the proportion of positive signs. According to international boxing rules, the fight would have been won by fighter B. Suppose we decided to use statistical hypothesis testing to determine who the winner was, or even if there was a winner at all in the fight. First decide on the null hypothesis. The null hypothesis (H_0) is that the fight was a draw (hypothesized population proportion = $p_0 = .5$). The alternate hypothesis (H_A) is that one of the combatants won the fight (the population proportion does not = .5).

H_0: $p = .5$ There is no difference between the boxers. The fight is a draw.

H_A: $p \neq .5$ There is a winner in the fight.

This problem is analogous to flipping a coin, except there can't be a draw on a coin flip. However, **since ties (draws) are discarded** in the sign test, the analogy to the coin flip is appropriate.

Table 14.1   Ranking Boxers According to the Sign Test
*Data File on MINITAB CD

Judge	Score: A	Score: B	Differences	Signs
1	100	89	+11	+
2	95	96	−1	−
3	97	84	+13	+
4	98	81	+17	+
5	89	91	−2	−
6	92	93	−1	−
7	89	90	−1	−
8	89	89	0	N/A
9	99	90	+9	+
10	91	92	−1	−
11	88	92	−4	−
12	94	96	−2	−
13	94	95	−1	−
14	96	88	+8	+
15	99	92	+7	+
16	95	96	−1	−
17	90	93	−3	−
18	88	90	−2	−
19	89	90	−1	−
20	94	89	+5	+
21	94	91	+3	+

For a one-tailed test, we would have to state that a particular fighter won the match. We have two columns of data, scores for fighter A and for fighter B. We subtract column A from column B to determine the sign. The sign (+ or −) will either have a positive or negative connotation; $\hat{p}$ is the number of positive signs divided by n. If we stated that fighter B won or tied the match then a + has a negative connotation (it means that fighter A won). The null hypothesis is that $p_0 \leq .5$. With the null hypothesis we would be stating that the negative signs exceed the positive signs.

We will now conclude with the rules to follow when using the sign test:

Rules to Follow when Using the Sign Test

1. The pairs of data must be independent and randomly selected.
2. Discard ties, and then determine the sign of differences between the paired points.
3. Count the positive and negative signs; $\hat{p}$ = proportion of positive signs and equals the proportion of negative signs.
4. MINITAB will convert the plus and minus signs into a z scale and perform either a one- or two-tailed test. As always we reject the null hypothesis whenever the significance coefficient is greater than or equals the p-value.

MINITAB will perform the sign test for us. First we enter the data in Table 14.1 with the first column being ScoreA and the second ScoreB. Using MINITABs calculator we subtract column B from column A to obtain C which is stored in C3.

Calc > Calculator
Enter **C3** into the **Store results in Variable** box.
Double click **ScoreA** into the Expressions box. Enter a minus sign (−), then double click **ScoreB** into the box.
OK

Now we can have MINITAB perform the sign test for us

Stat > Nonparametrics > 1-Sample Sign
Double click **C3** into Variable box.
Click **Test median (0.0)**. If half the judges favored A and half B the median of the differences should be 0.

MINITAB results of a two-tailed test.
Sign Test for Median

Sign test of median = 0.00000 versus not = 0.00000

	N	Below	Equal	Above	P	Median
C3	21	12	1	8	0.5034	−1.000

MINITAB results of a left-tailed test.
Sign Test for Median

Sign test of median = 0.00000 versus < 0.00000

	N	Below	Equal	Above	P	Median
C3	21	12	1	8	0.2517	−1.000

MINITAB results of a right-tailed test.
Sign Test for Median

Sign test of median = 0.00000 versus > 0.00000

	N	Below	Equal	Above	P	Median
C3	21	12	1	8	0.8684	−1.000

MINITAB results of a 95% confidence interval.
Sign Confidence Interval

Sign confidence interval for median

	N	Median	Achieved Confidence	Confidence interval	Position
C3	21	−1.000	0.9216	(−1.000, 5.000)	7
			0.9500	(−1.000, 5.653)	NLI
			0.9734	(−1.000, 7.000)	6

Note the confidence intervals include 0.0.

 Concept Check 14.A

The sign test merely counts how many times one of the paired data sets exceeds the other without regard to how much it exceeds it. True or false? If false, explain.

Exercises

14.1 The personnel department of a large company institutes a training program to reduce the number of defective parts going through a daily assembly line. The training program will only be considered a success if the number of defects after training is less than the number before training. The two sets of data below record the daily defective parts. Before training 7, 9, 11, 3, 7, 9, 8, 5, 2, 6, 11, 9, 3, 1. After training 5, 10, 14, 6, 5, 3, 9, 8, 1, 9, 11, 8, 2, 2

    a. Using MINITAB at a 5% level of significance, and the sign test, can it be concluded that the training program has been a success?

    b. If the program was not a success, could other factors have interfered with the analysis?

    c. If the program is determined to be a success, does this mean that further training could further reduce defects?

14.2 A medication is developed to reduce the bacteria count in the blood stream. The medication may only be deemed successful if the bacteria count after medication is less than what it was before medication. Blood tests are made on individuals before and after they have taken the prescribed medication. The data are:

No medication 3.2, 6.7, 9.1, 4.3, 8.4, 2.3, 7.9, 10.1, 5.3, 6.8
Medication 2.2, 5.6, 8.8, 4.4. 6.9, 8.6, 7.7, 8.9, 4.4, 5.9

    a. Using MINITAB at a 99% confidence level and the sign test, can it be concluded that the new drug is a success?

    b. Is the sample size sufficient to make a real determination concerning a new drug?

    c. Why do you think the FDA waits longer than most nations to allow a new drug on the market?

14.3   In the National Football League there are 14 games (28 teams) per week for 16 weeks. Over the year a football fan records the number of correct predictions made by a local sports reporter and himself, as follows:

Week	Sport Reporter	Fan
1	11	8
2	13	10
3	6	9
4	10	8
5	8	8
6	11	9
7	7	8
8	10	4
9	13	9
10	11	10
11	7	10
12	12	10
13	9	5
14	13	11
15	11	9
16	10	8

a.   Using MINITAB at the 5% level of significance and the sign test, is the fan equal to the sport reporter as a forecaster?

b.   The recorded wins do not account for the point spread or the amount of points the favorite team is expected to win. Would you expect the number of wins to be greater if the projections included the point spread?

14.4   University students are asked to evaluate a new pen. The students are asked to record the length of time it takes for them to run out of ink. Each student is asked to record the length of time for two pens, one the old model, the other the developmental pen. The students do not know which is which, because both have the same physical appearances. The results are shown in hours:

Student	Old Pen	Developmental Pen
1	19.6	28.9
2	17.6	21.7
3	15.1	24.9
4	16.2	16.1
5	21.9	37.8
6	22.4	24.8
7	14.6	16.4
8	17.6	17.4
9	25.0	28.7
10	13.9	27.3
11	28.2	21.3
12	22.0	23.8
13	17.1	16.4
14	29.8	36.1
15	18.9	18.3
16	19.9	19.3
17	21.9	23.4
18	21.9	21.2
19	16.9	27.9
20	26.7	23.4

436

a. Visually, do you believe that the developmental pen is superior to the old pen in terms of longevity?

b. Test your hypothesis at the 5% level of significance using MINITAB.

14.5 A pharmaceutical company has developed what it believes is a novocain that will dissipate the old variety. They test the time it takes for 24 dentist's patients' mouths to feel normal (in hours). The dentist records the same patient first using the old, then the new novocain. The results are:

Patient	Old	New	Patient	Old	New
1	3.2	1.7	13	2.2	2.8
2	4.1	2.6	14	1.8	2.9
3	3.7	1.5	15	1.5	1.4
4	2.4	2.7	16	1.1	3.5
5	1.1	3.2	17	0.9	2.3
6	2.3	2.1	18	1.6	3.1
7	1.9	1.8	19	0.8	4.2
8	1.4	3.7	20	1.0	3.7
9	2.1	1.9	21	1.6	2.6
10	0.6	4.1	22	2.0	3.2
11	1.7	1.7	23	1.1	2.5
12	1.3	3.5	24	2.8	2.3

Using the sign test and MINITAB, is the hypothesis correct at the 1% level?

14.6 A new machine is tested which is designed to reduce the errors in producing precision equipment. The new machine is placed alongside the older version and the differences between actual measurements and design measurements are recorded (in mm) for 20 bearings. It is important that the bearing not be too large or too small. The results are:

Part	Old	New	Part	Old	New
1	+1.2	−1.7	11	+0.7	−1.1
2	−0.9	+0.6	12	−0.9	+0.2
3	−0.7	−1.1	13	+0.5	+0.4
4	+1.4	−0.7	14	+1.1	+0.5
5	−0.2	+0.3	15	−1.3	−0.1
6	+1.3	+0.1	16	−0.6	+0.1
7	+0.9	−0.3	17	+0.8	−1.2
8	−0.7	−0.9	18	−0.1	+0.3
9	−0.8	+1.1	19	+1.2	−2.4
10	+0.4	−0.7	20	+0.9	−0.1

The new machine is much more efficient to operate than the old one; hence, to be superior to the old machine the new machine just needs to equal the old in terms of deviations from specifications. Using the sign test and MINITAB, is the performance of the new machine equal to that of the old (10% level)?

14.7   A new weight reduction plan is developed by a company. Paired individuals are selected based on demographics and psychographics. After 6 weeks, the weight loss is recorded for 30 patients under the new and old plans. The company wants to guarantee that the new plan is better than the old plan. The weight loss results are:

Patient	Old	New	Patient	Old	New
1	7	12	16	14	22
2	14	31	17	9	19
3	20	18	18	5	26
4	9	17	19	6	15
5	11	18	20	12	8
6	16	31	21	21	24
7	11	19	22	12	41
8	19	13	23	13	12
9	12	29	24	6	23
10	2	18	25	12	35
11	−3	10	26	16	14
12	14	22	27	15	26
13	9	15	28	19	22
14	0	13	29	15	11
15	12	19	30	16	19

Using the sign test and MINITAB, is the hypothesis correct at the 1% level?

14.8   A supermarket tests to determine if more boxes of Cereal X are purchased when the box is placed at eye level or when customers have to reach for the product. The supermarket chain uses two branches where the demographic and psychographic profiles of the customers are the same. Fifteen randomly selected hours are used to record the number of boxes purchased. The company believes that the boxes at eye level will sell at a greater volume than those not at eye level. The survey results are:

Hour	Sales Eye Level	Sales Not Eye Level	Hour	Sales Eye Level	Sales Not Eye Level
1	43	26	8	21	9
2	66	49	9	56	21
3	11	2	10	38	33
4	19	15	11	23	26
5	39	22	12	44	41
6	72	28	13	33	15
7	29	15	14	21	24
			15	46	18

Using the sign test and MINITAB at the 5% level, is the hypothesis correct?

14.3 The Wilcoxon Signed-Rank Test

The Wilcoxon signed-rank test is similar to the sign test, but it analyzes paired data more thoroughly, and so is a more powerful test. In addition to considering the sign differences between paired data points, the magnitudes of the differences are also measured.

Table 14.2 Computations for the Wilcoxon Signed-Rank Test Using the Boxers Example

Judge	Score: A	Score: B	Differences	Signs	Rank	T
1	100	89	+11	+	18.0	T_+
2	95	96	−1	−	4.0	T_-
3	97	84	+13	+	19.0	T_+
4	98	81	+17	+	20.0	T_+
5	89	91	−2	−	9.0	T_-
6	92	93	−1	−	4.0	T_-
7	89	90	−1	−	4.0	T_-
8	89	89	0	N/A	N/A	N/A
9	99	90	+9	+	17.0	T_+
10	91	92	−1	−	4.0	T_-
11	88	92	−4	−	13.0	T_-
12	94	96	−2	−	9.0	T_-
13	94	95	−1	−	4.0	T_-
14	96	88	+8	+	16.0	T_+
15	99	92	+7	+	15.0	T_+
16	95	96	−1	−	4.0	T_-
17	90	93	−3	−	11.5	T_-
18	88	90	−2	−	9.0	T_-
19	89	90	−1	−	4.0	T_-
20	94	89	+5	+	14.0	T_+
21	94	91	+3	+	11.5	T_+

Let us return to the example of the championship boxing match with 21 judges (Table 14.2). Note the similarity to Table 14.1. The differences between the scoring for fighters A and B are analyzed without regard to sign (absolute differences). The ties are discarded, which reduces the sample size from 21 to 20. The absolute differences are then ranked from small to large. Since ties are discarded, differences of 0 can't exist. Therefore, the smallest possible absolute difference is 1 (using whole integers). We have seven absolute differences of 1 (judges 2, 6, 7, 10, 13, 16, and 19). For each of these seven judges, the decision went to fighter B. We will give each of the seven judges the average of the first seven ranks, which is 4: Ranks $(1 + 2 + 3 + 4 + 5 + 6 + 7)/7 = 4$. The ranks are given in Table 14.2.

The second smallest absolute difference is 2. There are three −2 differences (judges 5, 12, and 18). We will average the three ranks and use the average for each judge: ranks $(8 + 9 + 10)/3 = 9$. The next absolute difference is 3. There is one −3 (judge 17) and one +3 value (judge 21). In this case, each judge voted for a different boxer. The average ranking is 11.5: ranks $(11 + 12)/2 = 11.5$. Since there are no other duplication of ranks, we assign 13 to 20 to the remaining judges without averaging: judge 11 = rank 13, judge 20 = rank 14, etc.

Test statistics T_W can be determined for the positive rankings T_{W+} and for the negative rankings T_{W-}. These T readings merely are the sums of the positive and negative ranks. The T readings are

$$T_{W+} = 18 + 19 + 20 + 17 + 16 + 15 + 14 + 11.5 = 130.5$$

$$T_{W-} = 4 + 9 + 4 + 4 + 4 + 13 + 9 + 4 + 4 + 11.5 + 9 + 4 = 79.5$$

The total for the two sums $= (n \bullet n + 1)/2$. In our example the total for the two sums is 20 • 21/2=210.

The closer T_{W+} is to T_{W-}, the greater the odds that the fight is a draw. The further apart they are indicates a winner has emerged. Hence,

H_0: the probability distributions for the paired groups are identical.

439

H_A: The probability distribution for the paired groups are not identical.

For hypothesis testing purposes, we may use either T_{W+} or T_{W-}.

It is possible to get opposing viewpoints from the sign and the Wilcoxon signed-rank test. In our boxer example, there were 21 judges. Of these, 12 selected boxer B and 8 chose fighter A. While judges who selected boxer A thought he won by a wide margin, judges who selected fighter B thought it was a close fight. Note that if the judges who selected fighter A thought he won by an even wider margin, we might have to reject the hypothesis that the fight was a draw. The sign test favored boxer B, while the Wilcoxon signed-rank test might favor boxer A. However, the favoring was not significant enough to determine a winner.

MINITAB will perform the analysis for us and test the various hypotheses. After we have entered ScoreA and ScoreB in two columns:

Calc > Calculator
Enter **C3** into the **Store results in Variable** box.
Double click **ScoreA** into the **Expression** box. Enter a minus sign (−), then double click **ScoreB** into the box.
OK

Now we can have MINITAB perform the Wilcoxon test for us.

Stat > Nonparametrics > 1-Sample Wilcoxon
Double click **C3** into Variable box.
Click **Test median (0.0)**. If half the judges favored A and half B the median of the differences should be 0.
OK

MINITAB results of a two-tailed test.

Wilcoxon Signed Rank Test
Test of median = 0.000000 versus median not = 0.000000

	N	N for Test	Wilcoxon Statistic	P	Estimated Median
C3	21	20	130.5	0.351	2.000

MINITAB results of a left tailed and right tailed test are left for a student exercise.

We will now turn to a summary of the rules to be followed when using the Wilcoxon signed-rank test.

Rules to Follow When Using the Wilcoxon Signed-Rank Test

1. The pairs of data must be independent and randomly drawn from continuous populations.

2. Discard any 0 differences and then rank the absolute difference between the paired data. If any absolute differences are equal, average. If the absolute differences have the same sign, either arbitrarily assign consecutive ranks or average the ranks. The outcome is the same.

3. Compare the test statistic to the critical value to determine if the null hypothesis is to be rejected.

 Concept Check 14.B

The sign test and the Wilcoxon signed-rank test always yield identical results with respect to rejecting the null hypothesis. True or false? If false, explain.

14.9 Two friends have taken a number of identical classes. The grades the two friends received from these classes are shown below:

Class	Friend 1	Friend 2
Psychology	76	81
Biology	92	71
Calculus	98	67
Sociology	75	87
Anthropology	81	93
World History	83	95
Art I	87	96
Statistics	91	64
Finance	86	81
Economics I	89	77
Law I	76	98
Marketing	81	86
Management I	83	91
Language I	72	93
Accounting I	88	77
Accounting II	84	77
Computer Science	98	85
International Business	84	84
Report Writing	74	87
Logistics	91	83
Political Science	81	99

a. Do you notice any relationship between the grades of the two friends?

b. Using the Wilcoxon signed-rank test and MINITAB at the 5% level of significance, test if the two friends have the same grades.

14.10 A medication is developed to reduce the bacteria count in the blood stream. The medication may only be deemed successful if the bacteria count after medication is less than what it is before medication. Blood tests are made on individuals before and after they have taken the prescribed medication. The data are:

No medication 3.2, 6.7, 9.1, 4.3, 8.4, 2.3, 7.9, 10.1, 5.3, 6.8
Medication 2.2, 5.6, 8.8, 4.4, 6.9, 8.6, 7.7, 8.9, 4.4, 5.9

Using the Wilcoxon signed-rank test and MINITAB at the 1 %, can it be concluded that the new drug is a success?

14.11   In the National Football League there are 14 games (28 teams) per week for 16 weeks. Over the year a football fan records the number of correct predictions made by a local sport reporter and himself; as follows:

Week	Sport Reporter	Fan
1	11	8
2	13	10
3	6	9
4	10	8
5	8	8
6	11	9
7	7	8
8	10	4
9	13	9
10	11	10
11	7	10
12	12	10
13	9	5
14	13	11
15	11	9
16	10	8

a.   Based on the 5% level of significance and the Wilcoxon signed-rank test (using MINITAB), is the fan equal to the sport reporter as a forecaster?

b.   Are the results different when the sign test was used (Exercise 14.3)?

14.12   University students are asked to evaluate a new pen. The students are asked to record the length of time it takes for them to run out of ink. Each student is asked to record the length of time for two pens, one the old model, the other the developmental pen. The students do not know which is which, because both have the same physical appearances. The results are shown in hours:

Student	Old Pen	Developmental Pen
1	19.6	28.9
2	17.6	21.7
3	15.1	24.9
4	16.2	16.1
5	21.9	37.8
6	22.4	24.8
7	14.6	16.4
8	17.6	17.4
9	25.0	28.7
10	13.9	27.3
11	28.2	21.3
12	22.0	23.8
13	17.1	16.4
14	29.8	36.1
15	18.9	18.3
16	19.9	19.3
17	21.9	23.4
18	21.9	21.2
19	16.9	27.9
20	26.7	23.4

a. Visually, do you believe that the developmental pen is equal to or superior to the old pen in terms of longevity?

b. Test your hypothesis at the 5% level using the Wilcoxon signed-rank test using MINITAB.

c. Do the results differ from when the sign test is used (Exercise 14.4)? Explain.

14.13 A pharmaceutical company has developed what they believe is a novocain that will dissipate the old variety. They test the time it takes for 24 dentist's patients' mouths to feel normal (in hours). The dentist records the same patient first using the old, then the new novocain. The results are:

Patient	Old	New	Patient	Old	New
1	3.2	1.7	13	2.2	2.8
2	4.1	2.6	14	1.8	2.9
3	3.7	1.5	15	1.5	1.4
4	2.4	2.7	16	1.1	3.5
5	1.1	3.2	17	0.9	2.3
6	2.3	2.1	18	1.6	3.1
7	1.9	1.8	19	0.8	4.2
8	1.4	3.7	20	1.0	3.7
9	2.1	1.9	21	1.6	2.6
10	0.6	4.1	22	2.0	3.2
11	1.7	1.7	23	1.1	2.5
12	1.3	3.5	24	2.8	2.3

Using the Wilcoxon signed-rank test, is the hypothesis correct at the 1 % level?

14.14 A new machine is tested which is designed to reduce the errors in producing precision equipment. The new machine is placed alongside the older version and the differences between actual measurements and design measurements are recorded (in mm) for 20 bearings. It is important that the bearing not be too large or too small. The results are:

Part	Old	New	Part	Old	New
1	+ 1.2	−1.7	11	+ 0.7	−1.1
2	−0.9	+ 0.6	12	−0.9	+ 0.2
3	−0.7	−1.1	13	+ 0.5	+ 0.4
4	+ 1.4	−0.7	14	+ 1.1	+ 0.5
5	−0.2	+ 0.3	15	−1.3	−0.1
6	+ 1.3	+ 0.1	16	−0.6	+ 0.1
7	+ 0.9	−0.3	17	+ 0.8	−1.2
8	−0.7	−0.9	18	−0.1	+ 0.3
9	−0.8	+ 1.1	19	+ 1.2	−2.4
10	+ 0.4	−0.7	20	+ 0.9	−0.1

The new machine is much more efficient to operate than the old one; hence, to be superior to the old machine, the new machine just needs to equal the old in terms of deviations from specifications.

Using the Wilcoxon signed-rank test and MINITAB, is the performance of the new machine equal to that of the old (10% level)?

14.15 A new weight reduction plan is developed by a company. Paired individuals are selected based on demographics and psychographics. After 6 weeks the weight loss is recorded for 30 patients under the new and old plans. The company wants to guarantee that the new plan is better than old plan. The weight loss results are:

Patient	New	Old	Patient	New	Old
1	7	12	16	14	22
2	14	31	17	9	19
3	20	18	18	5	26
4	9	17	19	16	15
5	11	18	20	12	8
6	16	31	21	21	24
7	11	19	22	12	41
8	19	13	23	13	12
9	12	29	24	6	23
10	2	18	25	12	35
11	−3	10	26	16	14
12	14	22	27	15	26
13	9	15	28	19	22
14	0	13	29	15	11
15	12	19	30	16	19

Using the Wilcoxon signed-rank test and MINITAB, is the hypothesis correct at the 1 % level?

14.16 A supermarket tests to determine if more boxes of Cereal X are purchased when the box is placed at eye level or when customers have to reach for the product. The supermarket chain uses branches where the demographic and psychographic pro files of the customers are the same. Fifteen randomly selected hours are used to record the number of boxes purchased. The company believes that the boxes at eye level will sell at a greater volume than those not at eye level. The survey results are:

	Sales				Sales	
Hour	Eye Level	Not Eye Level	Hour	Eye Level	Not Eye Level
1	43	26	8	21	9
2	66	49	9	56	21
3	11	2	10	38	33
4	19	15	11	23	26
5	39	22	12	44	41
6	72	28	13	33	15
7	29	15	14	21	24
			15	46	18

Using the Wilcoxon signed-rank test at the 5% level and MINITAB, is the hypothesis correct?

14.4 The Coefficient of Rank Correlation

In Section 9.5, we discussed the coefficient of correlation, which provided a measure of the degree of association between paired variables. Another measure of association is the Spearman rank correlation coefficient, The statistic is symbolized by R_S, where R is the correlation coefficient symbol, and the subscript S stands for Spearman's rank correlation coefficient. The statistic is a measure of the association existing between the ranks of two variables. The Spearman rank correlation coefficient is the same as R (sometimes called the Pearson correlation coefficient which was covered in Section 9.5) applied to ranks.

Spearman's rank coefficient of correlation ranges from -1 to $+1$. The positive reading means that high ranks of one variable are related directly to high ranks of the other variable. A negative coefficient R_S means that high ranks of one series are related to low ranks of the other series.

Let us return to the boxing example and determine the degree of rank correlation for the variables. We are involved with a two-tailed test. Our null hypothesis is that $R_s = 0 (H_A: R_S \neq 0)$.

Minitab will allow us to easily get an approximation for the rank correlation. First we rank both columns of the data, and then perform a coefficient of correlation (Chapter 9.5) on the ranks of the data. The command sequence is as follows:

Data > Rank
Double click **ScoreA** into **Rank data in**.
Enter **RankScoA** into **Store ranks in**.
OK
Data > Rank
Double click **ScoreB** into **Rank data in**.
Enter **RankScoB** into **Store ranks in**.
OK
Stat > Basic Statistics > Correlation
Click in **RankScoA** and **RankScorB** into **Variable** box.
OK

The Minitab results are "Pearson correlation of the ranks $= -0.171$ with a P-value 0.457." The P-value is interpreted here exactly as it has been in previous chapters. If $\alpha \geq P$-Value we may reject H_0. If we desire to be 95% confident $\alpha = 0.05$ and is less than 0.457. Hence, we are unable to reject the null hypothesis (ISER) and the contest is declared a draw.

We will now follow the steps necessary when using the rank correlation coefficient.

Rules to Follow when Using the Rank Correlation Coefficient

1. Rank the two columns of data.
2. Run a coefficient of correlation on the ranks.
3. Use the P-Value to reject/not reject the null hypothesis.

 Concept Check 14.C

With the rank correlation coefficient we want to determine if low rankings for one variable are associated with low/high ranking for another variable, or if there is little relationship between the two. True or false? If false, explain.

14.17 On a rainy weekend, you and a friend watch fifteen rented movies. You each decide to rank the movies from 1 to 15, with 1 for the best. The rankings are as follows:

Movie	Your ranking	Friend's ranking
Return of the Killer Apes	9	10
Re-return of the Killer Apes	4	7
No-return of the Killer Apes	3	5
WW III: A footnote	12	14
Booger and Me	8	9
Godzilla meets Bambi	1	2
Godzilla in Concert	11	1
The Life of Otto Skorzeny	15	3
A Fistful of Lira	10	11
Robo-President	13	13
Aliens from Ice-cream Cones	14	15
The Spy who Couldn't	5	6
Jesse James vs. Godzilla	2	4
Adolph Hitler: Humanitarian	7	8
The Greenhouse Effect on Bluejeans	6	12

a. Would you expect a relationship to exist between your rankings and your friend's? If you expected a relationship, how would this alter the null hypothesis?

b. Compute the rank correlation for the two rankings.

14.18 University students are asked to evaluate a new pen. The students are asked to record the length of time it takes for them to run out of ink. Each student is asked to record the length of time for two pens, one the old model, the other the developmental pen. The students do not know which is which, because both have the same physical appearances. The results are shown in hours:

Student	Old Pen	Developmental Pen
1	19.6	28.9
2	17.6	21.7
3	15.1	24.9
4	16.2	16.1
5	21.9	37.8
6	22.4	24.8
7	14.6	16.4
8	17.6	17.4
9	25.0	28.7
10	13.9	27.3
11	28.2	21.3
12	22.0	23.8
13	17.1	16.4
14	29.8	23.6
15	18.9	18.3
16	19.9	19.3
17	21.9	23.4
18	21.9	21.2
19	16.9	27.9
20	26.7	23.4

The manufacturer believes that there is no relationship existing between the ranks of the two pens. Test the hypothesis at the 5% level of significance using the rank coefficient of correlation.

14.19   Two friends have taken a number of identical classes. The grades the two friends received from the same classes are shown below:

Class	Friend 1	Friend 2
Psychology	76	81
Biology	92	71
Calculus	98	67
Sociology	75	87
Anthropology	81	93
World History	83	95
Art I	87	96
Statistics	91	64
Finance	86	81
Economics I	89	77
Law I	76	98
Marketing	81	86
Management I	83	91
Language I	72	93
Accounting I	88	77
Accounting II	84	77
Computer Science	98	85
International Business	84	84
Report Writing	74	87
Logistics	91	83
Political Science	81	99

Using the rank correlation coefficient at the 5% level of significance to test if both friends have performed equally at the university.

14.20   The following represents pets that people have. You would like to buy a pet that both you and your spouse will like. Both of you independently rank different pets.

Pet	Your Ranking	Spouse Ranking
Little dog	15	1
Big dog	17	2
Little cat	16	3
Big cat	19	8
Miniature rabbit	9	4
Rabbit	3	7
Guinea Pig	2	9
Goldfish	1	10
Tropical fish	14	11
Parrot	4	5
Cockatiel	13	6
Parakeet	12	12
Monkey	8	18
Small snake	18	20
Big snake	20	19
Gerbil	7	13
Snail	5	14
Horse	6	17
Turtle	10	16
Frog	11	15

a. You and your spouse believe either that no relationship between the ranks exists. State the null hypothesis.
b. Compute the rank correlation coefficient.

14.21   In the National Football League there are 14 games (28 teams) per week for 16 weeks. Over the year a football fan records the number of correct predictions made by a local sport reporter and himself, as follows:

Week	Sport Reporter	Fan
1	11	8
2	13	10
3	6	9
4	10	8
5	8	8
6	11	9
7	7	8
8	10	4
9	13	9
10	11	10
11	7	10
12	12	10
13	9	5
14	13	11
15	11	9
16	10	8

Compute the rank correlation coefficient.

14.22   Two friends take 8 college classes together over an academic year. At the end of the year each friend ranks the 8 professors. For the following rankings compute R_S:

Instructor	Your Rank	Friend's Rank
1	4	5
2	1	2
3	7	6
4	6	7
5	5	4
6	2	3
7	8	8
8	3	1

14.23   An artist and an engineer are asked to rank the top art pieces from 8 area schools. The ranks are:

Art Piece	Engineer's Rank	Artist's Rank
A	8	1
B	7	2
C	6	3
D	5	4
E	4	5
F	3	6
G	2	7
H	1	8

Compute R_S.

14.24   A supermarket tests to determine if more boxes of Cereal X are purchased when the box is placed at eye level or when customers have to reach for the product. The supermarket chain uses two branches where the demographic and psychographic profiles of the customers are the same. Fifteen randomly selected hours are used to record the number of boxes purchased. The company believes that there is no association between the ranks of the corresponding sales. At the 1% level of significance, is the company correct? The survey results are:

Hour	Sales Eye Level	Sales Not Eye Level	Hour	Sales Eye Level	Sales Not Eye Level
1	43	26	8	21	9
2	66	49	9	56	21
3	11	2	10	38	33
4	19	15	11	23	26
5	39	22	12	44	41
6	72	28	13	33	15
7	29	15	14	21	24
			15	46	18

14.5   The Mann–Whitney/Wilcoxon Rank-Sum Test

We can use two equivalent methods to compare two independent populations of unequal sample sizes. They are the **Wilcoxon Rank-Sum test** and the **Mann–Whitney U test**. Because they are equivalent tests, we cover them as though they are the same test.

Suppose two professors have taught all of the business statistics classes at a college over the last few years. Each class has the same number of students. The average grades for each professor are given in Table 14.3. Included are the ranks for all 23 classes. For ties, from the same professor we average the ranks. For ties between two professors, the ranks must be averaged (as was the case when each professor had a class with a 69.8 average). The ranks of the classes will be summed for comparison purposes. There will be a test statistic for professor A (W_A) and for professor B (W_B). The sum of the ranks are:

$$W_A = 1 + 2 + 3 + 5.5 + 7 + 12 + 13 + 15 + 18 + 23 = 99.5$$
$$W_B = 4 + 5.5 + 8 + 9 + 10 + 11 + 14 + 16 + 17 + 19 + 20 + 21 + 22 = 176.5$$
$$W_A + W_B = \frac{n(n+1)}{2} = \frac{23(24)}{2} = 276$$

The sum of $W_A + W_B$ is 276 and is constant for $n = 23$. Hence, if W_A increases then W_B must decrease. The closer W_A is to W_B, the more likely it is for us to have ISER for the null hypothesis (that there is no difference between the grades given by the two professors). The further W_A is from W_B, the more likely we are to reject the null hypothesis, which is

H_0: The professors give the same median grades.
H_A: The professors give different median grades.

Table 14.3   Class Averages for Two Business Statistics Professors
***Data File on MINITAB CD**

PROF A: 87.6, 67.9, 77.2, 69.8, 76.9, 62.1, 73.7, 80.2, 66.7, 70.4
PROF B: 83.2, 73.0, 84.7, 69.8, 80.4, 77.5, 79.7, 68.3, 72.4, 72.8, 77.1, 81.6, 72.5

Ranking of Class Averages for All 23 Classes: $n_A = 10$, $n_B = 13$

Rank 1	62.1	Prof A	Rank 13	76.9	Prof A
Rank 2	66.7	Prof A	Rank 14	77.1	Prof B
Rank 3	67.9	Prof A	Rank 15	77.2	Prof A
Rank 4	68.3	Prof B	Rank 16	77.5	Prof B
Rank 5.5	69.8	Prof A	Rank 17	79.7	Prof B
Rank 5.5	69.8	Prof B	Rank 18	80.2	Prof A
Rank 7	70.4	Prof A	Rank 19	80.4	Prof B
Rank 8	72.4	Prof B	Rank 20	81.6	Prof B
Rank 9	72.5	Prof B	Rank 21	83.2	Prof B
Rank 10	72.8	Prof B	Rank 22	84.7	Prof B
Rank 11	73.0	Prof B	Rank 23	87.6	Prof A
Rank 12	73.7	Prof A			

MINITAB will perform the Mann–Whitney test, give us our W values, and tell us if the test is significant. The data must be entered as it appears in its raw form (Table 14.3) with Prof A grades in the first column and Prof B grades in the second column. The command sequence is:

Stat > Nonparametrics > Mann–Whitney
Double click **ProfA** to **First Sample** box.
Double click **ProfB** to **Second Sample** box.
Specify confidence level and it a two-tailed or one tailed test (**Alternatives**).
OK

Mann–Whitney Confidence Interval and Test

ProfA   N = 10   Median =   72.05
ProfB   N = 13   Median =   77.10
Point estimate for ETA1-ETA2 is −3.20
95.6 Percent C.I. for ETA1-ETA2 is (−9.90, 3.10)
W = 99:5
Test of ETA1 = ETA2 vs. ETA1 $\neq$ ETA2 is significant at 0.2148
The test is significant at 0.2147 (adjusted for ties)

Cannot reject at alpha = 0.05

We will not summarize with the rules to follow when using the Wilcoxon rank sum test.

Rules to Follow when Using the Wilcoxon Rank Sum Test

1.   Uneven sample sizes for the two independent random continuous data sets are acceptable.

2.   Pool the data, then rank them from 1 to n. If ties exist from different samples, average the ranks. If ties exist from the same sample, either average the ranks or arbitrarily assign consecutive ranks. The two approaches are equivalent.

3.   Compare the test statistic to the critical value to determine if the null hypothesis is to be rejected.

450

The Wilcoxon Rank Sum test requires paired data while the Wilcoxon Signed-Rank test can have unequal sample sizes. True or false? If false, explain.

Exercises

14.25 A personnel department is developing a screening test for applicants. The company wants to determine if minorities score the same as non-minorities. In the pretesting process, the following scores are recorded.

Minorities: 87, 62, 17, 74, 91, 87, 64, 82, 91, 61, 59, 67
Non-Minorities: 76, 41, 82, 71, 66, 78, 71, 56, 82, 94, 74, 88, 55, 73, 65, 39, 53, 99, 81

a. As the personnel director, would you set this up as a one or two-tailed test? What is the null hypothesis? Explain.
b. Use the Wilcoxon rank sum test and MINITAB (5% level of significance), to test the null hypothesis.
c. If you were the director of personnel, what is the relationship that exists between having ISER or rejecting the null hypothesis and in being in compliance with the law in terms of discriminating against minorities?

14.26 The following lists represent the number of sick days for employees under and over 40 years of age, last year.

age ≤ 40: 12, 8, 5, 0, 1, 7, 23, 7, 0, 2, 6, 2, 9, 2
age 40+ : 2, 15, 8, 2, 0, 7, 3, 0, 2, 0, 0

a. Use the Wilcoxon rank sum test and MINITAB (1% level of significance) to test if there is a difference between the two groups.
b. Comment on how a personnel director might utilize such information.

14.27 A production line manager watches the number of defective parts produced daily by an old and new machine. The new machine has only been installed for two weeks. The following lists the number of defective parts produced by each machine.

Old: 6, 14, 8, 2, 20, 9, 13, 21, 23, 17, 11, 12, 15, 18, 16
New: 10, 7, 5, 2, 0, 1, 3, 4, 1, 2

For the new machine to be a success, it must be as error free as the old machine. Use the Wilcoxon rank sum test and MINITAB, at the 10% level of significance, to test if the new machine is a success.

14.28 Suppose you record your average grades for classes in which your instructors are under and over 5 ft. 5 in. tall and obtain the following results:

Over: 88.1, 77.6, 59, 64.3, 87.8, 90.4, 88.6, 71.1, 69.1, 79.9
Under: 76.4, 65.3, 86.3, 98.6, 78.5, 87.2, 64.9, 94.3, 87.5, 61.2, 73.2, 76

a. Is there a difference in your grades between instructors under and over 5 ft. 5 in. at the 5% level of significance (using MINITAB)?
b. If there is a difference, could you think of a cause for such a difference?

14.29 Suppose a company compares two brands of light bulbs (A and B) to determine if one lasts longer than the other. Since brand B is 10% more costly, the only way brand B would be preferred to A is if brand B lasts 10% longer than brand A. The manager attempts to equalize the data by reducing the life of product B by 10% (by multiplying the data by 0.9). The manager wants to determine if the life expectancy of A is equal to the life expectancy of the reduced product B. The following lists represent the lengths of a series of both brands:

A: 36.4, 62.1, 9.8, 55.3, 29.1, 45.8, 67.0, 38.9, 49.3, 55.6, 40.3
B: 65.9, 46.3, 77.9, 62.8, 43.2, 71.8, 39.3, 55.3, 68.9, 65.8

   a.   Are we involved in a one or two-tailed test?
   b.   Use the Wilcoxon rank sum test and MINITAB (5% level of significance) to test the null hypothesis.

Exercise 14.30   2000 Infant Mortality Figures per 1000 births

Developing Countries	Deaths	Developed Countries	Deaths
Iraq	63	Germany	5
Afghanistan	149	Great Britain	6
Bangladesh	72	Switzerland	5
India	65	U.S.	7
Laos	95	Belgium	5
Pakistan	83	Denmark	5
Angola	196	Greece	7
Boliva	60	Italy	6
Ecuador	35	Sweden	4
Haiti	97	France	5
Brazil	38	Russia	20
Mexico	26		
Peru	41		

If we hypothesize that the mortality rates for developing and developed countries were the same (at the 1% level), would we have ISER for this hypothesis using the Wilcoxon rank sum test?

14.31   We record the number of defects per hour from both old and new machines. We will purchase the new machines only if the hourly defects are less than the old machine. The data are:

Old: 7.2, 8.3, 9.7, 4.1, 5.3, 6.9, 2.7
New: 1.7, 2.2, 4.0, 1.9, 3.8, 2.5

Using $W_{A:test}$, $\alpha = 0.025$, is the null hypothesis rejected (use MINITAB)?

14.32   A golf club member has developed a new gold driver that is supposed to hit the ball farther. The club will buy the golf club if it equals the driving power of the old clubs. The clubs used and the distances measured are as follows:

Old: 301, 314, 290, 322, 318
New: 216, 225, 228, 247, 261, 218, 253

At the 5% level, using the Wilcoxon rank sum test and MINITAB, will the new clubs be purchased?

14.6 The Kruskal–Wallis H Test

When the Wilcoxon rank sum and the Mann–Whitney tests compare two independent random populations, the two groups of data are pooled and ranks are made for the pooled data. Then the sum of the ranks are tabulated for the different groups. When more than two populations are involved (equal sample sizes unnecessary), however, only the Kruskal–Wallis test can be used. This test is the nonparametric equivalent to the one factor completely randomized design ANOVA and uses the sum of the averaged individual squared sum of the ranks (T). The test statistic is

The Kruskal–Wallis Test Statistic

$$H_{\text{test}} = \frac{12 \bullet T}{n(n+1)} - 3(n+1) \qquad\qquad (14.1)$$

where

T = the average individual squared sum of the ranks

$T = (\Sigma \text{Rank}_A)^2/n_A + (\Sigma \text{Rank}_B)^2/n_B + \cdots + (\Sigma \text{Rank}_i)^2/n_i$

n = the pooled sample size

where T is the sum of the individual average squared sum of the ranks ($T = (\Sigma \text{Rank}_i)^2/n_i$: see Table 14.4 for computations). The H statistic follows a chi-square distribution with degrees of freedom equal to the number of populations (in our example, there are three different populations: $P = 3$) minus 1, or $3 - 1 = 2$ ($P - 1$) degrees of freedom. This is true as long as the sample size in each group is 5 or more ($n_i \geq 5$).

Table 14.4   Class Averages for Three Business Statistics Professors
***Data File on MINITAB CD**

PROF A: 87.6, 67.9, 77.2, 69.8, 76.9, 62.1, 73.7, 80.2, 66.7, 70.4
PROF B: 83.2, 73.0, 84.7, 69.8, 80.4, 77.5, 79.7, 68.3, 72.4, 72.8, 77.1, 81.6, 72.5
PROF C: 66.9, 64.3, 75.2, 58.3, 60.1, 59.2, 62.7, 67.5, 62.0, 55.1, 60.2

Rank	Value	Prof		Rank	Value	Prof
Rank 1	55.1	Prof C		Rank 18	72.4	Prof B
Rank 2	58.3	Prof C		Rank 19	72.5	Prof B
Rank 3	59.2	Prof C		Rank 20	72.8	Prof B
Rank 4	60.1	Prof C		Rank 21	73.0	Prof B
Rank 5	60.2	Prof C		Rank 22	73.7	Prof A
Rank 6	62.0	Prof C		Rank 23	75.2	Prof C
Rank 7	62.1	Prof A		Rank 24	76.9	Prof A
Rank 8	62.7	Prof C		Rank 25	77.1	Prof B
Rank 9	64.3	Prof C		Rank 26	77.2	Prof A
Rank 10	66.7	Prof A		Rank 27	77.5	Prof B
Rank 11	66.9	Prof C		Rank 28	79.7	Prof B
Rank 12	67.5	Prof C		Rank 29	80.2	Prof A
Rank 13	67.9	Prof A		Rank 30	80.4	Prof B
Rank 14	68.3	Prof B		Rank 31	81.6	Prof B
Rank 15.5	69.8	Prof A		Rank 32	83.2	Prof B
Rank 15.5	69.8	Prof B		Rank 33	84.7	Prof B
Rank 17	70.4	Prof A		Rank 34	87.6	Prof A

$\Sigma \text{Rank}_A = 7 + 10 + 13 + 15.5 + 17 + 22 + 24 + 26 + 29 + 34 = 197.5$
$\Sigma \text{Rank}_B = 14 + 15.5 + 18 + 19 + 20 + 21 + 25 + 27 + 28 + 30 + 31 + 32 + 33 = 313.5$
$\Sigma \text{Rank}_C = 1 + 2 + 3 + 4 + 5 + 6 + 8 + 9 + 11 + 12 + 23 = 84.0$

$T = (\Sigma \text{Rank}_A)^2/n_A + (\Sigma \text{Rank}_B)^2/n_B + (\Sigma \text{Rank}_C)^2/n_C$
$T = (197.5)^2/10 + (313.5)^2/13 + (84)^2/11$
$T = 3{,}900.625 + 7{,}560.173 + 641.455 = 12{,}102.253$

The H statistic for our class-average problem is

$$H_{\text{test}} = \frac{12 \bullet 12,102.253}{34(34+1)} - 3(34+1)$$
$$H_{\text{test}} = 122.040 - 105 = 17.04$$

Since H_{test} is $> \chi^2_{0.05(2)}$ (Appendix A: Table 6; 5.991), the null hypothesis
H_0: The 3 professors, grades are the same.
H_A: At least 2 professors, grades differ.
must be rejected. The grades given by at least one of the professors are different. In this example, Professor C gives lower grades than Professors A and B. However, this fact doesn't necessarily have a negative connotation. Maybe Professor C's grades are better representations of the students' work. Also, Professor C may give a more rigorous course, which may translate into better grades in other courses for which this course is a prerequisite. Hence, it is possible that Professor C may be preferred because the quality in teaching may correlate to higher grades in other classes.
We will now summarize the rules to follow when using the Kruskal–Wallis test.

Rules to Follow When Using the Kruskal–Wallis H Test

1. Uneven sample sizes for more than two independent random data sets drawn four continuous populations are acceptable.
2. $n_A, n_B, n_C, \ldots, n_i \geq 5$
3. Pool the data, then rank from 1 to n. If any ties are from different samples, average the ranks. If any ties are from the same sample, either average or arbitrarily assign consecutive ranks.
4. Use formula 14.2 to determine the test statistic H_{test}.

MINITAB will perform a Kruskal–Wallis analysis for us. When entering the data enter all of the class average into the first column (Class Av), then enter into the second column the professor (Prof) who gave the grade (either 1, 2, or 3) (see Table 14.5).

Stat > Nonparametrics > Kruskal–Wallis
Double click **ClassAv** into **Response** box.
Double click **Prof** into **Factor** box.
OK

Table 14.5   Kruskal–Wallis Test

KRUSKAL–WALLIS TEST ON CLASSAV

Prof	N	Median	Ave Rank	Z
A	10	72.05	19.7	0.85
B	13	77.10	24.1	3.05
C	11	62.00	7.6	−3.99
Overall	34		17.5	

$H = 17.04\ DF = 2\ P = 0.000$
$H = 17.04\ DF = 2\ P = 0.000$ (adjusted for ties)

When there are ties in the data, the significance level adjusted for ties is also printed. The unadjusted significance level is conservative if ties are present; the adjusted significance level is usually closer to the correct values, but is not always conservative.

The Kruskal–Wallis H test is essentially a weighted average of the sum of the means for the three or more populations. True or false? If false, explain.

Exercises

14.33 Listed are the 2000 death rates per 1,000 live births for randomly selected countries from four geographic regions.

2000 Death Rate per 1,000 Living Births

Region A		Region B		Region C		Region D	
Angola	149	Algeria	42	Afghanistan	149	Canada	5
Botswana	62	Egypt	62	Bangladesh	72	Denmark	5
Cameroon	71	Gaza Strip	26	Burma	75	Finland	4
Chad	97	Iraq	63	Cambodia	67	France	5
Congo	102	Israel	8	China*	29	Germany	5
Ethiopia	101	Jordan	21	Hong Kong	6	Greece	7
Ghana	57	Lebanon	29	India	65	Italy	6
Kenya	69	Libya	30	Indonesia	42	Norway	4
Mali	123	Morocco	50	Iran	30	Russia	20
Mozambique	140	Oman	23	Japan	4	U.K.	6
Nigeria	74	Syria	35	Laos	95	U.S.	7
Senegal	58	W. Sahara	133	Vietnam	31		
Swaziland	109						
Uganda	53						
Zimbabwe	62						

A = Sub-Saharan Africa B = Near East & North Africa C = Asia D = North America, Europe, U.S.S.R.
*China, Mainland
Source: World Population Profile; 1989, U.S. Department of Commerce, Bureau of the Census and www.census.gov

Using H_{test} at the 5% level with MINITAB, are the death rates per 1,000 births identical for the four regions?

14.34 A production line manager counts the defective parts produced by 6 employees on different days of the week. Absences result in an unequal number of employees throughout the week.

M: 16, 14, 12, 21, 19, 26
T: 1, 4, 2, 5, 0, 3
W: 0, 1, 5, 2, 8
Th: 7, 3, 9, 10, 0, 2
F: 24, 18, 22, 28, 43

a. The manager believes that on Mondays and Fridays employees are either thinking ahead to, or looking back, at the weekend. Use the Kruskal–Wallis H test and MINITAB (5% level of significance), to test if the manager is correct.

b. If the manager appears correct, can you come up with any ideas to remedy the situation?

14.35 A hardware store carries three different brands of equally priced hammers. The manager records the number of each unit sold over the last 6 days, as follows:

Brand A: 12, 8, 5, 0, 14, 11
Brand B: 6, 7, 2, 9, 1, 3
Brand C: 23, 21, 15, 16, 13, 17

a. The manager believes that all three hammers have equal sales. Use the Kruskal–Wallis test and MINITAB (5% level of significance) to test if the manager's hypothesis is correct.
b. Comment on how you might utilize this information.

14.36 Suppose over the last week two couch potatoes and a TV critic record the hours of TV watched per day for a week. The hours watched are

Potato A: 12.1, 6.2, 9.7, 10.4, 4.3, 18.1, 17.2
Potato B: 9.1, 8.7, 6.9, 19.3, 12.3, 9.8, 7.0
Critic C: 6.8, 13.6, 7.4, 4.4, 12.7, 13.3, 13.0

Based on the Kruskal–Wallis H test and MINITAB (1% level of significance), is at least one of the selections different from the rest?

14.37 A surfboard shop sells three surfboards priced from expensive to less expensive. Since for two days the store ran out of the least expensive boards, there are no data for those two days. The number of boards sold is:

Expensive: 5, 8, 9, 15, 9, 10, 7
Medium: 2, 0, 1, 3, 6, 4, 0
Cheap: 13, 12, 7, 17, 21

a. The manager believes that an equal number of the three boards are sold daily. Use the Kruskal–Wallis H test and MINITAB (10% level of significance) to test if the manager is correct.
b. Comment on how you might utilize this information in stocking inventory.

14.38 A university department wishes to determine if the average class grades are different when 3 different texts are used. The compiled data are as follows:

Text A: 74.7, 86.2, 68.3, 77.1, 72.8, 80.5, 69.9
Text B: 82.0, 70.7, 76.4, 72.4, 78.6, 72.2
Text C: 75.1, 79.3, 67.9, 81.4, 70.6

Using the 10% level of significance and H_{test} are the grades the same using the 3 different texts (use MINITAB)?

14.39 A consumer magazine asks individuals insured by 5 companies to rate them on 4 factors (each with a 0–100 scale), which are then averaged. The averages are as follows:

Company A: 81.7, 90.2, 76.1, 92.9, 77.2
Company B: 93.7, 69.1, 88.3, 76.5, 90.0, 83.9, 81.0
Company C: 78.8, 87.3, 90.3, 77.4, 85.1
Company D: 69.2, 42.8, 51.1, 41.0, 62.7, 68.5
Company E: 87.1, 74.8, 94.4, 81.6, 82.4, 77.7, 86.3

Using the 5% level of significance and H_{test}, are the ratings for the 5 insurance companies the same (use MINITAB)?

14.40 A football team records the points scored against opponents on grass, artificial turf outdoors, and artificial turf indoors. The points scored is as follows:

Grass: 27, 36, 14, 33, 16, 49
Art Out: 10, 37, 21, 28, 42
Art Ind: 9, 56, 18, 35, 30

Using the 1% level of significance and H_{test} are the points scored the same for grass, artificial turf outdoors and indoors (use MINITAB)?

14.7 The Runs Test (for a Single Sample)

Sometimes it is important to determine if a data set is random, such as for state lottery drawings. Lottery games use approximately 50 ping-pong balls with numerals 01 to 50 inscribed on them. Normally, a vacuum is used to select the winning numbers. During a game it is essential that every number have an equal chance of being selected. If odd numbered balls were lighter than even numbered balls, the lighter balls would have a greater chance of being sucked in by the vacuum. To test for randomness, we can select 16 balls and record the following even (E) and odd (O) sequence:

E, E, E, O, O, O, O, O, E, O, O, O, E, O, O, E

If the data were truly random, we would expect an approximate equal number of even and odd numbers. In addition, we would not be able to predict whether the next ball selected was even or odd. Even if a data set contained an equal number of even and odd numbers, non-randomness would show up in two extreme scenarios. First if all of the even numbers were followed by all of the odd numbers (E, E, E, E, E, E, E, E, O, O, O, O, O, O, O, O), this would indicate a clumping (or grouping) of even and odd numbers. Thus, the data are not random. Second, if the sequence alternated between even and odd (E, O, E, O, E, O, E, O, E, O, E, O, E, O, E, O), the data also would not be random. In this case, we would be able to predict the next ball (it would be an even number).

To utilize the runs test, we must begin by placing our pencil beneath the first outcome and drawing a line connecting all similar outcomes. When you reach a different outcome, a new run begins. That run continues as long the outcome remains the same. Each outcome change determines a new run. The first of the two extreme scenarios mentioned above ($n = 16$: n_a = even = 8: n_b = odd) yields one run for E and one run for O (total runs of $R_T = 2$), which the second scenario yields eight runs for E and eight runs for O ($R_T = 16$).

$$\underbrace{E, E, E, E, E, E, E, E}_{1_E}, \underbrace{O, O, O, O, O, O, O, O}_{1_O} \qquad R_T = 2$$

$$\underbrace{E}_{1_E}, \underbrace{O}_{1_O}, \underbrace{E}_{2_E}, \underbrace{O}_{2_O}, \underbrace{E}_{3_E}, \underbrace{O}_{3_O}, \underbrace{E}_{4_E}, \underbrace{O}_{4_O}, \underbrace{E}_{5_E}, \underbrace{O}_{5_O}, \underbrace{E}_{6_E}, \underbrace{O}_{6_O}, \underbrace{E}_{7_E}, \underbrace{O}_{7_O}, \underbrace{E}_{8_E}, \underbrace{O}_{8_O} \qquad R_T = 16$$

These cases represent the maximum and minimum number of runs and a case where the data set is nonrandom. The closer the number of runs for E and O is to the average for the two extremes (upper and lower limits), the greater the probability that the data sequence is random $[(R_{UL} + R_{LL})/2 = R_E = R_O = (8 + 1)/2 = 4.5)]$.

Let us return to our original example and determine the runs for even (E) and odd (O) data. In the drawing $n = 16$, $n_E = 6$, $n_O = 10$. Hence, the minimum number of runs is 1 each ($R_E = R_O = 1$: $R_T = 2$). The maximum number of runs is $R_T = 13$ ($R_E = 6$ and $R_O = 7$). In our example, there are actually four runs for even and three runs for odd numbers ($R_E = 4$, $R_O = 3$; $R_T = 7$).

$$\underbrace{E, E, E}_{1_E}, \underbrace{O, O, O, O, O}_{1_O}, \underbrace{E}_{2_E}, \underbrace{O, O, O}_{2_O}, \underbrace{E}_{3_E}, \underbrace{O, O}_{3_O}, \underbrace{E}_{4_E} \qquad R_T = 7$$

The null hypothesis is that the data are random.

H_0: the data are random.

H_A: the data are not random.

Rules to Follow When Using the Number of Runs Test

1. Data are sequentially analyzed for a single randomly selected sample.
2. We must be able to group data into only two categories such as man–woman, heads–tails, defective–or not.
3. Perform the runs analysis to determine R_T.

Minitab will perform the runs test for us (see Table 14.6). We enter the data into a single column (Data) with either a 1 or a 2. The commands are.

Stats > Nonparametric > Run Test
Double click **Data** into the **Variables** box.
OK

Table 14.6   Runs Test
*Data File on MINITAB CD

EvenOdd

$K = 1.6250$
 The observed number of runs $= 7$
 The expected number of runs $= 8.5000$
 10 Observations above K 6 below
 *N Small—The following approximation may be invalid
         The test is significant at 0.405
         Cannot reject at alpha $= 0.05$

 Concept Check 14.F

The basic logic of the number of runs test is that if the next value of a sequence can be predicted with a high degree of accuracy, it's nonrandom. If not, the sequence is random. True or false? If false, explain.

Exercises

14.41   A gambling casino fears that its roulette wheel is becoming unbalanced. It records the number of black and reds that turn up. They are:

$R, R, B, R, B, R, B, R, R, B, R, B, R, R, B, R, R, B, B, B, R$

     a. Use the runs test and MINITAB (5% level of significance) to test if there is a problem with the roulette wheel.

     b. How might management utilize this information?

14.42   A large tourist attraction checks daily to see if those entering the grounds are locals (L) or not (NL).

$L, NL, NL, NL, L, L, NL, L, L, L, NL, NL, L, NL, NL, L, L, L, NL, NL$

Use the runs test and MINITAB (5% level of significance) to test if there is any relationship between the customers entering the turnstiles.

458

14.43 A customs official selects passengers to determine if they are bringing anything illegal into the country. The following is the sequence of passengers who were searched (S) and who were not searched (NS).

S, NS, NS, NS, NS, S, NS, NS, NS, S, S, NS, NS, NS, NS, NS, S, NS, NS, S,
NS, NS, S, S

The custom official wants to be sure that the search procedure is done randomly.

a. Use the runs test and MINITAB (5% level of significance) to test the hypothesis of randomness.
b. If the process was not random, how could this information be used by those wanting to carry out illegal activities?

14.44 The number of even (E) and odd (O) numbers selected in a lotto drawing are:

E, O, O, O, E, O, E, E, O, E, O, O, E, E, E, O, O, E, E, E

Using MINITAB are you satisfied that the drawing is random based on the runs test (5% level of significance)?

14.45 A customs official searches 3 consecutive persons, lets 20 go by without a search, searches 3 consecutive persons, lets 20 go by without a search, searches 3 consecutive persons, then lets 20 go by without a search.

a. Do you believe the search process to be random? Explain.
b. Use the runs test and MINITAB at the 1% level to confirm your suspicions.

14.46 You are performing a least squares analysis and have MINITAB print the residuals. You note that there are 12 negative residuals followed by 24 positive residuals followed by 9 negative residuals. You remember that residuals are supposed to be random, including the signs. Perform a runs test and MINITAB at the 1 % level to determine if the residuals are random with regard to their signs.

14.47 For the data set of Chapter 10, Appendix A (duplicated below), we ascertained through d that autocorrelation was present in the data.

X	Y	e
1	10.779	+1.378
2	10.890	+0.451
3	11.642	+0.165
4	12.008	−0.507
5	13.416	−0.137
6	14.337	−0.254
7	15.006	−0.623
8	15.520	−1.147
9	17.688	−0.017
10	18.755	+0.012
11	19.355	−0.426
12	20.453	−0.366
13	21.562	−0.295
14	23.092	+0.197
15	23.883	−0.050
16	26.595	+1.624

a. Use the runs test and MINITAB to determine if the signs of the residuals are random at the 5% level.

b. If the results differ from the d statistic (which said the residuals are autocorrelated), which test do you believe is more powerful? Can you state a reason why the results are different?

14.48 A radio signal comes from space with just 2 signals, A and B. The signal sequence is as follows:

$A, B, A, B, A, B, A, B, A, B, A$

Is the signal from space random according to the runs test, at the 5% level (use MINITAB)?

14.8 The Friedman S Test Statistic

In Section 8.3, we used a randomized block design to compare similar blocks of experimental units in our analysis of variance section. In order to use the analysis of variance techniques, we had to assume that the individual populations (or k treatments) were from normal distributions with equal variances. These are restrictive assumptions not required by the Friedman S test analysis, which is the nonparametric equivalent to the ANOVA experimental block design.

As always, we will illustrate with the use of an example. A marketing research firm finds 50 randomly selected respondents who read all 4 weekly publications in their market. The research firm asks the respondents to rank the 4 weekly publications in terms of 11 characteristics. These include the variety of articles, business related articles, timeliness of the articles, etc. A "1" is given for the lowest and a "4" to the highest frequency by topic. The results and assigned ranks are given in Table 14.7. Ties are assigned the average of the ranks involved.

Table 14.7 The Rankings by 50 Respondents Who Read 4 Weekly Publications Regarding 11 Factors or Blocks
*Data File on MINITAB CD

	WEEKLY PUBLICATIONS							
Topic	AgeWeek	R_1	WeekWeek	R_2	LifeWeek	R_3	TimeWeek	R_4
Variety	16	4	12	2	13	3	9	1
Business	10	2.5	9	1	21	4	10	2.5
Timeliness	17	4	10	2	15	3	8	1
Appearance	9	1.5	17	4	15	3	9	1.5
Sports	6	2	14	3	5	1	25	4
Arts	14	3	12	2	15	4	9	1
International	15	3.5	10	1.5	15	3.5	10	1.5
National	15	3	7	1	16	4	12	2
Weather	16	3	7	2	21	4	6	1
Human Interest	20	4	8	1	12	3	10	2
Sensationalism	5	1	20	4	7	2	18	3
	$\Sigma R_1 = 31.5$		$\Sigma R_2 = 23.5$		$\Sigma R_3 = 34.5$		$\Sigma R_4 = 20.5$	

The marketing research firm wishes to determine the effectiveness of each of the 4 weekly publications concerning the 11 categories. The 11 categories act as blocks since each weekly magazine would attempt to specialize in certain characteristics.

The hypotheses are

H_0: The probability distributions are the same for the 4 weeklies.

H_A: The probability distributions are not the same for all 4 weeklies. At least one is different.
The formula for the Friedman test statistic (S) is

Friedman's Test Statistic (S)

$$S = \frac{12 \bullet T}{b \bullet L(L+1)} - 3 \bullet b(L+1) \qquad (14.2)$$

where

$b =$ the number of blocks

$L =$ the number of treatment levels

$T =$ the individual squared sum of rank

$T = (\Sigma \text{Rank}_A)^2 + (\Sigma \text{Rank}_B)^2 + \cdots + (\Sigma \text{Rank}_i)^2$

Hence, our data set

$$T = 31.5^2 + 23.5^2 + 34.5^2 + 20.5^2 = 3.155$$

$$S = \frac{12 \bullet 3.155}{(1)(4)(4+1)} - 3(11)(4+1) = 7.0909$$

The S test statistic has a sampling distribution that the chi-square distribution can approximate with $L - 1$ degrees of freedom. The approximation holds as long as either b or $L > 5$. If $S > \chi^2_{\alpha(df)}$, the null hypothesis must be rejected. Conversely, if $S \leq \chi^2_{\alpha(df)}$, the null hypothesis can't be rejected. With a 5% significance level, $\chi^2_{.05(3)} = 9.348$; hence, $S \leq \chi^2_{.05(3)}$ (7.0909 $\geq$ 9.348), and we have ISER for the null hypothesis.

We will now summarize the rules to follow when using the S statistic.

Rules to Follow when Using the Friedman S Statistic

1. In order to use the chi-square approximation, b or L must exceed 5.
2. The treatments are randomly assigned within the blocks and the probability distributions for the L treatments are continuous and identical (H_0).
3. Rank each of the observations within each block from the largest to the smallest rank. Ties are the average of the ranks involved.
4. Use formula 14.2 to determine S.

MINITAB will perform the Friedman test for us (see Table 14.8). We enter the data into three columns. The first column contains the rankings (**Rankings**). The second column contains which weekly is involved; AgeWeek= 1, WeekWeek= 2, LifeWeek= 3, TimeWeek= 4 (**labeled Weekly**). The third column contains the Topic: variety= 1, business= 2, timeliness= 3, etc. The commands are:

Stats > Nonparametric > Friedman
Double click **Rankings** into the **Response** box.
Double click **Weekly** into the **Treatment** box.
Double click **Topic** into the **Block** box.
OK

461

Table 14.8   Friedman Test

Friedman test for Rankings by Weekly blocked by Topic.

$S = 7.09$ $DF = 3$ $P = 0.069$
$S = 7.36$ $DF = 3$ $P = 0.061$ (adjusted for ties)

Weekly	N	Est Median	Sum of Ranks
1	11	14.125	31.5
2	11	10.375	23.5
3	11	14.625	34.5
4	11	9.375	20.5

Grand median = 12.125

✔ **Concept Check 14.G**

The Friedman test uses the logic that the closer the ranks of the treatment variables are to each other, the greater the chance the null hypothesis will be rejected. True or false? If false, explain.

Exercises

14.49   Three medications are being tested. The three medications are given to different age groups and a bacteria count is made after the application of the medicine with the following results:

Age Group	Medication A	Medication B	Medication C
20 to 29	67	89	43
30 to 39	76	91	41
40 to 49	81	87	39
50 to 59	71	85	56
60 to 69	73	86	60
70 to 79	69	71	76

Use the Friedman S test statistic and MINITAB to test that the three probability distributions are the same (1% level of significance).

14.50   A company is experimenting with 4 new strains of pine trees which will grow at accelerated rates. Based on preliminary research, the company wants to know which strain to press on with. Strain A is the cheapest; hence, if there are no differences in the growth patterns this is the one with which they will go. However, if one of the strains does yield superior growth, this is the one with which it will go. The growth in inches per year for a randomly selected tree from each strain.

a.   State the null and alternative hypotheses.
b.   Using S, is the null hypothesis rejected (5% level of significance)?

Blocks	Strain A	Strain B	Strain C	Strain D
Level 1	1.9	3.0	2.2	3.1
Level 2	2.1	2.9	2.3	3.3
Level 3	2.7	3.3	2.8	3.4
Level 4	2.8	3.6	2.7	3.6
Level 5	2.8	3.5	3.4	3.9
Level 6	2.7	3.7	3.3	3.5
Level 7	3.4	3.9	3.5	4.1

14.51 Two new cardboard boxes are designed to hold weight while wet. An experiment is made using the old design and the two new designs. The blocking factor is eight levels of wetness, The packages are picked up and the weight necessary to break the box is recorded. The results are:

Wetness Levels	Old Box	New Box #1	New Box #2
Level 1	41 lbs	37 lbs	40 lbs
Level 2	36	32	33
Level 3	29	34	29
Level 4	17	31	27
Level 5	24	28	29
Level 6	21	24	22
Level 7	18	17	14
Level 8	13	13	14

Using S and MINITAB, is the null hypothesis rejected (1% level of significance)?

14.52 You have a major league baseball team. You want to know if your team obtains the same number of hits during a day ball game, a night ball game, or at an enclosed stadium. You randomly select days when your club played against four specific pitchers, under the three conditions, and find:

Pitcher	Day Game	Night Game	Indoor Game
#1	6	12	7
#2	8	9	5
#3	5	8	5
#4	8	10	4
#5	10	11	4
#6	7	15	6
#7	2	8	5
#8	3	14	10
#9	5	7	9
#10	6	9	1

a. Why is it important to pick days when your club was facing the same pitcher under the 3 treatment levels?

b. Using S, is the null hypothesis rejected (1% level of significance)?

14.53 Consumer researchers are interested in 3 different displays for a grocery store product. They randomly select 6 stores for each demographic and psychographic mix in the region and record the sales of consumers going by the aisle. An observer waits for a customer to pick up the product, then counts the number of customers that walk by until the next customer buys a box. The results are:

	Display A	Display B	Display C
Store type 1:	46	26	68
Store type 2:	75	34	49
Store type 3:	51	49	77
Store type 4:	89	31	99
Store type 5:	95	18	88
Store type 6:	74	43	52

a. Using S (5% significance level) are the distributions the same (use MINITAB)?

b. Using S (1% significance level), are the distributions the same (use MINITAB)?

14.54   A surfboard shop sells three surfboards priced from expensive to inexpensive. The number of boards sold each day for the last week is:

	M	T	W	TH	F	S	SU
Expensive:	5	8	9	15	9	2	2
Less expensive:	2	0	1	3	2	4	1
Inexpensive:	9	12	7	17	8	3	2

Using S (5% significance level), are the distributions the same (use MINITAB)?

14.55   Four computer printers are set to print the same chapters from this textbook and are monitored to determine the time to complete the process. The publishing company believes the four printers have equal speed. Using S at the 5% level and MINITAB, test the null hypothesis.

Chapter	Printer #1	Printer #2	Printer #3	Printer #4
1	2.3 min	1.9 min	2.0 min	2.0 min
2	4.8	4.4	4.5	4.1
3	3.1	3.2	2.8	2.7
4	4.6	4.2	4.7	4.9
5	6.9	6.4	6.2	6.1
6	6.1	6.4	6.7	6.3
7	8.1	6.9	7.3	7.1
8	4.3	3.9	4.0	5.1
9	7.3	6.7	7.3	7.1
10	10.5	9.4	9.8	10.0
11	9.3	9.1	9.0	8.7

14.56   Five suppliers of floppy disks claim their product will hold 720k of memory. We select 1 disk from 6 production cycles from each supplier and record the memory capacity. The results are:

Cycle	Company A	Company B	Company C	Company D	Company E
1	689	715	745	722	728
2	718	722	736	719	716
3	712	724	751	726	720
4	702	718	739	721	701
5	716	720	744	718	722
6	729	724	732	716	722

Using MINITAB, are all of the floppy disks equivalent, at the 10% level using S?

14.9 Summary

In this chapter we discussed several new statistical procedures and tests. Essentially, the null hypothesis is the same for all of these tests. Each null hypothesis states that the different samples come from the same or identical populations. In other words, there is no difference between the different groupings of the data.

For each test, we must be careful to follow the conditions necessary to use each test. Some tests require paired data, some limit the data to two groups, some accommodate more than two groups, and others require sequential information from a single sample. All of the nonparametric tests are simple to use, which enables business professionals to use the tests with little formal knowledge of hypothesis testing. Thus, these tests are very important to the business community.

Mini-case 14.1: University Dating Service

A university dating service wants to know if a couple is compatible. They ask the couple to rank their favorite dates from 1–12. They believe that the couple is compatible only if the Spearman's rank correlation (R_S) is positive and significant at the 5% level. According to the dating service, is the couple compatible?

Table 14.9   Rankings of Favorite Dates

	Male	Female
Going to the movies	5	6
Watching TV	4	12
Playing miniature golf	9	11
Visiting friends	8	8
Go to a party	3	2
Go to a dance	10	1
Go to a concert	7	4
Out for dinner	9	3
Go to sporting event	2	9
Go shopping	11	7
Go for a drive	6	8
Go to the beach	1	5
Go to a play or drama	12	10

Mini-case 14.2: Long Distance Phone Preference

A research company wants to know if consumers prefer long distance phone service between two companies. The null hypothesis will be that there is no preference for either company. For 23 individuals, they connect one long distance phone company one week, then change companies the second week. The individuals have no knowledge of which company they have. They are asked to rate their long distance service (from 1–5) with respect to clarity, speed, and any other problems experienced. The research company will sum the ratings. A perfect rating would be 15 (a 5 for all three categories) and the worst rating possible is 3 (a 1 for all 3 categories). The sum of the ratings are:

Table 14.10 Sum of the Ratings for Long Distance Phone Service

Survey	Company A	Company B
#1	27	26
#2	24	22
#3	28	27
#4	30	29
#5	21	20
#6	21	30
#7	26	24
#8	30	30
#9	26	25
#10	21	20
#11	20	26
#12	29	28
#13	29	26
#14	23	22
#15	23	30
#16	28	26
#17	30	29
#18	17	16
#19	16	24
#20	27	26
#21	29	28
#22	21	26
#23	17	16
#24	27	23
#25	20	30

a. Using the sign test (5% level) are the two long distance phone companies viewed as equal?

b. Using the Wilcoxon Signed-Rank test (5% level) are the two long distance companies viewed as equal?

c. Compare the answers to parts a and b. Explain.

Review of Important Terms and Concepts

Nonparametric statistics: A series of test statistics that do not involve stringent assumptions concerning the parent population.

Measurement scales: The assignment of numbers on football uniforms is for the purpose of differentiating players or players' positions and would be called a nominal scale. If the assignment of a larger number meant that the higher numbered player was superior to the lower number player, we would be involved with an ordinal scale. If the player with the number 27 was three times as good as the player with the number 9, we would be involved with an interval scale.

The sign test: A test that requires paired data. Differences between the paired data are examined to determine if there are enough positive or negative signs, which would indicate that the two samples come from unlike populations.

The Wilcoxon signed-rank test: A test that examines differences between populations. Like the sign test, it examines the number of positive and negative signs, but now the magnitude of the differences are also examined.

The rank coefficient of correlation: A coefficient of correlation that measures the relationship between the ranks of paired data. The rank correlation coefficient is less susceptible to the problems caused by extreme data points then the normal coefficient of correlation.

The Wilcoxon rank sum test: A test that compares two groupings of independent data to determine whether or not they come from identical populations. Equal sample sizes are unnecessary.

The Mann–Whitney U test: An equivalent test to the Wilcoxon rank sum test.

The Kruskal–Wallis test: A test that compares multiple groupings of independent random data to determine whether or not they come from identical populations. Equal sample sizes are unnecessary.

The runs test: A test that determines whether or not successive values of a single sample are random. To use this test, the data must be divided into two categories, such as heads and tails, even and odd.

The Friedman test statistic: An alternative to the analysis of variance technique. The assumptions of the ANOVA table are not required in this nonparametric alternative.

Review of Important Formulas

The Kruskal–Wallis Test Statistic

$$H_{\text{test}} = \frac{12 \bullet T}{n(n+1)} - 3(n+1) \tag{14.1}$$

where

T = the average individual squared sum of the ranks
$T = (\Sigma \text{Rank}_A)^2/n_A + (\Sigma \text{Rank}_B)^2/n_B + \cdots + (\Sigma \text{Rank}_i)^2/n_i$
n = the pooled sample size

Friedman's Test Statistic (S)

$$S = \frac{12 \bullet T}{b \bullet L(L+1)} - 3 \bullet b(L+1) \tag{14.2}$$

where

b = the number of blocks
L = the number of treatment levels
T = the individual squared sum of rank
$T = (\Sigma \text{Rank}_A)^2 + (\Sigma \text{Rank}_B)^2 + \cdots + (\Sigma \text{Rank}_i)^2$

Using MINITAB for the sign test.

Using MINITABs calculator we subtract column B from column A to obtain C.

Calc > Calculator
Click **C3** into **Store result in Variable box**.
Double click Data in A into **Expressions** box. Enter a minus sign (–), then double click **Data in B** into the box.
OK

Now we can have MINITAB perform the sign test for us.

Stat > Nonparametrics > 1-Sample Sign
Double click **C3** into **Variable** box.
Click **Test median (0,0)**.
State if a one or two tailed test is involved.
Test hypothesis using P-value.

Using MINITAB for the Wilcoxon test.

Stat > Nonparametrics > 1-Sample Wilcoxon
Using MINITAB for and approximation of the rank correlation coefficient.
Stat > Basic Statistics > Correlation
Click in **RankScoA** and **RankScorB** into **Variable** box.
OK

Using MINITAB to perform the Mann–Whitney test.

Stat > Nonparametrics > Mann–Whitney
Double click **DataA** to **First Sample** box.
Double click **DataB** to **Second Sample** box.
Specify confidence level and if a two-tailed or one tailed test (**Alternatives**).
OK

Using MINITAB to perform a Kruskal–Wallis test.

Stat > Nonparametrics > Kruskal–Wallis
Double click **ClassAv** into **Response** box
Double click **Prof** into **Factor** box.
OK

Using MINITAB to perform the runs test.
We enter the data into a single columns (**Data**) with either a 1 or a 2. The commands are:

Stats > Nonparametric > Run Test
Double click **Data** into the **Variables** box.
OK

Using MINITAB to perform the Friedman test.

Stats > Nonparametric > Friedman
Double click **Rankings** into the **Response** box.
Double click **Treatment factor** into the **Treatment** box.
Double click **Block factor** into the **Block** box.
OK

14.57 Twenty students are asked to rate two perfumes (A and B) with regard to scent, lasting duration, and value for the price. They use one perfume one week and the other the following week. They do not know which perfume is which. They are to rate each factor, for both perfumes, on a 1–5 scale. If the perfume were to receive the highest rating for all 3 categories, it would receive a score of 15. If it received the lowest score possible, it would receive a score of 3. The scores for the students are:

Student	Rating for A	Rating for B	Difference
1	13	12	+ 1
2	15	13	+ 2
3	10	15	° 5
4	13	12	+ 1
5	8	14	° 6
6	6	15	° 9
7	5	11	° 6
8	12	11	+ 1
9	7	13	° 6
10	13	11	+ 2
11	4	12	° 8
12	10	15	° 5
13	3	14	° 11
14	5	13	° 8
15	7	10	° 3
16	11	15	° 4
17	12	15	° 3
18	9	12	° 3
19	10	15	° 5
20	7	14	° 7

a. Perfume B is an upgrade of perfume A. If the students feel that perfume B is not better than A, they will not market it. From a casual observation of the data, do you believe perfume B is superior to A?

b. Do you feel the sign test or the Wilcoxon Signed-Rank test will have a better chance of rejecting the hypothesis that the perfumes have the same statistical rating? Explain.

c. Test the hypothesis with the sign test (5% level) using MINITAB.

d. Test the hypothesis with the Wilcoxon signed-rank test (5% level) using MINITAB.

e. Compare your answers to "c" and "d."

f. Suppose we desired to perform a two-tailed test, 1% level of significance, using both the sign and the Wilcoxon signed rank test, Would Ho be rejected?

14.58 For Exercise 14.57, compute the rank correlation coefficient and ascertain if it is significant at the 5% level.

14.59 A total of 25 pollen sufferers were asked to rate two pain killers (aspirin and ibuprofen) with regard to their effect in reducing severe headaches. Specifically, they were asked to rate them regarding speed, lasting duration, and on possible side-effects. They are given one medication for the first two headaches, and the other medication for the following two headaches. The individuals do not know which headache medication they are taking. They are to rate both speed, lasting duration, and side-effects on a 1–10 scale. If the pain killer were to receive the highest rating for both categories, it would receive a score of 30. If it received the lowest score possible, it would receive a score of 3. The scores for the pain sufferers are:

Sufferer	Aspirin	Ibuprofen	Difference
1	22	17	+ 5
2	27	28	○ 1
3	24	25	○ 1
4	22	12	+ 10
5	24	16	+ 8
6	20	22	○ 2
7	21	17	+ 4
8	28	23	+ 5
9	29	17	+ 12
10	21	23	○ 2
11	16	12	+ 4
12	27	30	○ 3
13	25	21	+ 4
14	22	16	+ 6
15	23	15	+ 8
16	29	15	+ 14
17	30	24	+ 6
18	24	21	+ 3
19	22	23	○ 1
20	26	21	+ 5
21	22	23	○ 1
22	16	12	+ 4
23	29	22	+ 7
24	16	12	+ 4
25	28	12	+ 16

a. According to the sign test and MINITAB (1% level), test the hypothesis that there is no difference between the two pain killers.

b. According to the Wilcoxon signed-rank test and MINITAB (3% level), is there any difference in the painkillers?

c. Compare the answers to a and b. Explain.

14.60   Use MINITAB to compute the rank correlation coefficient for the data in Exercise 14.59.

14.61   The following data set is to be analyzed:

X	Y
1	1
2	3
3	9
4	18
5	29
6	21
7	16
8	11

Use MINITAB to compute the rank correlation coefficient.

14.62   The following data set is to be analyzed:

X	Y
1	1
2	3
3	9
4	18
5	29
6	21
7	16
8	11
9	2000

Use MINITAB to compute the rank correlation coefficient.

14.63   A local chamber of commerce asks 8 males and 6 females to predict the local unemployment rate for the upcoming year. The predicted rates are as follows:

Males	Females
5.7%	4.3%
6.9	3.3
10.2	5.1
4.4	4.7
6.7	5.6
8.1	4.5
9.3	
7.4	

Using the Wilcoxon rank sum test and MINITAB at the 3% level, are the predictions between males and females the same?

14.64   Frequent business travelers are asked to rate critically two car rental companies on seven factors (speed, cleanliness. etc.). Each factor receives a 1–10 scale; hence, the maximum score is 70 and the minimum 7. The ratings are as follows;

Company	Rating	Company	Rating
A	53	B	59
A	51	B	20
A	41	B	44
A	37	B	47
A	22	B	25
A	43	B	29
A	60	B	58
A	42	B	38
A	39	B	34
A	55	B	49
A	14	B	52
A	56		

Using the Wilcoxon rank sum test and MINITAB, determine if the two rental companies are equivalents at the 10% level.

471

14.65　A new monitoring device measures pain in the brain as a scale from 0–500. A 500 indicates maximum pain, and 0 no pain. A survey was taken of migraine sufferers who took one of three pain killers (aspirin, ibuprofen, and acetaminophen). The pain from the migraine was recorded one half hour after taking the medication. The results are:

Sufferer	Aspirin	Ibuprofen	Acetaminophen (Tylenol)
1	367	247	366
2	277	349	359
3	389	353	462
4	261	250	268
5	356	358	267
6	341	369	376
7	361	339	454
8	350	344	463
9		241	451
10			455

    a.　Using the Kruskal–Wallis U test and MINITAB, determine if the three pain killers are equivalents at the 5% level.

    b.　Why is the Wilcoxon Rank Sum test inappropriate for this exercise?

14.66　Frequent business travelers are asked to critically rate four car rental companies on seven factors (speed, cleanliness, etc.). Each factor receives a 1–10 scale; hence, the maximum score is 70 and the minimum 7. The ratings are as follows:

Company	Rating	Company	Rating	Company	Rating	Company	Rating
A	53	B	59	C	63	D	37
A	51	B	20	C	56	D	46
A	41	B	44	C	48	D	26
A	37	B	47	C	70	D	49
A	22	B	25	C	61	D	50
A	43	B	29	C	46	D	31
A	60	B	58	C	62		
A	42	B	38				
A	39	B	34				
A	55	B	49				
A	14	B	52				
A	56						

Using the Kruskal–Wallis H test and MINITAB, determine if the four rental companies are equivalents at the 1 % level.

14.67　A regression analysis is made and the signs of the residuals is as follows:

+, +, +, −, +, −, −, +, −, −, +, +, +, +, −, −, +, −, −, −, +, +, −, −, +, −, −, −, +, +, −, +, +, −, +, +, +, −, −, +, −, −, +, +, −

Using the runs test and MINITAB at the 5% significance level, are the signs of the residuals random?

14.68　A company receives parts in boxes of 50. Each box is opened and the first five parts are inspected for 10 consecutive boxes. Use the sign test at the 1% level to determine if the inspection process is random.

14.69   A major breeder of dogs analyzes the average sales prices for all dogs she sells in 4 geographic regions. The breeder believes that there are no geographical differences in prices, although prices are believed to differ by breed. Using S and MINITAB at the 1 % level, is the breeder correct?

Breeds	Area #1	Area #2	Area #3	Area #4
Sporting	$187	$211	$156	$196
Hounds	153	144	189	168
Working Dogs	317	302	376	412
Terriers	189	219	151	190
Toy	541	467	480	336
Non-Sporting	127	191	148	103
Herding	611	419	338	389

14.70   A major breeder of dogs analyzes the average sales prices for all dogs she sells in 7 breed categories. The breeder believes that the prices received for all breeds is the same even though there are geographical differences in prices. Using S at the 1% level and MINITAB, is the breeder correct?

Area	Sporting	Hounds	Working Dogs	Terriers	Toy	Non-Sport	Herding
#1	$187	$153	$317	$189	$541	$127	$611
#2	211	144	302	219	467	191	419
#3	156	189	376	151	480	148	338
#4	196	168	412	190	336	103	389

Concepts of Decision Theory

Where we are going

Chapters 15 and 16 begin a new thought process that students normally enjoy more than most. The reason is that the emphasis is on practical applications of decision-making and it is easy to understand that managers of both large and small businesses must learn to make "good" or optimal decisions. These decisions must be made after a careful evaluation of all the options that are open to them. Once the options are made clear, a method must be established to determine the optimum choice. This chapter concentrates on this thought process, that of determining the choices and then deciding on the best of the possible options. In this chapter we make our analysis based on the information at hand. However, in the next chapter we will expand to consider the possibility and practicality of obtaining additional information prior to decision making.

15.1 Introduction

We are now beginning a new section that concerns itself with making realistic business decisions using statistics, business logic, and a keen business acumen. Decision makers must constantly make evaluations based upon the options and choices that they have before them. These options are based on projections that may not be correct. Therefore, more than one scenario is usually analyzed based upon different projections. For instance, in management science courses, students are asked to project a normal activity time to perform a certain event in critical path analysis. Subsequently, they are asked to project the shortest and longest time the activity could take. One realistic problem faced is that it might not be possible to predict accurately the longest time for an activity because the decision maker is not totally in control of the environment. Therefore, he or she might not know of an impending labor dispute involving one of their suppliers.

Decision makers must decide on an optimum course of action. Yet this "optimum" decision must be made from two categories of information. First, there is the information based upon what the manager's options are. If a manager has options that means he or she has control over some of the factors influencing the outcomes. There is a certain aspect of control over whether to produce a certain product or service, or to decide to close operations. When you drive to class, there is a decision to be made about which route to take. The farther you live from the classroom, normally the greater the number of choices available. There is not a great deal of time spent in making this decision as it is performed almost automatically. Statisticians refer to these types of decisions as examples of decision-making under certainty. Decision-making under certainty refers to situations in which the decision maker knows with complete certainty the consequences of the relevant options. Unfortunately, decisions do not involve total certainty and it is possible that road crews or accidents will make our initial decision impossible or impractical. Yet, for all practical purposes this decision is treated as perfunctory in nature.

The other scenario is one in which there is only partial control by the decision maker. For example, a manager decides which supplier to use, but does not control the labor relations problems of those suppliers. Marketing controls the advertising medium to be used for our company, but cannot control the effectiveness of that medium.

These are examples of what statisticians call decision-making under uncertainty. Decision-making under uncertainty refers to situations in which the outcomes of the relevant alternatives are not known with certainty. So a decision analysis usually involves a combination of controllable and uncontrollable factors. The possible scenarios existing between controllable and uncontrollable facts can be developed and evaluated based upon their relative merits. This chapter analyzes the different methods for selecting an optimum business decision and the strengths and shortcomings of each.

15.2 New Terms and Concepts

All new statistical methods require an introduction of new terminology. Fortunately, the new terms in decision theory are easy to understand and grasp. The immediate terms to master are an **act**, an **event**, and an **outcome**. The basic distinction between an act and an event rests on the concept of managerial control. If a manager has control over a circumstance, it is termed an act. If the decision cannot be controlled, it is called an event or state of nature. Please remember that different authors and computer programs may use different words for the same concept, resulting in possible confusion and misunderstanding. To distinguish between an act and an event, the decision maker must evaluate the control that he or she has in a particular situation. Some examples for the decision maker are:

1. Whether you cut class today. An act because you control the selection.
2. Whether your instructor will give a pop quiz today. An event because you do not control the circumstance. Under unusual circumstances this could be classified as an act. If you released all the air from the instructor's tires this morning, there certainly would be an element of control.
3. Whether you will have a cup of coffee while reading this text. An act because there is decision maker control.
4. Whether you will invest in the stock market today. (Act)
5. Whether your stock price will go up or down in value. (Event)

The combination of the last two examples illustrates the concept of an outcome. An outcome is the result of combining an act with an event. If an individual were to invest in the market, and the market dropped, a loss would be incurred. Should the market subsequently increase, the investor would be the recipient of those gains. Of course, it is possible for the market to achieve substantial gains, yet individual stocks might be on the decline.

An analysis of events, acts, and outcomes can easily be placed in a matrix for convenience. Acts and events can either be placed in columns or rows. Not all authors, or computer programs, will use the same format, so careful attention must be paid to the terms and format of the matrix. Table 15.1 outlines the acts in columns and the events in rows. The acts represent your choices of whether or not to study for a pop quiz and the events are that either the teacher will or will not give the class a pop quiz. Note that two of the outcomes represent correct decisions and two denote incorrect decisions. Of course, to study and to learn can never be considered as an incorrect decision, yet the point is clear that in the short run time may be better utilized by doing something else.

Table 15.1 Decision Matrix for the Student Dilemma

	ACTS	
EVENTS	*Study*	*Don't Study*
Pop Quiz	"A" grade	"F" grade
No Pop Quiz	Studied Unnecessarily	No Wasted Time

15.3 Defining the Terms "Biggest" and "Best" (Optimal)

During the course of communicating with one another, there is a tendency to use nebulous terms such as the biggest or the best. Unfortunately, since all people have different backgrounds and reference points, these terms have different meanings to each. A classical example is used in business communication classes where a supervisor instructs a subordinate to "... burn" a copy of this report. Does the subordinate make a copy of the document or is it destroyed in the company shredder?

As another example, suppose you were asked to name the company that is the largest commercial airline in the world. The answer might depend upon the definition being used for the term "largest." It could mean which company had the largest assets (the most airplanes), which had the greatest number of employees, which flew the most passengers, or which flew the most passengers per air mile, etc. Therefore, before the question can be answered, a definition of biggest would be needed. Each different definition could yield a different air carrier as the biggest. Without knowing it, when the term biggest is used, a specific meaning comes into mind. Unfortunately, this definition might not coincide with others, and a lack of communication can result.

Which are the biggest or largest cities in the United States? Again the answer depends upon the definition being used. If biggest refers to population than the answer is New York, Los Angeles, and Chicago. If biggest were defined in terms of geographic square miles than it would be Juneau, Jacksonville, and Oklahoma City.

The same problems develop with the use of the word "best." Which is the best college football team in the country? Again there could be more than one way to define the term best. What is the best restaurant in town? What is the best Italian restaurant in town? All are examples of questions that can only be answered based upon individual knowledge and value judgments, but will all people have identical information bases? The same is true when making business decisions. Which is the best product to make when there is more than one choice? Again the answer depends upon the criterion being used.

By now it should be clear that a best or optimum business decision depends upon the framework from which the decision is made. After a digression on how to determine the outcomes of many business decisions, the question of defining the "best" business decision must be answered.

When stating a particular course of action to be best or optimum, it is first necessary to state the criteria that are being used. True or false? If false, explain.

Exercises

15.1   Most universities and community colleges select a yearly teacher and researcher of the year.

    a.   What are some of the criteria that should be considered in such a selection process?

    b.   Do you believe that it is possible to select one instructor as being statistically better than all others, for the year?

    c.   Who would be best qualified to make such a determination?

    d.   What factors do you believe might influence such a decision that you think might be inappropriate to consider?

15.2   The Academy Awards select the best movie of the year.

    a.   What are some of the criteria that you think should be considered in such a selection process?

    b.   Do you believe that it is possible to select one movie as being statistically better than all others for the year?

    c.   Who would be best qualified to make such a determination?

    d.   What factors do you believe might influence such a decision that you think might be inappropriate to consider?

    e.   Are there any similarities between the answers given to question 15.1 and 15.2? Explain.

15.4 Developing a Payoff Matrix

In most business problems, the outcomes are expressed in profits and losses and as such are termed payoffs. A payoff then is simply the profits/losses to be incurred from the selection of an act and the occurrence of an event. Since there are many events that can occur, and several business decisions from which to choose, it is convenient to place the possibilities in a matrix format. An example will best explain the concepts in developing a specific payoff matrix. For the upcoming Christmas season, a firm wishes to consider producing a robot toy called the atom smasher. Cosmic heroes have been popular as Christmas toys for several years, and our company has decided to produce a competitor to what has been selling on the market. Company decision makers are not sure whether to produce an inexpensive product, thereby attempting to maximize volume, or to produce an expensive highly automated version of the toy robot. In fact, four separate options are being evaluated. The four options are:

$$AS\text{-}1 = \text{A smasher with blinking lights only}$$

$$AS\text{-}2 = AS\text{-}1 + \text{prerecorded message communication}$$

$$AS\text{-}3 = AS\text{-}2 + \text{the ability to move on specified commands}$$

$$AS\text{-}4 = AS\text{-}3 + \text{the ability to pick up and retrieve objects}$$

These are obviously acts because of the control the firm has with respect to which of the four smashers will be produced. Because of budgetary and logistic reasons only one (or none) smasher will be produced. The production department is called and asked to estimate the fixed and variable costs involved in producing each of the smashers. The fixed costs represent the cost of the machinery used in the production cycle and the variable costs represent the different labor, maintenance, and energy costs associated with each toy. The following cost functions estimate both fixed and variable costs for all four robots.

478

$$AS\text{-}1 = \$100,000 + \$10(X)$$
$$AS\text{-}2 = \$400,000 + \$20(X)$$
$$AS\text{-}3 = \$700,000 + \$40(X)$$
$$AS\text{-}4 = \$2,000,000 + \$90(X)$$

where X represents the projected demand for the smasher.

Whereas each act represents the choice of producing just one smasher, the events represent the possible sales that might be expected at Christmas. The smasher will be advertised in an attempt to generate high sales volume. However, the sales volume will in all probability be dictated by general economic conditions and consumer's perceptions of the product. There is potential for thousands of different sales volumes, but, for simplicity, we will reduce the number to four categories (for analysis purposes).

$$E\text{-}1 = \text{Selling } 60,000 \text{ robots: Weak Sales}$$
$$E\text{-}2 = \text{Selling } 100,000 \text{ robots: ModerateSales}$$
$$E\text{-}3 = \text{Selling } 200,000 \text{ robots: Strong Sales}$$
$$E\text{-}4 = \text{Selling } 500,000 \text{ robots: Incredible Sales}$$

Remember that the sales are in physical units and do not represent dollar volumes.

The last factor that must be considered is the sales price for each of the four prospective smashers. Because there are competitors currently in retail stores for all four robots, it is felt that a price must be charged that is slightly under the price charged by our competitors. Research indicates that when consumers are faced with a choice between a known and an unknown product, they will normally choose the known product unless the price of the other is less (see Table 15.2).

Table 15.2   Our Price and the Competitors' Price for Atom Smashers

ATOM SMASHER	Competitors' Price	Our Price
AS-1	$15	$12
AS-2	$35	$25
AS-3	$65	$50
AS-4	$139	$110

Please note that federal regulations exist concerning child safety standards and these must be met when selling toys for children. The production department was considering a fifth alternative, which, in addition to the earlier smasher functions, would meet other toys in combat and destroy them. The legal staff recommended against such a toy because of the potential negative publicity that could occur.

Finally, it is possible to develop a payoff matrix for the smasher options. For example, if AS-1 were produced and E-1 occurred, then

$$\text{Total Revenue} = 60,000(\$12) = \$720,000$$
$$\text{Total Cost} = \$100,000 + \$10(60,000) = \$700,000$$
$$\text{Net Profit} = \$720,000 - \$700,000 = \$20,000$$

If AS-3 were produced and E-4 occurred, then

$$\text{Total Revenue} = 500,000(\$50) = \$25,000,000$$
$$\text{Total Costs} = \$700,000 + \$40(500,000) = \$20,700,000$$
$$\text{Net Profit} = \$25,000,000 - \$20,700,000 = \$4,300,000$$

It is now a simple process to complete the full payoff matrix (Table 15.3). Table 15.3 is often called a conditional profit table because it represents a union between supply, which is controlled by the decision maker, and demand, which is not controlled by the decision maker.

Table 15.3   Atom Smasher Payoff Matrix ($000's)

Events	AS-1	AS-2	AS-3	AS-4
E-1	20	(100)	(100)	(800)
E-2	100	100	300	0
E-3	300	600	1,300	2,000
E-4	900	2,100	4,300	8,000

 Concept Check 15.B

A payoff is a union between an event, which is controlled by the decision maker, and an act which is not controlled by the decision maker. True or false? If false, explain.

Exercises

15.3   A company must choose between three types of lawn sod to make which is sold in square feet. The estimated fixed and variable costs for each of the three sods are Type I = $10,000 + $0.03(X), Type II = $5,000 + $0.05(X), and Type III = $2,000 + $0.10(X), where X is the amount of square footage produced. The company estimates that it will either sell 100,000 (E-1), 500,000 (E-2), or 1,000,000 (E-3) square feet. The respective selling prices are for Type I = Type II = $0.10, Type III = $0.13 all per square foot. Develop the appropriate payoff matrix.

15.4   A major retailer is thinking about opening a new branch in a city. It must select between moving downtown (A-1), a short distance from downtown (A-2), or to a more rural area (A-3). The cost for the necessary land for A-1 = $2,000,000, A-2 = $1,000,000, and for A-3 = $500,000. The commercial construction costs are the same at $80 per sq. ft. The company has obtained a permit to build 10,000 sq. ft., but also has requested variances to build 30,000 sq. ft., and if denied to build a 20,000 sq. ft. building. The company does not know which square footage will be allowed. The estimated revenues per sq. ft. are $200 for downtown, $175 for a short distance from downtown, and $150 for the rural area. Develop the appropriate payoff matrix.

15.5   Reducing the Options

Company decision makers must choose one of the four acts (smashers) to produce. If it were possible to eliminate one or more of the acts, it would simplify the problem and make our decision easier. In fact, if it were possible to eliminate all but one act, the decision would be predetermined.

In looking at the four Atom Smashers it may be possible to detect illogical or irrational choices. To do this it is necessary to compare all combinations of acts taking two robots at a time. The different combinations would be AS-1 to AS-2, AS-1 to AS-3, AS-1 to AS-4, AS-2 to AS-3, AS-2 to AS-4, and finally AS-3 to AS-4. In evaluating the AS-2 to AS-3 combination, if E-1 occurs, then either smasher will yield the same loss. If E-2 occurs, AS-3 is the superior choice. Also, if E-3 or E-4 occurs, again AS-3 is the better of the two options. Therefore, no matter which event occurs, AS-3's payoff is either equal to or better than that of AS-2. Therefore, AS-3 dominates AS-2, and AS-2 is said to be inadmissible. By any standard AS-2 is an illogical choice and should be eliminated from further consideration.

One act dominates another if for at least one event its payoff is superior and for all other events the payoffs are equal to or superior to the payoffs associated with another act. In the smasher problem, no other combination of two acts meets this condition: therefore, only AS-2 is inadmissible. Act AS-2 can be and is eliminated from our payoff matrix (Table 15.4).

Table 15.4 Atom Smasher Revised Payoff Matrix ($000's)

Events	AS-1	AS-3	AS-4
E-1	20	(100)	(800)
E-2	100	300	0
E-3	300	1,300	2,000
E-4	900	4,300	8,000

 Concept Check 15.C

An act is inadmissible if one payoff is less than and all other payoffs are equal to or less than that of another act. True or false? If false, explain.

Exercise

15.5   The table represents payoffs contingent upon certain acts and events occurring. Define all the inadmissible acts.

	A-1	A-2
E-1	80	10
E-2	50	55

15.6   The table represents payoffs contingent upon certain acts and events occurring. Define all the inadmissible acts.

	A-1	A-2	A-3	A-4	A-5
E-1	50	70	60	20	10
E-2	100	40	10	10	20
E-3	80	90	70	80	90

15.7   The table represents payoffs contingent upon certain acts and events occurring. Define all the inadmissible acts.

	A-1	A-2	A-3	A-4	A-5	A-6
E-1	(10)	(15)	(20)	(25)	(30)	(35)
E-2	0	(5)	(10)	(15)	(20)	(25)
E-3	10	30	20	30	40	30
E-4	40	50	60	25	(10)	30

15.8   (A continuation of exercise 15.4) A major retailer is thinking about opening a new branch in a city. It must select between moving downtown (A-1), a short distance from downtown (A-2), or to a more rural area (A-3). The cost for the necessary land for A-1 = $2,000,000, A-2 = $1,000,000, and for A-3 = $500,000. The commercial construction costs are the same at $80 per sq. ft. The company has obtained a permit to build 10,000 sq. ft., but also has requested variances to build 30,000 sq. ft., and if denied to build a 20,000 sq. ft. building. The company does not know which square footage will be allowed. The estimated revenues per sq. ft. are $200 for downtown, $175 for a short distance from downtown, and $150 for the rural area. Develop the appropriate payoff matrix. Determine the inadmissible acts.

Company executives must now choose one of the three remaining robots as the "best" alternative available. Unfortunately, there is more than one definition for the word "best." The following represents some of the different definitions that are commonly used.

Criterion #1: Maximizing Expected Payoffs or Bayes' Decision Rule

The most frequently used measure of the optimal strategy involves computing the expected payoffs (weighted averages) and choosing the maximum value. In order to accomplish this, it is necessary to assign weights or probabilities for the possible events. In the real world, it is not easy to assign realistic probabilities to the possible events and there will be some subjectiveness to any values assigned to the weights. Assigning somewhat arbitrary weights is the vulnerable aspect of Bayesian analysis. Decision makers generally use historical data to estimate the weights. For example, maybe we have sold other similarly priced toys in the past, under similar economic conditions, and this historical information could be used for the upcoming Christmas. Or a retail trade professional organization could be contacted to see if they have performed any preliminary surveys and analyses. No matter what kind of business that is entered, there will normally exist a professional organization, started by retailers, to aid them in supplying information. There is even an association of associations that exists in the Washington, D. C. area. Such an association will have communicated with the major retailers (Wal-Mart, Target, Sears, K-Mart, J.C. Penny, etc.) to see what their purchasing intentions are for the upcoming Christmas season. Decisions have to be made early so that catalogs can be developed and printed prior to the upcoming season.

Based upon their findings, the following probabilities (Pr) are assigned:

$$\begin{array}{rcl}
Events & & Pr \\
\text{E-1} & = & .2 \text{ (Weak sales: sales} = 60,000 \text{ units)} \\
\text{E-2} & = & .4 \text{ (Moderate sales: sales} = 100,000 \text{ units)} \\
\text{E-3} & = & .3 \text{ (Strong sales: sales} = 200,000 \text{ units)} \\
\text{E-4} & = & .1 \text{ (Incredible sales: sales} = 500,000 \text{ units)} \\
\text{Total} & = & 1.0
\end{array}$$

It is now possible to develop a table obtaining the expected payoffs from each of the three choices remaining. The maximum expected payoff occurs for AS-4, which then represents the best or optimum choice available (Table 15.5). The outcome is partially determined by the weights. However, a different set of weights might lead to a different conclusion. The expected payoffs are often called the expected profit under uncertainty, because there is uncertainty about which event will occur. The probabilities are based on limited information and subjective analysis. Symbolically it is

The Expected Profit Under Uncertainty

$$E(x) = \Sigma x \bullet \Pr(x) \tag{15.1}$$

where

x is a discrete random variable with a probability distribution $\Pr(x)$

In our smasher problem, the random variable x is the respective payoffs, and the probability is the likelihood that each of the events (sales levels) will take place. In essence, the formula for AS-1 is

$$AS\text{-}1 = \Sigma x \bullet Pr(x)$$

or

$$AS\text{-}1 = .2(20) + .4(100) + .3(300) + .1(900) = \$224$$
$$AS\text{-}3 = .2(-100) + .4(300) + .3(1,300) + .1(4,300) = \$920$$
$$AS\text{-}4 = .2(-800) + .4(0) + .3(2,000) + .1(8,000) = \$1,240$$

Table 15.5 Expected Payoffs ($000's) for Atom Smashers

		AS-1		AS-3		AS-4	
Events	Pr	$	Pr•$	$	Pr•$	$	Pr•$
E-1	.2	20	4	(100)	(20)	(800)	(160)
E-2	.4	100	40	300	120	0	0
E-3	.3	300	90	1,300	390	2,000	600
E-4	.1	900	90	4,300	430	8,000	800
			Σ =224		Σ =920		Σ =1,240*

Company researchers have found that the different probabilities for the events remain constant regardless of the price of the Atom Smasher. In other words, it has the same probability of being successful, regardless of whether the price is $12 or $110. If it's to be a success, it will be a success for all prices less than $150.

Shortcomings

All rules of logic that are developed have inconsistencies which can appear. An inconsistency appears if the decision maker chooses one act but the decision criterion suggests a different act. Often large variations in profits and losses can create problems with our decision rules. In our robot example, with the selection of AS-4 we have a 60% chance of either sustaining a loss or in breaking even. Only a 40% probability exists in making any profit at all. Fortunately, that profit potential is substantial.

As another example of an inconsistency using Bayes' decision rule caused by a large variation in the payoffs we examine Table 15.6. The expected payoff from A-1 is $20,000 while that of A-2 is $20,400. Using the maximum expected payoff logic, A-2 should be chosen as optimum. Since most individuals could not afford a 60 percent chance of losing $100,000, they might prefer A-1. This inconsistency might be dealt with if either a different rule were applied or if the actual effect of the payoffs were taken into account. Later in this chapter the concept of converting payoffs into an impact scale and evaluation will be discussed.

Table 15.6 Expected Payoff Inconsistency ($)

		A-1		A-2	
Events	Pr	$	Pr•$	$	Pr•$
E-1	.6	0	0	(100,000)	(60,000)
E-2	.4	50,000	20,000	201,000	80,400
			Σ = 20,000		Σ = 20,400*

 Concept Check 15.D

From selecting AS-4 (Table 15.5), the manager may expect to receive exactly $1,240,000 from the decision. True or false? If false, explain.

483

15.9 The table represents payoffs contingent upon certain acts and events occurring. Compute the expected payoff for each of the following acts and determine the optimum act.

	Pr	A-1	A-2	A-3	A-4
E-1	.2	50	70	60	20
E-2	.3	100	40	10	50
E-3	.4	80	90	100	110
E-4	.1	(10)	(20)	20	40

15.10 A company must choose between three types of lawn sod to make which is sold in square feet. The estimated fixed and variable costs for each type of the three sods are Type I $= \$10,000 + \$0.03(X)$, Type II $= \$5,000 + \$0.05(X)$, and Type III $= \$2,000 + \$0.10(X)$, where X is the amount of square feet produced. The company estimates that they will either sell 100,000 (E-1), 500,000 (E-2), or 1,000,000 (E-3) square feet. The respective selling prices are for Type I $=$ Type II $= \$0.10$, Type III $= \$0.13$ all per square foot. Develop the appropriate payoff matrix.

Compute the expected payoffs for each act of problem 15.3 and determine the optimum act. Use the following weights: E-1 $= .5$, E-2 $= .2$, and E-3 $= .3$.

15.11 A major retailer is thinking about opening a new branch in a city. It must select between moving downtown (A-1), a short distance from downtown (A-2), or to a more rural area (A-3). The cost for the necessary land for A-1 $= \$2,000,000$, A-2 $= \$1,000,000$, and for A-3 $= \$500,000$. The commercial construction costs are the same at \$80 per sq. ft. The company has obtained a permit to build 10,000 sq. ft., but also has requested variances to build 30,000 sq. ft., and if denied to build a 20,000 sq. ft. building. The company does not know which square footage will be allowed. The estimated revenues per sq. ft. are \$200 for downtown, \$175 for a short distance from downtown, and \$150 for the rural area. Develop the appropriate payoff matrix.

Compute the expected payoffs for each act in problem 15.4 and determine the optimum act. Use the following weights: E-1 $= .2$, E-2 $= .5$, E-3 $= .3$.

15.12 a. For the following payoff matrix determine the optimum expected payoff.

	Pr	A-1	A-2
E-1	.5	$(5,000,000)$	$4,000
E-2	.5	$10,000,000	0

b. Suppose $P_r(\text{E-1}) = .9$ and $P_r(\text{E-2}) = .1$, determine the optimum expected payoff.
c. Compare your answers in "a" and "b." Explain.

Criterion #2: Maximin Payoff Criterion

A second definition of the "best" decision is based on the maximin payoff criterion, which must be viewed as a pessimistic way of observing the choices. The criterion essentially says, if I select this act, what is the worst financial scenario that can occur? As such, it represents a pessimistic viewpoint as you are assuming the worst scenario. For AS-1 it's to make \$20,000; for AS-3 it's to lose \$100,000; and for AS-4 it's to lose \$800,000. The best of these worst scenarios is to make \$20,000; therefore, AS-1 is the optimum choice of acts.

Table 15.7 The Maximin Decision Rule ($000's)

Events	AS-1	AS-3	AS-4
E-1	20*	(100)*	(800)*
E-2	100	300	0
E-3	300	1,300	2,000
E-4	900	4,300	8,000
Best of Worst Scenarios	20**	(100)	(800)

If this logic were applied to Table 15.6, the optimum act would be A-1 because the worst payoff for A-1 is $0; for A-2 it's to lose $100,000. The best of these two choices is A-1 and $0. The overwhelming advantage to the maximin technique is the guarantee of a floor income (if the best of the worst scenarios is positive), or a ceiling on the loss (if the best of the worst scenarios is negative). This feature can be particularly attractive to anyone disliking risk or who is currently in a bad financial situation. The maximin approach is often termed a non probabilistic decision criterion, since the outcomes are not dependent on the probabilities of the events occurring.

Shortcomings

There are two major shortcomings associated with the maximin criterion. First, most of the time the worst payoff is usually associated with the event with the lowest sales. If this is the case, as it is with our Atom Smasher example, the entire decision is being based on E-1 occurring. Of course, if it does occur the selection of acts is optimum. However, in our example, a probability of 20% was assigned to E-1 occurring. In a sense, we would be basing the entire decision on something that has a one in five chance of happening.

The second problem with maximin occurs when there is a great disparity between the payoffs of certain acts. A particular problem develops when the worst payoff for each act are numerically close, while the other payoffs differ widely. In Table 15.8, the worst payoff for A-1 is a $1 loss, while for A-2 it's a $2 loss, Using the maximin rule, it is better to lose $1 than $2; therefore, A-1 is superior. However, given the choices described by Table 15.8, it would clearly be a mistake to claim that A-1 would be the optimum choice for all decision makers.

Table 15.8   Shortcomings of Maximin Criterion ($)

Events	Pr	A-1 $	A-1 Pr•$	A-2 $	A-2 Pr•$
E-1	.4	(1)	(20)	(2)	(20.4)
E-2	.6	0	0	10,000,000	6,000,000
Best of Worst Scenario		(50)*	(20)	(51)	5,999,979.6

Please remember that each definition of the "best" act is based on a certain rationale. Should the logic of that rationale not be realized in a certain situation, then the rule may go awry. Sometimes the United States government runs into the same problem. Government officials may attempt to define a depressed region as an area in which a large percentage of the residents have no visible means of support. However, if such a definition were used, we might learn that the biggest poverty area in the country was Beverly Hills, California or West Palm Beach, Florida.

It must be remembered that circumstances could change and might dictate a change in the optimum choice of acts. If a person were given a choice of flipping a coin to win or lose $10, or to win or lose $100,000, he or she would probably choose the former (Table 15.9). Very few people can afford to lose $100,000 with a 50% probability. Yet circumstances could change so that A-2 would be preferred. Suppose upon leaving the next statistics class you have a heart malfunction and have to be rushed to the hospital. Your doctor confers with you the next morning that she has bad news and good news. The bad news is that you have a bum heart and have only a few days to live. The good news is that there is a compatible heart donor across the country and you must leave right away to have a transplant operation. The heart donor's family wants $200,000 for the transplant organ. You presently have $100,000. Under this strange scenario you would probably choose A-2 as the optimum choice. The $100,000 that you currently have has little value, but the $200,000 represents a chance at life. This is one of the rare times when it will pay to gamble, since what you may win has considerably more value to you than what you can lose.

Table 15.9   Flipping a Coin ($)

Events	Pr	A-1	A-2
E-1	.5	(10)	(100,000)
E-2	.5	10	100,000

 Concept Check 15.E

The maximin technique selects the maximum value from the minimums of each event. True or false? If false, explain.

Exercises

15.13   The table represents payoffs contingent upon certain acts and events occurring.

	Pr	A-1	A-2	A-3	A-4
E-1	.1	50	70	10	20
E-2	.4	100	40	20	50
E-3	.3	80	90	80	110
E-4	.2	(10)	(20)	20	10

a.   Do the probabilities have any bearing on the maximin payoff criterion?
b.   Determine the optimum act using the maximin payoff criterion.
c.   Determine the optimum act using the maximum expected payoff criterion.
d.   Do you feel more comfortable with the answer to "b" or "c"? Explain.

15.14   For the following payoffs, determine the optimum act using the maximin payoff criterion.

	A-1	A-2	A-3	A-4	A-5	A-6
E-1	20	70	100	200	(100)	(200)
E-2	200	70	60	50	200	(100)
E-3	80	(10)	80	110	60	(60)

Criterion #3:   Maximum Likelihood Criterion

The maximum likelihood criterion is based on which event has the greatest probability of occurring. It then assumes that event will occur and selects the highest payoff associated with it. Returning to the smasher problem, E-2 had the highest probability of occurring at 40%. If it is assumed that E-2 will take place, AS-3 is the optimum choice (Table 15.10).

Table 15.10 The Maximum Likelihood Criterion ($000's)

Events	Pr	AS-1	AS-3	AS-4
E-1	.2	20	(100)	(800)
E-2	.4	100	300*	0
E-3	.3	300	1,300	2,000
E-4	.1	900	4,300	8,000

486

Shortcomings

It is not wise to disregard much of the data in a given information set since it is so difficult to obtain accurate information. Also, in a real world situation, there can be hundreds of possible events. In such cases, there will be many events with identical or similar probabilities.

 Concept Check 15.F

The maximum likelihood technique discards all data except for the act with the greatest chance of occurring. True or false? If false, explain.

Exercises

15.15 The table represents payoffs contingent upon certain acts and events occurring.

	Pr	A-1	A-2	A-3	A-4	A-5	A-6
E-1	.6	10	20	25	15	30	5
E-2	.1	30	5	10	10	15	15
E-3	.3	40	30	15	20	0	50

a. Using the maximum likelihood criterion, determine the optimum act.
b. Determine if there are any inadmissible acts.
c. Using the maximum expected payoff criterion, determine the optimum act.
d. Using the maximin payoff criterion, determine the optimum act.
e. Compare and analyze your answers to "a," "c," and "d."

15.16 Use the maximum likelihood criterion to determine the optimum act for the following payoffs.

	Pr	A-1	A-2	A-3	A-4
E-1	.2	100	200	300	400
E-2	.4	400	300	200	100
E-3	.3	200	300	400	500
E-4	.1	900	900	900	900

Criterion #4: The Maximax Criterion

The maximax criterion is similar to the maximin in logic, but looks at it from a purely optimistic viewpoint. Whereas the maximin selects the best of the worst, the maximax chooses the best of the best (pure optimism). Using the Atom Smasher example, the best from AS-1 = $900,000; from AS-3 = $4,300,000; from AS-4 = $8,000,000. The maximax then would correspond to AS-4 and a payoff of $8,000,000.

Table 15.11 The Maximax Decision Rule ($000's)

Events	AS-1	AS-3	AS-4
E-1	20	(100)	(800)
E-2	100	300	0
E-3	300	1,300	2,000
E-4	900*	4,300*	8,000*
Best of Best Scenarios	900	4,300	8,000**

487

Shortcomings

Whereas most of the worst payoffs occur with low sales, many of the best payoffs are associated with the best sales. In our Atom Smasher example, all the best payoffs were associated with incredible sales (E-4). If E-4 were to occur, then an excellent decision would have been made. However, a 10% probability was assigned to E-4, therefore it will only occur in one of ten chances. Thus, the maximax criterion leads the decision maker to focus on an event with little chance of occurring.

Criterion #5:   Principle of Insufficient Information, Laplace Method

Suppose it is not possible to find any realistic method of weighting the events. If so, one can assume that the events were equally likely, and equal weights should be assigned to the events. In our Atom Smasher example, a 25% weight should be placed on each event. Of course, when the weights are equal, then weighted and non-weighted averages are identical. Therefore, it is only necessary to compute the straight arithmetic means of all the payoffs for each act. They would be $330,000 for AS-1; $1,450,000 for AS-3; and $2,300,000 for AS-4. Act four would then be optimal. This concept is usually termed the concept or criterion of insufficient information, reason, or logic. It is sometimes also called the Laplace method, named after the famous mathematician and astronomer Pierre-Simon Laplace (1749–1827).

Shortcomings

When business people use this technique, it usually means that they put forth little effort in attempting to track down information. If this little effort is to be put forth into a decision, then it is unlikely that the decision will yield the results desired by the decision maker. This being the case, it might be better to abort the entire decision at this point.

 Concept Check 15.G

The maximax technique involves finding the act associated with the highest payoff in the payoff matrix. True or false? If false, explain.

Exercises

15.17   The table represents payoffs contingent upon certain acts and events occurring.

	Pr	A-1	A-2	A-3	A-4	A-5	A-6
E-1	.3	10	20	30	30	20	10
E-2	.7	50	40	30	20	30	40

a.   Determine the inadmissible acts.

Determine the optimum act using:
b.   the maximum expected payoff criterion.
c.   the maximin criterion.
d.   the maximum likelihood criterion.
e.   the maximax criterion.
f.   the Laplace criterion (Assuming E-1 = E-2 = .5).

15.18   The table represents payoffs contingent upon certain acts and events occurring.

	Pr	A-1	A-2	A-3	A-4	A-5
E-1	.4	100	200	150	300	100
E-2	.1	200	150	300	100	300
E-3	.5	10	8	0	20	30

a.   determine the inadmissible acts.

Determine the optimum act using:

b. the maximum expected payoff criterion.
c. the maximin criterion.
d. the maximum likelihood criterion. Why might this criterion be inappropriate for this exercise?
e. the maximax criterion.
f. the Laplace criterion (assuming that the weights given are incorrect and that the real weights are unknown).

15.19   Repeat exercise 15.18, revising the probabilities to E-1 = E-2 = .05, E-3 = .90.

15.20   Use the following weights; E-1 = E-3 = .3, and E-2 = .4 for exercise 15.4 and determine the optimum act using:

a. the maximum expected payoff criterion.
b. the maximin criterion.
c. the maximum likelihood criterion.
d. the maximax criterion.
e. the Laplace criterion (assuming that the weights given are incorrect and that the real weights are unknown).

15.7 Converting Payoffs to Regrets (Opportunity Loss)

Sometimes it is convenient to analyze a decision problem in a different context. The payoffs of a matrix can be converted from a positive measurement to a negative one. Suppose a wizard would appear and tell you that E-1 would take place in the Atom Smasher example. If the wizard were to be believed, then AS-1 would be selected, and the company would make $20,000. However, suppose you did not believe the wizard and went on to produce AS-3, what would be the consequences? Your belief would have cost $120,000. Had there been faith in the wizard, there would have been a $20,000 profit; therefore, there will be a regret (opportunity loss) of the difference, which is $120,000 [$20,000 − (−$100,000)]. Had AS-4 been selected, then $20,000 − (−$800,000) equals a $820,000 regret. If the wizard was believed, then AS-1 would have been chosen, leaving $20,000 − $20,000 = $0 as the regret or lost opportunity. The opportunity loss or regret associated with an act is the profit or payoff foregone as a result of not selecting the best act for a specific state of nature.

It is easy to determine the regret table from the payoff table. Simply select the highest payoff for each event, then subtract all the payoffs in that event from it. The regrets for the complete Atom Smasher example are given in Table 15.12. Note that the definition of an opportunity loss or regret precludes the possibility of negative values since the payoffs of each act are subtracted from those of the best act. The smallest possible regret is zero, which implies you have the best act for the state of nature. In a sense, the data have been inverted. Here the smallest regret represents the most desirable outcome and the largest represents the worst outcome. Since the opportunity loss values are contingent upon the event that occurs, it is sometimes called a conditional loss or conditional opportunity loss.

Table 15.12 Computation of Regrets ($000's)

Events	AS-1			AS-3			AS-4		
E-1	20 −	20 =	0	20 −	(100) =	120	20 −	(800) =	820
E-2	300 −	100 =	200	300 −	300 =	0	300 −	0 =	300
E-3	2,000 −	300 =	1,700	2,000 −	1,300 =	700	2,000 −	2,000 =	0
E-4	8,000 −	900 =	7,100	8,000 −	4,300 =	3,700	8,000 −	8,000 =	0

REGRET TABLE

Events	AS-1	AS-3	AS-4
E-1	0	120	820
E-2	200	0	300
E-3	1,700	700	0
E-4	7,100	3,700	0

Criterion #6: Minimum Weighted Regret

Once the payoffs have been converted to regrets, the same set of criteria that were applied to payoffs can be applied to the regrets. The first would be an application of Bayes' rule, or to determine the minimum weighted regret. In Table 15.13, the regrets are multiplied by their respective weight to obtain the average weighted regret. Since the outcomes are described in a negative sense, the lowest or minimum regret is most desirable (AS-4).

Table 15.13 The Minimum Weighted Regret ($000's)

Events	Pr	AS-1 $	AS-1 Pr•$	AS-3 $	AS-3 Pr•$	AS-4 $	AS-4 Pr•$
E-1	.2	0	0	120	24	820	164
E-2	.4	200	80	0	0	300	120
E-3	.3	1,700	510	700	210	0	0
E-4	.1	7,100	710	3,700	370	0	0
			$\Sigma = 1,300$		$\Sigma = 604$		$\Sigma = 284*$

Shortcomings

All the techniques as they are applied to regrets essentially have the identical shortcomings as explained earlier under payoffs. Therefore, they will not be repeated under the regret (opportunity loss) section of the chapter. It is left as a student exercise to repeat the shortcomings as applied to regrets.

Criterion #7: Minimax (Regrets)

Earlier, the maximin concept was explained. A pessimistic approach was used and the worst payoff was taken from each act, and the maximum of the column minimums was deemed optimal. The same logic is applied with the minimax technique, except that it's applied to regrets (Table 15.14). Therefore, the worst scenario is not the lowest value, but rather the highest values, as they in a sense represent a mistake in judgment. The best of the worst scenarios occurs for AS-4. Remember that for the maximin and minimax techniques the probabilities play no role in the optimum act's determination.

Table 15.14 The Minimax Criterion ($000's)

Events	AS-1	AS-3	AS-4
E-1	0	120	820
E-2	200	0	300
E-3	1,700	700	0
E-4	7,100	3,700	0
Worst Scenario's	7,100	3,700	820*

Criterion #8:   The Maximum Likelihood Criterion (Regrets)

The maximum likelihood technique, as applied to regrets or payoffs, would yield the same choice as the optimum act. This is because only the event with the greatest probability of occurrence is evaluated. Therefore, it would not make any difference if the payoffs or the regrets are evaluated since the highest payoff would automatically concur with the zero regret. Since the maximum likelihood technique assumes E-2 will take place, the optimum payoff, $300, and the smallest regret, $0, are associated with AS-3.

 Concept Check 15.H

A regret is the absolute difference between a particular payoff and the largest payoff for that act. True or false? If false, explain.

Exercises

15.21   The following table is one of regrets.

	Pr	A-1	A-2	A-3	A-4
E-1	.1	50	40	20	0
E-2	.5	10	0	50	0
E-3	.4	0	10	20	30

    a.   Without being told that this is a regret table, there are two indications that this might not be a payoff table. What are the two indicators?

    b.   The respective payoffs for A-4 are E-1 = $200, E-2 = $400, and E-3 = $500. Determine the original payoffs.

    c.   What is the minimum weighted regret and with which act is it associated?

    d.   Using the minimax criterion, which is the optimum act?

    e.   Using the maximum likelihood criterion, which is the optimum act?

15.22   Convert the following payoff matrix into a regret (opportunity loss) table and determine the minimum weighted regret. Before transforming, remove all inadmissible acts.

	Pr	A-1	A-2	A-3	A-4	A-5
E-1	.2	20	40	30	40	40
E-2	.3	50	10	0	(10)	(10)
E-3	.1	50	60	10	0	(10)
E-4	.4	10	30	80	80	80

15.23 Convert the following payoff matrix into a regret (opportunity loss) table and determine the minimum weighted regret. Before transforming, remove all inadmissible acts.

	Pr	A-1	A-2	A-3	A-4
E-1	.2	20	40	30	50
E-2	.3	60	10	80	30
E-3	.1	20	20	20	20
E-4	.2	50	40	70	70
E-5	.2	30	40	40	40

15.24 Convert the payoffs into regrets and determine the act with the minimum weighted regret and the minimax act.

	Pr	A-1	A-2	A-3	A-4	A-5	A-6
E-1	.6	20	70	100	200	(100)	(200)
E-2	.3	200	70	60	50	200	(100)
E-3	.1	80	(10)	80	110	60	(60)

15.8 Expected Value of Perfect Information

In this section we will again be dealing with payoffs instead of regrets. Decision makers must begin to learn how to deal with the problem of seeking additional information before making a decision. Finally, the relationship between payoffs and regrets will be analyzed in terms of their interrelationships.

Expected Payoff of Perfect Information

Sometimes abstract concepts can be used to make very practical business decisions. Such an abstract concept, called the **expected payoff of perfect information** (EPPI), will be now introduced. Although it appears to be a concept without practicality, the EPPI has substantial value in decision-making. Why would we compute something that is difficult to achieve in the real world? After we make a few computations, however, we will learn how it will be used in a very practical manner.

Recalling our example with a wizard, if he were to tell us that E-1 would take place, AS-1 would be chosen netting the company $20,000. If E-2 were to occur, AS-3 would be chosen netting $300,000. If E-3 or E-4 were to occur, then the choice would be AS-4, and the respective payoffs would be $2,000,000 and $8,000,000. If $20,000 were made 20% of the time, and $300,000 made 40% of the time, and $2,000,000 made 30% of the time, and $8,000,000 made 10% of the time, the average weighted payoff would be $1,524,000 (Table 15.15). This is the expected payoff of perfect information. It represents how much the decision maker expects to make if perfect information is utilized prior to selecting an act.

Table 15.15 Computing the Expected Payoff of Perfect Information ($000's)

Events	Pr	AS-1	AS-3	AS-4	Row Maximum	Pr•Maximum
E-1	.2	$20	$(100)	$(800)	$20	$4
E-2	.4	100	300	0	300	120
E-3	.3	300	1,300	2,000	2,000	600
E-4	.1	900	3,700	8,000	8,000	800
					EPPI = $1,524	

Expected Value of Perfect Information (EVPI)

If perfect information is possible the company could expect to make $1,524,000 (EPPI). Suppose a decision had to be made right now based on the information already at hand. After reviewing all the different criteria for choosing an optimum act, and since the majority chose AS-4, this would probably be the company choice. In Table 15.5, the expected payoff from AS-4 is $1,240,000. The question that now arises is whether it is worthwhile to attempt to gather more and better information.

To gather new information might require the hiring of consultants, accountants, forecasters, financial experts, etc. The information received from such experts may increase the expected payoff of the optimal decision, yet it is not expected to be as valuable as perfect information. What is the maximum value of such experts? If $1,524,000 (EPPI) could be made if perfect information is available and $1,240,000 is the expected payoff under uncertainty, the maximum that would be considered paying the consultants is the difference, or $284,000. This difference is termed the **expected value of perfect information** (EVPI). The $284,000 difference represents a 22.9% increase over what could have been made by choosing to produce AS-4 immediately.

Since the EVPI value is a relatively large value, the company may wish to consider an option of obtaining more information prior to making a decision. This does not mean that additional information will definitely be obtained, merely that the option will be evaluated. Chapter 16 will deal in more detail with the consideration of gathering additional information. If the EVPI is relatively small, then it is often not wise to seek additional information as the cost will probably exceed the benefits to be derived.

Remember that we are selling a toy and must be ready for this Christmas season's retail market. Our firm can't afford to be faced with the situation that Coleco encountered when their small computer reached the retail market in January. All the Christmas sales were missed and the company stock dropped substantially. Similar circumstances surrounded Worlds of Wonder, Inc. and the company got itself into trouble by not meeting schedules. See "Worlds of Wonder: From Wall Street Charmon to Chapter 11," *BusinessWeek*, March 21, 1988, pp. 74–75, 78. Please remember that Christmas catalogs are sometimes printed in August and the major retailers must begin purchasing in March to meet the summer deadline. Timing is essential, and more information would be without value if it caused one to miss the Christmas retail sales, unless the EVPI was an extremely large value.

How "extremely large value" is defined is a management prerogative. Many believe that the management style in the United States is geared toward finding decisions which had negative consequences for the firm. The firm then penalizes the decision-makers who made those choices. This forces managers to become risk averters by obtaining more and more information prior to making any decisions, even if its not justified by the available facts. For example, physicians order needless tests as a precaution or to hedge against potential law suits. Managers may themselves be in a similar scenario. In order to avoid making a bad decision, needless feasibility studies and analyses may be performed. These feasibility studies may not only add little in the way of new information, but they may also delay the decision long enough for competitors to out-maneuver the Atom Smasher. This is not a condemnation of all, or even most of the feasibility studies, but merely a precaution against unnecessary overkill.

EVPI Equals the Lowest Weighted Regret

An interesting fact can be viewed by analyzing Bayes' rule as it's applied to payoffs and regrets. The expected payoff is what is monetarily expected from choosing a particular act. The expected regret represents what a decision maker expects to incur as a lost opportunity if an act is selected. When the two are added together it must sum to the expected payoff with perfect information. Table 15.16 combines the weighted payoffs of Table 15.5 with the weighted regrets of Table 15.13, to obtain the expected payoff with perfect information.

Table 15.16 Payoffs Plus Regrets ($000's)

	AS-1	AS-3	AS-4
Payoffs	224	920	1,240
Regrets	1,300	604	284
TOTAL	1,524	1,524	1,524

The lowest weighted regret (AS-4) will always be associated with the act that has the maximum payoff. Therefore, the EVPI and the lowest weighted regret will always be identical. The same value (284,000) can be obtained by two different computational processes.

 Concept Check 15.I

EVPI may be used as a guide to determine if the decision maker will want to consider additional information prior to making the decision. True or false? If false, explain.

Exercises

15.25 The table represents payoffs contingent upon certain acts and events occurring.

	Pr	A-1	A-2	A-3
E-1	.6	100	200	150
E-2	.3	300	100	200
E-3	.1	200	500	400

a. Determine the inadmissible acts.
b. Determine the optimal act using the maximum expected payoff criterion.
c. Determine the EVPI.
d. Convert the payoff matrix to a regret (opportunity loss) table and determine the minimum weighted regret.
e. Compare the answers to "c" and "d." Comment.

15.26 The table represents payoffs contingent upon certain acts and events occurring.

	Pr	A-1	A-2	A-3	A-4	A-5	A-6
E-1	.8	100	200	100	300	400	200
E-2	.1	700	2000	5000	600	100	900
E-3	.1	2000	4000	5000	0	0	10,000

a. Determine the inadmissible acts.
b. Determine the optimal act using the maximum expected payoff criterion.
c. Determine the EVPI.
d. Convert the payoff matrix to a regret (opportunity loss) table and determine the minimum weighted regret.
e. Compare the answers to "c" and "d." Comment.

15.27 For the following payoffs, find any inadmissible acts, then determine EVPI.

	Pr	A-1	A-2	A-3	A-4	A-5	A-6
E-1	.6	20	70	100	200	(100)	(200)
E-2	.3	200	70	60	50	200	(100)
E-3	.1	80	(10)	80	110	60	(60)

15.28 Determine all inadmissible acts from the following payoff matrix then compute EVPI.

	Pr	A-1	A-2	A-3	A-4	A-5
E-1	.2	20	40	30	40	40
E-2	.3	50	10	0	(10)	(10)
E-3	.1	50	60	10	0	(10)
E-4	.4	10	30	80	80	80

494

All of the analyses made have been in terms of profit, losses or a failure to make optimum profits or losses (regrets). It might be noted that it is really not money, or the loss of it that may be important, but rather the effect that money has on an individual's well being. To explain the concept an example from Greek mythology will be used.

The Myth of Achilles

One version of the Myth of Achilles is that at birth he was confronted by the leader of the Gods, Zeus, who gave Achilles a choice. The choices were to have a long normal life or to have a glorious, but shorter life. Legend has it that Achilles chose the latter and his mother held him by the heel while she dipped him into the Styx River (River of Death). He was unconquerable except for the area of his heel where his mother held him. He went on to great feats of mortal combat. After killing the great Trojan warrior Hector, Achilles knew his death was near. The following day, Achilles met his demise at the end of Paris's (Hector's brother) arrow.

Suppose you, the reader, were given a similar choice at birth. The choices were to have the life that you are now leading or to become someone that is envied. People frequently fantasize that they are popular entertainers, sports heroes, famous politicians, or super spies like James Bond (Jane Bond for the ladies). The catch is that you would die long before your normal life expectancy of 75+ years.

Examples of individuals who might fit this general category are Janis Joplin, John Belushi, Elvis Presley, John Lennon, Freddy Prinz, Jack and Robert Kennedy, Karen Carpenter, Bruce Lee, James Dean, Heath Ledger, Richie Valens, Buddy Holly, Ernie Davis, Marilyn Monroe, Len Bias, Andy Gibb, etc. These are the type of individuals some have dreamed of emulating in terms of their life and riches.

Although it might be tantalizing to dream of such a scenario, most people would prefer to have the life they are leading now. Of course, there could be extenuating circumstances that could make a person choose the shorter glamorous life. If one, because of a terminal illness, was not expected to lead the long normal life, they might consider selecting the short glamorous life. Or if an individual were from a Third World country where opportunities are not very plentiful, and life expectancies not very long, again one might sacrifice themselves for the good of their families. Most of the individuals mentioned had enormous revenue potential before their untimely deaths.

The main point of this informal discussion is that it is not money that is most important to many, but rather the effect that it has on their quality of life. Many students envision themselves as various superstars, yet students might find that they have a more fulfilling life as the person they are rather than the person they dream of being. The point to note is that increased monetary income does not necessarily correlate with an improved quality of life. The concept of utility is an attempt to measure the effect of different outcomes on the decision maker's well being.

Utility and an Example of Possible Use

Economists attempt to measure satisfaction in terms of the utility (or satisfaction) a consumer receives from the ownership of a product or service. In order to compare different products or services of different values, a ratio of the utility received, divided by the price, yields an optimization of one's budget. One should always maximize their utility per dollar spent.

When reviewing the maximum expected payoff criterion (Bayes' rule), an inconsistency appears (Table 15.6). With A-1, fate would net either $0 or $50,000, and with A-2 it's either ($100,000) or $201,000. The respective weights for the two events were E-1 = .4, E-2 = .6. The weighted payoff for A-1 was $20,000, and for A-2 it was $20,400. Since A-2 had the greatest payoff, it was the optimum act. Yet it had associated with it a 60% chance of losing $100,000, which some might find unacceptable.

What might be attempted is to rescale the data to reveal a displeasure with such a large loss. We might start by listing all the possible payoffs in descending order (Table 15.17).

Table 15.17 Assigning Utility Values

		UTILS	
Payoffs	A	B	C
$201,000	10	10	10
$50,000	9	4	5
$0	6	1	3.33
($100,000)	0	0	0

Normally, a 0–10 subjective utility scale, which attaches zero to the worst scenario and a 10 to the best, is used. Other common scales would be 0 to 1, or −5 to +5. A util is a unit of satisfaction. Its value must be determined subjectively, yet it must follow a rationale of either an ascending or descending scale. To rank in an ascending or descending order, it is assumed that an individual can always express preference for one choice over another or indifference between the two. A second requirement is that if X is preferred to Y, and Y is preferred to Z, then X must be preferred to Z. This particular property is sometimes called transitivity of preference.

Returning to our problem, and following the previously mentioned logic, $201,000 would be preferred to making $100,000, $100,000 is preferred to $50,000, and $0 is preferred to losing $100,000. The last difference is the one that is critical to most decision makers because few can afford to lose $100,000. Because of the latter fear a decision maker might show a large utility difference between making $0 and the loss. For a utility preference scale such as this, an individual (Table 15.17) would be called a risk averter. The utils show a consistent pattern in that the largest payoffs have a higher utility value than the lower ones.

If a decision maker shows a tendency to gamble on making the $200,000, he or she might place little value on the other payoffs (individual B in Table 15.17), As such they would be classified as risk takers. Individual C would be classified as risk neutral. For individual C, their utility function would just be a linear approximation to money (Figure 15.1).

Figure 15.1 Risk Averters, Risk Takers, and Risk Neutral

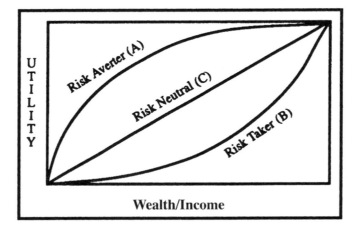

Once a consistent set of util values have been determined, they would replace the payoffs in the decision matrix. The weighted average would then be computed not for the payoffs, but rather for the utility values. If an individual were to receive 6 utils 60% of the time, and 9 utils 40% of the time, he or she would have an expected utility of 7.2 utils. If he or she had 0 utils 60% of the time and 10 utils 69% of the time, the expected utility would be 4 utils (Table 15.18). Since it would be desirable to maximize utility, A-1 should be chosen. Note that this leads to a different conclusion than obtained by strictly applying Bayes' rule to the original payoffs. Individual B would select act (A-2), which is the same act selected by maximizing the expected payoff. Individual C would be indifferent between both acts.

Table 15.18 Computation of Expected Utility

INDIVIDUAL A:

Events	Prob.	Payoffs	A-1 Utils	Weighted Utils	Payoffs	A-2 Utils	Weighted Utils
E-1	.6	0	6	3.6	(100,000)	0	0
E-2	.4	50,000	9	3.6	201,000	10	4
Totals				7.2			4.0

INDIVIDUAL B:

Events	Prob.	Payoffs	A-1 Utils	Weighted Utils	Payoffs	A-2 Utils	Weighted Utils
E-1	.6	0	1	0.6	(100,000)	0	0
E-2	.4	50,000	4	1.6	201,000	10	4
Totals				2.2			4.0

INDIVIDUAL C:

Events	Prob.	Payoffs	A-1 Utils	Weighted Utils	Payoffs	A-2 Utils	Weighted Utils
E-1	.6	0	3.33	2.0	(100,000)	0	0
E-2	.4	50,000	5.00	2.0	201,000	10	4
Totals				4.0			4.0

Shortcomings

An attempt has been made to personalize the data to incorporate the decision maker's attitudes (particularly about risk), beliefs, and fears into the analysis. This is truly important because it is not profits and losses that are important to us as much as the effect that those profits and losses have on the quality of life.

The real problem in trying to apply utility analysis in real life situations lies within the assumptions. It is necessary that the decision makers' preferences are transitive and preferences or indifference can be expressed for any two alternatives. However, there is a problem in trying to apply utility measurement consistently. In Table 15.19 there are a series of possible payoffs ranging from making $20,000 to losing $10,000. If scenario A is followed, the higher payoffs are preferred to the lower payoffs. Remember that a loss is something to be avoided. For scenario B, we are part of a conglomerate that needs a tax write-off. Therefore, the optimum payoff is the greatest loss. In this case, it might not be desirable to make the greatest profit. In scenario C, the individual is in a complicated tax situation. The individual is income-averaging and has a capital loss, and it will not be beneficial either to make too big a profit or too large a loss. Therefore, the worst util values are at the lower and higher ends of the payoff matrix. Finally, in scenario D the individual has just been through a bitter divorce, and in the final settlement the judge has decreed that the alimony payments would double as soon as reported income reached $20,000. If this is distasteful, it is the worst payoff, but the $15,000 payoff is optimum.

Table 15.19 **Possible Utility Ratings**

Scenario	A	B	C	D
Payoffs				
$20,000	10	0	1	0
15,000	9	3	3	10
10,000	8	6	9	9
5,000	7	7	10	8
0	6	8	8	5
(5,000)	3	9	2	3
(10,000)	0	10	0	1

There are obviously enormous complexities involved when attempting to apply utility analysis to payoffs. Because of the number and complexity of the variables involved, the technique is currently impractical to apply. Yet the technique has merit for the future. Ultimately, payoffs must be subjectively converted to the personal effect they would have upon the decision maker.

 Concept Check 15.J

With utility analysis and the util scale, we are attempting to evaluate not only the payoffs involved, but also the effect that payoff will have on us. True or false? If false, explain.

Exercises

15.29   If you were asked to take a promotion and move to a city where you would prefer not to relocate, might not the promotion in actuality be a demotion? Explain. Suppose you were offered two promotion possibilities, one in city A and one in city B. The move to city A represents a 30% pay increase, and a move to city B a 10% increase. Is it not possible that you would still prefer city B to city A? Note that the increases are above those of the increase in cost of living adjustments. Explain.

15.30   Some courses in college are required while others are elective. Listed are reasons students often give for taking elective courses. Rate (from 1 to 8) the reasons you most often use in selecting electives. Do you feel this makes you a risk taker, averter, or that you are risk neutral? Explain.

___ Courses I enjoy
___ Courses more closely related to my discipline
___ Courses where it is easier to obtain a better grade
___ Courses that pose less of a commitment on my time
___ Challenging courses
___ Courses recommended by my advisor
___ Courses that will heighten my quantitative skills
___ Courses taught by a particular instructor
___ Courses that fit my schedule
___ More courses with computers to increase my knowledge

15.31 The table represents payoffs and utils (with asterisk) contingent upon certain acts and events occurring.

	Prob.	A-1	A-2	A-3
E-1	.3	100 5*	200 7*	30 8*
E-2	.5	300 8*	200 7*	0 2*
E-3	.2	(1000) 1*	(2000) 0*	500 10*

a. Determine the optimum act using the maximum expected payoff rule.
b. Determine the optimum act using the maximum expected util rule.
c. Compare your answers to "a" and "b." Explain.

15.10 Summary

In this chapter we analyzed how business managers can analytically develop and evaluate alternatives under conditions of uncertainty. Matrices are used to develop a thought process involving controllable factors (acts) and non-controllable ones (events). The non-controllable factors often represent different possible sales levels for a particular product or service. By evaluating certain contingencies payoffs can be computed.

Once the payoffs are obtained, a series of thought processes can be used to determine the optimum course of action. Some of these thought processes require a determination of the probabilities with which the various events will take place. This can be troublesome as subjective judgment usually plays a large role. Some of the thought processes do not require a determination of the probabilities and are termed nonprobablistic techniques. All the techniques attempt to identify one act as being optimal. Since all use a different point of logic each has shortcomings. These shortcomings mean that the optimizing technique would select an act different from that of the manager.

Besides selecting an optimum act the process allows the computing of the expected value of perfect information (EVPI). With this information, decision makers can determine if it would be worthwhile to pursue the idea of obtaining additional information before making the final decision. This concept is pursued in the next chapter.

Mini-case 15.1: Problem Analysis, a Step by Step Approach

Problem. A payoff matrix has been developed for a decision maker confronted with five options and there are three possible events.

Events	Probability	A-1	A-2	A-3	A-4	A-5
E-1	.5	200	500	500	200	(300)
E-2	.3	100	100	0	500	700
E-3	.2	0	700	700	900	1,000

Determine or compute

a. the inadmissible acts.
b. the maximum expected payoff and the act associated with it.
c. the maximin payoff and the act associated with it.
d. the maximum likelihood payoff and the act associated with it.
e. the maximax payoff and the act associated with it.
f. the payoff from the concept of insufficient reason.
g. the minimum weighted regret.
h. the minimax payoff.
i. the EVPI.

Mini-case 15.2: Purchase of a Used Car

You are completing your second year of college. You need to purchase a used car so that you can work during your last two years. You are deciding between three used automobiles. The first (A-1) is nice and sporty, but the gas consumption and the maintenance costs are high. The last car (A-3) is the most efficient to operate, but the sales price is the highest. The following formulas represent the sales price (fixed cost) and the cost to drive per mile (variable cost) as given by an auto magazine.

$$A\text{-}1 = \$2,000 + .25 \text{ (Miles driven)}$$
$$A\text{-}2 = \$4,000 + .15 \text{ (Miles driven)}$$
$$A\text{-}3 = \$5,000 + .10 \text{ (Miles driven)}$$

You are not sure exactly how many miles you will drive, which will in part depend upon the part-time jobs you are trying to obtain. For simplicity, you stratify the miles into three groups.

$$E\text{-}1 = 7,000 \text{ Low Miles Driven}$$
$$E\text{-}2 = 12,000 \text{ Average Miles Driven}$$
$$E\text{-}3 = 18,000 \text{ High Miles Driven}$$

You estimate Automobile A-1 Will Have a resale of $1,000; A-2 $1,750; and A-3 $2,500 when you sell in two years when you graduate from college. You will assign a twenty percent probability for E-1, a fifty percent probability for E-2, and a thirty percent probability for E-3. Develop an appropriate payoff matrix for the problem. Which car should you purchase viewing the decision as an attempt to minimize your costs during your last two years at college?

Review of Important Terms and Concepts

Acts: Decision variables that can be controlled by management.

Events: Decision variables which cannot be controlled by management. In many business problems events are the possible sales that can occur.

Outcomes: A result that reflects the combination of an act (which is controllable) and an event (which is not controllable).

Payoffs: In many business problems, outcomes are denoted in profits and losses and are termed payoffs.

Decision table: A matrix of all possible elements of a decision problem. It includes the acts, events, and outcomes.

Inadmissible acts: Factors we have control over and are illogical because of payoffs of another act are always either greater than or equal to those of the inadmissible act.

Maximizing expected payoffs or Bayes' decision rule: A method of obtaining probability estimates for events, then using the respective payoffs by computing the weighted average for each act. The optimum act is the one with the greatest weighted payoff.

Maximin: A decision criterion that selects the smallest (worst) payoff per act, then selects the best of the worst possibilities. Probabilities do not enter into consideration. The term means to select the maximum value of the column (acts) minimums.

Maximum likelihood criterion: A method of selecting the event with the highest probability of occurring, then assuming that it will occur. If it occurs, the act with the highest payoff for that event is to be selected as optimum.

Maximax: Analogous to the maximin criteria, except the best payoff is selected for each act, then the best of the best is selected as optimum. The term means to select the maximum value of the column (acts) maximums. Probabilities do not enter into consideration.

Principle of insufficient reason: If probabilities cannot be assigned to the various events then an equal weight is assigned to them. This is analogous to computing a straight arithmetic mean for each act.

Regrets or opportunity losses: Regrets are obtained by taking the highest payoff for each event, then subtracting the payoffs of all other alternatives for that event. Since it is an absolute difference, negative numbers are not possible. The smallest number possible is zero, and this represents a positive condition since there would be no regrets. After the table is completed, each event should contain at least one zero value.

Minimum weighted regret: The regrets are multiplied by the assigned weights (probabilities) to determine the weighted regrets. The lowest weighted regret is selected as optimum.

Minimax: The worst regret (Largest value) is selected from each act (column) and the best (smallest value) is selected as optimum. The term means to select the minimum value of the column (acts) maximums. Probabilities do not enter into consideration.

EPPI, the expected payoff of perfect information: The highest payoff is selected for each event, then a weighted payoff is obtained using the assigned weights.

EVPI, the expected value of perfect information: The EVPI can be computed two ways. First, the lowest weighted regret can be obtained and it must be equal to EVPI. Second, the highest weighted payoff (Bayes' decision rule) can be subtracted from the expected payoff with perfect information.

Util: A measure of satisfaction derived from a product or service.

Transitivity of preference: A rule of consistency where if A was preferred to B, and B was preferred to C, A would be preferred to C.

Risk taker/neutral/averter: A decision maker is a risk taker if he or she desires to accept a fair gamble rather than an equivalent amount of money for certain. Risk neutral if indifferent between fair gamble and amount for certain. Risk averter if prefer certain amount rather than the fair gamble.

Review of Important Formulas

The Expected Profit Under Uncertainty

$$E(x) = \Sigma x \bullet \Pr(x) \tag{15.1}$$

where

x is a discrete random variable with a probability distribution $\Pr(x)$

15.32 The table represents payoffs contingent upon certain acts and events occurring.

	Prob.	A-1	A-2	A-3	A-4	A-5	A-6
E-1	.6	4	100	200	20	10	70
E-2	.3	90	80	70	60	70	10
E-3	.1	10	60	70	90	40	90

    a.   Identify any inadmissible acts.

Determine the optimum act using:
    b.   the maximum expected payoff criterion.
    c.   the maximin payoff criterion.
    d.   the maximum likelihood technique.
    e.   the maximax criterion.
    f.   the Laplace method.
    g.   Compute EVPI.

Convert the payoffs to regrets (opportunity losses) and determine the optimum act using:
    h.   the minimum weighted regret.
    i.   the minimax criterion.
    j.   the maximum likelihood technique.

15.33 In Exercise 15.32, we were told that the data represented payoffs. If we were not told this, how could we have figured that they indeed represented payoffs and not regrets?

15.34 A company must decide which one of three products to produce. For product A, the fixed costs are $100,000 with a variable cost of $3 per unit. For product B, fixed costs are $50,000 and variable costs $6 per unit, and for product C the respective figures are $20,000 fixed and $8 variable. The marketing department projects three possible sales levels. Either the company will sell 20,000 units (probability = .7), 40,000 units (probability = .2), or 60,000 units (probability = .1). The respective per unit selling prices are for A it's $9, for B it's $10, and for C it's $12.

    a.   Determine the appropriate payoff matrix.
    b.   Identify any inadmissible acts.

Determine the optimum act using:
    c.   the maximum expected payoff criterion.
    d.   the maximin payoff criterion.
    e.   the maximum likelihood.
    f.   the Laplace method.
    g.   Compute the EVPI.

15.35 a.   For Exercise 15.34, transform the payoffs into regrets.

Then determine the optimum using:
    b.   the minimum weighted regret.
    c.   the minimax criterion.
    d.   the maximum likelihood technique.

15.36   You have a choice of selecting between two acts. There are two possible events both equally probable.

	Prob.	A-1	A-2
E-1	.4	$10	$600
E-2	.6	(2)	(10)

     a.   Use the maximin payoff criterion and determine the optimum act.
     b.   Use the maximum likelihood criterion and determine the optimum act.
     c.   Determine the maximum expected payoff and with which act it is associated.
     d.   Would there be any way to avoid the difficulties found in the logic involved in answering "a" and "b"?

15.37   In Exercise 15.36, if the probabilities for the two events were reversed, would the answers to "a","b", and "c" change? Explain.

15.38   The following is a regret (opportunity loss) table.

	A-1	A-2	A-3	A-4	A-5
E-1	20	50	10	0	0
E-2	30	90	25	5	0
E-3	10	0	10	60	60

     a.   If you were not told this was a regret table, what two clues would lead you to this conclusion?
     b.   Use the minimax criterion to determine the optimum act.

15.39   For Exercise 15.38, if the probabilities were E-1 = E-2 = .2, E-3 = .6, determine the minimum weighted regret.

15.40   For Exercise 15.38, convert the regrets to payoffs utilizing the following information. Some respective payments are A-5: E-1 = 80, A-5: E-2 = 90, and A-5: E-3 = 30. After the payoffs are obtained determine the highest weighted payoff and with which act it is associated.

15.41   If you were a department store manager and knew that you would either have poor, normal, or strong Christmas sales, how might you go about the task of trying to ascertain exactly what those probabilities would be?

15.42   The following is a payoff matrix:

Events	Probability	A-1	A-2	A-3
E-1	.3	$10,000	$1,000	$4,000
E-2	.2	$10,000	$12,000	$14,000
E-3	.3	6,000	3,000	4,000
E-4	.2	20,000	18,000	12,000

     a.   Are there any inadmissible acts?
     b.   Which is the optimum act according to Bayes' rule?
     c.   Determine the EVPI.

15.43 The following is a payoff matrix:

Events	Probability	A-1	A-2	A-3
E-1	.5	$10,000	$12,000	$14,000
E-2	.3	6,000	3,000	5,000
E-3	.2	20,000	18,000	20,000

   a. Are there any inadmissible acts?
   b. Which is the optimum act according to Bayes' rule?
   c. Determine the EVPI.
   d. Evaluate the EVPI and ascertain if it would be worthwhile to obtain additional information.

15.44 The following is a payoff matrix:

Events	Probability	A-1	A-2	A-3
E-1	.5	$10,000	$12,000	$14,000
E-2	.3	6,000	3,000	6,000
E-3	.2	20,000	18,000	20,000

   a. Are there any inadmissible acts?
   b. Which is the optimum act according to Bayes' rule?
   c. Determine and evaluate the EVPI.

15.45 The following is a payoff matrix:

Events	Probability	A-1	A-2	A-3
E-1	.3	$10,000	$1,000	$4,000
E-2	.3	1,000	1,000	10,000
E-3	.4	2,000	10,000	2,000

   a. Are there any inadmissible acts?
   b. Which is the optimum act according to Bayes' rule?
   c. Determine and evaluate the EVPI.
   d. Obtain the regret table and compute the smallest weighted regret.
   e. Compare your answers to parts "c" and "d."

15.46 Convert the payoffs from exercise 15.45 to utils using the following scale:

Money Value	Utils
$10,000	10
4,000	2
2,000	1
1,000	0

   a. Based on the util values would the decision maker be considered a risk taker, risk averter, or risk neutral?
   b. Which act yields the largest weighted utils?
   c. Does the outcome differ from 15.45b?

15.47 Convert the payoffs from Exercise 15.45 to utils using the following scale:

Money Value	Utils
$10,000	10
4,000	9
2,000	8
1,000	0

   a. Based on the util values would the decision maker be considered a risk taker, risk averter, or risk neutral?

   b. Which act yields the largest weighted utils?

   c. Does the outcome differ from 15.45b and 15.46b?

15.48 Convert the payoffs from Exercise 15.45 to utils using the following scale:

Money Value	Utils
$10,000	10
4,000	3.3
2,000	1.1
1,000	0

   a. Based on the util values would the decision maker be considered a risk taker, risk averter, or risk neutral?

   b. Without making any computations, would the act yielding the largest weighted utils be any different from the act yielding the largest weighted payoff?

15.49   a. Think of a geographic area for which you do not care. How much money would a company have to offer you, over and above what you might be able to make in geographic areas for which you do care, to persuade you to move there?

   b. Is there a relationship between income and quality of life?

15.50 Why do many people play golf when they are not really very proficient at the sport?

Bayesian Analysis and Experimental Information

Where we have been

In Chapter 15, we learned to develop payoff tables based on certain contingencies involving controllable acts and uncontrollable events. We also developed rules or criteria on which to determine, or aid in the selection of, the "best" or optimal act. We completed the chapter by introducing the EVPI, which is the expected value of perfect information.

Where we are going

We will elaborate on the conceptual framework learned in the last chapter. If the EVPI turns out to be relatively large, it might be worthwhile to consider the possibility of obtaining additional information prior to making our decision. We will have to evaluate the specific benefits and the associated costs of additional information to make such a decision. Tree diagrams are very useful tools to aid in making this decision and they will be introduced in this chapter.

16.1   Introduction

In Chapter 15, we introduced the EVPI (expected value of perfect information), which essentially is the difference between the payoffs of perfect and imperfect information. If the value of EVPI is low it would be an indication that it might not be profitable to seek additional information (sometimes called **experimental information**). If the EVPI were relatively large, it certainly would be wise to consider obtaining additional information, possibly by hiring consultants. It is not a certainty that additional information will be obtained, but rather just a consideration of the costs and the possible benefits to be derived from obtaining additional information. It also must be remembered that in obtaining additional information a time delay in our business decision is inevitable, and depending on circumstances, the time delay could result in a substantial loss in revenue. Such a loss might occur if the delay meant we missed the Christmas season. One season like this often can account for more than half of an organization's yearly revenues. If the value of the EVPI is small on an absolute scale, then it is clear that any efforts to obtain additional or experimental information will be unjustified unless the cost of obtaining it is even smaller. Decision making based on the EVPI is referred to as **prior analysis** and Chapter 15 was an introduction to decision making based on prior information. Prior analysis is decision analysis based on the prior information and prior probabilities that are available without incurring any expense in information gathering. The decision maker bases the decision on the information immediately available.

In some instances, prior analysis can lead to decisions which seem inappropriate. For example, in legal litigations it is frequently less expensive for a lawyer to reach a settlement than to precede with a case in which their client is right and has a good chance of winning. In the court system, plea bargains are often made based upon the availability of confinement space, and the costs associated with that space, as opposed to the merits of an individual case. Yet, from the rationale of dollar costs, these plea bargains may represent an optimum decision, at least in the short run.

16.2 Drawing Tree Diagrams or Decision Trees

The development of tree diagrams provides an extremely useful tool in evaluating the options open to a decision maker. A tree diagram provides a visualization of the entire decision problem. A pictorial representation of alternatives, events, and the consequences or outcomes of each combination, helps the decision maker evaluate alternatives in a rational manner.

Control vs. No Control

When constructing a tree diagram, one of the main questions that must be answered is the control the decision maker has over a set of circumstances. In Chapter 15, we stratified the choices into two categories. First, there were acts over which the decision maker has total control; and second, the event (or state of nature) over which the decision maker has no control. An attempt has been made to standardize the use of symbols and the branching node for events will be depicted with a circle. The branching **node** for acts, where the control exists for the decision maker, will be differentiated with a square. A node is either a square or a circle from which all branches emanate. Again, if there is control at a given stage in a decision problem the node or branching point will be represented with a square, and if there is no control a circle will be used.

In Chapter 15, we discussed the possibility of reviving a pop quiz during your very next business statistics class. Your options were either to prepare for it or gamble that the instructor would not give the pop quiz and not prepare. In drawing the analysis on a tree diagram, we would draw whether the instructor gives a quiz or not as a circle (since you do not control that variable) and your option to study or not as a square (since that aspect is controlled by you, the decision maker).

Left to Right

In constructing a decision tree, it must be remembered that the drawing should be chronologically ordered from left to right. Since the analysis must be drawn chronologically, the basic consideration in drawing the tree structure is the sequencing of events and acts and their consequences or outcomes. In the pop quiz example, do you have to make the decision to study or not before or after your instructor walks into class and gives or doesn't give a pop quiz? Obviously, you must make your decision to study or not before. Therefore, the tree diagram will emanate from that decision point.

Figure 16.1 follows the chronological flow of the pop quiz decision problem. The tree originates with a square from which the two decisions, study and do not study, branch. As a student, there are only two choices, that of study or not. In other problems, there could be many more choices open to us and therefore, more options branching off the square. The branches from the square ultimately come to circles which reflect an aspect of the decision problem that you do not control but rather is under the control of your instructor. Note, even though your instructor has control over whether there will be a pop quiz, you, the decision maker do not. There are the four basic outcomes, two of which are essentially positive, and two which are negative. As mentioned in the last chapter, it would be hard to describe studying for an exam not given as a bad choice, yet in the short run, your time may have been more efficiently allocated to another course in order for you to maximize your grade point average.

Figure 16.1 Decision Tree for Pop Quiz Decision Problem

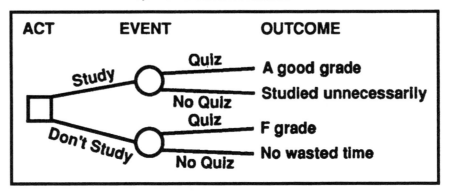

Atom Smasher Example

We will now utilize the Atom Smasher example of Chapter 15 to review the concept of decision trees. In the Atom Smasher problem the EVPI was $284,000; therefore, it would be wise to entertain the notion of obtaining additional information as long as the cost of such information is less than the EVPI. Let us ascertain that the additional information to be considered is to survey the nation's leading retailers, Sears, K-Mart, Wal-Mart, etc., to determine what their expectations might be for the upcoming Christmas season. Retailers might categorize their perceptions of the future Christmas season as optimistic or pessimistic. Of course, their own purchase of stock for inventory will depend upon their expectations. Several marketing research firms have been contacted and it is now believed that it will cost about $100,000 to obtain the information that is sought from the major retailers. For simplicity, it will be assumed that the marketing research findings can be categorized as either optimistic (for upcoming Christmas sales) or pessimistic.

At this point, a tree diagram would be a useful tool to visualize the structure of the decision problem and the options available to the decision maker. Since there is a great deal of information, it will be wise to list the acts and events of the problem (Table 16.1).

Table 16.1   Listing the Acts and Events: Atom Smasher Example

Acts: To be Drawn as Squares	Events: To be Drawn as Circles
To produce 1 of 3 robots: AS-1, AS-3, AS-4*	*Possible Sales:* Light, Moderate, Strong, Incredible
To hire a consulting firm: Hire or not hire firm	*Outcome of consulting firm:* Optimistic or Pessimistic

*Robot AS-2 was inadmissible

After listing the possible acts and events it is important to examine the chronological structure of the acts. Which act will precede the other? Obviously, we will make the decision concerning the consultant first, then decide which robot to produce. If we hire the consultant, we want that input in helping make the decision of which robot to produce.

509

Once the sequence of the acts is finished, the problem now turns to the events. After collecting additional information a set of outcomes will result. These outcomes will embody the possible results of the new information. In the problem, the outcome of the new information is a survey indicating either an optimistic or a pessimistic upcoming Christmas sale. The remaining set of events in the problem stem from the previously discussed potential sales levels. These were weak sales (E-1), moderate sales (E-2), strong sales (E-3), and incredible sales (E-4). We are now ready to draw the tree diagram (Figure 16.2). The tree will begin with a square representing the branching point for the alternatives, gather additional information and do not gather additional information. This aspect of the decision problem is controllable; hence, its branching node is represented by a square.

Figure 16.2 Drawing a Tree Diagram: Atom Smasher Example

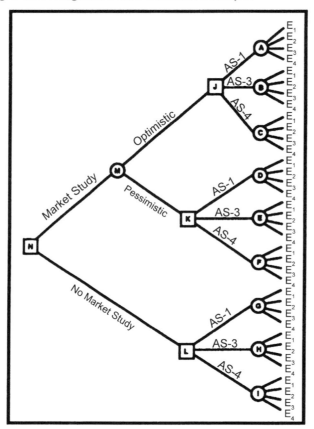

Following the path that new information is obtained leads to events over which there is no control. At this point, there are two possibilities: retailers are optimistic or retailers are pessimistic. Since these are events, their branching node is a circle. Subsequent to these outcomes, a decision must be made to produce one of three Atom Smasher models: Smasher AS-1, Smasher AS-3, or Smasher AS-4. Remember that Smasher AS-2 was eliminated as an inadmissible act. Since these are controllable they are acts and their branching node is a square.

Finally, after making the production decision, the set of events occur reflecting the eventual demand for the Atom Smasher. These events are: weak sales, moderate sales, strong sales, or incredible sales. Since these are noncontrollable, their branching point is a circle. In review, following a determination to obtain the additional information, there is no control over the outcome of that information, there subsequently is control over which robot to produce, but then no control over the ultimate sales at the retail level.

510

If it is decided not to obtain the new information, we obviously would not receive the survey results. Therefore, the tree diagram would go directly to the next decision (square) which is to decide which Atom Smasher to produce, and then finally to what is not controlled, which is the ultimate sales (circle) during Christmas. When drawing the tree diagram make sure that all of the squares or circles that involve the same essential decision are in the same vertical plane so that the decision frame along the various branches is consistent. In the lower branch, the circle (resulting from the new information) is absent. This is because if the new information is not obtained, there will not be a subsequent outcome to be derived from that information. The no new information branch goes from a square to a square.

Remember that the level of Christmas sales will also depend upon customers' expectations. An event like the 508 point one day drop in the Dow Jones industrial average on Monday, October 19, 1987, could have a very unpredictable effect on upcoming Christmas purchases.

Legal Example

Suppose you are a young attorney that has a run of eight straight acquittals for your clients. The ninth such acquittal would mean an elevation to a partnership in a prestigious law firm for which you work. You have been asked to defend a young person who is charged with the premeditated murder of his spouse. After listening to your prospective client, the question of guilt or innocence is unclear. Therefore, you feel that if you can't be convinced of the innocence, a jury may be equally inclined and you could lose the case. Winning the ninth case means a great deal to you and you are considering paying for a lie detector test for the defendant or paying a private investigator to substantiate part of the defendant's alibi.

To visualize the decision problem, a tree diagram will be used. Before constructing the tree, the first task is to differentiate the acts from the events (Table 16.2) and to chronologically order them. You can accept the case or not; so this is an act. Also, whether you gather additional information prior to making this decision is under your control. In fact, you have two avenues available for obtaining the desired information.

Which of the acts comes first—the decision to accept the case or the decision to gather additional information? You would obviously want the additional information, lie detector test results, or the private investigator's report, prior to the decision of whether to accept the case. You want the results from the decision to gather information to aid in decision making regarding the second set of acts. The tree will emanate from the initial act (square) of either paying for a lie detector test, paying a private investigator to substantiate part of the defendant's story, or to do neither.

Table 16.2   Listing the Acts and Events: Legal Example

Acts: To be Drawn as Squares	Events: To be Drawn as Circles
To take the case: Yes or no	*Outcome of Jury:* Guilty or innocent
A: *To pay for lie detector:* Yes or no	*Outcome of lie detector* Story; substantiated or refuted
B: *To hire private-eye:* Yes or no	*Outcome of private-eye:* Story; substantiated or refuted

Assume that the results of the lie detector test and of the private detective will either be to substantiate the defendant's story or refute it. Then from the acts to obtain additional information there will be two possible events (circle): Substantiate alibi or refute alibi. Following these two branches the decision must be made to defend or not (act/squares). However, you do not determine the judgment of the jury, which will be either innocent or guilty (event/circle). Your ultimate partnership in the firm depends on the judgment of the jury as to the innocence or guilt of the defendant. For the bottom branch, since there is no new information, the attorney must then directly choose to defend or not (Figure 16.3).

Figure 16.3 Drawing a Tree Diagram: Legal Example

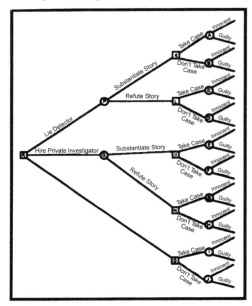

If the attorney does not take the case, the question of innocent or guilty will be a moot point (to the lawyer who does not take the case, not to the defendant). Hence, these event nodes can be eliminated from the decision tree. This reduces the total number of nodes (acts + events) from 18 to 13 (Figure 16.4).

There is also a second reason for eliminating some event nodes on some problems. If all the pay-offs emanating from an event node are identical, the tree diagram is usually collapsed into a single branch. This elimination of the event node can occur because regardless of the probabilities assigned to each event, the expected payoff of a constant is the constant itself.

Figure 16.4 Reducing the Number of Nodes: Legal Example

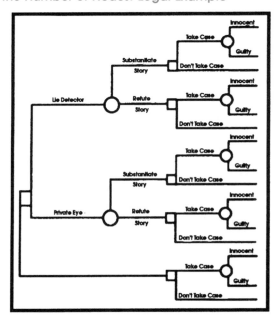

512

Although there are always exceptions to a general rule, tree diagrams as they are applied to business problems tend to follow a pattern. First, there is normally the choice of whether or not to obtain additional information (act/square). Second, if new information is obtained, there is no control over the result of that new information (event/circle). Third, the decision maker must finally "fish or cut bait." This refers to the decision maker's fundamental decision (act/square). Finally, there are a set of events that influence the ultimate outcome over which the decision maker has no control, which in many business examples refers to the potential sales levels (event/circle). Many business decision problems follow this same pattern; act, event, act, event for the branch involving the new information and act, act, event for the branch not obtaining the new (experimental) information.

 Concept Check 16.A

The fundamental decision in the problem will precede the decision to obtain additional Information. True or false? If false, explain.

Exercise

16.1   An internationally known artist is contemplating how to sell her latest lithograph. She can either make a limited edition of 100, and sell them at exclusive galleries, or make 1,000 and sell them at less exclusive galleries. She is thinking of hiring an art consulting firm to help her with the decision. The consulting firm's response will be either positive (Pos) or negative (Neg). In the end, the print selling will either be a financial success (S) or a failure (F) with the buying public. Draw the appropriate chronological tree diagram of the circumstances.

16.2   A manager must choose between two courses of action (A or B). He is thinking about having a market survey performed at a cost of $5,000. If the market survey is conducted, the outcome will either be favorable (Fav) or unfavorable (Unf). Ultimately, the outcome will either be a business success (S) or a business failure (F). Draw the appropriate chronological tree diagram of the circumstances.

16.3   A new company is contemplating either opening in a city or in a suburban area. The CEO is thinking about conducting a market study to give her more information in the making of the decision. The results of the research would be a strong sentiment (SS) in favor of the city, or no real sentiment either way (NS). The CEO believes ultimately that there will be either a strong sales (S), a normal sales (N), or a weak sales (W). Draw the appropriate chronological tree diagram of the circumstances.

16.4   A company is thinking about opening a new product line. They feel that the possible upcoming sales can be categorized as strong (S), normal (N), or weak (W). They are also thinking about hiring a consulting firm to aid in the decision making process. The results of such an analysis will either be positive (Pos) or negative (Neg). Draw the appropriate chronological tree diagram of the circumstances.

16.5   A company is contemplating placing a bid for a government contract. It may make a bid, and if so it may (S = Success) or may not (F = Failure) get the contract. It is thinking about hiring a consulting firm and lobbyist to help make the decision to bid or not. The consulting firm will either state that the conditions are favorable (Fav) for the bid or unfavorable (Unf). Draw the appropriate chronological tree diagram of the circumstances.

16.6   A company is thinking about opening one of 2 possible new product lines. It feels that the possible upcoming sales can be categorized as strong (S), or weak (W). It is also thinking about hiring a consulting firm to aid in the decision making process. The results of such an analysis will either be positive (Pos) or negative (Neg). Draw the appropriate chronological tree diagram of the circumstances.

16.7   A young producer has just completed a movie that turned out better than expected. The producer was going to sell the movie to cablevision but now also wants to consider selling to movie theaters. The producer is considering hiring a theatrical consulting firm to test show the movie overseas and to tabulate the responses of movie buffs. The result will either be extremely positive (EP), positive but reserved (PR), and a negative reaction (NR). Ultimately the movies will be a success (S) or a failure (F). Draw the appropriate chronological tree diagram of the circumstances.

16.8   A decision must be made to go or not with a small merger. If we go through with it, the outcome will either be a success (S) or a failure (F). We are thinking about hiring a consultant to aid in this decision making process. The outcome will be either favorable (Fav) or unfavorable (Unf). Draw the appropriate chronological tree diagram of the circumstances.

16.9   An executive must make a decision whether to go ahead with a new product or not. She is considering two possible sources of additional information. They are an econometric consulting firm and a market research consulting firm. In both cases, if the research is performed, the results will be either favorable (Fav) or unfavorable (Unf). If the product is marketed, the result will be either a success (S) or a failure (F). Draw the appropriate chronological tree diagram of the circumstances.

16.10   A rock group is making a comeback and thinks that it has a hot tune. However, it will hold it back if the public doesn't like it. The group is thinking about trial testing it in several cities. It believes that the trial test will either lead to super ratings (Sup), good ratings (Good), okay ratings (Ok), or poor ratings (Poor). Ultimately, the song will either be a success (S) or a failure (F). Draw the appropriate chronological tree diagram of the circumstances.

16.3 Determining Payoffs or Regrets

The easiest part of evaluating decision tree diagrams is the determination of the respective payoffs, or regrets, that would occur under the different scenarios. Since business students must take accounting and finance courses, they are well-versed in the determination of profits and losses for different scenarios.

Atom Smasher Example

Referring to the appropriate fixed and variable costs reviewed in Chapter 15, payoffs were computed and displayed in Tables 15.3 and 15.4. These payoffs refer only to the branch where no new information is collected. These payoffs are placed at the end of the respective branches of the decision tree.

The payoffs for the higher branches, based on the decision to collect new information, are smaller than the bottom branch by $100,000, the cost of conducting the market study. All of the payoffs are placed at the end of the relevant branches that sequentially lead to that outcome. These payoffs are reflected in Figure 16.5.

Figure 16.5 Placing Profits and Losses: Atom Smasher Example

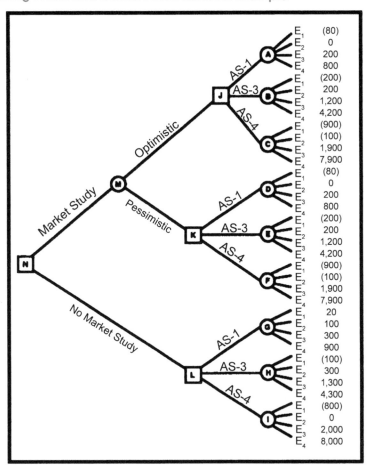

Legal Example

As a young attorney you know that if you can obtain an acquittal for your client you will become a partner in a prestigious law firm. You believe, if you don't get the partnership now, it will take an additional five years of hard work to get to that level. You estimate projected salary differentials, discount the future stream to present value, and realize that the present value of the salary differential is $160,000 over the next five years if the case is won.

If you take the case and receive a guilty verdict, you believe that you will be excluded from the more profitable clients. This will cost you approximately $50,000 in salary over the same five year period.

The cost incurred in hiring a private detective is estimated to be $15,000 and the cost of a lie detector test is $1,000. The respective payoffs are shown in Figure 16.6. The payoffs for the branch involving not obtaining any new information are $160,000 if an acquittal is achieved, and $(50,000) if the verdict is guilty, and $0 if you don't take the case. The payoffs on the lie detector branch are $1,000 less, and the payoffs on the private investigator branch are $15,000 less.

515

Figure 16.6 Placing Profits and Losses in Legal Example

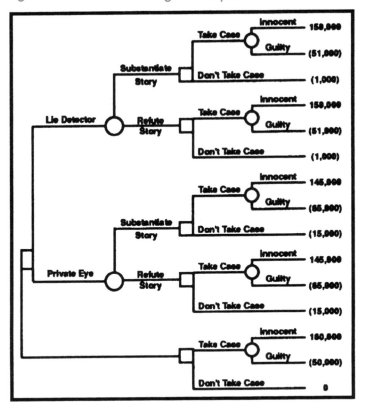

✔ Concept Check 16.B

Once the payoffs have been determined for the branch where no additional (experimental) information was obtained, to go to the branches where the information was obtained, we merely subtract the cost of obtaining the information. True or false? If false, explain.

Exercises

16.11 (Exercise 16.1 continued) An internationally known artist is contemplating how to sell her latest lithograph. She can either make a limited edition of 100, and sell them at exclusive galleries, or make 1,000 and sell them at less exclusive galleries. She is thinking of hiring a New York art consulting firm to help her with the decision. The consulting firm's response will say there is either positive (Pos) or negative (Neg) response to the print. In the end, the print selling will either be a success (S) or a failure (F) with the buying public.

The exclusive gallery will sell her prints for $10,000 each and the less exclusive galleries for $800 each. If the print is a success, the artist will sell all of her lithographs. If the print is a failure, the artist believes she will sell half of her expensive prints, but three fourths of the less expensive prints. This is because art consumers will still want her signature on a print in their house. The cost of the consulting firm would be $50,000. Determine the appropriate payoffs and place them alongside the appropriate branches in the chronological tree diagram.

516

16.12   (Exercise 16.2 continued) A manager must choose between two courses of action (A or B). He is thinking about having a market survey performed at a cost of $5,000. If the market survey is conducted, the outcome will either be favorable (Fav) or unfavorable (Unf). Ultimately, the outcome will either be a business success (S) or a business failure (F). For option A, success = $50,000 profit, failure = $5,000 loss. For option B, success = $30,000 profit, failure = $10,000 profit. The market survey, if performed, would cost $5,000. Place the appropriate payoffs alongside the chronological tree diagram.

16.13   (Exercise 16.3 continued) A new company is contemplating either opening in a city or in a suburban area. The CEO is thinking about conducting a market study to give her more information in the making of the decision. The results of the research would be a strong sentiment (SS) in favor of the city, or no real sentiment either way (NS). The CEO believes ultimately that there will be either a strong sales (S), a normal sales (N), or a weak sales (W).

The CEO believes if the company opens in the city that their profits will be $10.2 million for a strong sales, $6.2 million for a normal sales, $2.2 million loss for a weak sales. If the company opens in the rural area, the profits are expected to be $7.2 million for a strong sales, $5.2 million for a normal sales, and a $4.2 million loss for a weak sales. If it conducts the research, the cost would be $0.2 million, which is not included in the above figures. Place the appropriate payoffs alongside the chronological tree diagram.

16.14   (Exercise 16.4 continued) A company is thinking about opening a new product line. It feels that the possible upcoming sales can be categorized as strong (S), normal (N), or weak (W). It is also thinking about hiring a consulting firm to aid in the decision making process. The results of such an analysis will either be positive (Pos) or negative (Neg).

Finance has estimated that if no consultants are hired, if strong sales occur the profit will be $110,000; for normal sales, it's $50,000; and for weak sales, a $30,000 loss. The consulting firm, if hired, would cost $10,000. Place the appropriate payoffs alongside the chronological tree diagram.

16.15   (Exercise 16.5 continued) A company is contemplating placing a bid for a government contract. It may make a bid, and if it does it may (S = Success) or may not get the contract (F = Failure). They are thinking about hiring a consulting firm and lobbyist to help make the decision to bid or not. The consulting firm will either state that the conditions are favorable (Fav) for the bid or unfavorable (Unf).

The CEO believes that if it doesn't pay for the consulting firm it will make $20 million if it bids and makes it and lose $2 million if it bids and doesn't get it. If it pays for a consulting service, this will reduce its profits by another $2 million, which is the cost of the consulting fees. Place the appropriate payoffs alongside the chronological tree diagram.

16.16   (Exercise 16.6 continued) A company is thinking about opening one of 2 possible new product lines. It feels that the possible upcoming sales can be categorized as strong (S), or weak (W). They are also thinking about hiring a consulting firm to aid in the decision making process. The results of such an analysis will either be positive (Pos) or negative (Neg).

Finance estimates that if no additional information is obtained that from product A, a $70,000 profit will occur for strong sales, and a $30,000 loss for weak sales. For product B, a $30,000 profit will be realized under a strong sales, and a break-even under a weak sales. The consulting costs, if utilized, are expected to be $10,000. Place the appropriate payoffs alongside the chronological tree diagram.

16.17   (Exercise 16.7 continued) A young producer has just completed a movie that turned out better than expected. The producer was going to sell the movie to cablevision, but now also wants to consider selling to movie theaters. The producer is considering hiring a theatrical consulting firm to test show the movie overseas and to tabulate the responses of movie buffs. The result will either be extremely positive (EP), positive but reserved (PR), or a negative reaction (NR). Ultimately, the movie will be a success (S) or a failure (F).

If it is a success and sold to cablevision the producer believes it will net $12 million and net $2 million if its a failure. If it is sold to the theater and becomes a success, the net is $25 million, but a failure will result in a $5 million loss. The test survey, if performed overseas, will cost $2 million. Place the appropriate payoffs alongside the chronological tree diagram.

16.18   (Exercise 16.8 continued) A decision must be made to go or not with a small merger. If we go through with it the outcome will either be a success (S) or a failure (F). We are thinking about hiring a consultant to aid in the decision making process. The outcome will be either favorable (Fav) or unfavorable (Unf).

If no additional information is obtained, a successful merger will net $200,000, but an unsuccessful one will lose $75,000. The consulting firm, if utilized, will cost $10,000. Place the appropriate payoffs alongside the chronological tree diagram.

16.19   (Exercise 16.9 continued) An executive must make a decision whether to go ahead with a new product or not. She is considering two possible sources of additional information. They are an econometric consulting firm and a market research consulting firm. In both cases, if the research is performed, the results will be either favorable (Fav) or unfavorable (Unf). If the product is marketed, the result will be either a success (S) or a failure (F).

If the executive decides not to conduct any research and the project is a success, this will net a profit of $32 million. If it's a failure the result will be a loss of $17 million. If the project is abandoned, there will be no profit or loss involved. The econometric consulting firm will cost $2 million and the market research firm $1 million if utilized. Place the appropriate payoffs alongside the chronological tree diagram.

16.20   (Exercise 16.10 continued) A rock group is making a comeback and thinks that it has a hot tune. However, it will hold it back if the public doesn't like it. The group is thinking about trial testing it in several cities. It believes that the trial test will either lead to super ratings (Sup), good ratings (Good), Okay ratings (Ok), or poor ratings (Poor). Ultimately, the song will either be a success (S) or a failure (F).

If the record is a hit, $20 million in profits will be generated. However. if it's not, the image will be tarnished and the group will lose $6 million from advertising. The trial testing will cost $0.5 million, which is not included in the figures already given. Place the appropriate payoffs alongside the chronological diagram.

16.4   Determining the Appropriate Probabilities

So far we have learned how to construct a decision tree placing the acts, events, and outcomes in the proper chronological framework. The third phase in the analysis of decision tree diagrams is to determine the respective probabilities associated with all events. We must be careful since students normally have more difficulty in this phase of the analysis of decision problems than in any other.

The branch segments which involve the obtaining of additional or experimental information are essentially probabilities that are revised in light or lieu of additional information. This revision process, known as Bayes' theorem has already been covered in Section 3.5, and should be reviewed before continuing with this section.

There are four types of probabilities involved in the revision process. First there are the prior probabilities which are the original probabilities available at the start of a decision problem. The probabilities utilized in Chapter 15 were prior probabilities and were used to compute the EVPI. Most statisticians feel this is one of the weakest aspects of decision theory because these probabilities are normally obtained with some degree of subjectivity.

In addition to the prior probabilities, there is a second set of probabilities that reflect the accuracy of the experimental or additional information that is being considered. These probabilities are called conditional probabilities because they are conditional upon certain information being true. Third, the old and new information is combined into joint probabilities. The joint probabilities reflect the likelihood that a specific event is true and a particular experimental result occurs. Given the prior, conditional, and joint probabilities, posterior probabilities can be computed that reflect the likelihood of a particular event given the occurrence of a specific experimental result.

The theorem that established the posterior probabilities was developed over 200 years ago by the Reverend Thomas Bayes. It is as follows:

Bayes' Theorem

$$\Pr(E|S) = \frac{\Pr(E) \bullet \Pr(S|E)}{\Pr(E) \bullet \Pr(S|E) + \Pr(\text{Not } E) \bullet \Pr(S|\text{Not } E)} \tag{3.8}$$

where

$\Pr(E) = $ an event probability

$\Pr(S|E) = $ a conditional probability of sample information (S) given event E

$\Pr(E|S) = $ a posterior probability of event E given sample information (S)

Note that S is the outcome of the sample experimental information.

Atom Smasher Example

In the Smasher example, the prior probabilities were: $\Pr(E\text{-}1) = .2$, $\Pr(E\text{-}2) = .4$, $\Pr(E\text{-}3) = .3$, $\Pr(E\text{-}4) = .1$. The new information we were considering was based on a market study of the major toy retailers. If the study is made, there are only two possible outcomes, that of an optimistic (Opt) holiday season and that of a pessimistic (Pes) holiday season. The market research company is asked to estimate the conditional probabilities based upon their past surveys, for other clients. Their estimates are $\Pr[\text{Opt}|E\text{-}1] = .1$, $\Pr[\text{Opt}|E\text{-}2] = .2$, $\Pr[\text{Opt}|E\text{-}3] = .7$, and $\Pr[\text{Opt}|E\text{-}4] = .4$. Since the summation of all the $E\text{-}1$'s, $E\text{-}2$'s, etc., must equal 1 the remaining conditional probabilities are $\Pr[\text{Pes}|E\text{-}1] = .9$, $\Pr[\text{Pes}|E\text{-}2] = .8$, $\Pr[\text{Pes}|E\text{-}3] = .3$, and $\Pr[\text{Pes}|E\text{-}4] = .6$. Using these conditional probabilities in conjunction with the original prior probabilities, through Bayes' formula, yields joint and posterior probabilities.

Applying Bayes' formula directly yields

$$\Pr(E-1|\text{Opt}) = \frac{.2(.1)}{.2(.1)+.4(.2)+.3(.7)+.1(.4)} = \frac{.02}{.35} = .0571$$

$$\Pr(E-2|\text{Opt}) = \frac{.4(.2)}{.2(.1)+.4(.2)+.3(.7)+.1(.4)} = \frac{.08}{.35} = .2286$$

$$\Pr(E-3|\text{Opt}) = \frac{.3(.7)}{.2(.1)+.4(.2)+.3(.7)+.1(.4)} = \frac{.21}{.35} = .6000$$

$$\Pr(E-4|\text{Opt}) = \frac{.1(.4)}{.2(.1)+.4(.2)+.3(.7)+.1(.4)} = \frac{.04}{.35} = .1143$$

$$\Pr(E-1|\text{Pes}) = \frac{.2(.9)}{.2(.9)+.4(.8)+.3(.3)+.1(.6)} = \frac{.18}{.65} = .2769$$

$$\Pr(E-2|\text{Pes}) = \frac{.4(.8)}{.2(.9)+.4(.8)+.3(.3)+.1(.6)} = \frac{.32}{.65} = .4923$$

$$\Pr(E-3|\text{Pes}) = \frac{.3(.3)}{.2(.9)+.4(.8)+.3(.3)+.1(.6)} = \frac{.09}{.65} = .1385$$

$$\Pr(E-4|\text{Pes}) = \frac{.1(.6)}{.2(.9)+.4(.8)+.3(.3)+.1(.6)} = \frac{.06}{.65} = .0923$$

The probabilities presented in a matrix format are given in Table 16.3.

Table 16.3   Developing Posterior Probabilities: Atom Smasher Problem

A: Optimistic Scenario

	Prior	Conditional	Joint	Posterior
Events	*Pr*	*Pr*	*Pr*	*Pr*
E-1	.2	.1	.02 = (.2●.1)	.0571 = (.02/.35) = Pr(E-1|Opt)
E-2	.4	.2	.08 = (.4●.2)	.2286 = (.08/.35) = Pr(E-2|Opt)
E-3	.3	.7	.21 = (.3●.7)	.6000 = (.21/.35) = Pr(E-3|Opt)
E-4	.1	.4	.04 = (.1●.4)	.1143 = (.04/.35) = Pr(E-4|Opt)
			SUM .35	1.000

B: Pessimistic Scenario

	Prior	Conditional	Joint	Posterior
Events	*Pr*	*Pr*	*Pr*	*Pr*
E-1	.2	.9	.18 = (.2 ●.9)	.2769 = (.18/.65) = Pr(E-1|Pes)
E-2	.4	.8	.32 = (.4●.8)	.4923 = (.32/.65) = Pr(E-2|Pes)
E-3	.3	.3	.09 = (.3●.3)	.1385 = (.09/.65) = Pr(E-3|Pes)
E-4	.1	.6	.06 = (.1●.6)	.0923 = (.06/.65) = Pr(E-4|Pes)
			SUM .65	1.0000

These posterior probabilities are superimposed on the event branches of the decision tree in Figure 16.7. For the branch, not seeking the new information, the prior probabilities are relevant since there is no additional information available with which to revise the original probabilities. Thus, for the decision tree branch where no new information is sought, prior probabilities must be used and the payoffs on this branch are usually higher because there are no costs incurred in obtaining the new information.

Figure 16.7 Placing Probabilities After Event Nodes: Atom Smasher Example

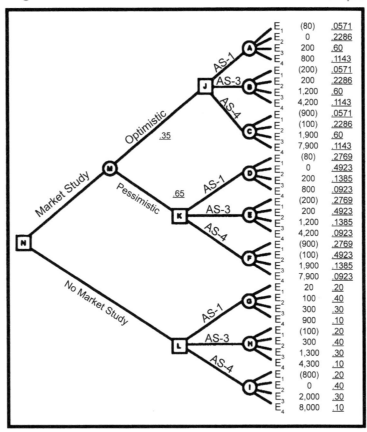

Usually, the posterior probabilities, the sum of the joint probabilities, and the prior probabilities will all appear in the completed decision tree diagram. The sum of the joint probabilities appears after the circle involving obtaining of the experimental information. The probability coming off the optimistic branch is .35 and from the pessimistic branch is .65 (both represent the sum of the joint probabilities).

Legal Example

Suppose that you always guess a client's innocence (I) or guilt (G) based upon an initial interview. In this case, you assess that there is a 30% chance that the client is innocent [$Pr(I) = .3$ and $Pr(G) = .7$]. You believe the guilt or innocence verdict will hinge on a story the defendant is giving concerning where he was during a critical hour. If the story is true the defendant is innocent and will be acquitted. If the story is false, the defendant is guilty and will be convicted.

You turn to experimental information to help you make your decision (to take the case or not). You believe that the lie detector will substantiate (Sub) the defendant's story, if it is true, 40% of the time [$Pr(Sub|I) = .4$] and refute (Ref) the story, if it is false, 30% of the time [$Pr(Ref|G)$]. The private investigator, by digging into the specifics of the alibi, will substantiate the client's story, if it is true, 80% of the time [$Pr(Sub|I) = .8$] and refute the story, if it is false, 90% of the time [$Pr(Ref|G) = .9$]. Again, we are assuming that if the client is lying, we will receive a guilty verdict and if he is telling the truth we will receive an innocent verdict.

In Table 16.4, the appropriate probabilities are computed and the posterior probabilities, prior probabilities, and sum of the joint probabilities appear next to their respective payoffs in Figure 16.8. Note where the sum of the joint probabilities appear in the tree diagram.

521

Table 16.4   Developing Posterior Probabilities: Legal Problem

A: Lie Detector Branch

Substantiate Claims

	Prior Pr	*Conditional Pr*	*Joint Pr*	*Posterior Pr*
Innocent	.3	.4	.12	Pr(I|Sub) = .197
Guilty	.7	.7	.49	Pr(G|Sub) = .803
		Total	.61	1.000

Refute Claims

	Prior Pr	*Conditional Pr*	*Joint Pr*	*Posterior Pr*
Innocent	.3	.6	.18	Pr(I|Ref) = .462
Guilty	.7	.3	.21	Pr(G|Ref) = .538
		Total	.39	1.000

B: Private Investigator Branch

Substantiate Claims

	Prior Pr	*Conditional Pr*	*Joint Pr*	*Posterior Pr*
Innocent	.3	.8	.24	Pr(I|Sub) = .774
Guilty	.7	.1	.07	Pr(G|Sub) = .226
		Total	.31	1.000

Refute Claims

	Prior Pr	*Conditional Pr*	*Joint Pr*	*Posterior Pr*
Innocent	.3	.2	.06	Pr(I|Ref) = .087
Guilty	.7	.9	.63	Pr(G|Ref) = .913
		Total	.69	1.000

Figure 16.8 Placing Probabilities After Event Nodes: Legal Example

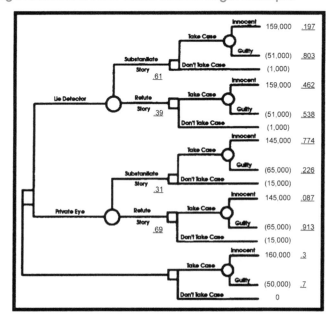

522

In many real world applications, particularly applications involving quality control examples, conditional probabilities can be ascertained with the use of the Bernoulli process (Section 4.3). The necessary conditions for the Bernoulli process are that there are only two possible outcomes, the probabilities of the events must remain constant, and the outcome of successive trials are independent.

Quality Control Example

All businesses are extremely concerned with control of the quality of their product or service. In these cases, statistical decision theory is invaluable. To aid in maintaining the proper level of quality, the organization could gather information regarding quality by sampling and evaluating the probability that the production process was out of control. The experimental information would be obtained by sampling and inspecting products as they come off the production line or as they are delivered to vendors. Assume that the inspected parts will either be defective or not according to some stated criterion. The probability of a defective item will normally remain constant and successive trials will be independent.

Suppose the production department wanted to sample three units from a batch of 100 parts. There could be four possible results from the survey. Either there will be no defective parts ($r = 0$), one defective part ($r = 1$), two defective parts ($r = 2$), or three defective parts ($r = 3$). Note that we are considering the finding of defective parts as successes.

There will be a need to use historical frequencies to determine in the past what percentage of the 100 parts have been defective. Suppose, that historically, the shipments have been 5% defective ($p = .05$) 50% of the time; 10% defective ($p = .10$) 30% of the time; and 20% defective ($p = .20$) 20% of the time. We will utilize our cumulative binomial tables (Appendix A, Table 2, a portion repeated in Table 16.5) to determine the condition probabilities of the sample outcomes given the events or states of nature.

For example, to find the probability of finding one defective part $\Pr(r = 1)$ in the sample of three ($n = 3$), when 10% overall is defective ($p = .10$), we would take $\Pr(r \leq 1)$ and subtract from $\Pr(r \leq 0)$ to obtain .243 (.972–.729). To find $\Pr(r = 2)$ we take $\Pr(r \leq 2) - \Pr(r \leq 1)$ to obtain .027 (.999–.972). To find $\Pr(r = 3)$ we take $\Pr(r \leq 3) - \Pr(r \leq 2)$ to obtain .001 (1.000 – .999). Of course, to obtain $\Pr(r = 0)$, we simply read $\Pr(r \leq 0)$, which is .729.

Table 16.5 Cumulative Values for the Binomial Probability Distribution

$n = 3$

r	p 0.5	.10	.20
0	0.8574	0.7290	0.5120
1	0.9927	0.9720	0.8960
2	0.9999	0.9990	0.9920
3	1.0000	1.0000	1.0000

Once the conditional probabilities are obtained, it is a fairly mechanical process to compute the probabilities as shown in Table 16.6.

Table 16.6   Computing Posterior Probabilities: Defective Parts Problem

$r = 0$

p	Prior Pr	Conditional Pr	Joint Pr	Posterior Pr
.05	.5	0.8574	0.4287	0.57175
.10	.3	0.7290	0.2187	0.29168
.20	.2	0.5120	0.1024	0.13657
			SUM 0.7498	

$r = 1$

p	Prior Pr	Conditional Pr	Joint Pr	Posterior Pr
.05	.5	0.1353	0.06765	0.31125
.10	.3	0.2430	0.0729	0.33540
.20	.2	0.3840	0.0768	0.35335
			SUM 0.21735	

$r = 2$

p	Prior Pr	Conditional Pr	Joint Pr	Posterior Pr
.05	.5	0.0072	0.0036	0.11650
.10	.3	0.0270	0.0081	0.26214
.20	.2	0.0960	0.0192	0.62136
			SUM 0.0309	

$r = 3$

p	Prior Pr	Conditional Pr	Joint Pr	Posterior Pr
.05	.5	0.0001	0.00005	0.02564
.10	.3	0.0010	0.0003	0.15385
.20	.2	0.0080	0.0016	0.82051
			SUM 0.00195	

 Concept Check 16.C

The sum of all the conditional probabilities, for each possible outcome for the new information, must equal 1. True or false? If false, explain.

Exercises

16.21   (Exercise 16.11 continued) An internationally known artist is contemplating how to sell her latest lithograph. She can either make a limited edition of 100, and sell them at exclusive galleries, or make 1,000 and sell them at less exclusive galleries. She is thinking of hiring a New York art consulting firm to help her with the decision. The consulting firm's response will say there is either a positive (Pos), or a negative (Neg) response to the print. In the end, the print selling will either be a success (S) or a failure (F) with the buying public.

   The exclusive galleries will sell her prints for $10,000 each and the less exclusive galleries for $800 each. If the print is a success, the artist will sell all of her lithographs. If the print is a failure, the artist believes she will sell half of her expensive prints, but three fourths of the less expensive prints. This is because art consumers will still want her signature on a print in their house. The cost of the consulting firm would be $50,000.

   The artist believes the probability for success to be .3 (failure = .7). The conditional probabilities are: Pr(Pos|S) = .9 and Pr(Neg|F) = .8. Determine the appropriate posterior probabilities [Pr(S|Pos), Pr(F|Pos), Pr(S|Neg), and Pr(F|Neg)] and place them alongside the appropriate payoffs.

524

16.22   (Exercise 16.12 continued) A manager must choose between two courses of action (A or B). He is thinking about having a market survey performed at a cost of $5,000. If the market survey is conducted, the outcome will either be favorable (Fav) or unfavorable (Unf). Ultimately, the outcome will either be a business success (S) or a business failure (F). For option A, success = $50,000 profit, failure = $5,000 loss. For option B, success = $30,000 profit, failure = $10,000 profit. The market survey, if performed, would cost $5,000.

The appropriate probabilities are Pr(F) = .6. Pr(Fav|S) = .9, and Pr(Unf|F) = .8. Determine the appropriate posterior probabilities [Pr(S|Fav), Pr(F|Fav), Pr(S|Unf), and Pr(F|Unf)] and place the probabilities alongside the appropriate payoffs.

16.23   (Exercise 16.13 continued) A new company is contemplating either opening in a city or in a rural area. The CEO is thinking about conducting a market study to give her more information in the making of the decision. The results of the research would be a strong sentiment (SS) in favor of the city, or no real sentiment either way (NS). The CEO believes ultimately that there will be either a strong sales (S), a normal sales (N), or a weak sales (W).

The CEO believes if the company opens in the city that their profits will be $10.2 million for a strong sales, $6.2 million for a normal sales, $2.2 million loss for a weak sales. If the company opens in the rural area the profits are expected to be $7.2 million for a strong sales, $5.2 million for a normal sales, and a $4.2 million loss for a weak sales. If it conducts the research, the cost would be $0.2 million, which is not included in the above figures.

In addition, the CEO believes the probability of strong sales is .1, for normal sales it's .6, and for weak sales is .3. The conditional probabilities are: Pr(SS|S) = .8, and Pr(SS|N) = .5, and Pr(SS|W) = .3. Determine the appropriate posterior probabilities [Pr(S|SS), Pr(N|SS), Pr(W|SS), Pr(S|NS), Pr(N|NS), and Pr(W|NS)] and place the probabilities alongside the appropriate payoffs.

16.24   (Exercise 16.14 continued) A company is thinking about opening a new product line. It feels that the possible upcoming sales can be categorized as strong (S), normal (N), or weak (W). It is also thinking about hiring a consulting firm to aid in the decision making process. The results of such an analysis will either be positive (Pos) or negative (Neg). Finance has estimated that if no consultants are hired, if strong sales occur the profit will be $110,000; for normal sales, it's $50,000; and for weak sales, a $30,000 loss. The consulting firm, if hired, would cost $10,000.

The appropriate prior probabilities are: Pr(S) = .2, Pr(N) = .1, and Pr(W) = .7. The appropriate conditional probabilities are Pr(Pos|S) = .9, Pr(Pos|N) = .4. and Pr(Pos|W) = .2. Determine the appropriate posterior probabilities [Pr(S|Pos), Pr(N|Pos), Pr(W|Pos), Pr(S|Neg), Pr(N|Neg), and Pr(W|Neg)] and place the probabilities alongside the appropriate payoffs.

16.25   (Exercise 16.15 continued) A company is contemplating placing a bid for a government contract. It may make a bid, and if so, it may (S = Success) or may not get the contract (F = Failure). It is thinking about hiring a consulting firm and lobbyist to help make the decision to bid or not. The consulting firm will either state that the conditions are favorable (Fav) for the bid or unfavorable (Unf).

The CEO believes that if it doesn't pay for the consulting firm it will make $20 million if it bids and makes it, and lose $2 million if it bids and doesn't get it. If it pays for the consulting service, this will reduce their profits by another $2 million, which is the cost of the consulting fees.

The original probability for winning the bid is .2 [Pr(S) = .2]. In addition, Pr(Fav|S) = .7 and Pr(Unf|F) = .8. Determine the appropriate probabilities [Pr(S|Fav), Pr(F|Fav), Pr(S|Unf) and Pr(F|Unf)] and place the probabilities alongside the appropriate payoffs.

16.26   (Exercise 16.16 continued) A company is thinking about one of 2 possible new product lines. It feels that the possible upcoming sales can be categorized as strong (S) or weak (W). It is also thinking about hiring a consulting firm to aid in the decision making process. The results of such an analysis will either be positive (Pos) or negative (Neg). Finance estimates that if no additional information is obtained that from product A, a $70,000 profit will occur for a strong sales, and a $30,000 loss for a weak sales. For product B, a $30,000 profit will be realized under a strong sales, and a break even under a weak sales. The consulting costs, if utilized, are expected to be $10,000.

It is believed that the overall probability for a strong sales = .4, and a weak sales = .6. In addition, $\Pr(\text{Pos}|S) = .9$, and $\Pr(\text{Pos}|W) = .2$. Determine the appropriate posterior probabilities [$\Pr(S|\text{Pos})$, $\Pr(W|\text{Pos})$, $\Pr(S|\text{Neg})$, and $\Pr(W|\text{Neg})$] and place the probabilities alongside the appropriate payoffs.

16.27   (Exercise 16.17 continued) A young producer has just completed a movie that turned out better than expected. The producer was going to sell the movie to cablevision, but now also wants to consider selling to movie theaters. The producer is considering hiring a theatrical consulting firm to test show the movie overseas and to tabulate the responses of movie buffs. The result will either be extremely positive (EP), positive but reserved (PR), or a negative reaction (NR). Ultimately the movie will be a success (S) or a failure (F). The producer believes the film, if it is a success and sold to cablevision, will net $12 million, but will only net $2 million if it's a failure. If it is sold to the theater and a success, the net is $25 million, but a failure will result in a $5 million loss. The survey, if performed overseas, will cost $2 million.

The producer believes that the following probabilities apply: $\Pr(S) = .3$, $\Pr(\text{EP}|S) = .7$, $\Pr(\text{PR}|S) = .2$, $\Pr(\text{NR}|F) = .8$, and $\Pr(\text{PR}|F) = .1$. Determine the appropriate posterior probabilities [$\Pr(S|\text{EP})$, $\Pr(F|\text{EP})$, $\Pr(S|\text{PR})$, $\Pr(F|\text{PR})$, $\Pr(S|\text{NR})$, and $\Pr(F|\text{NR})$] and place the probabilities alongside the appropriate payoffs.

16.28   (Exercise 16.18 continued) A decision must be made to go or not with a small merger. If we go through with it, the outcome will either be a success (S) or a failure (F). We are thinking about hiring a consultant to aid in this decision making process. The outcome will be either favorable (Fav) or unfavorable (Unf).

If no additional information is obtained, a successful merger will net $200,000, but an unsuccessful one will lose $75,000. The consulting firm if utilized, will cost $10,000.

The overall probability for a successful merger = .3. The appropriate conditional probabilities are $\Pr(\text{Fav}|S) = .8$ and $\Pr(\text{Fav}|F) = .4$. Determine the appropriate posterior probabilities and place the probabilities alongside the appropriate payoffs.

16.29   (Exercise 16.19 continued) An executive must make a decision whether to go ahead with a new product or not. She is considering two possible sources of additional information. They are an econometric consulting firm and a market research consulting firm. In both cases, if the research is performed, the results will be either favorable (Fav) or unfavorable (Unf). If the product is marketed, the result will be either a success (S) or a failure (F). If the executive decides not to conduct any research and the project is a success, this will net a profit of $32 million. If it's a failure, the result will be a loss of $17 million. If the project is abandoned, there will be no profit or loss involved. The econometric consulting firm will cost $2 million and the market research firm $1 million if utilized.

It is believed that the probability for overall success is .4. For the econometric firm, the probability of a favorable report given success is .8 [$\Pr(\text{Fav}|S) = .8$] and $\Pr(\text{Fav}|F) = .1$. For the market research firm $\Pr(\text{Fav}|S) = .7$ and $\Pr(\text{Fav}|F) = .2$. Determine the appropriate posterior probabilities and place the probabilities alongside the appropriate payoffs.

16.30   (Exercise 16.20 continued) A rock group is making a comeback and thinks that it has a hot tune. However, it will hold it back if the public doesn't like it. The group is thinking about trial testing it in several cities. It believes that the trial test will either lead to super ratings (Sup), good ratings (Good), okay ratings (Ok), or poor ratings (Poor). Ultimately, the song will either be a success (S) or a failure (F).

If the record is a hit, $20 million in profits will be generated. However, if it's not, the image will be tarnished and the group will lose $6 million from advertising. The trial testing will cost $0.5 million which is not included in the figures already given.

The group believes the probability of success is .4. The conditional probabilities are: Pr(Sup|S) = .4, Pr(Sup|F) = .1, Pr(Good|S) = .4, Pr(Good|F) = .2, Pr(Ok|S) = .1, Pr(Ok|F) = .3. Determine the appropriate posterior probabilities [Pr(S|Sup), Pr(F|Sup), Pr(S|Good), Pr(F|Good), Pr(S|Ok), Pr(F|Ok), Pr(S|Poor), and Pr(F|Poor)] and place the probabilities alongside the appropriate payoffs.

16.5 Backward Induction Analysis

The first phase in analyzing a decision problem with the use of a tree diagram is to draw the correct tree; the second is to determine the appropriate payoffs; and the third is to ascertain the probabilities associated with the uncertain events in the problem. The fourth and final phase is to evaluate the decision tree in a way that will generate an optimal strategy. The last phase is often called backward induction analysis because the optimal decision making strategy is best determined by working from right to left along the branches of the decision tree.

Weighted Averages and Pruning Branches

There are two basic rules to follow in performing backward induction analysis. At an event (circle) compute a weighted average and at an act (square) prune or remove all but the best option. Remember that probabilities only apply to events, never to an act.

Atom Smasher Example

Referring back to our decision tree diagram (Figure 16.9), we begin with the nine circles (sometimes referred to as nodes: both circles and squares are nodes) in the farthest right vertical plane. Weighted average payoffs must be computed for each of the act branches precipitating a set of events. For the first event circle (node "a"), if you were to lose $80,000, 5.71% of the time; make $0, 22.86% of the time; make $200,000, 60% of the time; and make $800,000, 11.43% of the time the expected payoff would be $206,872. The expected payoffs for all nine events are given in Figure 16.9. The full computations for a few of the nodes are as follows:

Nodes

"b" = $-\$200(.0571) + \$200(.2286) + \$1,200(.6) + \$4,200(.1143) = \$1,234.36$

"f" = $-\$900(.2769) - \$100(.4923) + \$1,900(.1385) + \$7,900(.0923) = \$693.88$

"g" = $\$20(.2) + \$100(.4) + \$300(.3) + \$900(.1) = \$224.$

Figure 16.9 Backwards Induction Analysis: Atom Smasher Example

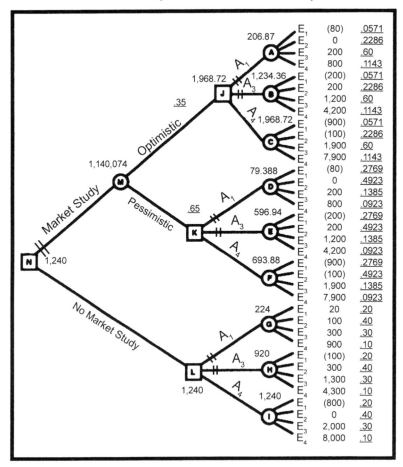

The expected payoffs for the remainder of the nodes in the further right vertical plane is "c" = $1,968.72, "d" = $79,388, "e" = $596.94, "h" = $920, and "i" = $1,240. We then move leftward to the next vertical plane, which reflects the acts related to the type of smasher to produce (remember that AS-2 was an inadmissible act). There are three acts in this vertical plane. For acts (squares) a choice must be made. For the first set, we are given a choice of making $206.87; $1,234.36; or $1,968.72 depending on the selected act. Since the $1,968.72 is optimum, the other choices are deemed illogical and would be pruned or eliminated (as indicated with a small parallel set of wavy lines). The expected payoff from AS-4 ($1,968,720) is brought backwards from the circle to the square. This would mean that if this square were to be reached, any decision maker would choose to produce AS-4 and expect slightly less than a two million dollar profit. For the middle act in that plane, again AS-1 and AS-3 would be pruned as illogical, and the same would be true for the last act in that vertical plane.

At this point we might notice an inconsistency in the problem that may appear in tree diagrams. Under all circumstances (if we obtained the survey information or not, and no matter what the survey concluded) we would select AS-4 as the optimum act. Hence, we would immediately decide not to pay for a survey, since we would not use the subsequent information. Thus, there is no need to complete the analysis, but, we will proceed with the analysis to understand the procedure used.

Having completed the two vertical planes on the right of the decision tree, we would now move backwards to the single event which yielded the possible outcomes of the market study. Since this is an event, a weighted average must be computed. Neither the prior nor the posterior probabilities are appropriate. These branches reflect the possible outcomes of the sample. In Table 16.3, probabilities are grouped by optimistic versus pessimistic sample outcomes. The sum of the joint probabilities for optimistic is .35 and for pessimistic it is .65. If $1,968,720 is expected 35% of the time and $693,880 is expected 65% of the time, the average weighted payoff would be $1,140,074. This represents the payoff to be expected if the market survey is conducted.

Finally, move to the farthest left plane to the originating square in which there are the choices of conducting the market study and expect to make $1,140,074 or not performing a market study and go directly into the production of Smasher AS-4 and expect to make $1,240,000. Since $1,240,000 is the larger amount, the $1,140,074 branch would be pruned. The ultimate answer to the problem then would be not to perform the market study and go directly to producing AS-4. When the decision making analysis incorporates the question of whether to collect additional information or not, it is called preposterior analysis.

Remember that posterior analysis is decision analysis based on combining original information and the new information for a decision problem and revising the probabilities of the events. The revised probabilities are utilized in the decision making. Thus, posterior analysis is decision making after collecting additional information. Preposterior analysis is decision analysis designed to determine the net economic value of gathering additional information prior to making a final decision. It requires the determination of the expected benefits of the information and compares these to the known costs.

Legal Example

The backward induction analysis begins with the vertical plane on the extreme right of the tree (Figure 16.10). The weighted payoffs are computed for each of the five events. For the first weighted payoff, if we expect a payoff of $159,000 19.7% of the time and lose ($51,000) 80.3% of the time the weighted payoff would be ($9,630). For the second event, if we expect a payoff of $159,000 46.2% of the time and lose ($51,000) 53.8% of the time the weighted payoff is $46,020. For the third event, if we expect $145,000 77.4% of the time and ($65,000) 22.6% of the time the weighted average is $97,540. For the fourth event if we make $145,000 8.7% of the time and ($65,000) 91.3% of the time the weighted average is ($46,730). Finally, the branch we receive no additional information, if make $160,000 30% of the time and ($50,000) 70% of the time the weighted average is $13,000.

Once the five weighted payoffs are tabulated, we move leftward to the next vertical plane. Since these represent acts, all of the illogical branches are pruned from the tree. For the first square in this vertical plane, we have a choice of losing ($9,630) or ($1,000). Hence, the ($9,630) branch is pruned and the ($1,000) is brought back and placed above the square. For the second square, we have the choice of making $46,020 or ($1,000). Hence, the ($1,000) branch is pruned and the $46,020 brought back. The optimum selection for the third square is $97,540, for the fourth ($15,000), and for the fifth $13,000.

Next are the events to the left of the decision either to take the case or not. At this phase, sums of the relevant joint probabilities are used to compute the expected payoffs. The weighted average for the first event is $17,337.40 [.61 − $1,000 + .39 • $46,020], and for the second event is $19,887.40 [.31 • $97,540 + .69 • $15,000].

Finally, we are left with the choice of obtaining additional information or not. If we go ahead with the lie detector, the expected payoff is $17,337.80. If we contract with the private detective, our expected payoff is $19,887.40. If we decide not to obtain the additional information and directly decide to take the case, the payoff is $13,000. Since the payoff is greater for the private detective, we decide to hire the detective agency. If the results from the detective substantiates the defendant's story, we will take the case. If the results refute the defendant's story, we will not take the case. Note that the expected payoff from the lie detector test is greater than not receiving any additional information. However, the payoff from the lie detector test is not greater than the payoff from hiring the private investigator.

Figure 16.10   Backwards induction Analysis: Legal Example

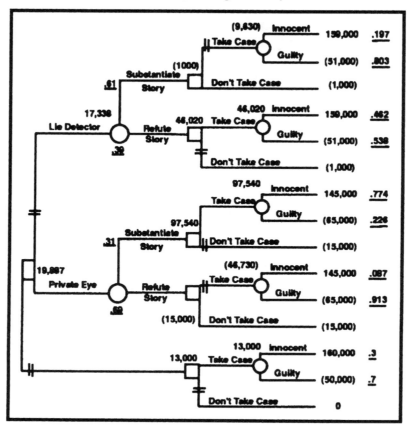

Quality Control Example

In the quality control example, the posterior probabilities were developed for the outcome of sampling three items to test for defective units as developed in Table 16.6. A tree diagram for this analysis is shown in Figure 16.11. The tree is drawn under the assumption that the quality control sample of three items will take place. That is why the tree goes directly from the original square to the event. There are three possible results in terms of the number of defective items found in the sample. These are $r = 0$, $r = 1$, $r = 2$, and $r = 3$.

This type of problem usually leaves the decision maker with the option of either accepting the incoming shipment of 100 units, or rejecting it. To reject means a complete census of the 100 units will be made to determine the specific defective parts. These parts would then be returned to the manufacturer and replaced with non-defective parts. Unfortunately, the replacement parts would also have to be tested to determine if they were defective or not. If the lot of 100 is accepted then the buyer will be the one to find the defective part and will probably return it to our firm for replacement. Unfortunately, we will lose goodwill and the effect of such a loss may be cumulative.

Finally, after the decision to accept or reject the lot our firm does not control the decision of whether the proportion of defective parts is 5%, 10%, or 20%. This is determined, even if involuntarily, by the manufacturer.

The total cost for surveying all 100 parts is obviously greater than the cost associated with sampling three units. However, the per unit costs of small samples is usually considerably higher than the per unit costs of a census. Since sampling three units means a random sample of three units, if the units purchased come in a box of 100, then random numbers must be used to select the three units. If a random number generator found the numbers 26, 49, and 93, then these are the three specific products to be tested. It will take time, hence money, to find and test the three units. Sampling three units does not mean opening a box and surveying the first three units grabbed. It is easier to be more efficient in dealing with a census as we will obtain the benefits of a learning curve.

Returning to our problem of buying and selling computer hard disks, we must order them in groups of 100 to be able to get the wholesale discount. However, past experience indicates that 5 (5%) of the group are defective 50% of the time, 10 (10%) are defective 30% of the time, and 20 (20%) are defective 20% of the time. The units are sold for a profit of $100 each. The costs of a small sample are $50 per unit, and census costs are $20 per unit. The accounting department informs us that it estimates that it costs the firm $200 in lost goodwill and in the labor and parts to replace the disk for each one returned.

The respective profits are given at the end of the branches. For the rejection branches, the payoffs are all identical. The profit is $10,000 minus sampling costs for three units ($50 • 3) and census costs of ($20 • 97), equaling $7,910. Remember that after sampling the three units a census must be performed (if the lot is rejected and returned to manufacturer), yet the first three sampled would not be included in the census; otherwise, they would be tested twice.

To review the computation of the payoffs, node "a" will be evaluated. Remember that for an accepted group of 100 disks either 5, 10, or 20 will be defective. Basically, it is the $10,000 profit minus the $150 sampling costs minus the return cost of $200 per returned unit.

$$\text{node ``a''} = \$10,000 - \$150 - 5(\$200) = \$8,850$$
$$\$10,000 - \$150 - 10(\$200) = \$7,850$$
$$\$10,000 - \$150 - 20(\$200) = \$5,850$$

Based on the previously given posterior probabilities,

$$\text{node ``a''} = \$8,850(.572) + \$7,850(.292) + \$5,850(.136) = \$8,150$$

For node "b," the payoffs are larger than that of node "a" increased by $200, because a defective disk was caught in the survey and it will be replaced with a good unit prior to consumers purchasing it.

$$\text{node ``b''} = \$10,000 - \$150 - 4(\$200) = \$9,050$$
$$\$10,000 - \$150 - 9(\$200) = \$8,050$$
$$\$10,000 - \$150 - 19(\$200) = \$6,050$$
$$\text{node ``b''} = \$9,050(.311) + \$8,050(.335) + \$6,050(.354) = \$7,653$$

for the remaining two nodes the computation is

$$\text{node ``c''} = \$9,250(.117) + \$8,250(.262) + \$6,250(.621) = \$7,125$$
$$\text{node ``d''} = \$9,450(.026) + \$8,450(.154) + \$6,450(.820) = \$6,836$$

Moving to the next vertical plane to the left, the rejection branch is pruned for the $r = 0$ scenario, and the acceptance branch is pruned for the $r = 1$, $r = 2$, and $r = 3$ scenarios.

Therefore, the weighted average for sampling units is node "i" = $8,150(.7498) + $7,910(.2502) = $8,089.95 which represents the weighted payoff from sampling three units. In fact with some additional effort, backward induction analysis can be used to determine the optimum sample size. In our problem the expected payoff from sampling three items was obtained. However, if the expected payoffs from $n = 0$, $n = 1$, $n = 2$, $n = 4$, $n = 5$ were obtained, the optimum sample size could be determined by selecting the sample with the largest expected payoff. A computer is needed for efficiently determining the optimal sample size.

The vast majority of the time backwards induction analysis is performed using payoffs. However, it is possible to substitute regrets or utils for payoffs. With utils the analysis is exactly the same. At each circle (event), compute a weighted util, and at each square (act), prune all but the highest expected util value. Be careful when pruning a regret because all but the lowest (optimum) regret would be pruned.

Figure 16.11   Backwards Induction Analysis: Quality Control Example,
Assuming Inspection Will Be Made

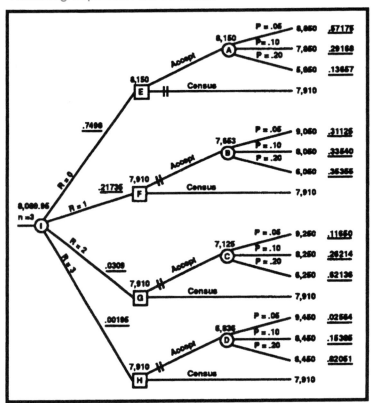

   Concept Check 16.D

In backwards induction analysis, we prune at each event and compute a weighted average at each act. True or false? If false, explain.

Exercises

16.31   (Exercise 16.21 continued) An internationally known artist is contemplating how to sell her latest lithograph. She can either make a limited edition of 100, and sell them at exclusive galleries, or make 1,000 and sell them at less exclusive galleries. She is thinking of hiring a New York art consulting firm to help her with the decision. The consulting firm's response will say there is either a positive (Pos), or a negative (Neg) response to the print. In the end, the print selling will either be a success (S) or a failure (F) with the buying public.

The exclusive galleries will sell her prints for $10,000 each and the less exclusive galleries for $800 each. If the print is a success, the artist will sell all of her lithographs. If the print is a failure, the artist believes she will sell half of her expensive prints, but three fourths of the less expensive prints. This is because art consumers will still want her signature on a print in their house. The cost of the consulting firm would be $50,000.

The artist believes the probability for success to be .3 (failure = .7). The conditional probabilities are: $Pr(Pos|S) = .9$ and $Pr(Neg|F) = .8$. Determine the appropriate posterior probabilities $[Pr(S|Pos), Pr(F|Pos), Pr(S|Neg), and Pr(F|Neg)]$ and perform a backwards induction analysis to see if the experimental information should be obtained.

16.32   (Exercise 16.22 continued) A manager must choose between two courses of action (A or B). He is thinking about having a market survey performed at a cost of $5,000. If the market survey is conducted, the outcome will either be favorable (Fav) or unfavorable (Unf). Ultimately, the outcome will either be a business success (S) or a business failure (F).

For option A, success = $50,000 profit, failure = $5,000 loss. For option B, success = $30,000 profit, failure = $10,000 profit. The market survey, if performed, would cost $5,000.

The appropriate probabilities are $Pr(F) = .6$, $Pr(Fav|S) = .9$, and $Pr(Unf|F) = .8$. Determine the appropriate posterior probabilities $[Pr(S|Fav), Pr(F|Fav), Pr(S|Unf), and Pr(F|Unf)]$ and perform a backward induction analysis to determine if the experimental information should be obtained.

16.33   (Exercise 16.23 continued) A new company is contemplating either opening in a city or in a suburban area. The CEO is thinking about conducting a market study to give her more information in the making of the decision. The results of the research would be a strong sentiment (SS) in favor of the city, or no real sentiment either way (NS).The CEO believes ultimately that there will be either a strong sales (S), a normal sales (N), or a weak sales (W).

The CEO believes if the company opens in the city that its profits will be $10.2 million for a strong sales, $6.2 million for a normal sales, $2.2 million loss for a weak sales. If the company opens in the rural area, the profits are expected to be $7.2 million for a strong sales, $5.2 million for a normal sales, and a $4.2 million loss for a weak sales. If it conducts the research the cost would be $0.2 million, which is not included in the above figures.

In addition the CEO believes the probability of strong sales is .1, for normal sales, it's .6; and for weak sales it's .3. The conditional probabilities are: $Pr(SS|S) = .8$, and $PR(SS|N) = .5$, and $Pr(SS| W) = .3$. Determine the appropriate posterior probabilities $[Pr(S|SS), Pr(N|SS), Pr(W|SS), Pr(S|NS), Pr(N|NS), and Pr(W|NS)]$ and perform a backwards induction analysis and determine if the experimental information should be obtained.

16.34   (Exercise 16.24 continued) A company is thinking about opening a new product line. It feels that the possible upcoming sales can be categorized as strong (S), normal (N), or weak (W). It is also thinking about hiring a consulting firm to aid in the decision making process. The results of such an analysis will either be positive (Pos) or negative (Neg).

Finance has estimated that if no consultants are hired, if strong sales occur, the profit will be $110,000; for normal sales, it's $50,000, and for weak sales a $30,000 loss. The consulting firm, if hired, would cost $10,000.

The appropriate prior probabilities are: $Pr(S) = .2$, $Pr(N) = .1$, and $Pr(W) = .7$. The appropriate conditional probabilities are $Pr(Pos|S) = .9$, $Pr(Pos|N) = .4$, and $Pr(Pos|W) = .2$. Determine the appropriate posterior probabilities $[Pr(S|Pos), Pr(N|Pos), Pr(W|Pos), Pr(S|Neg), Pr(N|Neg), and Pr(W|Neg)]$ and perform a backwards induction analysis to determine if the experimental information should be obtained.

16.35   (Exercise 16.25 continued) A company is contemplating placing a bid for a government contract. It may make a bid, and if so, it may (S = Success) or may not get the contract (F = Failure). It is thinking about hiring a consulting firm and lobbyist to help make the decision to bid or not.

The consulting firm will either state that the conditions are favorable (Fav) for the bid or unfavorable (Unf).

The CEO believes that if it doesn't pay for the consulting firm it will make $20 million if it bids and makes it, and lose $2 million if it bids and doesn't get it. If it pays for the consulting service, this will reduce its profits by another $2 million, which is the cost of the consulting fees.

The original probability for winning the bid is .2 [Pr(S) = .2]. In addition. Pr(Fav|S) = .7 and Pr(Unf|F) = .8. Determine the appropriate probabilities [Pr(S|Fav), Pr(F|Fav), Pr(S|Unf), and Pr(F|Unf)] and perform a backwards induction analysis and determine if the experimental information should be obtained.

16.36   (Exercise 16.26 continued) A company is thinking about opening one of 2 possible new product lines. It feels that the possible upcoming sales can be categorized as strong (S) or weak (W). It is also thinking about hiring a consulting firm to aid in the decision making process. The results of such an analysis will either be positive (Pos) or negative (Neg).

Finance estimates that if no additional information is obtained from product A, a $70,000 profit will occur for a strong sales, and a $30,000 loss for a weak sales. For product B, a $30,000 profit will be realized under a strong sales, and a break even under a weak sales. The consulting costs, if utilized, are expected to be $10,000.

It is believed that the overall probability for a strong sales = .4, and a weak sales = .6. In addition, Pr(Pos|S) = .9, and Pr(Pos|W) = .2. Determine the appropriate posterior probabilities [Pr(S|Pos), Pr(W|Pos), Pr(S|Neg), and Pr(W|Neg)] and perform a backwards induction analysis to determine if the experimental information should be obtained.

16.37   (Exercise 16.27 continued) A young producer has just completed a movie that turned out better than expected. The producer was going to sell the movie to cablevision, but now also wants to consider selling to movie theaters. The producer is considering hiring a theatrical consulting firm to test show the movie overseas and to tabulate the responses of movie buffs. The result will either be extremely positive (EP), positive but reserved (PR), or a negative reaction (NR). Ultimately, the movie will be a success (S) or a failure (F).

The producer believes the film if it is a success and sold to cablevision, will net $12 million and net $2 million if it's a failure. If it is sold to the theater and is a success, the net is $25 million, but a failure will result in a $5 million loss. The survey, if performed overseas, will cost $2 million.

The producer believes that the following probabilities apply: Pr(S) = .3, Pr(EP|S) = .7, Pr(PR|S) = .2, Pr(NR|F) = .8., and Pr(PR|F) = .1. Determine the appropriate posterior probabilities [Pr(S|EP), Pr(F|EP), Pr(S|PR), Pr(F|PR), Pr(S|NR), and Pr(F|NR)] and perform a backwards induction analysis to determine if the experimental information should be obtained.

16.38   (Exercise 16.28 continued) A decision must be made to go or not with a small merger. If we go through with it, the outcome will either be a success (S) or a failure (F). We are thinking about hiring a consultant to aid in the decision making process. The outcome will be either favorable (Fav) or unfavorable (Unf).

If no additional information is obtained, a successful merger will net $200,000, but an unsuccessful one will lose $75,000. The consulting firm, if utilized, will cost $10,000.

The overall probability for a successful merger = .3. The appropriate conditional probabilities are Pr(Fav|S) = .8 and Pr(Fav|F) = .4. Determine the appropriate posterior probabilities and perform a backwards induction analysis to determine if the experimental information should be obtained.

16.39   (Exercise 16.29 continued) An executive must make a decision whether to go ahead with a new product or not. She is considering two possible sources of additional information. They are an econometric consulting firm and a market research consulting firm. In both cases, if the research is performed the results will be either favorable (Fav) or unfavorable (Unf). If the product is marketed, the results will be either a success (S) or a failure (F).

If the executive decides not to conduct any research and the project is a success, this will net a profit of $32 million. If it's a failure the result will be a loss of $17 million. If the project is aborted, there will be no profit or loss involved. The econometric consulting firm will cost $2 million and the market research firm $1 million if utilized.

It is believed that the probability for overall success is .4. For the econometric firm, the probability of a favorable report given success is .8 [Pr(Fav|S) = .81 and Pr(Fav|F) = .1]. For the market research firm Pr(Fav|S) = .7 and Pr(Fav|F) = .2. Determine the appropriate posterior probabilities and perform a backwards induction analysis to determine if the experimental information should be obtained.

16.40   (Exercise 16.30 continued) A rock group is making a comeback and think that they have a hot tune. However, it will hold it back if the public doesn't like it. It is thinking about trial testing it in several cities. The group believes that the trial test will either lead to super ratings (Sup), good ratings (Good), okay ratings (Ok), or poor ratings (Poor). Ultimately, the song will either be a success (S) or a failure (F).

If the record is a hit $20 million in profits will be generated. However, if it's not, the image will be tarnished and the group will lose $6 million from advertising. The trial testing will cost $0.5 million which is not included in the figures already given.

The group believes the probability of success is .4. The conditional probabilities are: Pr(Sup|S) = .4, Pr(Sup|F) = .1, Pr(Good|S) = .4, Pr(Good|F) = .2, Pr(Ok|S) = .1, Pr(Ok|F) = .3. Determine the appropriate posterior probabilities [Pr(S|Sup), Pr(F|Sup), Pr(S|Good), Pr(F|Good), Pr(S|Ok), Pr(F|Ok), Pr(S|Poor), and Pr(F|Poor)] and perform a backwards induction analysis to determine if the experimental information should be obtained.

16.6 Summary

In Chapter 15, we developed the logic of business decisions based on prior information. If the EVPI is larger than the cost of obtaining additional information, additional information must be considered prior to making the basic decision. This does not mean that new information will be obtained, but rather that it will be considered. If the costs of the additional information exceed the possible benefits, then the decision maker would use the rules established in the last chapter. However, if the information is critical it can prove invaluable in avoiding incorrect choices.

Mini-case 16.1

A small but prestigious college enjoys an excellent reputation as an elite liberal arts school for women. However, declining enrollment over the past year, due in part to a steady increase in the number of late night assaults, has motivated college administrators to consider instituting two options to make the campus safer.

Both options will result in either a high (H), medium (M), or small (S) degree of success. Each student who fails to enroll because of the problems will cost the school $10,000 in tuition each year for four years, or $40,000. For option A, a high success will mean 100 new students, a medium success will equate to 50 new students, and a small degree of success will mean 10 new students. For option B, a high success will mean 70 new students, a medium success will equate to 50 new students, and a small degree of success will mean 40 new students. The cost of implementing Plan A is $300,000, and for Plan B is $200,000.

The prior probabilities are: $\Pr(H) = .35$, $\Pr(M) = .40$, and $\Pr(S) = .25$. The college is considering conducting a survey to pretest both plans. Based on information from other colleges, the results of the pretest will either be favorable (Fav) or unfavorable (Unf). Some expected conditional probabilities are: $\Pr(\text{Fav}|H) = .9$, $\Pr(\text{Fav}|M) = .5$, and $\Pr(\text{Unf}|S) = .9$.

    a.   Using the historical statistics available, construct a decision tree diagram featuring expected payoffs, probabilities, and information chronology.

    b.   Use backward induction analysis to determine the optimal strategy for the college.

Mini-case 16.2

    Attempt to draw a tree diagram tracing your career path since you were a junior in high school. Did the selection of high school courses affect the present career you are seeking? As you perceive them, draw the tree diagram for what you believe lies ahead. What are the major options that are open to you? Evaluate the subjective probabilities and payoffs for each of the options. What do you believe will be the optimum career path decision for you in the future?

Review of Important Terms and Concepts

Control vs. no control: If an aspect of the decision problem is under the control of the decision maker, it is an act and will emanate from a square node in a tree diagram. If an aspect of the problem is not controllable, it is an event or state of nature and emanates from a circle in the tree diagram.

Node: A circle or square drawn on a tree diagram.

Decision chronology: Tree diagrams are drawn from left to right in the chronological sequence of the decision problem.

Prior analysis: Decision analysis based on prior information, without the aid of additional information. Prior analysis was the basis for Chapter 15. Different decision rules may lead to different choices on the optimum act.

Posterior analysis: Decision analysis based on the prior information and the additional information that is obtained. The prior probabilities of the events are reversed in light of the additional or experimental information. The posterior or revised probabilities are then used to compute new expected payoffs on which to base the decision.

Preposterior analysis: The gathering of experimental information normally involves considerable survey expense. There must be an analysis of whether the expense will be worth the potential gains. Should the survey take place from a cost-benefit standpoint?

Prior probabilities: Prior probabilities are those probabilities known in advance. They usually have been predetermined on the basis of historical relative frequencies or subjective analysis. They are often the weak link in decision theory because of the subjectivity involved.

Conditional probabilities: Probabilities of the sample outcomes given the states of nature. Note conditional probability is a generic term that has taken on a special meaning in Chapter 16.

Joint probabilities: Probabilities of the specific research or sample outcomes. These are by-products of the process of computing revised probabilities.

Posterior probabilities: Probabilities that are revised based on additional information. They incorporate the prior information (prior probabilities), and the accuracy of the sample or additional information (conditional probabilities) into a new set of event probabilities that are specific to the occurrence of a specific sample result.

Bernoulli process: Many business quality control problems follow the format of a Bernoulli process. As such, the Binomial Probability Distribution Table can be used to determine conditional probabilities.

Backward induction analysis: the analysis of a decision problem that uses inductive logic by moving from right to left on a decision tree.

End of Chapter Exercises

16.41 We are a small firm producing canoes. We can either produce a framed canoe or take a large tree trunk and hollow one out. We considering conducting a market study to determine which type would consumers prefer, because we only want to produce one of the two canoes. There is a belief that the upcoming sales will either be strong (S), moderate (M), or weak (W) and the outcome of the market research (if conducted) would either be favorable (Fav) or unfavorable (Unf). Draw the complete decision tree for the scenarios involved.

16.42 Continuing with exercise 16.41, the payoffs for a framed canoe for a strong sales = $250,000, for a moderate sales = $100,000, and for a weak sales will result in a loss of $100,000. The payoffs for a hollowed out canoe for a strong sales = $200,000, for a moderate sales = $50,000, and for a weak sales will cause $0 profits, hence a break even situation. The market research will cost $10,000.

The following probabilities relate to the problem: $Pr(S) = .2$, $Pr(M) = .4$. $Pr(Fav|S) = .8$, $Pr(Fav|M) = .2$, and $Pr(Fav|W) = .1$. Determine the posterior probabilities and perform a backwards induction analysis and determine the optimum course of action.

16.43 In a quality control problem, you are going to sample two units from a shipment of twenty parts. The inspection will yield information that the parts are either defective or not. As such we believe that it will follow the Bernoulli process and the binomial probability distribution may be used. Researching our historical records reveals that 10% of the fifty are defective 50% of the time, 20% of the fifty are defective 40% of the time, and 30% of the fifty are defective 10% of the time. Compute the posterior probabilities for the problem.

16.44 Continuing with Exercise 16.43, we sell the 20-unit shipments for a profit of $1,000. When a 20-unit shipment comes in, we must accept or reject it. If we reject the shipment we must do a census and find all the defective parts, which are replaced with nondefective parts by the manufacturer. It costs us $300 to conduct such a census of the 20 parts and to mail defective parts back, then monitor our incoming parts. Hence, our profit is only $700 if a rejection occurs and we do not survey. If we decided to perform a census (after having decided to sample 2 units), it would occur right after sampling 2 parts and we estimate the census costs to be $265, with the $25 survey costs, profits = $710 ($1,000 − $25 − $265). If we accept the shipment of 20, we then pass them along to our customers who are the ones who find the defective parts. We believe it costs about $100 per part for a returned defective part due to handling costs and losses to goodwill.

Perform a backwards induction analysis assuming we were to survey 2 parts and determine the expected payoff for $n = 2$.

16.45 Continuing with exercise 16.43 and 16.44, determine the posterior probabilities and perform a backward induction analysis involving $n = 1$. The cost of surveying one item is $15. If we decide to perform a census (after deciding to sample 1 unit), it would occur right after sampling 2 parts and we estimate the census costs to be $280 with the $15 survey costs, profits = $705 ($1,000 − $15 − $280).

16.46 Continuing with exercises 16.43, 16.44, and 16.45 draw a tree diagram of the scenarios $n = 2$, $n = 1$, and $n = 0$ and determine which is optimum.

16.47 An undefeated boxer is thinking of ending his retirement to engage in one last fight. To fight the current champion, he has been offered 40 million for a win (W), 20 million for a draw (D), and 0 if he loses (L). He is afraid that if he loses his popularity will drop, and he will forfeit the 5 million he will make if he doesn't fight. So a loss in the fight will result in a 5 million dollar loss.

His former manager assesses that he has a 10% chance of beating the current champion, and a 5% chance of a draw, in his current condition. However, if he were to train successfully (Suc) in the mountains with special equipment for six months, it would greatly improve his chances. The trainer assesses the conditional probabilities to be: $Pr(Suc|W) = .6$, $Pr(Suc|D) = .4$, and $Pr(Suc|L) = .2$. The cost of the special training is 1 million dollars.

a. Determine the posterior probabilities for the problem.
b. Perform a backwards induction analysis and the optimum course of action.

16.48 Repeat exercise 16.47 changing the following probabilities: $Pr(Suc|W) = .9$. $Pr(Suc|D) = .7$, and $Pr(Suc|L) = .1$. Has the optimum course of action changed?

16.49 A rock group is making a comeback and thinks that it has a hot tune. However, it will hold it back if the public doesn't like it. It is thinking about trial testing it in several cities. The group believes that the trial test will either lead to super ratings (Sup), good ratings (Good), Okay ratings (Ok), or poor ratings (Poor). Ultimately, the song will either be a success (S) or a failure (F).

If the record is a hit $20 million in profits will be generated. However, if it's not the image will be tarnished and the group will lose $6 million from advertising. The trial testing will cost $1 million which is not included in the figures already given.

The group believes the probability of success is .4. The conditional probabilities are: $Pr(Sup|S) = .4$. $Pr(Sup|F) = .1$, $Pr(Good|S) = .4$, $Pr(Good|F) = -.2$, $Pr(Ok|S) = .1$, $Pr(Ok|F) = .3$. Determine the appropriate posterior probabilities [$Pr(S|Sup)$, $Pr(F|Sup)$, $Pr(S|Good)$, $Pr(F|Good)$, $Pr(S|Ok)$, $Pr(F|Ok)$, $Pr(S|Poor)$, and $Pr(F|Poor)$].

a. Perform a backwards induction analysis to determine if the experimental information should be obtained.
b. The only difference between exercises 16.40 and 16.49 was in the cost of the consultant. Did the outcome change as the cost of the consultant changed?

538

Deming's 14 Points and Quality Control Concepts

Where we have been

We have completed an analysis of hypothesis testing and we now conclude with one of its main applications, that of quality control.

Where we are going

With increased world competition, the term quality control has received new attention. Although much of the theory has been developed in the United States, Japan has specialized in its applications. The Japanese believe that some of their accomplishments in becoming a world economic power are attributable to the pursuit of quality in workmanship. The techniques themselves are fairly simple; what is difficult is to allow for an environment that will foster them.

17.1   Introduction

"The world is becoming a smaller place" is an often used cliché. Now it is a business reality. New competitors are constantly entering world markets. The new competitors often attempt to be innovative to gain the competitive edge they need. Companies in so called First World countries have grown bureaucratic and find it difficult to accept innovation as an ongoing process. Yet this is the inevitable management process of the future.

Just like you, as a student, avoided your first experience with computers, the confrontation was inevitable. Our first reaction is to fight change. Yet, if we do, we are just losing our competitive advantage. The earlier we accept the notion that computers are essential to data analysis, and data analysis is essential for business survival, the better off we will be.

The management of the future involves managing a process, a process that continually needs updating. One early leader of this philosophy was W. Edwards Deming. Deming, born on October 14, 1900, went on to receive a Ph.D. in physics, from Yale University. He worked at the Western Electric plant where the famous Hawthorne studies were conducted. The plant was a sweatshop turning out telephone equipment. He viewed piecework as a method to ensure low productivity and morale.

While working for the Department of Agriculture, Deming met Walter A. Shewhart of Bell Telephone Laboratories, New York. Shewhart had developed the forerunner of today's statistical quality control and associated charts. Shewhart had the foresight to understand that workers themselves could and should be trained to detect aberrations in process variances. After detection, an analysis could be made to determine cause. The workers themselves could alter processes to allow for corrections.

Deming had studied with the world renowned statistician, Ronald Fisher, and was placed in charge of sampling procedures for the 1940 census. He utilized concepts learned from Shewhart in reducing errors and in increasing productivity. He helped prepare the 1951 Japanese census and the Japanese have given Dr. Deming numerous awards. They have put the Deming philosophy into practice, and despite serious resource shortcomings, Japan is one of the leaders in being the most productive nation on the planet. The Japanese honor Deming by giving the Deming Prize to worthy recipients in two categories. The first is for an individual accomplishment in statistics, and the second for a company in the area of statistical applications whose work has resulted in increased quality and productivity.

W. Edwards Deming was a Stern Professor of Statistics at New York University. His tenure with New York University began in 1946 and continued for nearly 50 years. Shortly before his death, an NYU publication wrote in 1992 that "every Monday he takes a train from his home in Washington, D.C., to a studio apartment in New York City. In the afternoon, he teaches a packed course on quality to 115 MBA students, undergraduates, and visiting executives."

Deming also realized that, even though scientists were being trained in the new management philosophies, it would be of little practical help if top management did not buy into the scheme of things. Management had to give up some of its authoritarian concepts in order for workers to develop a fundamental ability to change the economic process that is their environment.

We review the Deming concept because it is of little value to learn concepts in colleges and universities if their utilization does not expand beyond this scope. We must use data to the degree that a baseball manager does. We must know not only batting averages, but batting averages against left, and right handed pitchers, between day and night, on regular and artificial turf, etc. These data must be revised to take account of changes, both positive and negative. Hence, we review the man, and his points, prior to reviewing the statistical quality control charts.

17.2 Deming's 14 Points

Deming's 14 points are:

#1   *Create consistency of purpose for improvement of product and service.* Deming believed the short term goal of maximizing profits could result in long term morale and productivity problems. Managers tend to treat workers as overhead capital that must be manipulated and used to obtain the optimum financial ratios. However, in accomplishing these goals, it becomes evident to workers that they have no stake in the company and hence have no desire to improve it.

#2   *Adopt the new philosophy.* The new philosophy is that mistakes and poor workmanship are not inevitable. In addition, negativism will not lead to the elimination of poor work habits.

#3   *Cease dependence on mass inspection.* Inspecting parts for tolerances usually occurs at some point on the assembly line. Parts not meeting tolerances are reworked or discarded. Such policies require the company to pay for the defects and to correct them. More inspection will not solve the problem. We have to eliminate the need to inspect, which requires change in the process itself.

#4   *End the practice of awarding business on price tag alone.* Many resources purchased by a company are based on the lowest price at a point in time given the specifications. Firms know that they may be the lowest price for one bid, but not for another. Hence no loyalty is developed between company and supplier. The supplier knows that it is simply being used. Hence, the supplier feels that he or she in return must use your company.

#5   *Improve constantly and forever the system of production and service.* Improvement is not a one-time hot topic, but rather a way of life.

#6   *Institute training.* Since companies view labor as overhead capital, the worker will leave as soon as a better opportunity presents itself. This being the case, it would not be wise to spend money to train workers so that they can utilize learned skills to make another company more efficient. This process must be eliminated.

#7   *Institute leadership.* Leadership is not autocratic management. It entails helping others to develop. The best referee at a sporting contest is not the one blowing the whistle most often. Rather it is the one who exerts some controls to make sure that overall goals and rules are established and who then allows individuality to occur.

#8   *Drive out fear.* Employees are often afraid to ask questions for fear it will mark them as "inferior employees." Often they will continue making mistakes rather than brand themselves as "unable to follow instructions." Companies spend incredible sums because of such errors.

#9   *Break down barriers between staff areas.* Most companies are departmentalized by function, product, or some other criterion. Departments then compete against one another based on a fixed pie syndrome. "I get mine or it will go to them." There is no realization that if one department is unable to accomplish its goals, the entire organization will fail. The chain is only as strong as its weakest link.

#10   *Eliminate slogans, exhortations, and targets for the work force.* Slogans fostered by management will not instill morale and productivity. If slogans are to be effectively developed, it must come from the workers themselves. It must have grass roots support.

#11   *Eliminate numerical quotas for workers and numerical goals for management.* Some countries that have a centrally based economy have tried quotas, without success. One country increased the quotas on the number of nails being produced at a factory. At the end of the year the country had an overabundance of small nails, and virtually none of the larger nails that were required in construction. The quota was met at the expense of overall productivity.

#12   *Remove barriers to pride of workmanship.* Individuals want to perform well and take pride in their personal accomplishments. Without this pride, their activities change from a profession to a job. With this change comes the elimination of productivity. All factors that stand in the way of pride in workmanship, such as bureaucratic management, inefficient equipment, and poor resources, must be eliminated.

#13   *Institute a vigorous program of education and retraining.* For a new system to work, all must know and be part of the new goals and techniques. The new techniques must include the statistical analysis of quality control.

#14   *For everyone to take action to accomplish the transformation.* Only top management can establish the environment which will foster a new era of quality workmanship. This can't be accomplished by a grass roots approach.

Following Deming's beliefs, in order to keep you prepared for this class, you should be given pop quizzes. True or false? If false, explain.

Exercises

17.1 Which of the 14 points do you feel is the most

a. significant?
b. neglected?

17.2 In your own terms, briefly review Deming's 14 points.

17.3 Deming's 7 Deadly Sins

#1 *Lack of constancy of purpose.* Many companies have no clear sense of direction. Often, when this occurs, upper level managers will try to make their mark on the company by going in this direction or that. Employees know when direction is absent and act accordingly. The optimum course of action, under this scenario, is to do as little as possible. What you accomplish today will be undone by a new direction tomorrow.

#2 *Emphasis on short term profits and performance.* A new manager may improve certain financial ratios by laying off 20% of the workplace, then having the remaining 80% do 100% of the work. However, this short term improvement will be more than offset by the eventual long term decline in the company's conditions.

#3 *Evaluation by performance, merit rating, or annual review of performance.* Annual reviews of employees create rivalries and eliminate teamwork. Employees assign their own tasks which will yield the greatest ratings for themselves, even if it's at the expense of company goals. Police forces have been known to arrest individuals for minor infractions when they must appear before finance committees requesting additional funds. It's easier to justify additional funds when arrest records are up. It might not matter that the entire judicial system is about to collapse under the weight of the increased prisoner loads.

Deming *feels* that the ranking of employees is counterproductive towards an efficient work force. In his classes, Professor Deming *awards* only Pass/Fail grades and *to date no one has failed his courses.*

#4 *Mobility of management.* With increased mobility of managers, they can often initiate plans that will make them look good in the short run, but which will create long term productivity problems. The manager doesn't care because he or she won't be with the company when the problems develop. In addition, managers who are with a company for a short term never really understand how it operates. They tend to specialize in corporate areas where they feel more comfortable. Hence, a company may be entirely operated by financial ratios if finance is the CEO's specialty.

#5 *Running a company by visible figures alone.* Much information can be learned from a company's financial ratios, yet much more can't be known. The heart of a company is its employees, and if management doesn't know how they feel, it knows little about the company.

#6 *Excessive medical costs.* Excessive medical costs can be merely a symptom of poor management and/or poor work environment. Both are the responsibility of management.

#7   *Excessive costs of warranty, fueled by lawyers that work on a contingency fee.* Excessive warranty costs correlate directly to poor workmanship. The U.S. has by far the highest ratio of lawyers to population in the world. The long term impact of such a ratio can be damaging to a productive work force.

 Concept Check 17.B

Following Deming's beliefs, periodic employee evaluations are disruptive to a team effort. True or false? If false, explain.

Exercises

17.3   Which of the 7 sins do you feel is the most

   a.   significant?
   b.   neglected?

17.4   In your own terms, briefly review Deming's 7 deadly sins.

17.4 Quality Control Concepts

Quality control comes from the basic logic of patterns. By plotting a process over time, we can categorize two types of variability in the data set. The first is the natural or explained variability in the data set. All processes have variations within them. A natural (common) variation is one which can be explained by the conditions of the process itself and must be considered random variations. If we monitor late incoming aircraft, the natural variations would include unscheduled maintenance problems, crew problems, etc. These are problems that (if not excessive) are natural to that system, and they result in reasonable delays. When a process is involved with random variation, it is considered in control.

A second variation to the system is the variation due to assignable causes. Assignable causes can't be explained by the system's past variation. It is a variation unexplained by past data variations. We can view a natural variation in Figure 17.1A, and a variation by assignable causes in Figures 17.1B and C. In Figure 17.1B, a trend is developing in terms of lateness of airline arrival times that will put us at a competitive disadvantage if it continues. In Figure 17.1C, there appear to be radical changes in the pattern of late times. This trend may have been caused by a slowdown from a union which received sympathy support from other unions. When the disagreement was settled, the process returned to its normal mode.

Figure 17.1 Late Times for Arriving Flights in Minutes

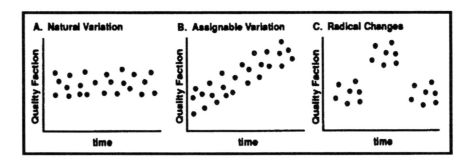

The main difference in terms of natural or assigned variation is in the area of responsibility. An assigned variation is a management problem because it usually involves a change in the process itself. This change involves either correcting the process or taking advantage of opportunities that have presented themselves. If Figure 17.1B had shown a trend of declining late flights, we might want to investigate the new comparative advantage we seem to have had over our competitors.

Since it is important to distinguish between common and assigned variation, control charts (as in Figure 17.1) are used. Two types of errors can occur for which control charts can help. First, we may believe a variation to be due to assigned variation when it is, in fact, due to common causes. This error is common when processes are adjusted too frequently and overadjustment creates a process that is out of adjustment. If you are driving on ice and begin to lose control, an adjustment process is necessary to put you in control. However, an overadjustment will probably be worse than no adjustment at all.

The second type of error is in believing that a common variation is occurring, but, in fact, an assigned variation is the cause. Under this scenario, we will be content in maintaining the process status quo, when change is needed. Control charts will not eliminate the two types of errors, but rather they reduce the probability of their occurrence.

 Concept Check 17.C

An assignable cause means that a new variation in the process can't be explained by past variation. True or false? If false, explain.

Exercises

17.5   When is a system "in control"?

17.6   What is a variation due to an assignable cause?

17.5 Quality Control Charts and Analyses

It is now time to begin to develop the control charts that will enable us to continuously monitor our business systems or processes. The first such charts will be the control chart of means ($\bar{x}$ chart), and ranges (R chart).

Throughout our analysis, we will utilize information concerning an example involving airline delays. In Table 17.1, we have randomly selected 5 domestic flights each day for an airline carrier, and recorded the estimated time of arrival (ETA), and the minutes the plane landed from this time. A positive value means our flight arrived early, and a negative value indicates tardiness. We feel the system is currently in control, or else we would not be justified in using the data as a basis of detecting assignable causes.

544

Table 17.1 Arrival Times Stated in Terms of Minutes from ETA: k Daily Samples of Size 5
($k = 20, n = 5$)
*Data File on Minitab CD

Sample	RECORDED INFORMATION FROM SAMPLE					$\bar{x}$	R	s
	1	2	3	4	5			
$k = 1$	−12	+2	−38	+1	−6	−10.6	40	16.3340
$k = 2$	+13	−42	+10	+4	−2	−3.4	55	22.3338
$k = 3$	+17	+2	0	+6	+20	+9.0	20	9.0000
$k = 4$	−5	+7	+2	−1	+7	+2.0	12	5.1962
$k = 5$	−15	+1	+19	−51	+6	−8.0	70	26.9444
$k = 6$	+8	+4	+25	+2	+10	+9.8	23	9.0664
$k = 7$	+12	−16	+17	+1	0	+2.8	33	12.7554
$k = 8$	+4	−9	−2	−18	−1	−5.2	22	8.5264
$k = 9$	+6	+1	−41	+15	−3	−4.4	56	21.5360
$k = 10$	+1	0	+23	−19	−1	+0.8	42	14.9064
$k = 11$	−79	+6	+19	−3	+9	−9.6	98	39.5828
$k = 12$	−12	−6	−16	−1	+17	−3.6	33	12.8569
$k = 13$	+10	−123	+1	+6	−8	−22.8	133	56.4154
$k = 14$	−8	−19	+4	−12	+6	−5.8	25	10.6395
$k = 15$	0	+17	+2	+4	−1	+4.4	18	7.3007
$k = 16$	−6	−2	−18	+7	+2	−3.4	25	9.4763
$k = 17$	+9	+1	+16	+2	+8	+7.2	15	6.0581
$k = 18$	+17	+2	+12	−16	−71	−11.2	88	35.7309
$k = 19$	+6	+1	+14	+17	+9	+9.4	16	6.3482
$k = 20$	−3	−13	−18	+11	−98	−24.2	109	42.7165
					$\Sigma = $	−66.8	933	373.7200

Control Chart of Means

The control chart of means is based on the pooled mean of all the sample data, or merely the mean of the various sample means denoted by $\bar{\bar{X}}$ (the double bar is symbolic for a mean of a number of means). The centerline is:

Centerline for $\bar{\bar{X}}$ Chart

$$\bar{\bar{X}} = \frac{\Sigma \bar{X}_i}{k} \qquad (17.1)$$

where

Σ occurs from 1 to k

$\bar{X}_i$ = the individual sample means, k in number

k = the number of samples taken of size n

For our airline problem,

$$\bar{\bar{X}} = \frac{-66.8}{20} = -3.34$$

We will now develop the upper control limits (UCL) and the lower control limits (LCL) from the centerline. Once we have the mean we will rely on Minitab to develop our Upper and Lower Control Limits (LCL, UCL) for both means and ranges.

Control Chart of Ranges

Because ranges tend to be unstable and volatile in large samples, we normally keep the sample sizes to single digits ($n \leq 9$). We notice in Table 17.1 that the R values are unstable, even with a sample size of 5. This is due to the nature of the data set. Since flights can't take off earlier than scheduled departure time, and can't normally exceed certain air speeds, to arrive much before the estimated time of arrival is difficult. Yet one minor problem requiring an inspection and/or replacement of parts can cause enormous delays.

We will now construct an R control chart. Remember that the range is simply the difference between the largest and smallest values. The control chart will have a centerline, which is the mean of the ranges (symbolically denoted as $\bar{R}$).

Centerline for R Chart

$$\bar{R} = \frac{\Sigma R_i}{k} \tag{17.2}$$

where

Σ occurs from 1 to k

R_i = the individual sample ranges, k in number

K = the number of samples taken on size n

For our time of arrival problem, $\bar{R} = 46.65$.

$$\bar{R} = \frac{933}{20} = 46.65$$

As we view the control chart for both means and ranges, (Figure 17.2), we note that two sample ranges appear beyond the UCL and one is extremely close to it. However after inspecting the reasons for these very long delays, we have concluded that the system is still in control. The delays were caused by an FAA plane inspection and two bomb threats that forced us to take extraordinary procedures.

Note: enter the data into a single column (ETA Time).

Stat > Control Charts > Variables Charts for Subgroups > Xbar-R
Double click the **Data** into **Variable** box.
Enter n as the **Subgroup size** ($n = 5$).
Click on Tests, click on Perform all eight tests.
OK

Figure 17.2 MINITAB Output for the Range Control Chart

Xbar-R Chart of Data

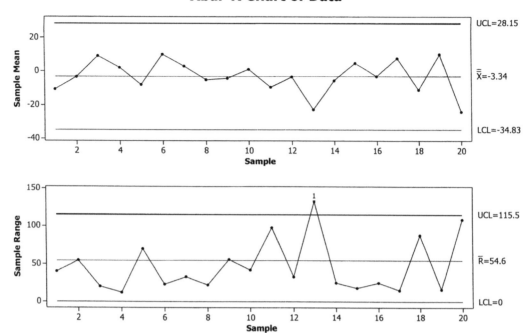

As an alternative to a control chart of ranges we could also have developed a control chart of sample S values. All of the sample S values are recorded in Table 17.1. The centerline would be

Centerline for S Chart

$$\overline{S} = \frac{\Sigma S_i}{k} \tag{17.3}$$

where

Σ occurs from 1 to k

S_i = the individual sample standard deviations, k in number

k = the number of samples taken of size n

For our time of arrival problem,

$$\overline{S} = \frac{373.72}{20} = 18.686$$

547

From viewing Figure 17.2 we obtain essentially the same information yielded in Figure 17.3. Surveys #13 and #20 are clearly above UCL. The only difference in results is with survey #11. In Figure 17.2 it is barely below UCL, and in Figure 17.3, it is barely above UCL. Since both control charts for ranges and standard deviations yield almost the same information, the range has historically been used because it is much simpler to compute (if a computer is not available).

Note: enter the data into a single column (ETA Time).

Stat > Control Charts > S
Double click the **Data** into **Variable** box.
Enter *n* as the **Subgroup size** ($n = 5$).
Click on **Rbar estimate**.
OK

Figure 17.3 *S* Control Charts

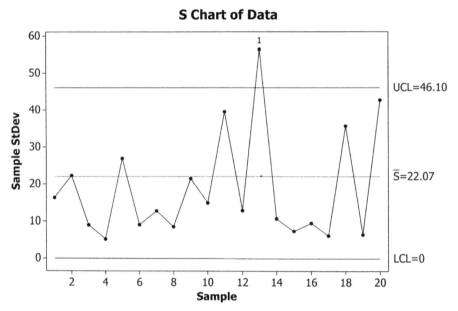

The *P* Control Chart

The control charts previously completed involved continuous data. We will now turn our attention to qualitative data. Hence, a variable either will contain a certain attribute or it won't, as is often the case in quality control. As an example, we could monitor parts coming off an assembly line to determine if they meet certain specified tolerances.

Let's say we record the number of machine parts coming from an assembly line each day for a month (Table 17.2). The number of *k* samples should be at least 25 ($k \geq 25$). The proportion defective is simply the defective parts divided by *n*. If the parts are sampled per hour or per day, it will be rare that the individual sample sizes would be the same.

548

Table 17.2 Defective Parts Coming Off an Assembly Line
*Data File on MINITAB CD

Day	Defective	n_i	P_i
1	29	810	0.0358
2	37	962	0.0385
3	9	767	0.0117
4	21	916	0.0229
5	14	902	0.0155
6	18	1006	0.0179
7	17	826	0.0206
8	16	698	0.0229
9	41	1076	0.0381
10	19	973	0.0195
11	24	789	0.0304
12	12	817	0.0147
13	28	751	0.0373
14	16	865	0.0185
15	7	719	0.0097
16	27	947	0.0285
17	15	1021	0.0147
18	16	861	0.0186
19	23	717	0.0321
20	28	866	0.0323
21	43	1101	0.0391
22	28	919	0.0305
23	11	897	0.0123
24	23	747	0.0308
25	19	862	0.0220
26	36	941	0.0383
27	21	818	0.0257
28	40	847	0.0472
29	50	967	0.0517
30	51	893	0.0571
31	44	719	0.0612

The formula for the centerline is

Centerline for P Chart Using a Weighted Proportion

$$\overline{P}_{wt} = \frac{\Sigma P_i \bullet n_i}{\Sigma n_i} \qquad (17.4)$$

where

P_{wt} = the weighted average proportion

S occurs from 1 to k

P_i = the individual sample proportions, k in number

k = the number of samples taken of size n_i

Σn_i = the sum of the individual sample sizes

For the computations for UCL and LCL, we will rely on MINITAB to obtain the limit.

We have 5 proportions outside of our control limits (Figure 17.4). Two proportions are below LCL (day 15). Having defects below the norms do not concern us except to be able to determine why we have become more efficient and to see if we can't always operate efficiently. What concerns us is days 28, 29, 30, and 31. We are out of control and must find the assignable cause to correct the system.

Note: enter the data into two columns. The first we titled Failed and the second Inspect. If we desire we can use MINITAB's calculator to compute the proportion of failures (Failed/Inspect).

Stat > **Control Charts** > **Attribute Charts** > *P*
Double click the **Failed** into **Variable** box.
Activate the **Subgroup sizes** in box and enter **Inspect**.
OK

Figure 17.4 MINITAB Output for the *P* **Control Chart**

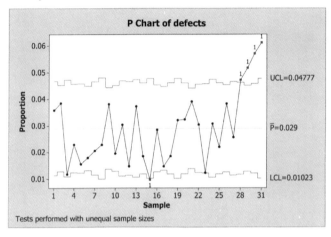

We note that days 28, 29, 30, and 31 are clearly above UCL and the system is out of control.

The *C* Chart

In the *P* control chart, we monitored the number of defective parts. In the control charts for ranges and means, we monitored late arrivals. Now we wish to consider not only a late arrival as a defect, but also lost luggage, incorrect airline tickets, etc. We wish to note the specific number of defects involved in a flight. Suppose we randomly select five airplane flights to ascertain how many defects they have. We record the number of defects that the five planes have for five weeks (see Table 17.3). This is referred to as the inspection unit.

Table 17.3　The Total Number of Defects Involving 5 Flights Over 35 Days

Inspection Unit	# of Defects	Inspection Unit	# of Defects
1	21	19	7
2	27	20	18
3	17	21	19
4	27	22	21
5	16	23	11
6	11	24	9
7	24	25	16
8	7	26	25
9	15	27	12
10	9	28	28
11	22	29	16
12	4	30	22
13	28	31	13
14	19	32	16
15	10	33	8
16	9	34	11
17	17	35	21
18	12		

The number of defects (per inspection unit) is symbolically denoted as C. The centerline formula for the control chart is

Centerline for C Chart

$$\overline{C} = \frac{\Sigma C_i}{k} \qquad (17.5)$$

where

Σ = occurs from 1 to k

C_i = the number of defects per inspection unit, k in number

K = the number of samples taken of size n

Substituting the appropriate numerical equivalents into Formula 17.5 yields

$$\overline{C} = \frac{568}{35} = 16.229$$

MINITAB can be used to develop our C control chart and the process is as follows:
Note: enter the data into a single column (Defects).

Stat > Control Charts > Attributes Charts > C
Enter **Defects** into **Variable** box.
Click on **Tests ... Perform all four tests**.
OK

Figure 17.5 MINITAB Output for the C Control Chart

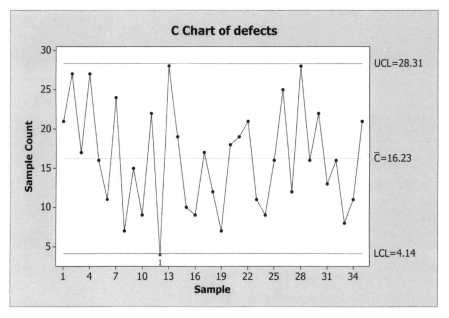

Only one inspection unit (#12) is outside the bounds. However, it represents fewer number of defects; hence, it does not concern us. Inspection units #13 and #28 are very close to the UCL, and this might concern us. We must monitor the system closely to be sure it is in control.

 Concept Check 17.D

A control chart is used to ascertain if a system is in control, based on its past variations. True or false? If false, explain.

Exercises

17.7   Why do we not use large samples when analyzing ranges?

17.8   Should a control chart of ranges not be similar to a control chart of standard deviations?

17.9   We have recorded parts as they come off an assembly line. The part is supposed to weigh x grams. We record the number of grams (plus or minus) that the part is off. The following is recorded information from sample:

Sample	1	2	3	4
#1	−12	+16	−11	+1
#2	+13	−42	+17	+9
#3	+17	+2	−19	0
#4	−5	+45	+2	−7
#5	−25	+19	+49	−51
#6	+28	+14	+2	−39
#7	+12	−16	+17	+1
#8	+24	−9	−1	+9
#9	+61	+1	−51	+15
#10	+41	0	+29	−19
#11	−79	+61	+19	−13
#12	−17	−6	+61	−1
#13	+19	−91	−1	+36
#14	−28	−19	+46	−12
#15	+8	+47	+2	−27
#16	−16	−2	−18	+67
#17	+49	+1	+16	−40
#18	+21	+12	+22	−16
#19	+46	+1	−14	−37
#20	−31	−13	−18	+41
#21	−11	+43	−28	+2
#22	+37	+10	−16	−5
#23	+16	−19	+31	−2
#24	−14	+41	+8	−9
#25	−7	+37	−26	+1

Have MINITAB perform a mean control chart analysis and determine if the system is in control.

17.10 For the data in Exercise 17.9, have MINITAB perform an R control chart analysis and determine if the system is in control.

17.11 For the data in Exercise 17.9, have MINITAB perform an S control chart analysis and determine if the system is in control.

17.12 Compare your answers to Exercises 17.9, 17.10, and 17.11 in terms of being in control.

17.13 The following information is recorded:

Sample	Information			Sample	Information		
1	6	7	1	11	12	9	13
2	0	5	9	12	10	12	9
3	3	9	2	13	16	10	13
4	4	2	7	14	14	11	15
5	1	8	4	15	12	18	14
6	9	2	3	16	21	12	18
7	4	4	7	17	17	24	19
8	8	0	1	18	23	17	22
9	2	7	5	19	21	27	24
10	4	9	1	20	24	25	27

Have MINITAB perform a mean control chart analysis and determine if the system is in control.

17.14   Use the data for Exercise 17.13, and have MINITAB perform an R and S control chart analysis and determine if the system is in control.

17.15   The following information is recorded from a process involving samples of size six.

Sample	Mean	Range	Sample	Mean	Range
1	72.9	41	13	77.4	22
2	69.5	51	14	62.8	73
3	64.9	39	15	75.1	27
4	74.2	29	16	65.8	51
5	80.3	17	17	71.1	46
6	72.4	36	18	62.5	49
7	64.1	55	19	81.0	19
8	59.7	61	20	67.7	45
9	82.6	16	21	72.3	32
10	66.8	53	22	76.2	38
11	76.0	32	23	67.4	36
12	71.1	41	24	77.9	26

Have MINITAB perform a mean and range control chart analysis and determine if the system is in control.

17.16   Why are the sample sizes much greater in P control charts than in mean or range control charts?

17.17   For 26 time periods, the number of defective parts is recorded from that period's production.

Time Period	# Defective	n_i	Time Period	# Defective	n_i
1	7	97	14	7	102
2	11	78	15	15	136
3	14	109	16	12	99
4	9	111	17	8	94
5	11	94	18	10	121
6	12	112	19	9	89
7	10	132	20	8	100
8	13	106	21	11	114
9	8	81	22	13	140
10	7	113	23	14	122
11	10	84	24	11	101
12	8	91	25	7	76
13	9	107	26	12	107

Have MINITAB perform a P control chart analysis.

17.18   For Exercise 17.17. is the system in control? Determine if each proportion is within the bounds of the weighted proportion using formula 17.5.

17.19 A company records the number of phone calls made during the same hour for 30 consecutive days. They also record the number of calls involving defective connections.

Time Period	# Defects	n_i	Time Period	# Defects	n_i
1	39	1,026	16	25	1,201
2	21	1,291	17	39	1,826
3	41	1,789	18	27	1,317
4	29	1,483	19	47	2,631
5	46	2,146	20	2	117
6	3	142	21	0	55
7	1	81	22	32	997
8	26	992	23	16	1,182
9	32	1,198	24	25	1,563
10	36	1,605	25	30	1,298
11	31	1,326	26	43	2,287
12	51	2,672	27	3	110
13	4	161	28	1	42
14	2	73	29	47	1,252
15	27	1,176	30	53	1,301

a. Compute a centerline for the P chart (using MINITAB).
b. Is the process in control?

17.20 For Exercise 17.19, have MINITAB perform the analysis.

17.21 A company monitors the first 1,000 calls and counts the number of defects in their communication process.

Inspection Unit	# of Defects	Inspection Unit	# of Defects
1	68	21	81
2	76	22	73
3	86	23	66
4	71	24	69
5	80	25	84
6	129	26	72
7	79	27	166
8	73	28	71
9	86	29	70
10	82	30	77
11	78	31	65
12	81	32	80
13	143	33	79
14	84	34	152
15	69	33	68
16	76	36	74
17	70	37	78
18	84	38	72
19	65	39	81
20	131	40	66

a. What is the grouping of 1,000 calls named?
b. Using MINITAB, compute the centerline for the C chart and UCL plus LCL.

17.22 A large shipper of packages wishes to know if the number of defects per 100 boxes shipped is in control. The types of defects include damaged boxes, incorrect addresses, incorrect charges, etc. Hourly, 10 boxes are surveyed and the number of defects are:

Inspection Unit	# of Defects	Inspection Unit	# of Defects
1	18	21	17
2	16	22	13
3	16	23	6
4	11	24	9
5	10	25	14
6	7	26	12
7	9	27	8
8	13	28	11
9	6	29	17
10	12	30	17
11	8	31	5
12	11	32	18
13	16	33	9
14	14	34	11
15	6	35	14
16	7	36	7
17	7	37	8
18	14	38	12
19	15	39	11
20	14	40	16

a. What is the grouping of 100 packages called?
b. Using MINITAB, compute the centerline for the C chart and determine UCL and LCL.
c. Is the process is in control?

17.6 Summary

We began with a brief history of W. Edwards Deming, a pioneer in the field of quality control and control charts. Deming believed that quality control should not simply be a process of sampling completed parts to ascertain if they were produced within specified tolerances. This, in effect, is rewarding and paying for unacceptable performance. What is necessary is to develop processes that monitor the system itself and allow for corrective changes prior to the system being out of control. Our analysis then covered four control charts and their respective upper and lower control limits.

Mini-case 17.1: Number of Mistakes on 10 Real Estate Contracts

A large real estate office feels there have been too many errors on sales contracts for purchases of homes. It inspects the first 23 contracts to close each week. For the first 20 weeks, the traditional contract is used, while for the last 20 weeks, an experimental contract is used. The number of defects is as follows:

Inspection Unit	# of Defects	Inspection Unit	# of Defects
1	18	21	31
2	16	22	13
3	6	23	26
4	17	24	19
5	8	25	14
6	7	26	12
7	19	27	28
8	17	28	21
9	3	29	20
10	12	30	17
11	10	31	9
12	11	32	18
13	6	33	19
14	4	34	21
15	9	35	28
16	16	36	24
17	10	37	17
18	14	38	12
19	5	39	28
20	14	40	26

a. Which control chart is appropriate for this data set?
b. Determine the appropriate centerline.
c. Determine UCL and LCL.
d. Is the system in control?

 Mini-case 17.2: Mistakes on Examinations

Record the number of mistakes that you make on the next 25 to 30 exams and for assigned projects you have. Is your system in control? Do you know of a friend that is currently not in control? If so, what factors do you believe have contributed to your friend being out of control? What can your friend do to regain control?

Review of Relevant Terms and Contracts

Process variations: Process variations are changes that occur within a system. The changes can be caused by the natural or explained variation inherent within the system, or by assignable causes not inherent in the system.

Control charts: A chart which will allow us to discern more readily if variations in a process are natural.

Upper and lower control limits: The bounds of a control chart to determine if a process is in a steady state, or is in control.

Types of control charts: Control charts reviewed were of ranges, standard deviations, means, and proportions.

Review of Important Formulas

Centerline for $\overline{\overline{X}}$ Chart

$$\overline{\overline{X}} = \frac{\Sigma \overline{X}_i}{k} \tag{17.1}$$

where

Σ occurs from 1 to k

$\overline{X}_i$ = the individual sample means, k in number

k = the number of samples taken of size n

Centerline for R Chart

$$\overline{R} = \frac{\Sigma R_i}{k} \tag{17.2}$$

where

Σ occurs from 1 to k

R_i = the individual sample ranges, k in number

k = the number of samples taken of size n

Centerline for S Chart

$$\overline{S} = \frac{\Sigma S_i}{k} \tag{17.3}$$

where

Σ occurs from 1 to k

S_i = the individual sample standard deviations, k in number

k = the number of samples taken of size n

Centerline for P Chart Using a Weighted Proportion

$$\overline{P}_{Wt} = \frac{\Sigma P_i \bullet n_i}{\Sigma n_i} \qquad\qquad (17.4)$$

where

$\overline{P}_{Wt} =$ the weighted average proportion

Σ occurs from 1 to k

$P_i =$ the individual sample proportions, k in number

$k =$ the number of samples taken of size n_i

$\Sigma n_i =$ the sum of the individual sample sizes

Centerline for C Chart

$$\overline{C} = \frac{\Sigma C_i}{k} \qquad\qquad (17.5)$$

where

Σ occurs from 1 to k

$C_i =$ the number of defects per inspection unit, k in number

$k =$ the number of samples taken of size n

Review of MINITAB Commands

Main MINITAB commands for control charts.

Stat > Control Charts > Variables Charts for Subgroups > Xbar
Stat > Control Charts > R
Stat > Control Charts > S
Stat > Control Charts > Attributes Charts > P
Stat > Control Charts > Attributes Charts > C

559

17.23 A student records the time that her three professors arrive at their respective classes in terms of minutes early (+) or late (−). The appropriate recorded times for 30 classes are:

Day	Recorded Times			Day	Recorded Times		
1	+7	−1	−5	16	−2	−3	+7
2	0	−12	+6	17	−1	+8	−2
3	+7	+2	+11	18	+1	+9	−4
4	−6	+7	+3	19	+7	+5	+2
5	+2	−1	+9	20	−6	+8	+14
6	+4	0	−2	21	+1	−5	+4
7	+2	+4	−1	22	+1	+8	0
8	−6	−19	+3	23	+3	−1	−5
9	−2	−3	+6	24	−1	−1	0
10	0	+7	+1	25	−4	+9	−2
11	+6	+3	+1	26	+2	+7	−5
12	+2	+6	−3	27	+2	−1	+8
13	−1	−6	+4	28	+1	−5	+3
14	0	−6	+1	29	+6	+2	+3
15	−3	+4	+2	30	−1	−4	−2

Have MINITAB perform a range control chart analysis.

17.24 For the data in Exercise 17.23, have MINITAB perform a mean control chart analysis.

17.25 The following information is recorded from monitoring motorists' speeds at a particular point on new interstate. The monitoring occurs for the first 6 cars of each hour for 24 hours.

Sample	Mean	Range	Sample	Mean	Range
1	53.7	22	13	54.8	22
2	49.5	16	14	57.6	22
3	51.0	28	15	52.0	17
4	56.2	27	16	57.2	29
5	58.3	36	17	55.9	22
6	52.4	26	18	58.3	31
7	54.1	18	19	72.4	70
8	49.7	16	20	77.2	62
9	48.6	23	21	80.1	77
10	45.2	17	22	76.1	73
11	48.3	25	23	84.3	79
12	51.1	28	24	87.0	81

Have MINITAB perform a range and mean control chart analysis and determine if the system is in control.

17.26 A health-care company surveys 7 hospitals with equal number of beds. For 31 days they tabulate the number of deaths occurring at each hospital.

Day			Recorded Deaths					Day			Recorded Deaths				
1	0	5	2	1	1	0	3	16	0	8	0	4	0	5	1
2	1	8	1	4	3	1	1	17	0	6	1	1	0	1	0
3	4	4	1	2	2	4	1	18	1	5	0	1	0	1	3
4	2	3	5	2	1	1	4	19	4	17	8	7	10	13	5
5	1	12	1	7	2	4	3	20	3	14	3	7	8	11	9
6	3	3	7	2	0	0	2	21	7	16	9	5	4	10	7
7	6	10	2	1	1	4	6	22	4	12	7	4	8	5	9
8	4	7	4	4	1	2	0	23	7	8	10	9	7	8	6
9	2	7	1	2	0	4	0	24	8	10	7	6	7	6	8
10	1	9	1	3	1	2	1	25	5	2	1	0	1	0	4
11	0	5	0	1	0	2	1	26	2	1	1	2	1	0	3
12	2	6	3	3	0	1	0	27	0	3	0	3	1	1	0
13	2	12	4	3	6	2	3	28	0	0	4	2	4	1	0
14	5	10	3	2	3	2	3	29	2	1	2	1	0	1	4
15	2	14	2	0	4	1	1	30	1	0	0	0	3	4	3
								31	0	1	1	2	3	1	0

Have MINITAB perform a mean, range, and S control chart analysis and determine if the system is in control.

17.27 A utility company desires that the electric monitoring devices it has distributed to households to measure electrical consumption be in control. Each week for half a year, the company randomly monitors as many meters as possible with the following number of defective meters and sample sizes:

DEFECTIVE ELECTRIC METERS

Week	Defective	n_i	Week	Defective	n_i
1	2	81	15	7	76
2	7	62	16	2	84
3	1	79	17	5	63
4	5	98	18	3	79
5	6	68	19	5	82
6	4	73	20	6	91
7	6	84	21	4	85
8	3	77	22	8	92
9	4	62	23	7	89
10	6	76	24	2	71
11	1	42	25	5	77
12	5	84	26	4	88
13	7	96	27	3	72
14	4	82			

a. Compute a centerline for the P chart.
b. Compute UCL and LCL using an average sample size.
c. Is the process in control?

17.28 For Exercise 17.27, have MINITAB perform the analysis.

17.29 A company that produces floppy disks wishes to know if its production process is in control. It monitors disks produced in one hour for 25 days. The results of that accounting are:

DEFECTIVE FLOPPY DISKS

Week	Defective	n_i	Week	Defective	n_i
1	28	1,281	14	17	1,192
2	13	978	15	31	1,789
3	11	791	16	25	1,632
4	15	987	17	23	1,179
5	25	1,511	18	15	826
6	14	673	19	26	918
7	26	1,284	20	221	855
8	21	1,177	21	18	921
9	14	662	22	12	890
10	16	976	23	10	791
11	11	842	24	26	1,377
12	15	840	25	11	880
13	19	963	26	74	1,067
			27	11	976

a.   Using MINITAB, compute a centerline for the P chart and find UCL and LCL.
b.   Is the process in control?

17.30 A consumer testing group follows the first car off a production line each day. After it is purchased they ask the owner to keep a detailed diary of all defects for 30 production days. The defects are recorded and they are:

Inspection Unit	# of Defects	Inspection Unit	# of Defects
1	18	16	17
2	16	17	13
3	23	18	16
4	21	19	19
5	14	20	14
6	22	21	17
7	25	22	20
8	19	23	23
9	22	24	17
10	17	25	24
11	18	26	19
12	17	27	10
13	24	28	6
14	17	29	3
15	15	30	2

Have MINITAB perform a C chart analysis.

17.31 Record the number of junk food purchases made each day for the next month. Think of a junk food purchase as a defect. Is your system in control?

Buckwalter, Robert. *Discovering Deming*, Stern School of Business, New York University, Summer 1992, pp. 24–26.

Burr, Irving W. *Statistical Quality Control Methods*, New York: Marcel Dekker, 1976.

Deming, W. E. *Quality, Productivity, and Competitive Position*, Cambridge, MA: MIT Center for Advanced Engineering Study, 1982.

Deming, W. E. *Some Theory of Sampling*, New York: John Wiley and Sons, 1966.

Evans, J. R. and Lindsay, W. M. *The Management and Control of Quality*, St. Paul, MN: West, 1989.

Ghosh, Subir. *Statistical Design and Analysis of Industrial Experiments*, New York: Marcel Dekker, 1990.

Grant, E. L. and Leavonworth, R. S. *Statistical Quality Control*, 6th edition, New York: McGraw-Hill, 1988.

Liepins, Gunar E. and Uppuluri, V. R. R. *Data Quality Control: Theory and Pragmatics*, New York: Marcel Dekker, 1990.

Ryan, Thomas P. *Statistical Methods for Quality Improvement*, New York: John Wiley and Sons, 1989.

Walton, Mary. *The Deming Management Method*, New York: Dodd and Mead, 1986.

Solutions to Chapters

Chapter 1 Solutions

 Answers to Concept Checks

1.A   True

1.B   False. The data involves a single point in time.

1.C   False. In sampling we may include individuals who represent extreme observations which will cause the sample mean to be different than the population mean.

1.D   False. We are dealing with ratio data; one item costs twice the other.

1.E   True.

Answers to Odd-Numbered Exercises

1.1   Patterns are determined which lead to high risk categories.

1.3   Yes.

1.5   We are really defining the class as the population.

1.7   The advantages are in the area of speed and reduced costs.

1.9   A variable is a characteristic/property that an individual population unit possesses.

1.11   Nominal data, such as social security number, just identifies employees. With ordinal data, employees with a higher evaluation had a superior years to those with a lower evaluation. With interval data, the superiority of employees with evaluations of 100 and 95 is exactly proportional for employee evaluations with 85 and 80. With ratio data an employee with a 100 evaluation is twice as good as an employee with an evaluation of 50.

1.15   For interval data, the intelligence difference between IQ scores of 130 and 120 is the same as between 100 and 90. For ratio data an individual with an IQ score of 120 is twice that of an individual with an IQ of 60.

1.17   Student project.

1.19   A survey could be taken in which students could state what courses to offer and at what times.

1.21   Yes. However statistics can be used to yield a conclusion beyond a reasonable doubt.

1.23   Time series data reflect data based on time as the observational unit. Thus, each observation differs in the relevant time period for which it is measured. The observational units for cross-sectional data are not time-based. That is, each observation is associated with a different individual, state, region, firm, country, industry, etc. However, in cross-sectional data the observations are fixed in time. Examples are left to your imagination.

1.25   The Gallup Poll is based on a sample.

 Answers to Mini-cases

Mini-case 1.1

Sherlock Holmes deduced clues from information and facts he observed. However, he also made inferences from these clues in terms of expanding his observations to the population at large.

Mini-case 1.2

By looking at the demographic and psychographic profiles of the population surrounding the hospital we can ascertain the probabilities of certain illnesses occurring.

Mini-case 1.3

Statistics is frequently used in quality control problems.

Mini-case 1.4

A very elaborate sample is used to ascertain what the average family spends on housing, food, etc.

Mini-case 1.5

Graduate schools and employers develop formulas and/or profiles which are based on historical findings. These findings may cause you to be accepted or rejected as a candidate.

Mini-case 1.6

Retailers monitor inventory and learn what merchandise sells. If a particular brand name product does not sell, it will be replaced with one that does. This is called consumer sovereignty.

Chapter 2   Solutions

 Answers to Concept Checks

2.A   True.

2.B   True.

2.C   False. The mean, median, and mode are only equal in a symmetric distribution. If the distribution is substantially skewed, the arithmetic mean would be a poor measure of central tendency. Thus, one should examine the distribution before selecting a measure of central tendency which represents the distribution.

2.D   False. The variance is a measure of absolute variation. The only measure of relative variation discussed in the text was the coefficient of variation which scales the standard deviation relative to the arithmetic mean of the distribution.

2.E   False. An outlier is a data point far into the tail of a distribution.

Answers to Odd-Numbered Exercises

2.1

Class Standing	Frequency	Relative Frequency	Cumulative Frequency
Freshman	2	2/20 = .10	2/20 = 0.10
Sophomore	4	4/20 = .20	6/20 = 0.30
Junior	6	6/20 = .30	12/20 = 0.60
Senior	8	8/20 = .40	20/20 = 1.00
Totals	20	20/20 = 1.00	

2.3

Region	Frequency	Relative Frequency
E	11	11/25 = .44
M	3	3/25 = .12
W	11	11/25 = .44
Totals	25	25/25 = 1.00

2.5   In the case of quantitative data, there are no natural groupings or categories other than the individual values. These individual values often are too numerous; hence we categorize by grouping observations into numeric intervals.

2.7   Student project using a MINITAB data base.

2.9   a. $722.50

b. $695. Since there is an even number of observations (6), the median is the average of the middle two (observations 3 and 4).

c. The mode is the most frequently occurring number. Only 595 repeats itself, hence it's the mode. Note that the mode has little meaning in small sample sizes.

2.11   Note that there is no definitive answer to this question. Each measure of central tendency has some advantages and disadvantages. Also we stress the fact that all measures of central tendency should be computed and differences in their values also will tell you something about the distribution. However, the following answers have some basis.

a. The median. Income distributions are notably skewed and there are almost certain to be some extreme values that would distort the arithmetic mean.

b. The mode. The arithmetic mean would again possibly be distorted by the sick leave records of a small minority of workers. The median may be atypical because workers are probably sick a lot or very infrequently. The mode would reflect the number of sick days most frequently occurring.

c. The mean (probably measured in months rather than years). The ages of students in a typical high school day class are likely to be tightly clustered. If so, the mean, median, and mode would all be close. However, the mean uses all the information in the distribution. The median and the mode do not.

2.13   The sample mode of a distribution is the value with the highest frequency of occurrence.

2.15   In contract negotiations, management will generally prefer to use the arithmetic mean. This conclusion is based on the assumption that worker's salaries will be skewed to the right. In other words, there will be some workers earning salaries substantially higher than most (due to longevity or managerial responsibilities). Thus, the mean will be biased upwards by the high salaries of a few. Union negotiators will probably prefer the mode. Since it is likely that most frequently earned salary is quite low.

2.17   Mean $= 72.6$, median $= 75.5$, mode $= 75$.

2.19   Mean $=$ median $= 2$; mode $= 2$.

2.21   **Descriptive Statistics**

Variable	N	Mean	Median	TrMean	StDev	SE Mean
First	31	70.65	73.00	70.74	14.83	2.66
Second	31	75.77	79.00	76.33	15.92	2.86

Variable	Minimum	Maximum	Q1	Q3
First	42.00	95.00	57.00	83.00
Second	44.00	98.00	67.00	88.00

2.23   A measure of dispersion is a statistic used to describe the variability in a data distribution. The statistics developed in this chapter to describe dispersion in a data distribution include the range, standard deviation, variance, mean absolute deviation, and coefficient of variation.

2.25   Range $= 11$

2.27   MAD $= 2$

2.29 $\overline{X} = 10$, $s^2 = 30$; $s = 5.48$

2.31   A coefficient of variation is a relative measure of dispersion that takes into consideration the measurement levels involved.

2.33   Stock A: $7.91/3.00 = .2637$ *Stock B: $2.24/5.00 = .448$

2.35 $S = 3.472$; $Q_i = 62.425$; $Q_3 = 68.225$

2.37   Employee J's salary is substantially different than the mean salary of $34,600. In addition, employee C's salary of $12,000 is also well below the mean.

2.39   Employee A's salary is $-.757$ standard deviations from the mean as evidenced in the following calculation, $z = -.757$. Thus, employee A's salary is slightly less than three-fourths of a standard deviation below the mean salary.

2.41   Student Exercise using MINITAB.

2.43 $z = 1.22$

568

Answers to Mini-cases

Mini-case 2.1

a. The stem-and-leaf plot and output show a minimum salary of $7.4(000) and a maximum salary of $38.8(000) for the 20 employees. Thus, the range is $30.9(000). Thus, there appears to be significant variation in the salaries. The median salary is $18.1(000). The first quartile and third quartiles are $15.2(000) and $22.45(000) respectively. Thus the middle 50 percent of the distribution differ in salary by at most $7.25(000).

b. The mean salary of the group is $19.28(000) which is larger than the median. However, this is expected since the stem-and leaf display indicated positive skewness in the distribution.

Mini-case 2.2

Many salary distributions are positively skewed. The most tenured persons in an organization are generally the highest paid in a particular job class. Therefore, replacing senior personnel with new young hires would usually involve replacing persons with high salaries with persons of low salary. All measures of central tendency can be affected by such a move. However, the arithmetic mean would be influenced very quickly and substantially with such a move.

Mini-case 2.3

The bar graph is misleading because only the vertical scale has meaning. Portfolio A has a higher return. However the bar graph has a width scale much wider for portfolio B than for portfolio A. The area for the bar graph for portfolio A is less than that of B. By area, portfolio B's bar is far greater than portfolio A's bar. Unfortunately, the vertical scale is the only scale of significance; hence, A is superior to B.

Chapter 3 Solutions

 Answers to Concept Checks

3.A   True.

3.B   True. We tend to store information in our minds and recall it incompletely. In a sense our minds are making relative frequencies, but the aggregations may be very inaccurate.

3.C   False. They could not overlap if they were mutually exclusive events.

3.D   False. $Pr(A|B) = Pr(B)$ for independent events.

3.E   False. This describes a posterior probability.

3.F   False. From reviewing the formulas we could see that the opposite is true.

Answers to Odd-Numbered Exercises

3.1   Statement A reflects intentions that are certain and statement B reflects uncertainty in the plans. Thus, adding the term probability added doubt to the statement.

3.3   If two events are mutually exclusive, the occurrence of one precludes the occurrence of the other during a specified period of time. Thus, if an instructor told you that you were to have mutually exclusive exams, there would be no overlapping of subject matter.

3.5
a. These events are overlapping but are not mutually exclusive.
b. These events are overlapping but are not mutually exclusive.
c. These events are overlapping but are not mutually exclusive.
d. These events are overlapping but are not mutually exclusive.
e. These events do not overlap but are mutually exclusive.

3.7   a. classical   b. subjective   c. relative frequency   d. subjective   e. relative frequency

3.9   a. 1317   b. .7137   c. They would be considered relative frequencies, since they are based on observed frequencies from the survey.

3.11   a. .3534   b. .5567

3.13   The Pr(A & B) is where two events occur jointly, whereas, Pr(A or B) is the entire sample space involving either of the two events.

3.15   a. 0.1538   b. 0.3077   c. 0.0192

3.17   a. 0.3333   b. 0.4111   c. 0.1333   d. 0.4111

3.19   a. 0.4615   b. 0.6154   c. 0.444   d. 0.8

3.21   Multiplication rules involve at lease two events. For conditional probabilities, we will want to know the probability of event A occurring, given event B has already occurred.

3.23   a. .12   b. .6, .2

3.25   a. .3   b. .3   c. .7

3.27   Event b: B-1 Tossing a tail

	Prior	Conditional	Joint
Event A:	Pr	Pr	Pr
A-1: Legitimate coin	.5	.5	0.25
A-2: Two-tailed coin	.5	1.0	0.50

Marginal Probability of tossing a tail: $\Sigma = 0.75$

Event B: B-2 Tossing a head

	Prior	Conditional	Joint
Event A:	Pr	Pr	Pr
A-1: Legitimate coin	.5	.5	0.25
A-2: Two-tailed coin	.5	0.0	0.00

Marginal Probability of tossing a head: $\Sigma = 0.25$

3.29   .18, .16, .02, .64

3.31   .3/.1 = 3; this is not possible, the subset is larger than the whole.

3.33   a. 1 = 100%   b. 2/3 = 0.6667   c. 1/3 = 0.3333   d. 0

3.35 a. Pr(S|Fav) = 0.6585

b. Pr(F|Fav) = 0.3415
c. Pr(S|Unf) = 0.0508
d. Pr(F|Unf) = 0.9492

3.37 .5000 = Pr(S|SS), .1111 = Pr(N|SS), .3889 = Pr(W|SS), .03125 = Pr(S|NS), .09375 = Pr(N|NS), .87500 = Pr(W|NS)

3.39 .75 = Pr(S|EP), .25 = Pr(F|EP), .4615 = Pr(S|PR), .5385 = Pr(F|PR), .05985 = Pr(S|Neg), .94915 = Pr(F|Neg)

3.41 A factorial for a numeric value is the product of that number and the sequence of all positive discrete values between the number and zero.

3.43 a. 3,024   b. 126

3.45 a. (10)5   b. (10)9

3.47 15

3.49 a. combination   b. 35

3.51 2,450

3.53 a. Subjective   b. classical   c. relative frequency

3.55 a. classical   b. subjective

3.57 a. 0.677   b. 0.871   c. Knowing the content of the exam and the grading scale would help.

3.59 a. 0.043   b. 0.763   c. Yes, 930/1093 (0.851) oppose the increase.

3.61 120

3.63 a. 30

b. Order is now important; hence, the problem involves a permutation and not a combination.

3.65 1.17,576

3.67 a. 0.583   b. 0.708   c. 0.396   d. 0.559

3.69 a. 0.5827   b. 0.2913   c. 0.4475

3.71 .75 = Pr(S|Sup), .25 = Pr(F|Sup), .75 = Pr(S|Good), .25 = Pr(F|Good), .60 = Pr(S|OK), .40 = Pr(F|OK), .2727 = Pr(S|Poor), .7273 = Pr(F|Poor)

 Answers to Mini-cases

Mini-case 3.1

Yes, using Bayesian analysis, the probability of guilt increases from .9 to .9863. Whether this is significant to be reasonable doubt depends one one's own perspective. Of course, there are many issues that have not been discussed including the accuracy and validity of lie detector tests.

Result	Prior Pr		Conditional Pr	Joint Pr	Posterior Pr
X	G	.9	.8	.72	.72/.73 = .9863
X	I	.1	.1	.01	.01/.73 = .0137
				Total .73	
Y	G	9	.2	.18	.18/.27 = .6667
Y	I	.1	.9	.09	.09/.27 = .3333
				Total .27	

Mini-case 3.2

a. If sequence of numbers is not important, we have a combination.

$$\frac{49 \bullet 48 \bullet 47 \bullet 46 \bullet 45 \bullet 44}{6 \bullet 5 \bullet 4 \bullet 3 \bullet 2 \bullet 1} = 13{,}983{,}816 \text{ to } 1$$

There are almost 14 million ways of drawing six numbers from 49.

b. If sequence is important, we have a permutation. The number of possibilities is

$$49 \bullet 48 \bullet 47 \bullet 46 \bullet 45 \bullet 44 = 10{,}068{,}000{,}000$$

c. California

$$\frac{53 \bullet 52 \bullet 51 \bullet 50 \bullet 49 \bullet 48}{6 \bullet 5 \bullet 4 \bullet 3 \bullet 2 \bullet 1} = 22{,}515{,}900 \text{ to } 1$$

Illinois

$$\frac{54 \bullet 53 \bullet 52 \bullet 51 \bullet 50 \bullet 49}{6 \bullet 5 \bullet 4 \bullet 3 \bullet 2 \bullet 1}$$

Mini-case 3.3

As you begin to work the puzzle you may realize that there are a large number of ways to arrange the numbers, and very few of these meet the conditions of the problem. How many ways are there to arrange the numbers? For the first box you choose to place a number, you may place any 1 of the 8 numbers (1 to 8). After this initial selection, the box you use to place the second number may contain any 1 of 7 numerical values (7 because one of the numbers has already been used up). For the third box, any 1 of the 6 remaining numbers may be placed there. Therefore, the number of ways the numbers may be placed in the box is 8 factorial ($8! - 8 \bullet 7 \bullet 6 \bullet 5 \bullet 4 \bullet 3 \bullet 2 \bullet 1$), or 40,320. Hence, it may not be wise to try to find the solution by randomly placing numbers.

The solution should target the two central boxes. These two boxes have every box touching it except one. Hence, the numbers that only have one number touching them (1 and 8) must be placed in the central boxes. If 1 is placed in the A space then 2 must be placed in the C space. If 8 is placed in the B space, then 7 must be placed in the D space. The rest of the puzzle is easy to complete. There are 4 correct solutions in 40,320 possibilities. The probability of randomly obtaining the correct answer is 4/40,320 = 0.0000992. The puzzle is only meant to initiate you to counting concepts. If we count the number of correct solutions (events) and divide by the complete set of possible outcomes (sample space), we obtain the probability of success.

Answers to Concept Checks

4.A   True.

4.B   False. As stated this is false, since, if members are not replaced, the probability does not remain constant from trial to trial. Also, as stated there are three possible outcomes rather than two.

4.C   False. All normal distributions are not identical. Normal distributions differ due to differences in the means and variances. However, note that after standardization, each normal distribution is reduced to the standard normal curve which is homogeneous.

Answers to Odd-Numbered Exercises

4.1   A random variable is a rule or function that assigns numerical values to the outcomes of a random process.

4.3   Yes. The statement includes all possible values of the random variable and their probabilities.

4.5

x	$Pr(x)$
0	1/16
2	4/16
4	6/16
6	4/16
8	1/16

4.7   Yes, it's a random variable the value of which can range from 0 to the maximum limit of people who can see the movie.

4.9   The length of stay, the money spent, and the number of times they have been there.

4.11   a.   Because each sample contains five parts, we are interested in the sum of two events: exactly four of five parts and five of five parts being flawed. The calculations would be:

$$Pr(4 \text{ flawed out of } 5) = \frac{5 \bullet 4 \bullet 3 \bullet 2 \bullet 1}{4 \bullet 3 \bullet 2 \bullet 1(1)} .2^4(1 - .2)5 - 4 = 5(.0016)(.8) = 0064$$

$$Pr(5 \text{ flawed out of } 5) = \frac{5 \bullet 4 \bullet 3 \bullet 2 \bullet 1}{5 \bullet 4 \bullet 3 \bullet 2 \bullet 1(1)} .2^5(1 - .2)5 - 5 = 1(.00032)(1) = .00032$$

Therefore, the probability of the sample containing four or more flawed parts is .00672 (.00640 + .00032)

b.   Cumulative Table: $Pr(\geq 4) = 1 - Pr(3) = 1 - .9933 = .0067$.

c. $\mu = n \bullet p = 5 \bullet .2 = 1; \sigma^2 = n \bullet p \bullet q = 5 \bullet .2 \bullet .8 = 0.8; \sigma = \sqrt{0.8} = 0.894$.

4.13 r $\Pr(x)$; $n = 5$, $p = .4$, $q = .6$

               0   .07776
               1   .2592
               2   .3456
               3   .2804
               4   .0768
               5   .01024

4.15 $\mu = n \bullet p = 50 \bullet .3 = 15$; $\sigma^2 = n \bullet p \bullet q = 50 \bullet .3 \bullet .7 = 10.5$; $\sigma = 3.2404$.

4.17 $n = 4$, $p = .1$, $\Pr(r = 3) = .0036$

4.19 $n = 10$, $p = .4$

     a. $\Pr(r = 4) = .2508$
     b.   Cumulative table; $\Pr(r > 4) = 1 - \Pr(r = 4) = 1 - .6331 = .3669$
     c.   Cumulative table; $\Pr(r < 3) = \Pr(r - 2) = .1673$

4.21   The one with the largest σ would be the shortest and widest. The distribution would have to be wide to encompass many different values. The one with the smallest σ would be the tallest and the narrowest.

4.23   In a symmetrical distribution, the mean, median, and mode are identical.

4.25   a. $\Pr(z > 0.56) = .2877$, 28.77% $(.5 - .2123)$
     b. $\Pr(-0.45 < z < 1.96) = .6486$, 64.86% $(.1736 + .4750)$
     c. $\Pr(-0.32 > z > -1.34) = .2844$, 28.44% $(.4099 - .1255)$
     d. $\Pr(0 < z < 1.64) = .4495$, 44.95%
     e. $\Pr(z < 1.76) = .9608$, 96.08% $(.5 + .4608)$

4.27   a.   Stock A: $z = (.15 - .10)/.05 = 1.00$, $\Pr(z > 1.00) = 15.87\%$ $(.5 - .3413)$
     b.   Stock B: $z = (.12 - .10)/.03 = 0.67$, $\Pr(z > 0.67) = 25.14\%$ $(.5 - .2486)$
     c.   Stock B, it has a greater probability of a rate exceeding. 10.

4.29 $\Pr(z > 0.00) = 50\%$; or half of the normal distribution.

4.31   We may use the normal distribution to approximate the binomial distribution when $n \bullet p > 5$ and $n \bullet q > 5$.

4.33 $n = 60$, $p = .1$, $q = .9$ $(\mu = n \bullet p = 60 \bullet .1 = 6$ and $n \bullet q = 60 \bullet .9 = 54)$

     so we can use the normal approximation. $\sigma^2 = 60 \bullet .1 \bullet .9 = 5.4$; $\sigma = 2.32379$

     $z = (5–6)/2.32379 = -0.43$ and $z = (9–6)/2.32379 = 1.29$; $\Pr(-0.43 < z < 1.29) = 56.79\%$ $(.1664 + .4015)$

Answers to Mini-cases

Mini-case 4.1

     a.   .10
     b.   .34868
     c.   .38742
     d.   Since the probability of 3 or more defective in this case is very small (.0128) if the probability of a defective item is in fact .10, we would have to question whether the shipment contains a larger proportion of defective items than historically observed.

e. Another choice is to reserve judgment until further sampling is done and base your decision on the larger sample size.

Mini-case 4.2

a. City B will experience the larger percentage of days with temperatures below 65 degrees.
b. Additional clothing expenses in the two cities would be:
City A—$8.76
City B—$33.40

Chapter 5 Solutions

 ## Answers to Concept Checks

5.A False. The mean of a population is called a parameter.

5.B False. Such surveys do not allow each member of the population an equal chance of being selected. Hence, the only comments that can be made are in terms of the sample itself; however, no inferences can be made concerning the general population.

5.C True.

5.D False. A sampling error is a difference between a sample mean and a population mean caused by chance.

5.E True.

5.F True.

5.G False. The sample size must be large enough before the approximation can be made.

5.H True.

Answers to Odd-Numbered Exercises

5.1 a statistic b. Parameter.

5.3 In a random sample, the survey results may be projected to the population (termed making inferences). In a nonrandom sample, inferences are not possible. From nonrandom samples, results can only be made in terms of the sample itself. For example, 70% of those who responded favored the President's policy, but no statement can be made concerning the population.

5.5 Yes, it is possible that poorer families do not own phones, and they may feel they do not receive the same treatment from public utilities companies as the rich.

5.7 Weights may change from hour to hour. Hence, it may actually be impossible to know your exact weight for any day. The exact weight might not be important, but rather a general reduction in weight is.

5.9 a. Systematic surveys are usually used with telephone interviews.
b. Long interviews can't be performed over the phone. Cluster samples are frequently used with personal interviews.
c. As long as the population is easy to reach, an unrestricted random sample would probably be used.
d. A stratified survey into first and second class.

5.11   We all have personal prejudices which could alter the way we ask a question, and hence alter the outcome.

5.13   a.   A stratified survey using different class times and using an unrestricted random sample of the strata.

        b.   Probably a telephone survey utilizing a systematic approach to reduce costs.

5.15   The difference is not important for large samples; however, in small samples the changes in the probabilities for random selection are important.

5.17   You will probably be remembering a number or address, and these numbers will repeat, making the randomness of the data sequence questionable.

5.19   A sampling error is the difference between a sample statistic and population parameter caused by the random process.

5.21   a.   Population mean = 30.333.
        b.   Sample mean = 30.25
        c.   A systematic survey.
        d.   Due to chance or random selection process. The difference between 30.333 and 30.25 is called a sampling error.

5.23   Because the extreme values have been averaged or smoothed and because of the concentration of different sample means concentrated near μ.

5.25   a. & b.   The possible combinations for $n = 3$, $N = 5$: 46.67, 22.67, 47.67, 38.00, 45.67, 70.67, 61.00, 37.00, 62.00, 46.67; $\mu = 47.8$; $\sigma = 13.229$.

5.27   Sampling with replacement: $\sigma_{\overline{X}} = 1.581$

        Sampling without replacement

        $$\sigma_{\overline{X}} = \frac{2.236}{\sqrt{2}} \times \sqrt{\frac{4-2}{4-1}} = 1.291$$

5.29   Sampling with replacement: $\sigma_{\overline{X}} = 5.774$

        Sampling without replacement

        $$\sigma_{\overline{X}} = \frac{8.165}{\sqrt{2}} \times \sqrt{\frac{3-2}{3-1}} = 4.082$$

5.31   1.2

5.33 s and n

5.35   a.   Whenever $n/N \geq .05$.

        b.   An adjustment must be made in sampling without replacement when the sample size is 5% or more of the population.

5.37   The Central Limit Theorem allows us to use the normal distribution as an approximation of virtually any other distribution as long as the sample size is large enough.

5.39 $n \bullet p > 5$ and $n \bullet q > 5$

5.41   0.01897

5.43 $\hat{p} = .167$

25.14%

5.45   a.   15.
        b.   4.97 and 2.363.
        c.   4.97 and 1.671.
        d.   The mean of the sampling distribution equates with the mean of the population. The standard error will always be smaller than the standard deviation of the population because extreme values are smoothed in the standard error.

5.47   You may be able to determine the number of new firms, the number no longer listed. By comparing the population of the geographic areas, you may be able to learn about the number of competitors vs. population ratio to support this business.

5.49   a.   Yes, because we would have to use the finite correction factor
        b.

$$\sigma_{\overline{X}} = \frac{220}{\sqrt{25}} \times \sqrt{\frac{100 - 25}{100 - 1}} = 382.97$$
$$z = -0.52; \ 30.15\%$$

5.51

$$z = \frac{27.8 - 29}{\frac{3.1}{\sqrt{21}}} = -1.77$$
$$5 - .4616 = 3.84\%$$

5.53   Sampling error can be corrected by increasing the sampling size; sampling bias can't.

 Answers to Mini-cases

Mini-case 5.1

        a.   Since the results of such a survey might appear in a court of law, it would be essential to state that each and every customer who entered the store had an equal chance of being selected in the survey.
        b.   To make this statement in reality, each and every server must agree to participate in the survey. If they are selected, they must agree to be followed by the umpire.
        c.   If the survey results indicate a lower tip rate than what the IRS claims, the judicial system then must decide whose facts are superior. Generally speaking, if each and every customer had an equal chance of selection, the court will normally side with the more narrowly defined survey than one broadly defined. The IRS data cover all tips left at all stores across a city or throughout a region or the country.

Mini-case 5.2

        a.   There are two basic objectives of the survey. Since most of the revenues come from advertisers, the sample size must be large enough to obtain a relevant sample around major retail stores (Sears, K-Mart, J. C. Penny, etc.). This is so the paper can approach these retailers and inform them if they want to reach households in their relevant market, they must use their paper. A second aspect of the study involves asking questions concerning likes and dislikes, and time preferences for delivery.

b. Because of the large numbers of questions to be asked, we will conduct personal interviews at households. One possible experimental design uses the telephone directory for randomly selecting starting points for clusters. At each starting point, we will move clockwise (counter clockwise) and select every kth house, up to a maximum of 5 households. The skip pattern and clockwise (counterclockwise) rotation will be developed randomly and will change at each cluster. Once at a household, a series of qualifying questions will be asked to determine which adult at the household is to be interviewed. The individuals conducting the sample must have no choice in the selection of the individual to be surveyed.

c. No, because of preconceived biases.

Chapter 6   Solutions

 Answers to Concept Checks

6.A   False. A point estimate is more precise than an interval estimate.

6.B   True.

6.C   True.

6.D   True.

6.E   False. It is true when $n \bullet p$ and $n \bullet q > 5$.

6.F   False. We replace z with a t when σ is unknown.

6.G   False. It's directly related to the desired confidence and the variation in the population, and inversely related to the allowable error.

6.H   False. The sample size will be larger when the population proportion is near 0.5, and smaller when near 1.0 or 0.0.

Answers to Odd-Numbered Exercises

6.1   a.   Point estimate
        b.   Interval estimate
        c.   We would have no confidence in the point estimate. We would have more confidence in the interval estimate as it increased.

6.3   Bias and efficiency deal with taking repeated samples of a given size, whereas consistency deals with allowing one sample to become larger and larger.

6.5   a.   Bias
        b.   Consistency

6.7   a. $\overline{X}$, s, and n b. n and p

6.9   39.4 and 2.1

6.11   a. 46.9 ± 0.849
        b.   If we were to perform 100 surveys of size 36, μ would fall within the interval 95 times.
        c. 46.9 ± 0.683

6.13 2.89 ± 0.0730

6.15 12.8 ± 0.6219

6.17   a. 0.69 ± 0.0806 b. $0.69 \pm .0773$

6.19 0.419 ± 0.0250

6.21   The t distribution should be used to replace the normal distribution whenever Σ is unknown and must be estimated using s, and we may assume the population is approximately normal.

6.23 567 ± 10.9249

6.25   a. 43.9 ± 3.6137 b. 43.9 ± 1.0818

6.27   MINITAB printouts

6.29   471.0 to 520.0

6.31   Direct relationship: confidence desired and dispersion of the population. Inverse relationship: allowable error.

6.33 $n = 49$

6.35 $n = 61$

6.37 $n = 35.$

6.39   Yes.

6.41 $n = 1205$

6.43 $n = 421$

6.45   a. $n = 247$

6.47   Biased.

6.49   The t distribution should be used to replace the normal distribution whenever Σ is unknown and must be estimated using s, and we may assume the population is approximately normal.

6.51   a. 76.8 ± 1.463 b. 76.8 ± 3.825 c.   With the smaller sample size, the interval widens.

6.53 2.32 ± 0.2156

6.55 $\hat{p} = 0.269; 0.269 \pm 0.064$

6.57 $n = 98$

6.59 $n = 462$

Answers to Mini-cases

Mini-case 6.1

a.
$$n = \frac{(1.96)^2(.09961)(.90039)}{(.02)^2} = 862$$

b. Because it is an accumulation of past files and includes deceased individuals.
c. Yes, the distribution is based on major immigration from Europe, particularly Germany and England. Major concentrations from immigration areas will greatly alter the percentages.

Mini-case 6.2

$$n = \frac{(1.645)^2(.94)(.06)}{(.02)^2} = 382$$

Chapter 7   Solutions

Answers to Concept Checks

7.A   False. The difference between the sample mean and the hypotheses may be attributable to sampling error.

7.B   False. It would be an example of a Type I error, the rejection of a true hypothesis.

7.C   True.

7.D   True. However, remember that the critical value of z will be different for a one- and two-tailed test.

7.E   False. We must use t_{test} in lieu of z_{test} whenever σ is unknown regardless of the sample size.

7.F   True.

7.G   False. We develop a test that is more powerful but also riskier.

7.H   True.

7.I   True.

Answers to Odd-Numbered Exercises

7.1   A hypothesis is a belief or a theory. It is a belief statement of fact, not a statement of a fact.

7.3   a.   2-tail   b.   1-tail   c.   1-tail   d.   1-tail   e.   2-tail

7.5   The null hypothesis is the hypothesis to be tested in the problem. It maintains the status quo.

7.7   Null hypotheses $= H_o$: Alternative hypothesis $= H_A$

7.9   A Type I error refers to rejecting a correct null hypothesis and a Type II error refers to the acceptance of an incorrect null hypothesis.

7.11   Since we do not know the population parameter, we are unable to reject the null hypothesis. All we can say is that there is insufficient statistical evidence to reject H_o (ISER).

7.13   a.   No.   b.   Yes, a reduction of α will increase β.

7.15   a. 39.4 ± 0.510 b.   no   c.   rejected   d. $z_{\text{test}} = -9.982$; p-value $= 0.000$
       e. p-value $= 0.000$

7.17 89 ± 1.839 and 90 seconds is in the interval: there is ISER the null hypothesis.

7.19 $z_{\text{test}} = -5.656$; since $|z_{\text{test}}| > z_\alpha$ (2.576), we must reject H_o. Since the results are superior to the claim, there is no harm done.

7.21   a. $.92 - .50 = .42$ $(z = 1.405)$ b. $.80 - .50 = .30$ $(z = 0.842)$

       c. $.98 - .50 = .48$ $(z = 2.054)$ d. $.94 - .50 = .44$ $(z = 1.555)$

7.23   We are not in the tail of rejection. $z_{\text{test}} = -6.462$; $z_{.05/1} = 1.641$

7.25   a. $900 - 24.211 = 875.789$. Since the sample mean is 863, we reject H_o.

       b. $z_{\text{test}} = -2.995$: Since $z_{\text{test}} < -z_{.05/1}$ (-1.645): reject H_o.

7.27   Since the sample result is superior to the null hypothesis, a test is not really necessary. $z_{\text{test}} = +5.284$; Since $z_{\text{test}} \geq -z_{.01/1}$ (-2.33): ISER H_o.

7.29   Because when s replaces Σ, our test statistic conforms to a t distribution.

7.31   a. $t_{.05/1(16)} = 1.746$ b. $t_{.01/1(6)} = 3.143$ c. $t_{.10/1(26)} = 1.315$

7.33   a.   2-tail

       b. $t_{\text{test}} = +0.931$; Since $|t_{\text{test}}| \leq t_{.05/2(6)}$ (2.447): ISER H_o.

       c. $t_{\text{test}} = +1.075$; Since $|t_{\text{test}}| \leq t_{.05/2(6)}$ (2.447): ISER H_o.

7.35   a.   at least $= $ 1-tail, a lower tailed test

       b.   **T-Test of the Mean**
          Test of $\mu = 500.00$ vs $\mu < 500.00$

Variable	N	Mean	StDev	SE Mean	T	P
Tensiles	24	503.83	37.81	7.72	0.50	0.69

          Since $.01 < 0.69$ we have ISER H_o.

7.37   a.   at most $= $ 1-tail, an upper tail test

       b. $t_{\text{test}} = +1.764$; Since $t_{\text{test}} > +t_{.05/1(27)} = 1.703$: reject H_o.

7.39   When $n \bullet p$ and $n \bullet q > 5$

7.41   a.   2-tail

       b. $\hat{p} = 180/410 = .439$; Since z_{test} (1.612) $< z_{.05/2}$ (1.960): ISER H_o.

7.43 $p = 32/61 = 0.525$; Since the sample result is superior to the null hypothesis, a test is not really necessary. Since z_{test}(1.215) $\leq z_{.01/1} = -2.326$: ISER H_o.

7.45 a. Since there is no reason to assume equal variances, we should not pool the data.

b. Two Sample T for CompA vs CompB

	N	Mean	StDev	SE Mean
CompA	20	216.8	25.3	5.7
CompB	15	211.9	36.5	9.4

95% CI for mu CompA − mu CompB: (−17.8, 27.7)

Ttest mu CompA = mu CompB (vs >): $T = 0.45$ $P = 0.45$ $DF = 23$

Since $\alpha < P$-value (.05 < .45), we are unable to reject H_o. The products are of equal quality.

7.47 a. Definitely not, there is no reason to assume equal variances.

b. Two Sample T for UndevNa vs DevNa

	N	Mean	StDev	SE Mean
UnderNa	13	87.3	49.6	14
DevNa	11	8.73	6.07	1.8

95% CI for mu UndevNa − mu DevNa: (48, 108.8)

TTest mu UndevNa = mu DevNa (vs GT): $T = 5.67$ $P = 0.0001$ $DF = 12$

7.49 a. Probably not.

b. Two Sample T for Younger vs Older

	N	Mean	StDev	SE Mean
Younger	14	6.00	6.11	1.6
Older	11	3.55	4.70	1.4

95% CI for mu Younger − mu Older: (−2.0, 6.9)

Ttest mu Younger − mu Older (vs not): $T = 1.13$ $P = 0.27$ $DF = 22$

c. If H_o has been rejected, it would mean that one of the age groups was more dependable than the other.

d. $T = 1.10$, $P = 0.28$, $DF = 23$, Pooled STDV $= 5.54$

7.51 Paired T for OldPen − NewPen

	N	Mean	StDev	SE Mean
OldPen	20	20.36	4.51	1.01
NewPen	20	23.13	5.36	1.20
Difference	20	−2.77	6.18	1.38

95% CI for mean difference: (−5.66, 0.12)

T-Test of mean difference = 0 (vs not = 0): T-Value $= −2.00$ P-Value $= 0.060$

7.53 a. To allow a compared analysis.

b. Since $\alpha < P$-value; .05 < .978, we must conclude the grades were the same.

c. Paired T for Friend1 − Friend2

	N	Mean	StDev	SE Mean
Friend1	21	84.29	7.38	1.61
Friend2	21	84.38	9.85	2.15
Difference	21	−0.10	15.41	3.36

95% CI for mean difference: (−7.11, 6.92)

T-Test of mean difference = 0 (vs not = 0): T-Value $= −0.03$ P-Value $= 0.978$

7.55   a. To allow for a compared analysis.

b. Since $\alpha < P$-value; $.10 < .97$, we believe that there is no difference between the speeds of the two software packages.

c. Paired T for StatPac1 $-$ StatPac2

	N	Mean	StDev	SE Mean
StatPac1	9	21.1	38.4	12.8
StatPac2	9	21.8	35.8	11.9
Difference	9	-0.71	4.60	1.53

95% CI for mean difference: $(-4.24, 2.82)$

T-Test of mean difference $= 0$ (vs not $= 0$): T-Value $= -0.46$ P-Value $= 0.655$

7.57 $F_{\text{test}} = 36.453^2/25.337^2 = 2.070$; Since $F_{\text{test}} \leq F_{.05(14/19)}$; $2.070 \leq 2.23$; we have ISER H_o; the population variances are equal.

7.59 $F_{\text{test}} = 40.903^2/5.334^2 = 58.804$; Since $F_{\text{test}} > F_{.05(12/10)}$; $58.804 > 2.91$; we reject H_o; the population variances are not equal.

7.61 $F_{\text{test}} = 6.114^2/4.698^2 = 1.694$; Since $F_{\text{test}} \leq F_{.05(13/10)}$; $1.694 \leq 3.07$, we have ISER H_o; the population variances are equal.

7.63   a. 2-tail   b. 2-tail   c. 1-tail   d. 1-tail   e. 1-tail

7.65   A left tailed test

T-Test of the Mean

Test of $\mu = 720.00$ vs $\mu < 720.00$

Variable	N	Mean	StDev	SE Mean	T	P
Memory	17	722.29	11.11	2.69	0.85	0.80

Since $.10 < 0.80$ we have ISER H_o.

7.67   a. $t_{.05/1(17)} = 1.740$ b. $t_{.01/2(9)} = 3.250$ c. $t_{.10/1(25)} = 1.1316$ d. $t_{.05/2(2)} = 2.571$.

7.69 $z_{\text{test}} = -1.787$; Since $|z_{\text{test}}|(1.787) \leq z_{.05/2}(1.96)$, we have ISER H_o.

7.71 $z_{\text{test}} = -1.787$; Since $|z_{\text{test}}|(-1.787) < -z_{.05/1}(-1.645)$, we must reject H_o

7.73   A lower tailed test: $p = 157/200 = .785$; Since $z_{\text{test}}(-1.775) < -z_{.05/1}(-1.645)$, we have to reject H_o.

7.74   a. No, equal sample sizes are not necessary

b. Yes, equal sample sizes are necessary.

7.75   a. No, it is not paired data; 2-tailed test.

b. Two sample T for Survey1 vs Survey2

	N	Mean	StDev	SE Mean
Survey1	7	306.57	5.32	2.0
Survey2	9	308.44	6.17	2.1

95% CI for mu Survey1 $-$ mu Survey 2: $(-8.1, 4.3)$

T-Test mu Survey1 $=$ mu Survey2 (vs not $=$): $T = -0.65$ $P = 0.53$ $DF = 13$

7.77   Paired T for Printer1 $-$ Printer2

	N	Mean	StDev	SE Mean
Printer1	11	6.118	2.575	0.776
Printer2	11	5.682	2.378	0.717
Difference	11	0.436	0.441	0.133

95% CI for mean difference: (0.140, 0.733)
T-Test of mean difference $= 0$ (vs not $= 0$): T-Value $= 3.28$ P-Value $= 0.008$

Answers to Mini-cases

Mini-case 7.1

a. We are involved with a two-tailed test because we will take the class if the new instructor's grades equal that of existing instructors.

b. **Z-Test**
Test of $\mu = 2.300$ vs μ not $= 2.300$
The assumed sigma $= 0.620$

Variable	N	Mean	StDev	SEMean	Z	P
GPAs	12	2.155	0.160	0.179	-0.81	0.42

5% level: Since α (.05) $<$ P-value (0.0095) we have ISER.
1% level: Since α (.05) $<$ P-value (0.42) we have ISER.

c. An α of .421, or a confidence level of .579.

d. We are unable to reject the hypothesis that the new instructor's grades are equal to that of existing instructors.

Mini-case 7.2

$P = 46/100 = .46$. The standard error of the proportion $= \sqrt{65 \bullet .35/100} = 0.0477$; $z_{test} = (.46 - 65)/0.0477 = -3.083$. Since $|z_{test}| > z_{.05/2}(1.96)$, we must reject H_o. The students prefer Friday off during the accelerated summer term.

Mini-case 7.3

a. to negate the impact of square feet. The more square feet to a home, the greater is the time necessary to clean it.

b. Paired T for 1890 $-$1990

	N	Mean	StDev	SE Mean
1890	14	13.471	2.222	0.594
1990	14	14.364	2.816	0.752
Difference	14	-0.893	1.089	0.291

95% CI for mean difference: $(-1.521, -0.264)$
T-Test of mean difference $= 0$ (vs not $= 0$): T-Value $= -3.07$ P-Value $= 0.009$
Since $P = .009$, the hypothesis that the two means equate would be rejected at the 10% level, for either a one- or two-tailed test (it could be viewed either way). The second hypothesis appears correct; labor saving devices have increased the definition of cleanliness.

c. A good question. For certain individuals, it will go one way, for other the opposite direction.

584

Mini-case 7.4

    a.   To negate demographic and psychographic profiles as much as possible.

    b.   In 1930, the topics covered were considerably different than today's topics. It would be unfair for either group to take an exam designed for the other.

    c.   Paired T for 1930 –1990

	N	Mean	StDev	SE Mean
1930	15	639.3	102.2	26.4
1990	15	594.7	89.8	23.2
Difference	15	44.7	47.2	12.2

95% CI for mean difference: (18.5, 70.8)

T-Test of mean difference $= 0$ (vs not $= 0$): T-Value $= 3.66$ P-Value $= 0.003$

Since P-value $= .003$, we must reject the hypothesis that means are the same. The 1930 students scored higher than the 1990 students.

Mini-case 7.5

    Yes.

Mini-case 7.6

    Yes, people live longer in the developed nations; 12.1% of the population of the developed nations are 65+ while only 4.2% of the developing nations' people are 65+. As a point of interest, Florida, with the oldest population in the U.S., has 18.3% of its population in the 65+ category.

Chapter 8 Solutions

 Answers to Concept Checks

8.A   True.

8.B   False: SSE $=$ SST $-$ SSTR.

8.C   False: The blocking variable is not a second treatment variable but rather a block to the original treatment variable.

8.D   True.

Answers to Odd-Numbered Exercises

8.1   Analysis of Variance. A NOVA is the analysis of several variations.

8.3   If the sample size was ≤ 30, we would use the t_{test} of Chapter 7. If the sample size exceeded 30 it would be z_{test} of Chapter 7.

8.5   SST $=$ total variation in the data set. SSTR is the variation explained by the treatment variable. Either a variation is explained by the treatment variable or it isn't.

8.7   Divide by the appropriate degrees of freedom.

8.9 The F distribution has distinct characteristics, which are

1. The curve of F distribution is positively skewed, continuous, and whose values go from 0 to infinity (no negative values).
2. Like the t distribution, there is a different F distribution for each degree of freedom involved. Since F_{test} is a ratio, there is a degree of freedom in the numerator and in the denominator. Hence, there is a different F distribution based on the paired degrees of freedom.

8.11
a. $F_{.05(2/8)} = 4.459$ b. $F_{.05(4/20)} = 2.87$
c. $F_{.05(6/24)} = 2.508$ d. $F_{.05(2.22)} = 3.443$
e. $F_{.01(2/8)} = 8.649$ f. $F_{.01(4/20)} = 4.431$
g. $F_{.10(2/10)} = 2.295$ h. $F_{.10(2/22)} = 2.56$

8.13
a. H_o: all the means are identical, H_A: at least two of the means differ.

b. There are 4 treatments and 7 levels of treatments.

c. Since $.05 \geq 0.000$ we must reject H_0.
d. Analysis of Variance for Data.

Source	DF	SS	MS	F	P
Strains	3	5.2925	1.7642	44.37	0.000
Error	24	0.9543	0.0398		
Total	27	6.2468			

INDIVIDUAL 95% CIs FOR MEAN
BASED ON POOLED STDEV

Level	N	Mean	StDev	
1	7	2.4714	0.2215	(—*—)
2	7	3.4286	0.1380	(—*—)
3	7	2.5857	0.2268	(—*—)
4	7	3.3571	0.1988	(—*—)

2.45   2.80   3.15   3.50

Pooled StDev = 0.1994
Tukey's pairwise comparisons
  Family error rate = 0.0500
  Individual error rate = 0.0110
Critical value = 3.90

Intervals for (column level mean) − (row level mean)

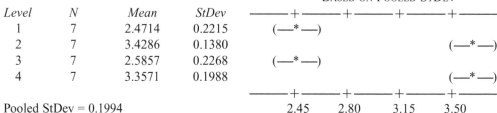

	1	2	3
2	−1.2511		
	−0.6632		
3	−0.4082	0.5489	
	0.1796	1.1368	
4	−1.1796	−0.2225	−1.0654
	−0.5918	0.3654	−0.4775

e. A new strain that grows fast may have negative side effects, such as wood not being as durable. In addition, the data may be tarnished by unequal amounts of moisture and/or fertilizer, etc.

8.15   a. H_o: all the means are identical, H_A: at least two of the means differ.

       b.   Since .05 ≥ 0.002, we must reject the null hypothesis.

8.17   a. H_o: all means are identical.

       b.   Since .01 < 0.498, we have ISER the null hypothesis.

8.19   a. H_o: all means are identical.

       b.   Since .05 ≥ 0.019, we must reject the null hypothesis.

ANALYSIS OF VARIANCE FOR DATA

Source	DF	SS	MS	F	P
Tr	2	164.7	82.3	4.99	0.019
Error	18	297.1	16.5		
Total	20	461.8			

INDIVIDUAL 95% CIs FOR MEAN
BASED ON POOLED STDEV

Level	N	Mean	StDev	
1	7	7.143	4.598	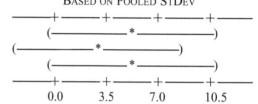
2	7	1.857	1.345	
3	7	8.286	5.155	

                                                               0.0   3.5   7.0   10.5

Pooled StDev = 4.063

Tukey's pairwise comparisons

     Family error rate = 0.0500

     Individual error rate = 0.0200

Critical value = 3.61

Intervals for (column level mean) − (row level mean)

	1	2
2	−0.258	
	10.829	
3	−6.687	−11.972
	4.401	−0.885

The inexpensive board sells more than the less expensive boards.

8.21   In the randomized block design, the data are entered in pairs in an attempt to minimize or eliminate the influence of a particular factor or set of factors. No such attempt is made for the completely randomized design.

8.23   Because age was an influencing factor and if not accounted for would constitute a large portion of the error factor.

8.25   a. H_o: all means are identical, H_A: at least two of the means differ.

      b.   Since .05 > 0.000, we must reject H_o for strains and for levels.

Source	DF	SS	MS	F	P
Levels	6	4.1136	0.6856	22.24	0.000
Strains	3	4.4300	1.4767	47.89	0.000
Error	18	0.5550	0.0308		
Total	27	9.0986			

INDIVIDUAL 95% CI

Levels	Mean	−+———+———+———+———+
1	2.550	(—*—)
2	2.650	(—*—)
3	3.050	(—*—)
4	3.075	(—*—)
5	3.400	(—*—)
6	3.300	(—*—)
7	3.725	(—*—)

```
        −+———+———+———+———+
       2.400   2.800   3.200   3.600   4.000
```

INDIVIDUAL 95% CI

Strains	Mean	−+———+———+———+———+
1	2.571	(—*—)
2	3.414	(—*—)
3	2.886	(—*—)
4	3.557	(—*—)

```
        −+———+———+———+———+
       2.450   2.800   3.150   3.500   3.850
```

8.27   Because visual interpretations are subject to error because of sampling variation problems.

8.29   a. H_o: all means are identical

b.   Because demographic and psychographic profiles greatly impact buying habits.

c-d.

Source	DF	SS	MS	F	P
Type	4	1154	288	1.08	0.428
Display	2	3297	1648	6.16	0.024
Error	8	2139	267		
Total	14	6590			

INDIVIDUAL 95% CI

```
Type   Mean        ————+————+————-+————-+—
1      46.7      (————*————)
2      52.7       (————*————)
3      59.09         (————*————)
4      73.0             (————*————)
5      56.3          (————*————)
                   ————+————+—-+————-+—
                   40.0     60.0     80.0    100.0
```

INDIVIDUAL 95% CI

```
Display  Mean       ————+————+—-+—-+—
1        67.0            (————*————)
2        36.6       (————*————)
3        69.0            (————*————)
                    ————+————+—-+—-+—
                    32.0     48.0     64.0     80.0
4        73.0           (————*————)
5        56.3        (————*————)
                    ——+——-+————-+—-+—
                    40.0 60.0 80.0 100.0
```

INDIVIDUAL 95% CI

```
Col    Mean         ————+—-+—-+—-+—
1      67.0             (————*————)
2      36.6        (————*————)
3      69.0            (————*————)
                    ————+—-+—-+—-+—
                    32.0  48.0  64.0  80.0
```

8.31   In the randomized block design, we had only 1 treatment variable and we tried to block the influence of another. In the two factor experiment, we deal with 2 treatment variables plus their interaction.

8.33   Add it to SSE.

8.35   It may be impossible to understand the independent impact of the factors or treatments.

8.37 a. Factor A is significant, factors B and AB are not.

b.

Factor	Type	Levels	Values	
FactA	fixed	2	1	2
FactB	fixed	2	1	2

ANALYSIS OF VARIANCE FOR DATA

Source	DF	SS	MS	F	P
FactA	1	1870.56	1870.56	29.29	0.000
FactB	1	5.06	5.06	0.08	0.783
FactA*FactB	1	0.06	0.06	0.00	0.976
Error	12	766.25	63.85		
Total	15	2641.94			

c. To plot 2 points would be of little value in ascertaining a trend.

8.39 a. H_o: All means are identical.

b. Factors A (Display type) and B (Store type) are significant, but their interaction is not.

c. Mean Differences $\pm 5.37 \bullet \sqrt{(270.417/5)}$; mean differences ± 38.491.

Cells	Cell differences	Confidence Interval	Includes 0
A1–B1:	$67.0 - 36.6 = +30.4$;	$+30.4 \pm 39.491$	Yes
A1–C1:	$67.0 - 69.0 = -2.0$;	-2.0 ± 39.491	Yes
A1–A2:	$67.0 - 90.6 = -23.6$;	-23.6 ± 39.491	Yes
A1–B2:	$67.0 - 66.8 = +0.2$;	$+0.2 \pm 39.491$	Yes
A1–C2:	$67.0 - 86.8 = -19.8$;	-19.8 ± 39.491	Yes
B1–C1:	$36.6 - 69.0 = -32.4$;	-32.4 ± 39.491	Yes
B1–A2:	$36.6 - 90.6 = -54.0$;	-54.0 ± 39.491	No
B1–B2:	$36.6 - 66.8 = -30.2$;	-30.2 ± 39.491	Yes
B1–C2:	$36.6 - 86.8 = -50.2$;	-50.2 ± 39.491	No
C1–A2:	$69.0 - 90.6 = -21.6$;	-21.6 ± 39.491	Yes
C1–B2:	$69.0 - 66.8 = +2.2$;	-2.2 ± 39.491	Yes
C1–C2:	$69.0 - 86.8 = -17.8$;	-17.8 ± 39.491	Yes
A2–B2:	$90.6 - 66.8 = +23.8$;	$+23.8 \pm 39.491$	Yes
A2–C2:	$90.6 - 86.8 = +3.8$;	$+3.8 \pm 39.491$	Yes
B2–C2:	$66.8 - 86.8 = -20.0$;	-20.0 ± 39.491	Yes

8.41 One factor completely randomized design just deals with one treatment variable. The one factor randomized block design attempts to block out the impact of another factor. Two factor ANOVA attempts to use two treatment variables, plus their interaction.

8.43 Since $.10 \geq 0.00$, we will reject the null hypothesis. The mean complaints are not the same.

8.45 Factor B is significant, factors A and AB are not.

8.47 a. No, they are not the same. Null hypothesis is rejected ($.10 > 0.000$).

b. Because of the unequal sample sizes, there are few common intervals.
Comparing A & B: -12.857 ± 7.921 Does not include 0
Comparing A & C: -38.19 ± 7.526 Does not include 0
Comparing A & D: -13.571 ± 7.231 Does not include 0
Comparing B & C: -25.333 ± 8.192 Does not include 0
Comparing B & D: -25.333 ± 7.921 Includes 0
Comparing C & D: $+24.619 \pm 7.256$ Does not include 0

8.49 Since $.10 < .164$, we must have ISER the null hypothesis that the voltages are the same.

Mini-case 8.1

a. H_o: the mean grades from all the texts are identical. H_A: at last two mean grades differ.
b. She grouped the students by GPA because she wanted to block out the influence of this factor.
c-d.

ANALYSIS OF VARIANCE DATA

SOURCE	DF	SS	MS	F	P
GPA	56	1717.08	343.42	73.96	0.000
Textbook	2	189.23	94.62	20.38	0.000
ERROR	10	46.44	4.46		
TOTAL	17	1952.75			

INDIVIDUAL 95% CI

GPA	Mean	
1	64.9	
2	68.3	
3	73.2	
4	79.3	
5	86.0	
6	92.9	

```
——+——+——+——+——
                        (——*——)°
                        (——*——)°
                        (——*——)°
                        (——*——)°°
                        (——*——)°
                        (——*——)°
——+——+——+——+——
 64.0    72.0    80.0    88.0
```

INDIVIDUAL 95% CI

Textbook	Mean
1	78.47
2	80.70
3	73.03

```
——+——+——+——+——
              (——*——)
                  (——*——)
   (——*——)
——+——+——+——+——
72.00   75.00   78.00   81.00
```

ANALYSIS OF VARIANCE FOR DATA

Source	DF	SS	MS	F	P
Day	4	1507.88	376.97	50.32	0.000
Error	45	337.10	7.49		
Error	45	337.10	7.49		
Total	49	1844.98			

INDIVIDUAL 95% CIS FOR MEAN
BASED ON POOLED STDEV

Level	N	Mean	StDev	
1	10	9.300	2.669	
2	10	6.000	3.162	
3	10	5.400	2.591	
4	10	4.700	2.497	
5	10	19.500	2.718	

```
——+——+——+——+——
        (—*—)
    (—*—)
    (—*—)
  (—*—)
                        (—*—)
——+——+——+——+——
5.0     10.0    15.0    20.0
```

Pooled StDev = 2.737
Tukey's pairwise comparisons
    Family error rate = 0.0500
Individual error rate = 0.00670
Critical value = 4.0

Intervals for (column level mean) − (row level mean)

	1	2	3	4
2	−0.179			
	6.779			
3	0.421	−2.879		
	7.379	4.079		
4	1.121	−2.179	−2.779	
	8.079	4.779	4.179	
5	−13.679	−16.979	−17.579	−18.279
	−6.721	−10.021	−10.621	−11.321

Chapter 9   Solutions

 Answers to Concept Checks

9.A   True

9.B   False. The independent variable is used to help predict the dependent variable.

9.C   False. One states that we can predict expenditures based on knowledge of income. The latter states we can predict income based on expenditure patterns.

9.D   True.

9.E   False. The larger the residual values are the larger is the standard error of the estimate.

9.F   False. The independent variable is not significant to the model.

9.G   True.

9.H   False. It refers to the fact that this individual's salary is considerably above that of fellow workers with similar tenure at the company. If the salary can't be justified by other factors (advanced degrees or certifications, consistently above average evaluations, etc.), it can create a morale problem for the company.

9.I   True.

Answers to Odd-Numbered Exercises

9.1   Educational attainment and achievements, company of employment and their goals, the state of the economy, etc.

9.3   If we could answer this question, we would be wiser than all who preceded us.

9.5   The more inventory we carry, the greater our costs will be. A proportional relationship exists.

9.7   Some of the relevant explanatory variables might be the population base and its expected changes, changes in the demographics in the population base, the number of competitors and the expected changes in the number of competitors, the attitudes of local business firms and their commitment to employee's education, etc.

9.9   a. 40   b.   168   c.   0   d.   no

9.11   It is considered the best fit equation because it's the one with the smallest sum of the residuals squared. Any other estimated value for the equation intercept and slope will increase the sum of the residuals squared.

9.13   a.   The necessary sums are ΣY, ΣX, ΣXY, ΣX^2 and n.

      b.   The summing takes place last. The variable is squared, then summed.

      c. $b = 1.034$, $a = 21.107$

      d. $\hat{Y} \approx 89.35$

9.15   a.   As X increases, Y decreases for an inverse relationship.

      b.   Yes, direct relationships yield a positive linear slope, inverse relationships yield a negative slope, and no relationship, yields a 0 slope.

      c. $\Sigma Y = 60$, $\Sigma X = 76$, $\Sigma XY = 591$, $\Sigma X^2 = 14338$

      d. $b = -1.1351$, $a = 29.25318$

      e.   28.1181

      f.

Predictor	Coef
Constant	29.253
X	−1.135

9.17   a.   As X increases, Y increases for a direct relationship.

      b. $\Sigma Y = 60$, $\Sigma X = 76$, $\Sigma XY = 1225$, $\Sigma X^2 = 1438$

      c. $a = -4.832$, $b = 1.1068$

      d.   The regression equation is

Predictor	Coef	Stdev	T	p
Constant	−4.832	3.663	−1.32	0.279
X	1.11068	0.2160	5.12	0.014

No data entry is necessary. Just reverse Predictor and Response variables.

9.19   a.   There are five paired data points; therefore, there will be five residual values.

      b.   2.287, −3.903, 0.907, 0.582, 0.123

      c.   They represent a vertical difference.

      d.   Since the residuals represent a vertical variation, they must be compared to the variation in the Y data set. From this perspective, the variation in the residuals appear to be small.

9.21   a.   Since $n = 5$, there will be five residuals.

      b.   −2.280, −0.335, 0.799, 4,177, −2.366

      c.   The residuals represent a vertical difference.

      d.   The residuals appear to be small.

      e. $S_{Y \bullet X} = 3.109$

9.23 $\hat{Y} = -4.823 + 1.1068(X)$: When X increases by 1, $\hat{Y}$ increases by 1.1068. $S_{Y \bullet X} = 3.632$. If we added and subtract 3.632 to the regression equation, 68.3% of the data will lie within the interval. If we add and subtract $2 \bullet 3.632$ to the regression equation, 95.5% of the data will lie within the interval. If we add and subtract $3 \bullet 3.632$ to the regression equation, 99.7% of the data will lie within the interval. 89.7% of the variation is Y is explained by the regression equation. There is a direct relationship between X and Y.

9.25   a.   The coefficient of determination is an absolute scale from zero to one which measures the impact of independent variables inside and outside the equation. The coefficient of correlation ranges from minus one to plus one. A positive sign indicates that the data is directly related, and a negative sign that the data are inversely related.

      b.   SSR = 0; SST = SSE = 0.

9.27   a.   We can see that Y increases by 2 each time X increases by 1, hence $b = 2.0$. Since when $X = 0$, $Y = 2$, our equation is $= 2 + 2(X)$. Since there is no deviation from this pattern, SSE $= 0$, and SSR $=$ SST. $r^2 = 1$.

        b.   Confirmed.

9.29   Yes. See exercise 9.25 a, when there was no variation in Y at all.

9.31   In simple linear regression analysis, there is but one predictor (independent) variable in the regression model. Hence, the global approach of testing to see if the true r^2, or to see if the true slope equals zero, are the same test.

9.33   a.   If we expect a direct relationship between X and Y, H_o: $B \leq 0$.

        b.   If we expect an inverse relationship between X and Y, H_o: $B \geq 0$.

9.35   a.   Since $\alpha \geq p$-value $(.05 \geq 0.006)$, we reject H_o: true $r^2 = 0$.

        b.   Since we have no knowledge of the data, we must use a two-tailed test. Since $\alpha \geq p$-value $(.05 \geq 0.006)$, we reject H_o: true $B = 0$.

        c.   Since a simple linear regression model has a single predictor variable, the two approaches lead to identical results.

        d.   The interval does not include $B = 0$.

9.37   a.   Since $\alpha < p$-value $(.10 < 0.189)$, we have ISER H_o: true $r^2 = 0$.

        b.   Since we have no knowledge of the data, we must use a two-tailed test. Since $\alpha < p$-value $(.10 < 0.189)$, we can't reject H_o: true $B = 0$.

        c.   Since a simple linear regression model has a single predictor variable, the two approaches lead to identical results.

        d.   The interval does include $B = 0$.

9.39   a.   We would expect a direct relationship between income and consumption. H_o: $B \leq 0$, H_A: $B > 0$.

        b.   Since $\alpha \geq p$-value we reject H_o.

9.41

Fit	Stdev. Fit	95% C.I.	95% P.I.
17.31	1.93	(11.18, 23.44)	(4.23, 30.40)

The interval involving a single X value is always greater than that involving the mean of several X values.

9.43   a.   FIT $= 3.176$

        b.   3.0783 to 3.2737

        c.   2.7927 to 3.5994

9.45   a.   FIT $= 60.673$

        b.   55.356 to 65.991

        c.   52.187 to 68.160

9.47   An outlier can have a large or small impact on the regression equation. The closer the outlier comes to falling on the old regression equation, the less it will affect the new regression equation.

9.49   a.   No warning is given.

        b. $Y = 28.253 - 1.135(100) = -84.247$ and $Y_i = -69$.
           The new data point is slightly below that from the regression equation to cause a minor change. The change should rotate the new regression equation counterclockwise; hence, the slope should decrease and the slope should increase.

        d. $Y = 26.757 - 0.9633(X)$.

9.51   a.   Yes, in case #18 we have recorded UGPA as 37.10 of 3.71.

       b.   With such an outlier we will probably receive both warnings.

       c.   Unusual Observations.

Obs.	UGPA	GGPA	Fit	Stdev. Fit	Residual	StResid
18	37.1	3.5200	3.6075	0.3701	−0.0875	−3.56RX

          R denotes an obs. with a large st. resid.

          X denotes an obs. whose X value gives it large influence.

9.53   We have had a great many disappointments in the past. Many times premature statistical results are released to the media that appear more promising than can be delivered.

9.55   a.   Yes, we would want salary increases to be directly related to performance (independent variable).

       b.   We reject H_o: predictor variable and model are significant.

       c. 0.060 ± 0.061

       d. $\hat{Y} = 3.3554$

       e.   CI: 3.1493 to 3.5616   PI: 2.8488 to 3.8621

9.57   a.   It depends. If all the apartments were in the same location, probably yes. If not, good location is more important a predictor than sq. ft. Rent $= f$(Sq. Ft.).

       b.   Rent $= \$135.788 + 0.369$(Sq. Ft.), $r^2 = .862$, and with p-values $= 0$, supposedly we have a predictive equation for any reasonable α value.

       c.   Rent $= \$837.299$ when Sq. Ft. $= 1900$.

9.59   a.   Board length $= f$(surface height).

       b.   Since $\alpha \geq p$-value $(.05 \geq 0)$ we reject H_o: that true $r^2 = 0$.

       c. $0.735 \pm .120$

       d.   6.8766

       e.   CI: 6.7472 to 7.0060   PI: 6.6719 to 7.0813

9.61   a.   The data seem to have risen, but are now falling. A parabola may fit the data better than a linear equation.

       b.   Profits $= 24500 + 2.172$(output); residuals are $−24500.00$, $−18218.182$, $−5936.364$, 6324.455, 7626.273, 20908.091, 30190.909, 44472.727, 13754.545, $−19963.636$, $−54681.818$. The signs to the residuals are grouped or clumped, possibly indicating a non-linear function.

9.63   a.   Yes.

       b.   Gas consumed $= 1.112 + 0.031$ (miles driven); $r^2 = .945$; since p-values $= 0$, the model is significant at the 1% level.

9.65   a. $\hat{Y} = 4.285 + 0.351(X)$: $S_{Y \bullet X} = 16.038$: $r^2 = .058$, which is not significant at any normally used confidence levels. For case #27, we will receive and outlier warning. The outlier substantially altered the regression equation; however, had little impact on r^2.

       b. $\hat{Y} = −0.748 + 0.440(X)$: $S_{Y \bullet X} = 5.144 r^2 = .899$ which is significant at any confidence level (p-value $= 0$). The outlier substantially affected both the regression equation and r^2, which is why we received a larger Cook distance value in addition to an unusual leverage and standardized residual value.

9.67   Use average distance as the independent variable. The variation due to omitted variables (SSE $= 1.44$) is extremely small; hence, r^2 nears 1.0. The model and the independent variable are significant at any level since p-value $= 0$. $\hat{Y} = 44.5 − 0.02(X)$.

Mini-case 9.1

a. Although a linear relationship is assumed, there is reason to expect a lower limit to household size. If average household size equals 1, then each citizen on average, regardless of age, would have their own dwelling. It is possible, though not probable, for the lower limit to be less than 1. This would mean that each citizen would have an average of more than one household. Although it is possible for a wealthy individual to have a main residence, a beach house, and a mountain house, it is unlikely that our society will in the near future attain an average of more than one household per citizen. Therefore, at some future point in time, average household size either has to approach a lower limit or start increasing again. Only time will tell which of the two scenarios is inevitable. Census forecasters currently believe the fertility rate has leveled off. Thus, average household size probably won't go much lower or its rate of decline will diminish. In addition, although the percentage of citizens younger than 18 years old is still decreasing, the rate at which it is decreasing has slowed considerably. Actually, the size of the under-18 group is now increasing after years of decline. It is not certain, however, if this represents a new trend or merely an aberration from the old trend.

b. The MINITAB printout yields

The regression equation is

AHS = 8.82 − 0.0809 ALE

Predictor	Coef	Stdev	T	p
Constant	8.8223	0.3838	22.99	0.000
ALE	−0.080861	0.005737	−14.15	0.000

$s = 0.1108$ $R - sq = 97.1\%$ $R - sq(adj) = 96.6\%$

ANALYSIS OF VARIANCE

SOURCE	DF	SS	MS	F	P
Regression	1	2.4600	2.4600	200.35	0.000
Error	6	0.0737	0.0123		
Total	7	2.5337			

An analysis of the preliminary results reveals that the variables are inversely related. Hence, the slope b and the coefficient of correlation r are negative. As the life expectancy increases by 1 year, the average household size decreases by .081766 members. Note how erroneous the results would be if we substituted $X = 0$ into the equation. At life expectancy of 0, we have an average household size of 8.875. If the life expectancy were 100, the average household size would be less than 1. Because S_e is fairly small, the sum of the residuals is small. Thus, the model should have (and does) a high coefficient of determination (0.971). The SSR, as a percentage of the total variation (SST) is 97.1%.

Although empirically it is reasonable to have a high r^2, note that the data being analyzed are two time series that normally change proportionately over time. While life expectancy increases over time, the average household size decreases over time. Of course, a false predictability may be distorting the results, as was the case with the INDY 500 and GNP example. Once again, we will see how to factor out time in Chapter 10.

Marketing specialists pay close attention to average household size. Many products and services are specifically purchased for the home, such as refrigerators, lawn mowers, and newspapers. It is rare for two members of the same household to purchase their own copies of a newspaper. Thus, the demand for some products depends on the number of households. However, the demand for many other products is heavily dependent on the size of households.

Mini-case 9.2

  a. Since we would theorize a direct relationship, we are involved in a one-tailed test.

  b. Yes

The regression equation is

Pop% = −13.8 + 1.97 Area%

Predictor	Coef	Stdev	T	p
Constant	−13.781	9.986	−1.38	0.226
Area%	1.9725	0.6121	3.22	0.023

$s = 12.97$ R-sq $= 67.5\%$ R-sq $= 61.0\%$

ANALYSIS OF VARIANCE

SOURCE	DF	SS	MS	F	p
Regression	1	1746.5	1746.5	10.39	0.023
Error	5	840.8	168.2		
Total	6	1587.3			

UNUSUAL OBSERVATIONS

Obs.	Area%	Pop%	Fit	Stdev.Fit	Residual	St.Resid
1	29.7	59.70	44.80	10.67	14.90	2.02R

R denotes an obs. with a large st. resid.

  c. Temperature, natural resources, logistics.

Mini-case 9.3

  a. We would theorize that we need to invest more money in teachers to obtain better qualified professionals (a direct relationship). We would theorize that smaller class size would allow a greater focus by teachers, hence a greater opportunity to increase performance (an inverse relationship).

  b. Many experts argue this point. What they learn in high school should make students more efficient and productive either in advanced schools or in occupational choices.

  c. Again, this is a difficult question. Since salary information is not normalized to the cost of living in different geographic areas, I would vote for the student–teacher ratio.

  d. Many factors would impact SAT scores. State's investment into the educational process, if incentives are given to teachers for superior performances, even if Latin is taught in the schools, is believed to greatly increase SAT scores. There are those that claim there is a sex and minority bias in SAT scores. If so, these would have to be removed.

  e. Competitive universities would want GPA and to know whether the student has taken the most difficult classes their high school has to offer.

  f. The regression equation is

SAT = 886 + 0.00017 ATS

Predictor	Coef	Stdev	T	p
Constant	885.90	51.18	17.31	0.000
ATS	0.000165	0.001901	0.09	0.932

$s = 30.24$ R-sq $= 0.0\%$ R-sq (adj) $= 0.0\%$

ANALYSIS OF VARIANCE

SOURCE	DF	SS	MS	F	p
Regression	1	6.9	6.9	0.01	0.932
Error	20	18289.8	914.5		
Total	21	18296.8			

UNUSUAL OBSERVATIONS

Obs.	ATS	SAT	Fit	Stdev.Fit	Residual	St.Resid
9	23190	832.00	889.74	9.29	−57.74	−2.01R

R denotes an obs. with a large st. resid.

The regression equation is

SAT = 931 − 2.40 PTR

Predictor	Coef	Stdev	T	p
Constant	930.76	44.72	20.81	0.000
PTR	−2.398	2.625	−0.91	0.372

$s = 29.63$ R-sq = 4.0%   R-sq (adj) = 0.0%

ANALYSIS OF VARIANCE

SOURCE	DF	SS	MS	F	p
Regression	1	732.9	732.9	0.83	0.372
Error	20	17563.8	878.2		
Total	21	18296.8			

UNUSUAL OBSERVATIONS

Obs.	PTR	SAT	Fit	Stdev.Fit	Residual	St.Resid
1	23.0	906.00	875.62	17.29	30.38	1.26X
7	22.6	881.00	876.58	16.32	4.42	0.18 X

X denotes an obs. whose X value gives it large influence.

Neither variable is significant at the 5% level.

Educational attainment and achievements, company of employment and their goals, the state of the economy, etc.

Mini-case 9.4

a. Many retailers believe that the hiring of Santa simply to be a promotion, which is not needed in a strong company.

b. As the economy weakens there is more competition; hence, a greater need to stand out.

Chapter 10   Solutions

 Answers to Concept Checks

10.A   False. Each independent variable would have its own estimated slope plus a constant. Hence, there are 7 estimated parameters.

10.B   False. It is determined by the respective discipline.

10.C   False. It involves one dependent and two predictor variables.

10.D   True.

10.E   True.

10.F   False. It means only that one predictor variable is significant.

10.G   True.

10.H   False. Multicollinearity is caused by a high correlation between different independent variables.

10.I   True.

10.J   False. Statistics must play second fiddle to sound logic.

10.1 False. Multiple regression analysis deals no longer with a two-dimensional approach, but rather deals with a plane. The simplest form of multiple regression analysis is a 3-variable model; hence, graphs are 3-dimensional.

10.3 Population density, a growing population rather than a declining one, a population in certain age groups and interests, business and community support, number and quality of competitors, if you are to a general or special interest university, etc.

10.5 1. Time to put into course* 2. my background coming into the course* 3. the individual instructor* 4. getting free from my job to get to class on time** 5. whether the exams are multiple choice or problem oriented* or ** 6. whether the class is a large lecture group or a small group*, etc.

10.7 Pretty much the same variables that will account for the sales of any product or service (population density, traffic flow and ease of entry into and out of the store area, the number of competitors, price, demographics of the population, etc.).

10.9 The sales price increases an average of $35.75 for each sq. ft. of house (keeping other variables constant) and an average of $4,986 for each bedroom (keeping other variables constant).

$$\hat{Y} = 3{,}000 + 35.75(2{,}000) + 4{,}986(4) = \$94{,}444$$

10.11 a. $\Sigma Y = an + b_1 \Sigma X_1 + b_2 \Sigma X_2$

$\Sigma X_1 Y = a\Sigma X_1 + b_1 \Sigma X_1^{\alpha} + b_2 \Sigma X_1 X_2$

$\Sigma X_2 Y = a\Sigma X_2 + b_1 \Sigma X_1 X_2 + b_2 \Sigma X_2$

b. $\hat{Y} = 74.530 + 8.794(X_1) + 2.832(X_2)$

c. 184.53.

10.13 a. As Y increases there appears to be no linear relationship to X_1, hence $b_1 = 0$. As Y increases by 1, X_2 drops by 5, hence the slope should be -0.2.

b. Confirmed: $\hat{Y} = 21.000 - 0.000(X_1) - 0.200(X_2)$; estimated $Y = 85.000$

10.15 SST = total sum-of-squares; SST yields the total variation in Y_i: SSR = regression sum-of-squares; SSR yields the variation in Y_i caused by predictor variable within the regression equation: SSE = error sum-of-squares; SSE yields the variation in Y_i caused by omitted variables from the regression model.

10.17 a. SSR = 9085.867; SSE = 1230.800; SST = 10316.667

b. $S_e = 11.694$; $R^2 = .881$

10.19 $s_e = 0.000$, meaning there is no variation from the multiple regression equation. All residuals = 0. Since SSE = 0, SSR = SST, hence $r^2 = 1$.

10.21 The subscript refers to a dependent variable being regressed on two predictor variables defined as X_1 and X_2.

10.23 a. Because $\alpha \geq p$-value $(.05 \geq .037)$ we reject H_o.

b. H_o: true $r^2 = 0$.

10.25 If test statistic is negative, make a negative. Direct relationship between Y and X_i; H_o: $B_i \leq 0$, reject H_o when $\alpha \geq P(2\ \text{TAIL})/2$. Inverse relationship between Y and X_i, make p-value negative; H_o: $B_i \geq 0$, reject H_o when $-\alpha \leq -P(2\ \text{TAIL})/2$.

10.27   a.   Yes, $\alpha \geq p$-value $(.05 \geq 0)$.
      b.   Realizing Murphy's law, the more employees and the longer production cycle, the more defects there will be. Hence, direct relationship between Y with X_1, and Y with X_2.
      c. X_1 is significant to the model. X_2 is not significant to the model.
      d. b_1: 8.974 ± 3.798 b_2: 2.832 ± 2.884

10.29   a. $SSE = 0$.

      b. $SSR = SST = 82.5$.

10.31 It will either raise r^2 or remain unchanged. Adding variables will not increase SSE.

10.33 $\hat{Y} = 12.307 + 9.01(X_1) + 2.396(X_2) + 32.546(X_3)$. Concerning F_{test}, since $.05 \geq 0$, the model is significant. We would expect direct relationships between Y and each of the three X variables. Each X variable is significant at the 5% level.

10.35   a.   Yes, there is no variation from the equation.

      b.   Hard to discern from the printout. Since there is perfect correlation between Y and X_2, the other independent variables are of no consequence.

10.37 If made Monday, we have two defects, and if made Friday, we have 5.6 defects. Obviously, there are more errors if made on a Friday, so we would want one made on a Monday.

10.39 In an attempt to reduce SSE and increase R^2, we may be adding variables at a frenzied pace. Unfortunately, the inclusion of so many variables affects df. To adjust for the lost degrees of freedom, we adjust the R^2 formula.

10.41 Stepwise regression of Defects on 3 predictors, with $N = 12$

Step	1	2	3
Constant	96.79	23.63	12.31
Days to C	10.9	10.8	9.0
T-Value	6.64	8.82	8.11
Surges		36.3	32.5
$T =$ Value		3.01	3.55
NoEmpl			2.40
T-Value			2.81
S	13.8	10.3	7.73
R-Sq	81.53	90.79	95.37

10.43 Stepwise regression of Salary on 3 predictors, with $N = 15$

Step	1	2	3
Constant	-11.236	-5.675	-3.032
MeanAge	0.358	0.189	0.100
T-Value	12.94	3.03	1.35
NoEmploy		0.0100	0.0100
T-Value		2.90	3.19
Assets			0.0110
T-Value			1.87
S	0.787	0.628	0.571
R-Sq	92.79	95.77	96.79

10.45 Variables Y and X_2 are perfectly correlated.

10.47 Multicollinearity exists where there is high correlation between the independent (predictor) variables themselves.

10.49 None of the tolerances nears 0 and the largest Pearson correlation is between X_1 and X_2, but it's only .562. There is no serious problem involving multicollinearity.

10.51 a. Unable to compute.

   b. There are perfect correlations existing between X_2 and X_3, hence a multicollinearity problem. ERROR #8, Multicollinearity (a variable is weighted sum of others)
   Using the correlate command, $r = 1$ between X_2 and X_3.
   c. Eliminate either X_2 or X_3.

10.53 $Y = a + bX = cX_2$; a U shape or upside down U. The trend of the parabola changes directions once. The linear equation never changes directions.

10.55

SOURCE	DF	Seq SS	F	P
Linear	1	562.181	7.0781	2.39E-02
*Quadratic	1	708.872	74.3016	1.21E-05
Cubic	1	34.413	5.35077	4.94E-02

10.57

SOURCE	DF	Seq SS	F	P
Linear	1	5846.48	8373.23	0
*Quadratic	1	0.17	0.229579	0.641120

10.59 The manager knows the appropriate predictor variables that should be tested. The manager knows the model, the statistician merely formalizes it, which allows for improvements.

10.61 The regression models of Chapter 9 had but a single predictor (independent) variable, while those of Chapter 10 have ≥ 2 predictor variables.

10.63 a. Probably not. There are so many factors influencing SAT scores it will be hard to find a significant variable. Sometimes teacher's salary is just a stepwise factor based on tenure and not performance. In fact, performance itself is hard to define. Sometimes the student/teacher ratio is not really as important as the instructor.

   b. We are involved in a one-tailed test because salary would be expected to be related directly and pupil–teacher ratio indirectly.
   c. X_1; since $.05 < .978/2$, $B_1 = 0$: X_2; since $-.05 > -386/2$, $B_2 = 0$.
   d. B_1: $0.0000531 \pm 2.093 \bullet 0.0062465$; B_2: $-2.3926642 \pm 2.093 \bullet 2.6988301$.
   e. CI: 907.192 ± 51.195 PI: 907.192 ± 81.672.

10.65 a. $S_{Y \bullet 12345} = 6.7859$: $n = 27$, $m = 6$, SSE $= \Sigma e^2 = 967.017$.

   b. No, we have SSE (Σe^2), but need either SSR or SST.

Mini-case 10.1

a. The regression equation is

SalesPR = −55.8 + 0.0666 SqFt + 40.3 LotSize − 8.8 Interior + 72.1 Exterior

Predictor	Coef	Stdev	T	p
Constant	−55.79	51.33	−1.09	0.303
SqFt	0.06662	0.03357	1.98	0.075
LotSize	40.25	52.72	0.76	0.463
Interior	−8.78	30.22	−0.29	0.777
Exterior	72.12	18.89	3.82	0.003

$S = 33.63$ R-sq = 76.8% R-sq (adj) = 67.5%

ANALYSIS OF VARIANCE

SOURCE	DF	SS	MS	F	p
Regression	4	37413	9358	8.27	0.003
Error	10	11312	1131		
Total	14	48725			

SOURCE	DF	SEQ SS
SqFt	1	20617
LotSize	1	273
Interior	1	36
Exterior	1	16486

Fit	Stdev.Fit	95% C.I.	95% P.I.
200.85	25.41	(144.22, 257.48)	(106.90, 294.80)

	Sqft	Interior	Exterior
Interior	0.806		
Exterior	0.039	0.111	
LotSize	0.644	0.492	−0.223

Stepwise regression of SalesPr on 4 predictors, with $N = 15$

Step	1	2	3	4
Constant	−16.62	−51.78	−45.44	−55.79
SqFt	0.074	0.072	0.060	0.067
T-Value	3.09	4.37	2.66	1.98
Exterior		67	71	72
T-Value		3.99	3.98	3.82
LotSize			41	40
T-Value			0.80	0.76
Interior				−9
T-Value				−0.29
S	46.5	31.7	32.2	33.6
R-Sq	42.31	75.22	76.59	76.78

Mini-case 10.2

a. The regression equation is

$$Y = 44353 - 2.5\ X1 + 10.7\ X2$$

Predictor	Coef	Stdev	T	p
Constant	44353	20010	2.22	0.069
$X1$	-2.53	24.17	-0.10	0.920
$X2$	11.682	7.840	1.49	0.187

$s = 28602$ R-sq $= 30.6\%$ R-sq (adj) $= 7.5\%$

SOURCE	DF	SS	MS	F	p
Regression	2	2167932416	1083966208	1.33	0.334
Error	6	4908289536	818048256		
Total	8	7076221952			

SOURCE	DF	SEQ SS
$X1$		1351370656
$X2$	1	181651920

b. Correlation of $X1$ and $X2 = 0.461$

Mini-case 10.3-A

The main problem of multicollinearity is between variables X_3 and X_1. It might be wise to remove X_1 from the analysis. The removal of X_1 will probably have little impact on the over-all analysis since correlation is not that great. It would be expected that the standard error of the coefficient would decline a little, t_{test} should increase a little, and P should drop a little. Remember that there are so many factors influencing ACT scores that the entire analysis must be questioned. Even ACT scores between states might not be equivalent. For example, some states may require all or most students to take the exam while other states might make it voluntary. In such a case, only students interested in college would take the test.

Mini-case 10.3-B

The main problem of multicollinearity is between variables X_3 and X_1. It might be wise to remove X_1 from the analysis. The removal of X_1 will probably have little impact on the over-all analysis since correlation is not that great. It would be expected that the standard error of the coefficient would decline a little, t_{test} should increase a little, and P should drop a little. Remember that there are so many factors influencing SAT scores that the entire analysis must be questioned. Even SAT scores between states might not be equivalent. For example, some states may require all or most students to take the exam while other states might make it voluntary. In such a case, only students interested in college would take the test.

Mini-case 10.4

Boys' Average Height and Weight from Birth to 14

a. Height $= 56.223 + 2.42(\text{Weight})$; p-values significant. The height and weight of boys is affected by their age. So both data increase somewhat proportionately over time yielding an appearance of a relationship.

b. Height $= 70.619 - 0.827(\text{Weight}) + 9.271\ (\text{Age})$; age is significant $(.05 \geq .004)$ but weight is not significant $(.05 < 0.389)$. Our suspicions are confirmed.

c. Height $= 70.619 - 0.827(80) + 9.271(40) = 375.299$cm. Your instructor should be about to sign with a professional basketball team. We can see the problems of extrapolating the data beyond the data base where a linear relationship might change to a nonlinear one.

Answers to Concept Checks (Appendix)

10.K   True.

10.L   True.

10.M   False. Values closest to 0 indicate the presence of positive autocorrelation, and closest to 4 the presence of negative autocorrelation. Values close to 2 indicate that neither positive nor negative autocorrelation is present.

10.N   False. It is not a relationship between e and X but rather between $|e|$ and X.

Answers to Even-Numbered Exercises (Appendix)

10.66   If two variables (X and Y) are independent, then the covariance of X and Y equals 0. This follows, since the covariance measures the extent that two variables move or vary in unison. Thus, if the covariance is 0, the variables do not move together and would be independent.

10.68   Constant variation in the errors is referred to as homoselasticity.

10.70   Positive autocorrelation can be seen if the residuals are grouped by signs. There might be a group of positive residuals, followed by a group of negative residuals, followed by a group of positive residuals, etc.

10.72   Negative autocorrelation would be seen by the residuals consistently going from positive, to negative, to positive, etc.

10.74   a.   No, not with $d = 2.103$. However, in order to find the critical values for d_1 and d_u, $n \geq 15$.

          b.   No, this is not a data series over time. Autocorrelation has a greater probability of occurring when X moves in a consistent time phase.

10.76   It is when the absolute values of the residual are related to X.

Chapter 11   Solutions

Answers to Concept Checks

11.A   False. There can be no missing values and needs to be in constant intervals.

11.B   True. The relevant type period increases as we move from analysis of seasonal variation to cyclical to trend.

11.C   False. The additive model assumes independence, the multiplicative assumes dependence.

11.D   True.

11.E   False. The word "log" does not appear before Y.

11.F   False. In a trend, you are actually attempting to remove the very increases and declines that a tenth degree polynomial would ensure.

11.G   True.

11.H　False. We should use a two-parameter exponential smoothing procedure.

11.I　True.

11.J　False. The Delphi technique is a qualitative, not quantitative, technique.

Answers to Odd-Numbered Exercises

11.1　Projections into the future are based upon the assumption that what happened in the past will continue into the future. If this assumption is violated, projections will prove fruitless.

11.3　History does tend to repeat itself, which enables us to predict some upcoming events.

11.5　Many scientists now believe that the weather of the earth follows a very detailed cycle. The only problem is that the cycle can be many millions of years, making it difficult to predict from the one hundred years of observations we currently have.

11.7　If there is a trend, this infers predictability. The irregular component would be the most difficult to predict because there are no recurring patterns.

11.9　$Y_t = T_t \bullet C_t \bullet S_t \bullet I_t$

11.11　It has been rejected because the implication is that there are no cross relationships existing within the four components.

11.13　$\hat{Y} = 111.440 + 5.38901(y)$; 192.275

11.15　Company A: $111.321 + 17.929(X)$;

Company B: $207.286 + 6.798(X)$;
They will catch each other when the two equations equate. To solve, set both equations equal to each other. $111.321 + 17.929(X) = 207.286 + 6.798(X)$; $95.965 = 11.131(X)$; $X = 8.621$, they equate on approximately July 14, 1993.

11.17　a.　$\hat{Y} = 506.481 + 7.89568(X) - 0.32284(X^2)$
　　　b.　$\hat{Y} = 535.936\ (1.00089)^x$
　　　c.　517.299 and 547.029

11.19　$Y = a + b(X) + c(X^2)$

11.21　What the percentage change (not absolute change) in successive data points is approximately equal.

11.23　a.　No, the data appear to fall, then rise again.
　　　b.　$\hat{Y} = 11.6776 - 2.08748(X) + 0.138578(X^2)$
　　　c.　6.583

11.25　Two times or one less than the highest power of X.

11.27　The purpose of the trend is to determine the overall direction of the data set void of the short term increases and declines in the data set. Each time an additional power is added to the trend question, the very increases and declines that we are trying to eliminate are returned to the equation.

11.29　We attempt to subdivide the four time series components in half, then half again to isolate S.

11.31   Trend Line Equation

$$Yt = 9.6159 + 5.38E - 02^*t$$

SEASONAL INDICES

Period	Index
1	1.16376
2	0.868214
3	0.768795
4	1.19923

Accuracy of Model

MAPE:	6.97245
MAD:	0.79031
MSD:	0.92632

ROW	Price	Trend	Seasonal	Detrend	Deseason	Model	Error
1	12	10.6697	1.16376	1.12468	10.3114	12.4169	−0.41693
2	10	10.7235	0.86821	0.93253	11.5179	9.3103	0.68973
3	9	10.7773	0.76879	0.83509	11.7066	8.2855	0.71450
4	13	10.8311	1.19923	1.20025	10.8403	12.9890	0.01105
5	14	10.8849	1.16376	1.28619	12.0300	12.6674	1.33265
6	10	10.9387	0.86821	0.61419	11.5179	9.4971	0.50290
7	9	10.9924	0.76879	0.81874	11.7066	8.4509	0.54906
8	15	11.0462	1.19923	1.35793	12.5080	13.2470	1.75299
9	11	11.1000	1.16376	.099099	9.4521	12.9178	−1.91778
10	9	11.1538	0.86821	0.80690	10.3661	9.6839	−0.68392
11	8	11.2076	0.76879	0.71380	10.4059	8.6164	−0.61637
12	12	11.2614	1.19923	1.06558	10.0064	13.5051	−1.50507
13	11	11.3152	1.16376	.097214	9.4521	13.1682	−2.16820
14	10	11.3690	0.86821	0.87958	11.5179	9.8708	0.12925
15	10	11.4228	0.76879	0.87544	13.0074	8.7818	1.21819
16	13	11.4766	1.19923	1.13274	10.8403	13.7631	−0.76313
17	15	11.5304	1.16376	1.30091	12.8893	13.4186	1.58137
18	11	11.5842	0.86821	0.94957	12.6697	10.0576	0.94242
19	9	11.6380	0.76879	0.77333	11.7066	8.9472	0.05276
20	14	11.6918	1.19923	1.19742	11.6741	14.0212	−0.02118
21	13	11.7456	1.16376	1.10680	11.1707	13.6691	−0.66905
22	9	11.7994	0.86821	0.76275	10.3661	10.2444	−1.24441
23	8	11.8532	0.76879	0.67492	10.4059	9.1127	−1.11267
24	14	11.9070	1.19923	1.17578	11.6741	14.2792	−0.27924
25	13	11.9608	1.16376	1.08688	11.1707	13.9195	−0.91948
26	10	12.0146	0.86821	.083232	11.5179	10.4312	−0.43124
27	9	12.0684	0.76879	0.74575	11.7066	9.2781	−0.27811
28	14	12.1222	1.19923	1.15491	11.6741	14.5373	−0.53730
29	15	12.1760	1.16376	1.23193	12.8893	14.1699	0.83009
30	12	12.2298	0.86821	0.98121	13.8215	10.6181	1.38194
31	10	12.1836	0.76879	.081410	13.0074	9.4435	0.55646
32	16	12.3374	1.19923	1.29687	13.3419	14.7954	1.20464
33	15	12.3912	1.16376	1.21054	12.8893	14.4203	0.57967
34	11	12.4450	0.86821	0.88389	12.6697	10.8049	0.19511
35	9	12.4988	0.76879	0.72007	11.7066	9.6090	−0.60898
36	15	12.5526	1.19923	1.19498	12.5080	15.0534	−0.5342

FORECASTS

ROW	Period	Forecast
1	37	14.6708

11.33   a.   Trend Line Equation

$Yt = 3.96632 + 0.186541*t$

SEASONAL INDICES

Period	Index
1	0.963786
2	0.951084
3	0.966428
4	1.11870

Accuracy of Model

MAPE: 2.42574
MAD: 0.13849
MSD: 0.02518

ROW	Sales	Trend	Seasonal	Detrend	Deseason	Model	Error
1	4.2	4.15286	0.96379	1.01135	4.35781	4.00247	0.197534
2	4.3	4.33940	.095108	0.99092	4.52116	4.12713	0.172869
3	4.6	4.52594	0.96643	1.01636	4.75979	4.37400	0.226003
4	5.1	4.71248	1.11870	1.08223	4.55886	5.27186	−0.171862
5	4.8	4.89920	0.96379	0.97979	4.98036	4.72161	0.078391
6	5.0	5.08556	0.95108	0.98318	5.25716	4.83680	0.163203
7	5.0	5.27211	0.96643	0.94839	5.17369	5.09511	−0.095112
8	6.2	5.45865	1.11870	1.13581	5.54214	6.10660	0.093401
9	5.4	5.64519	0.96379	0.95657	5.60290	5.44075	−0.040753
10	5.5	5.83173	0.95108	0.94312	5.78288	5.54646	−0.046463
11	5.7	6.01827	0.96643	0.94712	5.89801	5.81623	−0.116227
12	6.9	6.20481	1.11870	1.11204	6.16786	6.94134	−0.041335
13	6.0	6.39135	0.96379	0.93877	6.22545	6.15990	−0.159897
14	6.1	6.57789	0.95108	0.92735	6.41374	6.25613	−0.156128
15	6.4	6.76444	0.96643	0.94612	6.62232	6.53734	−0.137343
16	7.5	6.95098	1.11870	1.07898	6.70420	7.77607	−0.276072
17	6.8	7.13752	0.96379	0.95271	7.05551	6.87904	−0.079041
18	6.9	7.32406	0.95108	0.94210	7.25488	6.96579	−0.065794
19	7.6	7.51060	0.96643	1.01190	7.86401	7.25846	0.341542
20	8.5	7.69714	1.11870	1.10431	7.59809	8.61081	−0.110809

FORECASTS

ROW	Period	Forecast
1	21	7.59819

b. The regression equation is

Sales = 3.85 + 0.176 Time − 0.056 SecQtr + 0.067 ThirdQtr + 0.871 FourthQtr

Predictor	Coef	Stdev	t-ratio	p
Constant	3.8537	0.1071	35.98	0.000
Time	0.176250	0.007409	23.79	0.000
SecQtr	−0.0563	0.1188	−0.47	0.643
ThirdQtr	0.0675	0.1195	0.56	0.580
FourthQt	0.812	0.1206	7.22	0.000

$s = 0.1874$ R-sq = 98%   R-sq (adj) = 97.5%

ANALYSIS OF VARIANCE

SOURCE	DF	SS	MS	F	p
Regression	4	25.9305	6.4826	184.51	0.000
Error	15	0.5270	0.0351		
Total	19	26.4575			

SOURCE	DF	SEQ SS
Time	1	23.1405
SecQtr	1	0.4935
ThirdQtr	0.4633	
FourthQt	1	1.8332

UNUSUAL OBSERVATIONS

Obs.	Time	Sales	Fit	Stdev.Fut	Residual	St.Resid
4	4.0	5.1000	5.4300	0.1027	−0.3300	−2.10R
19	19.0	7.6000	7.2700	0.1027	0.3300	2.10R

R denotes an obs. with a large st. resid.

Fit	Stdev.Fit	95% C.I.	95% P.I.
7.5550	0.1222	(7.2945, 7.8155)	(7.0780, 8.0320)

11.35 $\alpha = 0.061$; Forecast = 17.0481

11.37 $\alpha = 0.687$; Forecast = 8.14994

11.39 $\alpha = 0.156310$

$\gamma = 0.206297$
Forecast = 7.48776

11.41   The consumer price index would more than likely have an upward trend; hence, the single parameter exponential smoothing technique is inappropriate.

11.43   An autoregressive model refers to the independent variable being a previous value of the dependent variable.

11.45 $\hat{Y} = 35.213 + 0.943(587) = 588.754$

11.47 $\hat{Y} = 4.769 + 1.011(90) = 95.759$

11.49   In class project.

11.51   a. $\hat{Y} = 64.920 − 0.191(7) = 63.583$

b.   With so little data and no visual trend, it would be unwise to believe a relationship exists.

c.   Yes, we would want to know if we are pricing homes beyond the means of the ordinary citizen. We could be losing the American dream of home ownership.

11.53 a. The price of such a commodity can't rise proportionately without substitute products coming on the market. Hence, there is a theoretical basis for a parabola.

b. Linear projection: $\hat{Y} = 1736.545 + 60.273(12) = 2{,}458.821$; parabolic projection: $\hat{Y} = 1208.364 + 304.049(12) - 20.315(122) = 1931.64$.

11.55 No. Fluctuations in price are not dependent on time, but rather on many economic and political variables.

11.57 There is probably less effect from omitted variables in space than in business interrelationships. The natural sciences are normally more predictable than business relationships which often can be illogical.

11.59 a. Revenue; $\hat{Y} = 840 + 500(6) = 3840$: Profit; $\hat{Y} = 38.820 + 111.960(6) = 632.616$

b. No, the sample size is much too small.

c. There are many variables, some beyond the control of the company, that can affect such data.

11.61 a. Linear: $\hat{Y} = -108{,}881 + 24{,}438.5(X)$ and log $\hat{Y}$

b. The plot will show for the exponential equation a linear fit. Hence, this is the appropriate equation.

c. Linear: $\hat{Y} = 233{,}258$ and exponential $\hat{Y} = 1{,}599{,}216$. The exponential forecast is much more rational.

11.63 a. Trend Line Equation

$Yt = 4223.14 + 25.3436{}^{*}t$

SEASONAL INDICES

Period	Index
1	0.662593
2	1.02106
3	1.54309
4	0.773254

Accuracy of Model
MAPE: 4.7
MAD: 189.6
MSD: 49567.2

ROW	Customer	Trend	Seasonal	Detrend	Deseason	Model	Error
1	2530	4248.49	0.66259	0.59315	3803.24	2815.02	−295.015
2	4714	4273.83	1.02106	1.10299	4616.76	4363.85	350.155
3	6819	4299.17	1.54309	1.58612	4419.05	6634.85	184.984
4	3692	4324.52	0.77325	0.85374	4774.63	3343.95	348.051
5	2671	4349.86	0.66259	0.61404	4031.13	2882.19	−211.186
6	4658	4375.20	1.02106	1.06464	4561.92	4467.35	190.645
7	7102	4400.55	1.54309	1.61389	4602.45	6790.45	311.554
8	3219	4425.89	0.77325	0.72731	4162.93	3422.34	−203.337
9	2819	4451.23	0.66259	0.63331	4254.50	2949.36	−130.355
10	4612	4476.58	1.02106	1.03025	4516.87	4570.86	41.136
11	6967	4501.92	1.54309	1.54756	4514.96	6946.88	20.124
12	3591	4527.27	0.77325	0.79319	4644.01	3500.73	90.275
13	3116	4552.61	0.66259	0.68444	4702.74	3016.53	99.475
14	4538	4577.95	1.02106	0.99127	4444.39	4674.37	−136.374
15	7019	4603.30	1.54309	1.52478	4548.66	7103.31	−84.306
16	3457	4628.64	0.77325	0.74687	4470.72	3579.11	−122.113
17	3276	4653.98	0.66259	0.70391	4944.21	3083.70	192.305
18	4498	4679.33	1.02106	0.96125	4405.22	4777.88	−279.884
19	6799	4704.67	1.54309	1.44516	4406.09	7259.74	−460.736
20	3698	4730.01	0.77325	0.78182	4782.39	3657.50	40.499

b. The regression equation is

Customer = 2749 + 9.57 Time + 1714 Qtr2 + 4042 Qtr3 + 622 Qtr4

Predictor	Coef	Stdev	t-ratio	p
Constant	2749.2	113.3	24.67	0.000
Time	9.575	7.836	1.22	0.241
Qtr2	1714.0	125.6	13.64	0.000
Qtr3	4041.6	126.4	31.99	0.000
Qtr4	622.3	127.6	4.88	0.000

$s = 198.2$ R-sq = 98.8% R-sq (adj) = 98.5%

ANALYSIS OF VARIANCE

SOURCE	DF	SS	MS	F	p
Regression	4	47714184	11928546	303.54	0.000
Error	15	589468	39298		
Total	19	48303652			

SOURCE	DF	SEQ SS
Time	1	427129
Qtr2	1	108514
Qtr3	1	46243352
Qtr4	1	935188

11.65 $\alpha = 0.087$

$\alpha = 0.156027$
$\gamma = 0.157977$

11.67 a. The regression equation is

Sales = 5.19 + 0.984 C2

10 cases used 1 case contain missing values

Predictor	Coef	Stdev	t-ratio	p
Constant	5.1939	0.5053	10.28	0.000
C2	0.98372	0.01809	54.37	0.000

$s = 0.7973$ R-sq = 99.7% R-sq (adj) = 99.7%

ANALYSIS OF VARIANCE

SOURCE	DF	SS	MS	F	p
Regression	1	1878.9	1878.9	2955.60	0.000
Error	8	5.1	0.6		
Total	9	1884.0			

b. The regression equation is

Sales = 10.2 + 0.974 C3

9 cases used 2 cases contain missing values

Predictor	Coef	Stdev	t-ratio	p
Constant	10.2316	0.5676	18.03	0.000
C3	0.97406	0.02259	43.12	0.000

$s = 0.8493$ R-sq = 99.6% R-sq (adj) = 99.6%

ANALYSIS OF VARIANCE

SOURCE	DF	SS	MS	F	p
Regression	1	1341.2	1341.2	1859.46	0.000
Error	7	5.0	0.7		
Total	8	1346.2			

11.69   Student exercise. Update the data file and process with MINITAB

11.71   Student exercise. Update the data file and process with MINITAB.

Mini-case 11.1

a. As long as the time sequence is in consistently spaced intervals, we will be able to attempt a forecast.

b. This depends on the question being asked. Since the question concerned winning bids, and not actual expenditures, there is no problem.

c. Linear equation: $\hat{Y} = -193.639 + 84.9833(X)$; Prediction: 656.2 million.

d. Second degree polynomial: $\hat{Y} = 31.619 - 37.8846(X) + 12.2868X^2$; Prediction: 881.5 million.

e. Exponential equation: $\hat{Y} = 4.09539(1.86245)^x$; Prediction: 2056.6 million.

f. The data appear to be exploding; hence, the exponential equation makes more sense at this point in time. However, this trend can't continue indefinitely.

g. There are several reasons including the enormous increases in advertising revenues. However, the main reason is probably that the major networks will sell off some of the rights to cablevision companies. Some sports that will not yield high ratings will be sold to the smaller stations which have select market niches.

h. There is always a problem with small sample sizes. Yet, in the real world, estimates must be made from limited information.

Mini-case 11.2

a. It is possible that some distortions have occurred but they occurred at a time when the acquired areas had relative sparsely populated areas. Hence, these distortions probably would have little effect on the data base.

b. Wars can have a major impact on population data bases. The United States has been very fortunate to have few confrontations within the confines of its own borders (with the exception of the Civil War). The respective casualties from some of the United States wars are as follows:

Revolutionary War (1775 to 1783): 33,769 casualties

Civil War: (1861–1865) 780,213 casualties ; sketchy information on the Confederate Side; casualties probably closer to 929,820

World War I (1917 to 1918): 320,710 casualties

World War II (1941 to 1945): 1,078,162 casualties

Korean War (1950 to 1953): 157,530 casualties

Vietnam War (1964 to 1973): 214,074 casualties

Iraqi War (1990–1991): 180 casualties

Considering casualties per 100,000 people, the Civil War had by far the biggest effect on the population rates. However, its effect was not large enough to decrease the population in absolute numbers. Note that wars also create baby booms that usually offset the casualty figures.

For some countries, wars will have a large effect on population data. The Soviet Union believes that it had over 20 million casualties during World War II and its population is only about 10 to 15% larger than that of the United States.

c. The only year that the population declined was in 1918. The decline was not really precipitated by World War I, but rather by a world epidemic of the swine flu. The modern world is not acquainted with the tragedies that have occurred in the past. For example, some cities in Europe had 95% casualties due to plagues during the first 16 centuries A.D.

d. The least squares equation by decades (1790 to 1990) is

1790	3,929	1840	17,120	1890	63,056	1940	132,122
1800	5,297	1850	23,261	1900	76,094	1950	151,684
1810	7,224	1860	31,513	1910	92,407	1960	180,671
1820	9,618	1870	39,905	1920	106,461	1970	205,052
1830	12,901	1880	50,262	1930	123,188	1980	227,757
						1990	252,100*

*estimate

The linear least squares equation (1780 = 0) and forecast is
$\hat{Y} = -48,754.068 + 12,328.028(22)$; 2000 $\hat{Y} = 222,462.55$

The parabolic least squares equation and forecast is
$\hat{Y} = 6,057.759 - 1,937.352(22) + 649.387(222)$; 2000 = 277,739.32

Of the two, the parabolic estimate is closer to the census predicted value. To determine which equation is superior, it might be wise to review the residuals. The residuals for the linear equation have a clumping (grouping) effect. There are some positive residuals, followed by a series of negative residuals, followed by a series of positive residuals. One cause of the clumped (grouped) values is an improper curve fit.

Year	Linear Residuals	Quadratic Residuals
1790	40355.040	−84.795
1800	29395.012	516.396
1810	18993.984	1133.813
1820	9059.956	919.457
1830	14.928	295.327
1840	−8094.100	−691.577
1850	−14281.128	−1055.255
1860	−18357.156	−606.706
1870	−22293.184	−1316.931
1880	−24264.212	−1360.930
1890	−23798.239	−266.703
1900	−23088.267	−277.249
1910	−19103.295	1788.431
1920	−17377.323	246.337
1930	−12989.351	67.470
1940	−4044.351	9012.470
1950	−9138.407	−9111.586
1960	7520.565	−915.775
1970	19573.537	1375.263
1980	29950.509	691.527
1990	41965.481	347.017

e. The linear least squares equation from 1975 to 1988 is
$\hat{Y} = 213,453 + 2,348.4291(16)$; 1990 = 252,483.43

The parabolic least squares equation is
$\hat{Y} = 213,213.56 + 2,438.058(16) - 5.975(162)$; 1990= 250,708.89

Again, to determine which is the best-fit equation you should compare the residuals of the two series. The simplest form of the two equations appears to be optimal.

f. The exponential least squares equation (1790 to 1990) is
$\log \hat{Y} = 8.462095 + 0.209135(22) = 13.063065$; $\hat{Y} = 471,212.76$

The data move in an arithmetic relationship and not geometrically. If the function were plotted on semilog paper, it would not be linear. The population of the United States does not increase by a constant percentage, which is fortunate.

g. Countries such as Germany and Italy have experienced either declines in population growth or even actual absolute declines in populations. A given land mass can support only so many people. The former West Germany was a country the approximate size of Oregon with 65 to 70 million people (that is the equivalent of having about 30% of our population reside in one state). Japan has one-half of our population in an area slightly smaller than Montana. Experts say that only about one-fourth of the land mass in Japan is inhabitable. Needless to say, the real estate values of Japan and Montana are quite different, The most densely populated city in the world is Hong Kong with 247,000 people per square mile. This, of course, also affects real estate values. It is expected that the United States population will eventually level off, then decline. Comment: The Census predictions as of February 1989 are that the population will follow the parabolic form, peaking in the year 2038 with a population of 301,881,000. The predictions are for the under age 35 group, which now comprises 55% of the population, to comprise 41% in the year 2030. This will have far reaching implications in terms of changing patterns of consumer spending.

Mini-case 11.3

We certainly hope not. There certainly will be a lot of people keeping an eye on things.

Mini-case 11.4

Update file: Student exercise.

Chapter 12   Solutions

 Answers to Concept Checks

12.A   False. Since the Fahrenheit scale includes only one variable or factor (temperature), it is not considered an index.

12.B   False. W is directly related to Y and inversely related to X.

12.C   True.

12.D   False. We would need quantities for all years.

12.E   True.

Answers to Odd-Numbered Exercises

12.1   An athlete has only so much energy to expend. To achieve a maximum point total one must maximize the point total. This might involve a decision of going all out on your best events and coasting in your poorer events, or just the opposite.

12.3   Index = (A + B)/C, if A and B are independent of each other, or Index = (A•B)/C, if A and B are dependent.

12.5   Index = (A + B)/C or Index (AS•B)/|C.

12.7   a.   1999 = 100.0%; 2000 = 300.0%; 2001 = 700.0%; 2002 = 1,000%

       b. | Year | 1999 | 2000 | 2001 | 2002 |
            |---|---|---|---|---|
            | Product B: | 100.0% | 150.0% | 200.0% | 250.0% |
            | Product C: | 100.0% | 133.3% | 200.0% | 266.7% |

       c.   1999 = 14.3%, 2000 = 42.9%, 2001 = 100.0%, 2002 = 142.9%

       d.   The price relatives are the same with a different base. The 2000 value is still 3 times that of 1999, etc.

12.9 | | *1999* | *2000* | *2001* | *2002* |
       |---|---|---|---|---|
       | a. | 100.00 | 200.0% | 250.0% | 400.0% |
       | b. | 40.0% | 80.0% | 100.0% | 160.0% |

       a.   1999 = 100.0%,   2000 = 200.0%,   2001 = 250.0%,   2002 = 400.00

       b.   1999 = 40.0%,   2000 = 80.0%,   2001 = 100.0%,   2002 = 160.0%

12.11 a.
            A: 1999 = 100.0%,   2000 = 150.0%,   2001 = 250.0%,   2002 = 400.0%
            B: 1999 = 100.0%,   2000 = 150.0%,   2001 = 220.0%,   2002 = 300.0%
            C: 1999 = 100.0%,   2000 = 133.3%,   2001 = 133.3%,   2002 = 116.7%
            D: 1999 = 100.0%,   2000 = 180.0%,   2001 = 220.0%,   2002 = 250.0%
            E: 1999 = 100.0%,   2000 = 140.0%,   2001 = 300.0%,   2002 = 500.0%

       b.
            A: 1999 = 40.0%,   2000 = 60.0%,   2001 = 100.0%,   2002 = 160.0%
            B: 1999 = 45.5%,   2000 = 68.2%,   2001 = 100.0%,   2002 = 136.4%
            C: 1999 = 75.0%,   2000 = 100.0%,   2001 = 100.0%,   2002 = 87.5%
            D: 1999 = 45.5%,   2000 = 81.8%,   2001 = 100.0%,   2002 = 113.6%
            E: 1999 = 33.3%,   2000 = 46.7%,   2001 = 100.0%,   2002 = 166.7%

12.13 a.   1999 = 100.0%, 2000 = 211.5%, 2001 = 430.8%, 2002 = 603.8%

       b.   1999 = 100.0%, 2000 = 166.7%, 2001 = 283.3%, 2002 = 383.3%
            Since prices of all three products are not too different, the index is essentially weighting the 3 products equally.

       c.   A weighted index would seem more logical than an unweighted index using only prices. Since the consumer expenditures are much heavier for product A followed by product C, A should be weighted more than C, and C should be weighted more than B.

12.15 a.   1999 = 100.0%, 2000 = 257.9%, 2001 = 438.5%, 2002 = 638.5%

       b.   The Value Index uses the summation of $P_o \bullet Q_n$ as the numerator (as does the Paasche index) but as the denominator it selects one of the years as the base and divides each basket value by that year's basket value.

12.17 a.   1999 = 100.0%, 2000 = 207.4%, 2001 = 345.6%, 2002 = 500.0%

       b.   1999 = $10; 2000 = $18; 2001 = $27; 2002 = $39.
            1999 = 100.0%, 2000 = 180.0%, 2001 = 270.0%, 2002 = 390.0%
            An unweighted index always weights the product with a price that is higher than products with prices that are lower. Hence, products D and A are weighted more heavily than C and B.

       c.   A weighted index would seem more logical than an unweighted index using only prices. The weights should be based on consumer expenditures.

12.19 a.   1999 = 100.0%, 2000 = 216.2%, 2001 = 494.1%, 2002 = 860.3%

       b.   The Value Index uses the summation of $P_o \bullet Q_n$ as the numerator (as does the Paasche index), but as the denominator it selects one of the years as the base and divides each basket value by that year's basket value.

12.21   1999 = 100.0%, 2000 = 144.0%, 2001 = 286.1%, 2002 = 462.8%

12.23   1999 = 100.0%, 2000 = 172.7%, 2001 = 383.9%, 2002 = 773.2%

12.25   1998 = 1.000; 1999 = 0.888; 2000 = 0.789; 2001 = 0.736; 2002 = 0.677: The value of the currency dropped 32.3% (1.000 − .677/1).

12.27   a.   1998 = \$24,987.00; 1999 = \$22,835.70; 2000 = \$21,437.50; 2001 = \$20,268.92; 2002 = \$17,530.73. Real purchasing power has dropped 29.84%.

          b.   1998 = \$24,987.00; 1999 = \$31,633.54; 2000 = \$37,180.66; 2001 = \$39,954.21; 2002 = \$46,750.68.

12.29   A consumer price index is a broad based fixed basket of goods that is purchased every month and indexed to a base period.

12.31   If our wages keep pace with inflation, there is no attempt to trim fat off of our purchases and to become more efficient consumers.

12.33   See Mini-case 12.1.

12.35   1999 = 1.000; 2000 = 0.514; 2001 = 0.257; 2002 = 0.154

        The value of the currency dropped 84.6%.

12.37   1999 = 1.000; 2000 = 0.478; 2001 = 0.293; 2002 = 0.152

        The value of the currency dropped 84.8%

12.39   a.

Year	Country A CPI Shifted	Country B	Country C CPI Shifted
1998	(158.2/158.2)(100) = 100.0	100.0	(796.9/796.9)(100) = 100.0
1999	(181.8/158.2)(100) = 114.9	126.9	(803.2/796.9)(100) = 100.8
2000	(206.3/158.2)(100) = 130.4	147.6	(807.8/796.9)(100) = 101.4
2001	(237.4/158.2)(100) = 150.1	155.3	(820.6/796.9)(100) = 103.0
2002	(249.4/158.2)(100) = 157.6	176.2	(829.5/796.9)(100) = 104.1

          b.

Year	Country A	Country B	Country C
1998	1/1.000 = 1.000	1/1.000 = 1.000	1/1.000 = 1.000
1999	1/1.149 = 0.870	1/1.269 = 0.788	1/1.008 = 0.992
2000	1/1.304 = 0.767	1/1.476 = 0.678	1/1.014 = 0.986
2001	1/1.501 = 0.666	1/1.553 = 0.644	1/1.030 = 0.971
2002	1/1.576 = 0.635	1/1.762 = 0.568	1/1.041 = 0.961

          c.   Country B has experienced the worst inflation and Country C the least.

Answers to Mini-cases

Mini-case 12.1

          a.   They certainly are important variables. However, they may be difficult to define and quantify.

          b.   Yes, we leave it as a student exercise to comment on additional variables.

          c.   Yes. We might be shocked to see where the U. S. stands in terms of infant mortality and education drop out rates. This might be a clue to future quality of life if these trends are not reversed.

          d.   Yes. Even though not all variables are included, it may yield insight into the perceptions of the population.

Mini-case 12.2

    a.-b.   Grade points can be misleading. Competitive universities look at the different levels of the courses at the school from which you came. They also determine if these courses were taken or avoided. If avoided, the probability of acceptance at a highly competitive college is low.

Mini-case 12.3

            It is difficult to determine using subjective analysis, but because of recent increases in food, housing, and medical costs, these components have probably increased.

Mini-case 12.4

    a.

YEAR	DM	CPI/100	Real Value of DM
1914	1	1.000	1.0000000
1915	1	1.053	1.9496676
1916	1	1.525	0.6557377
1917	1	1.788	0.5592841
1918	1	2.168	0.4612546
1919	1	4.126	0.2402691
1920	1	14.883	0.0674172
1921	1	22.960	0.0435540
1922	1	1474.800	0.0006781
1923	1	1,261,600,000,000.000	0.0000000

    b.   Yes.

Mini-case 12.5

    a.   An almost infinite number of variables or factors contribute to intelligence.
    b.   The probability of achieving such a goal must be placed at 0.

Chapter 13 Solutions

 Answers to Concept Checks

    13.A   False. The null hypothesis is that there exists no relationship between the rows and columns of data.

Answers to Odd-Numbered Exercises

    13.1   a. H_o states that there is no relationship between sex and the color of car purchased. The same proportion of male/female holds for all car colors. H_A states that at least one proportion is different.

            b.   67.84
            c.   Given at 87.
            d. $df = 4$
            e. $X^2_{test} = 75.1714$
            f.   5% level: $X^2_{test} = 75.1714 > X^2_{.05(4)} = 9.488$, Reject H_o.
               1% level: $X^2_{test} = 75.1714 > X^2_{.01(4)} = 13.277$, Reject H_o.

               Using MINITAB: since .05 & .01 ≥ .000, we reject H_o.

            g.   I would check to see if my customer base was more male or female. Then I would stock the colors that each sex likes. For example, males seem to prefer white and gray, while females prefer red and blue.

13.3   a. H_o: there is no relationship between age and employment.

         b.   10% level: $X^2_{\text{test}} = 2.733 > X^2_{.10(1)} = 2.706$, Reject H_o.
Using MINITAB, since $.10 \geq .098$, we reject H_o.

         c.   10% level: $X^2_{\text{test}} = 2.064 \leq X^2_{.01(1)} = 2.706$, ISER H_o.

         d.   We can go through an analysis department by department to ensure that there is no age discrimination taking place now. If there is, we must correct immediately.

13.5   a.   Since $X^2_{\text{test}} = 165.038 > X^2_{.05(3)} = 7.815$, Reject H_o.

           Using MINITAB, since $.05 \geq .000$ we reject H_o. Yes, there is a relationship between sex and the hours of play.

         b.   Maybe most of the female members are housewives. They frequent the club during the day. When the males return from work they go to the club for a game.

13.7   a.   Since $X^2_{\text{test}} = 64.88 > X^2_{.05(3)} = 7.815$, Reject H_o.

           Using MINITAB, since $.05 \geq .000$ we reject H_o. Yes there is a relationship between sex and the hours of play.

         b.   Since $X^2_{\text{test}} = 64.88 > X^2_{.01(3)} = 11.345$, Reject H_o.
Using MINITAB, since $.01 \geq .000$ we reject H_o. Yes, there is a relationship between sex and the hours of play.

13.9   a.   Since $X^2_{\text{test}} = 2.65 \leq X^2_{.01(2)} = 9.210$, ISER H_o.

           Using MINITAB, since $.01 < .265$ we have ISER H_o. There is no relationship between age and delinquent payments.

         b.   No, $df = 2$, not 1.

13.11   a.   Since $X^2_{\text{test}} = 1.168 \leq X^2_{.05(4)} = 9.488$, ISER H_o.

           Using MINITAB, since $.05 < .883$ we have ISER H_o. There is no relationship between professions and beer consumption.

         b.   In terms of marketing, we would have wished that a relationship did exist, then we could exploit the marketing niche.

13.13   a. H_o: there is no relationship between air-to-air missiles in terms of their destructive capability.

         b.   27.29

         c. $df = 4$

         d.   No, Yates' correction factor is used only when $df = 1$.

         e. $X^2_{\text{test}} = 2.6649 \leq X^2_{.10(4)} = 7.779$, ISER H_o.
Using MINITAB, since $.10 < .616$, we have ISER H_O. There is no relationship between professions and beer consumption.

13.15   a.   Since $X^2_{\text{test}} = 36.89 > X^2_{.05(8)} = 15.5073$, reject H_O.

           Using MINITAB, since $.05 \geq .000$, we reject H_O. There is a relationship between the continent of birth and rankings.

         b.   It certainly appears possible barring any mitigating circumstances.

13.17   Since $X^2_{\text{test}} = 56.509 > X^2_{.05(4)} = 9.488$, reject H_O.

       Using MINITAB, since $.05 \geq .000$, we reject H_O.

13.19   a.   Since $X^2_{\text{test}} = 26.854 > X^2_{.05(12)} = 21.026$, reject H_O.

           Using MINITAB, since $.05 \geq .008$, we reject H_O,

         b.   To concentrate on their market niche and to know where to advertise, and to see the draw the store has.

13.21 Since $X^2_{\text{test}} = 5072 \le X^2_{.05(4)} = 9.488$, ISER H_O.

Using MINITAB, since $.05 < .280$ we have ISER H_O.

13.23 Since $X^2_{\text{test}} = 20.67 > X^2_{.05(6)} = 12.592$ reject H_O.

Using MINITAB, since $.05 \ge .002$, we reject H_O.

13.24 a. 56.17

b. $df = 3$

c. Since $X^2_{\text{test}} = 27.46 > X^2_{.05(3)} = 7.815$, reject H_O.
Using MINITAB, since $.05 \ge .000$, we reject H_O. There is a relationship between age and the color of Christmas trees.

13.26 a. Since $X^2_{\text{test}} = 1.6503 \le X^2_{.01(3)} = 11.345$, ISER H_O.

Using MINITAB, since $.01 < .648$, we have ISER H_O.

b. It may be possible to gear curricula to excel at standardized tests. An example would be to make Latin a requirement. Some educators believe that taking Latin will improve SAT scores by over 100 points.

13.28 Since $X^2_{\text{test}}(17.76) > X^2_{.05(3)}(7.815)$, reject H_O.

13.30 The expected frequencies are generated by assuming that the observations are normally distributed with a specified mean and standard deviation. Therefore, the probability of finding an observation within a given interval can be determined. Subsequently, these probabilities can be used to generate expected frequencies by multiplying by the number of observations in the distribution. A comparison of observed with expected frequencies serves as the base for the goodness of fit test.

Answers to Mini-cases

Mini-case 13.1

a. $X^2_{\text{test}} = 4.1075 > X^2_{.05(1)}3.841$; hence, the test discriminates against minorities.

f_o	f_e	$f_o - f_e$	$(f_o - f_e)^2$	$(f_o - f_e)^2/f_e$
43	34.654	8.346	69.6557	2.0100339
53	61.346	−8.346	69.6557	1.1354565
105	113.346	−8.346	69.6557	0.6145406
209	200.654	8.346	69.6557	0.3471434
			$X^2_{\text{test}} = 4.1074795$	

b. $X^2_{Y\text{-test}} = 3.6298 \le X^2_{.05(1)}3.841$; hence, the test does not discriminate against minorities.

f_o	f_e	$|f_o - f_e| - .5$	$[|f_o - f_e| - .5]^2$	$[|f_o - f_e| - .5]^2/f_e$
43	34.654	7.846	61.5597	1.17764101
53	61.346	7.846	61.5597	1.0034838
105	113.346	7.846	61.5597	0.5431133
209	200.654	7.846	61.5597	0.3067954
			$X^2_{\text{test}} = 3.6298026$	

c. The chi-square test statistic, with and without Yates' correction factor, yields different results. The inclusion of the Yates' correction factor reduced the test statistic so that it fell in the ISER region. To have ISER for the hypothesis means the test does not discriminate against minorities.

Mini-case 13.2

a. No, because $df > 1. (df = 2)$

b.

f_o	f_e	$f_o - f_e$	$(f_o - f_e)^2$	$(f_o - f_e)^2/f_e$
19	17.5	1.5	2.25	0.1285714
6	7.5	−1.5	2.25	0.3000000
16	17.5	−1.5	2.25	0.1285714
9	7.5	1.5	2.25	0.3000000
7	7.0	0.0	0.00	0.0000000
3	3.0	0.0	0.00	0.0000000

$$X^2_{\text{test}} = 0.8571428$$

Since $X^2_{\text{test}} = (08571428) \le X^2_{.05(2)}(5.991)$, we have ISER for the null hypothesis that the home court advantage does not exist. The team has statistically the same percentage at home, away, or on neutral courts.

Chapter 14 Solutions

 Answers to Concept Checks

14.A   True, as long as ties are discarded.

14.B   False. They can yield opposite results.

14.C   True.

14.D   False. The Wilcoxon signed-rank test requires paired data while the Wilcoxon rank sum test can deal with unequal sample sizes.

14.E   False. It is essentially a weighted average of the sum of the medians for the 3 or more populations.

14.F   True.

14.G   False. The greater chance the null hypothesis will not be rejected.

Answers to Odd-Numbered Exercises

14.1   a.   Sign test of median $= 0.00000$ versus > 0.00000

	N	Below	Equal	Above	p	Median
C3	14	6	1	7	0.5000	0.5000

        b.   Many factors could be intervening such as labor management problems, a holiday season in which there may naturally be more defective parts, etc.
        c.   Possibly.

14.3   a.   Sign test of median $= 0.00000$ versus not $= 0.00000$

	N	Below	Equal	Above	p	Median
C3	16	3	1	12	0.0352	2.000

        b.   It is much more difficult to predict teams using the point spreads as the purpose of the point spread is to equalize the teams for betting purposes.

14.5   Sign test of median = 0.00000 versus > 0.00000

	N	Below	Equal	Above	p	Median
C3	24	15	1	8	0.9534	−1.050

14.7   Sign test of median = 0.00000 versus > 0.00000

	N	Below	Equal	Above	p	Median
C3	30	23	0	7	0.9993	−8.000

14.9   a.   Friend 1 seems to be better at quantitative courses and friend 2 is better in the arts.

   b.   Test of median = 0.00000 versus median not = 0.00000

	N	N for Test	Wilcoxon Statistic	p	Estimated Median
C3	21	20	99.0	0.837	−0.5000

14.11   a.   Test of median = 0.00000 versus median not 0 0.00000

	N	N for Test	Wilcoxon Statistic	p	Estimated Median
C3	16	15	97.5	0.036	2.000

   b.   The results were the same with the sign test.

14.13   Test of median = 0.00000 versus median > 0 0.00000

	N	N for Test	Wilcoxon Statistic	p	Estimated Median
C3	24	23	61.5	0.990	−9.500

14.15   Test of median = 0.00000 versus median < 0.00000

	N	N for Test	Wilcoxon Statistic	p	Estimated Median
C4	30	30	38.5	0.000	−8.000

14.17   a.   Not necessarily, sometimes opposites attract (this would make the null hypothesis $r_s \leq 0$) and sometimes people with the same interests pal around (this would make the null hypothesis $r_s \geq 0$). If we had no reason to believe we were opposites or not, the null hypothesis is $r_s = 0$.

   b. $r_s = 0.5143$

   c. $z_{test} = 1.924$. Since $1.924 \leq z_{.05/2}$ (1.96), we have ISER for H_o; there is no difference in movie preference. Note that at a 10% level of significance we would reject the null hypothesis.

14.19 $z_{test} = -2.6676$. Since $|-2.6676| > z_{.05/2}$ (1.96), we must reject H_o, there is a difference in the ranks of the two friends. This refers to one student being superior in the quantitative classes and one superior in the arts.

14.21   a.   That $R_s \leq 0$.

   b. $R_s = 0.5169$; $z_{test} = 2.0019$. We are in the tail of rejection. Since $2.0019 > z_{.05/2}(1.960)$, we must reject H_o; there is a difference in the ranks of the predictions.

14.23   The sample size is too small to use z_{test}. For a two tailed test, $R_{s:.01/2(8)} = 0.881$. Since $|1.0| > 0.881$, we must reject H_o. There is an inverse relationship between the ranks given by the engineer and the artist.

14.25 a. As a 2-tailed test, we want to be sure the performances of minorities and non-minorities are the same.

b. Mann-Whitney Confidence Interval and Test

Min $N = 12$ Median $= 70.50$
NonMin $N = 19$ Median $= 73.00$
Point estimate for ETA1 − ETA2 is 1.50
95.1 Percent C.I for ETA1 − ETA2 is (−12.00, 14.01)
$W = 196.5$
Test of ETA1 = ETA2 vs. ETA1 $\sim$ = ETA2 is significant at 0.8711.
The test is significant at 0.8710 (adjusted for ties).
Cannot reject at alpha $= 0.05$
There is no difference between performance between minorities and non-minorities.

c. A rejection of H_o means our screening test is breaking the law. Ignorance of this fact is not an excuse for breaking the law.

14.27 Mann-Whitney Confidence Interval and Test

old $N = 15$ Median $= 14.000$
new $N = 10$ Median $= 2.500$
Point estimate for ETA1 − ETA2 is 11.000
95.1 Percent C.I. for ETA1 − ETA2 is (6.001, 15.001)
$W = 260.0$
Test of ETA1 = ETA2 vs. ETA1 > ETA2 is significant at 0.0002.
The test is significant at 0.0002 (adjusted for ties).

14.29 Mann-Whitney Confidence Interval and Test

a. $N = 11$ Median $= 45.80$
b. $N = 10$ Median $= 64.30$
Point estimate for ETA1 − ETA2 is −14.55
95.5 Percent C.I. for ETA1 − ETA2 is (−29.40, −0.49)
$W = 90.5$
Test of ETA1 = ETA2 vs. ETA1 $\sim$ = ETA2 is significant at 0.0346.
The test is significant at 0.0346 (adjusted for ties).

14.31 We are involved in a 1-tailed test. Mann-Whitney Confidence Interval and Test

old $N = 7$ Median $= 6.900$
new $N = 6$ Median $= 2.350$
Point estimate for ETA1 − ETA2 is 3.500
98.2 Percent C.I. for ETA1 − ETA2 is (0.300, 6.599)
$W = 68.0$
Test of ETA1 = ETA2 vs. ETA1 > ETA2 is significant at 0.0041.

14.33

LEVEL	NOBS	MEDIAN	AVE. RANK	Z VALUE
1	15	121.000	37.1	3.67
2	12	69.500	24.5	−0.26
3	12	92.000	27.7	0.61
4	11	8.000	8.3	−4.43
OVERALL	50			

$H = 25.06$ d. f. $= 3$ $p = 0.000$
$H = 25.09$ d. f. $= 3$ $p = 0.000$ (adjusted for ties)
Area D has less deaths per 1,000 births than the other areas.

14.35 a.
LEVEL	NOBS	MEDIAN	AVE. RANK	Z VALUE
1	6	9.500	8.0	−0.84
2	6	4.500	5.2	−2.44
3	6	16.500	15.3	3.28
OVERALL	18			

$H = 11.59$ d. f. $= 2$ $p = 0.003$

Brand C outsells B and probably C as well.

b.   Since we reject the null hypothesis, we will no longer need to inventory the three makes of hammers.

14.37 a.
LEVEL	NOBS	MEDIAN	AVE. RANK	Z VALUE
1	7	9.000	11.9	1.14
2	7	2.000	4.1	−3.47
3	5	13.000	15.5	2.55
OVERALL	19			

$H = 13.18$ d. f. $= 2$ $p = 0.001$
$H = 13.22$ d. f. $= 2$ $p = 0.001$ (adjusted for ties)

We must reject the null hypothesis that an equal number of boards are sold daily.

b.   We should not stock the medium priced board.

14.39
LEVEL	NOBS	MEDIAN	AVE. RANK	Z VALUE
1	5	81.70	18.2	0.75
2	7	83.90	18.3	0.96
3	5	85.10	19.2	1.03
4	6	56.90	3.7	−3.68
5	7	82.40	18.3	0.96
OVERALL	30			

$H = 13.60$ d. f. $= 4$ $p = 0.009$

We must reject that all insurance companies are rated equally. Clearly Company D has lower ratings than the other companies.

14.41 a. $K = 1.4286$

The observed no. of runs $= 15$
The expected no. of runs $= 11.2857$
9 Observations above K 12 below
The test is significant at 0.0895
Cannot reject at alpha $= 0.05$

b.   If the gambling mechanism was becoming predictable we may find ourselves out of business.

14.43 a. $K = 1.6667$

The observed no. of runs $= 11$
The expected no of runs $= 11.6667$
16 Observations above K 8 below
The test is significant at 0.7529
Cannot reject at alpha $= 0.05$

b.   If searches were predictable, it would be easy to engage in illegal activities.

14.45   a.   A definite pattern exists. The data are nonrandom.
         b. $K = 1.8696$
               the observed no. of runs $= 6$
               The expected no. of runs $= 16.6522$
               60 Observations above K 9 below
               The test is significant at 0.0000

14.47   a. $K = 1.6250$
               The observed no. of runs $= 7$
               The expected no. of runs $= 8.5000$
               10 Observations above K 6 below
               *N Small — Following approx. may be invalid
               The test is significant at 0.4056
               Cannot reject at alpha $= 0.05$
               The data is random.
         b.   The results differ from that of the Durbin–Weston test, which stated that autocorrelation was
               present in the data. The Durbin–Weston d statistic is the more powerful test. In the area of
               going from positive to negative residuals (and vice versa), there was some variation causing
               the runs to increase making the runs test believe the residuals were random.

14.49   Friedman test for Bac Count by med

         $s = 7.00$ d.f. $= 2$ $p = 0.031$

Med	N	Est Median	Sum of RANKS
1	6	71.50	11.0
2	6	86.50	17.0
3	6	50.50	8.0

         Grand median $= 69.50$

14.51   Friedman test of C1 by C2 blocked by C3

         $S = 0.19$ d.f. $= 2$ $p = 0.911$
         $S = 0.29$ d.f. $= 2$ $p = 0.905$ (adjusted for ties)

C2	N	Est Median	Sum of RANKS
1	8	26.500	15.0
2	8	27.833	16.5
3	8	27.167	16.5

         Ground median $= 27.167$

14.53   Friedman test of C1 by C2 blocked by C3

         $s = 9.00$ d.f. $= 2$ $p = 0.011$

C2	N	Est Median	Sum of RANKS
1	6	75.17	15.0
2	6	40.00	6.0
3	6	75.83	15.0

         Grand median $= 63.67$

14.55   Friedman test of C1 by C2 blocked by C3

         $s = 7.72$ d.f. $= 3$ $p = 0.053$
         $s = 7.86$ d.f. $= 3$ $p = 0.050$ (adjusted for ties)

		Est	*Sum of*
C2	*N*	*Median*	*RANKS*
1	11	6.6625	36.5
2	11	6.2375	21.0
3	11	6.3625	29.0
4	11	6.2875	23.5

Grand median = 6.3875

14.57 a. Yes, it does appear that perfume B has superior ratings to perfume A.

b. Those students who preferred A did so by a narrow margin. Hence the Wilcoxon signed-rank test should have a better chance of rejection of the null hypothesis.

c. Sign Test of Median = 0.00000 vs < 0.00000

	N	*Below*	*Equal*	*Above*	*p*	*Median*
C3	20	15	0	5	0.0207	−5.000

d. Test of Median = 0.00000 vs Median < 0.000000

		N for	*Wilcoxon*		*Estimated*
	N	*Test*	*Statistic*	*p*	*Median*
C3	20	20	15.0	0.000	−4.500

e. There is a difference in the results at the 1% level, but not at the 5% level.

f. For the sign test, $|z_{test}|$ (2.236) $\leq z_{.01/2}$ (2.576), we have ISER for H_o (the per fumed are equal) and for the Wilcoxon rank sum test, since $|z_{test}|$ (3.360) $> z_{.01/2}$ (2.576), we reject H_o (perfume B exceeds the ratings of perfume A).

14.59 a. Sign Test of median = 0.00000 vs not = 0.00000

	N	*Below*	*Equal*	*Above*	*p*	*Median*
C3	25	7	0	18	0.0433	4.000

b. Test of Median = 0.000000 vs Median not = 0.000000

		N for	*Wilcoxon*		*Estimated*
	N	*Test*	*Statistic*	*p*	*Median*
C3	25	26	296.5	0.000	4.500

c. The sign test could not reject H_O, while the Wilcoxon rank sum test rejected it. Those that favored ibuprofen did so by a narrow margin.

14.61 MULTIPLE $R = R_S = .595$

14.63 Mann-Whitney Confidence Interval and Test

C1 $N = 8$ Median = 7.50
C2 $N = 6$ Median = 4.60
Point estimate for ETA1 − ETA2 is   3.20
95.5 Percent C.I. for ETA1 − ETA2 is (0.11, 5.89)
$W = 76.0$
Test of ETA1 = ETA2 vs. ETA1 $\sim$ = ETA2 is significant at 0.0454.
The test is significant at 0.0452 (adjusted for ties).

14.65 a.

LEVEL	*NOBS*	*MEDIAN*	*AVE. RANK*	*Z VALUE*
1	8	353.0	13.0	−0.42
2	9	344.0	9.2	−2.21
3	10	413.5	19.1	2.56
OVERALL	27		14.0	

$H = 7.52$ d.f. = 2 $p = 0.024$

b. The Wilcoxon rank sum test and the Mann–Whitney test can only deal with 2 treatments of unequal sample sizes.

14.67 $K = 1.4889$

The observed no. of runs $= 24$
The expected no. of runs $= 23.4889$
22 Observations above K 23 below
The test is significant at 0.8775.
Cannot reject at alpha $= 0.05$
The residuals are random with respect to sign.

14.69   Friedman test of Cl by C2 blocked by C3

$s = 0.43$ d. f. $= 3$ $p = 0.934$

C2	N	Est Median	Sum of RANKS
1	7	198.50	18.0
2	7	204.50	19.0
3	7	161.25	16.0
4	7	190.75	17.0

Grand median $= 188.75$

Answers to Mini-cases

Mini-case 14.1

Rankings of Favorite Dates

	Male	Female	Difference	Squared
Going to movies.	5	6	−1	1
Watching TV.	4	12	−8	64
Playing miniature golf.	9	11	−2	4
Visiting friends.	8	8	0	0
Go to a party.	3	2	+1	1
Go to a dance.	10	1	+9	81
Go to a concert.	7	4	+3	9
Out for dinner.	9	3	+6	36
Go to a sporting event.	2	9	−7	49
Go shopping.	11	7	+4	16
Go for a drive.	6	8	−2	4
Go to the beach.	1	5	−4	16
Go to a play or drama.	12	10	+2	4
				$\Sigma = 285$

$r_{S\text{-test}} = 1 - [(6 \bullet 285)/(13 \bullet 168)] = 0.217$, $R_{S\text{-}.05(13)} = 0.566$,
Since $|R_{S\text{-test}}| \leq R_{S\text{-}.05(13)}$, we have ISER for the null hypothesis that there is no relationship between the rankings. Hence, the couple is not compatible.

Mini-case 14.2

Survey	Company A	Company B	Difference	Rank
#1	27	26	+1	7+
#2	24	22	+2	15+
#3	28	27	+1	7+
#4	30	29	+1	7+
#5	21	20	+1	7+
#6	21	30	−9	22−
#7	26	24	+2	15+
#8	30	30	0	N/A
#9	26	25	+1	7+
#10	21	20	+1	7+
#11	20	26	−6	19
#12	29	28	+1	7+
#13	29	26	+3	16+
#14	23	22	+1	7+
#15	23	30	−7	20−
#16	28	26	+2	15+
#17	30	29	+1	7+
#18	17	16	+1	7+
#19	16	24	−8	21−
#20	27	26	+1	7+
#21	29	28	+1	7+
#22	21	26	−5	18
#23	17	16	+1	7+
#24	27	23	+4	17+
#25	20	30	−10	23−

a. Sign Test of Median = 0.00000 vs not = 0.00000

	N	Below	equal	Above	p	Median
C3	23	6	1	18	0.0227	1.000

b. Test of Median = 0.000000 vs Median not = 0.000000

		Not for	Wilcoxon		Estimated
	N	Test	Statistic	p	Median
C3	25	24	171.0	0.558	1.000

$$z_{test} = \frac{100 - \dfrac{22(23)}{4}}{\sqrt{\dfrac{22(23)(45)}{24}}} = -0.8603$$

Since $z_{test} \le z_{.05}$, we have ISER for the null hypothesis that there is no difference between the performances of the two long distance companies.

c. The reason for the different results is because those who favored company A do so by a small margin, while those who preferred company B did so by a wider margin. The sign test is unaffected by the margin difference, but the Wilcoxon signed-rank test is.

Answers to Concept Checks

15.A   True.

15.B   False. A payoff is a union between an event, which is not controlled by the decision maker, and an act, which is controlled by the decision maker.

15.C   True.

15.D   False. The manager will receive either (800), 0, 2000, or 8000. The 1240 represents a weighted pay-off of all four payoffs.

15.E   False. The maximin technique selects the maximum value from the minimums of each act.

15.F   False. It disregards all data except for the event with the greatest chance of occurring.

15.G   True.

15.H   False. A regret is the absolute difference between a particular payoff and the largest payoff for that event.

15.I   True.

15.J   True.

Answers to Odd-Numbered Exercises

15.1   a.   Student evaluations and comments, evaluation by peers, etc.

b.   Probably not. There will be a number of outstanding teachers and the selection of the best will be arbitrary.

c.   Possibly a diversified committee including students, faculty, alumni, and administrators.

d.   It is possible that political factors could weigh heavily.

15.3

	ACT-I	ACT-II	ACT-III
E-1 (100,000)	−3,000	0	1,000
E-2 (500,000)	25,000	20,000	13,000
E-3 (1,000,000)	60,000	45,000	28,000

15.5   There are no inadmissible acts.

15.7   A-2 dominates A-4 and A-6. A-4 and A-6 are inadmissible.

15.9   A-1* = 71, A-2 = 60, A-3 = 57, A-4 = 67 *Optimal

15.11   Remember that ACT-I was inadmissible and no computation is actually needed for it. ACT-II = 995,000*; ACT-III = 970,000 *Optimal

15.13   a.   No, the maximin criterion is nonprobabilistic, meaning probabilities play no part in the decision.

b.   The worst payoff for each act is: A-1 = (10); A-2 = (20); A-3 = 10*; A-4 = 10*. *Optimal

c.   A-1* = 67; A-2 = 46; A-3 = 37; A-4 = 57 *Optimal

d.   More comfortable with "c." The readings for "b" came from the two smallest weighted events.

15.15   a.   The maximum likelihood criteria states that E-1 will take place, and if it does, we should select A-5 and make 30.

          b.   There are no inadmissible acts.

          c.   A-1 = 21; A-2* = 21.5; A-3 = 20.5; A-4 = 16; A-5 = 19.5; A-6 = 19.5 *Optimal

          d.   The worst payoff for each act is: A-1 = 10*; A-2 = 5; A-3 =10*;A-4 = 10*; A-5 = 0; A-6 = 15: *Optimal

          e.   We can obtain different results by using the different rules.

15.17   a.   The inadmissible acts are A-4, A-5, and A-6.

          b.   A-1* = 38, A-2 = 34, A-3 = 30 *Optimal

          c.   The worst payoff for each act is: A-1 = 10; A-2 = 20; A-3 = 30*, A-4 = 20; A-5 = 20; A-6 = 10 *Optimal

          d.   A-4 = 50.

          e.   The highest payoff is 50 and it occurs under A-1.

          f.   With the Laplace criterion, we merely compute the arithmetic mean for each act. The means are A-1 = A-2 = A-3 = 30*, A-4 = A-5 = A-6 = 25.

15.19   a.   A-1 is inadmissible

          b.   A-2 = 24.7, A-3 = 22.5, A-4 = 38, A-5* = 47 *Optimal

          c.   The worst payoff for each act is: A-1 = 10; A-2 = 8; A-3 = 0, A-4 = 20, A-5 = 30* *Optimal

          d.   A-5 =30

          e.   The highest payoff is 300 and it occurs under A-3, A-4, and A-5.

          f.   The means are: A-1 = 103.33; A-2 = 119.33; A-3 = 150*, A-4 = 140; A-5 = 143.33: *Optimal.

15.21   a.   There is at least one zero per event and there are no negative values.

          b.

	A-1	A-2	A-3	A-4
E-1	150	160	180	200
E-2	390	400	350	400
E-3	530	520	510	500

          c.   A-1 = 10, A-2* = 8, A-3 = 35, A-4 = 12 *Optimal

          d.   A-1 = 50, A-2 = 40, A-3 = 50, A-4 = 30*: *Optimal

          e.   The maximum likelihood criterion states that E-2 will still take place, and if it does we would like to select A-2 or A-4 with 0 regrets.

          f.   The mean regrets are: A-1 = 20; A-2 = 16.67; A-3 = 30; A-4 = 10*: *Optimal

15.23   A-1 and A-2 are inadmissible. A-3* = 4, A-4 = 15 *Optimal

15.25   a.   There are no inadmissible acts.

          b.   A-1 = 170, A-2* = 200, A-3 = 190 *Optimal

          c.   EPPI = 260, EVPI = 60

          d.   A-1 = 90, A-2* = 60, A-3 = 70

          e.   EVPI and the minimum weighted regrets are synonyms.

15.27   A-5 and A-6 are inadmissible. EPPI = 191, EVPI = 45

15.29   A new city might require my quality of life to decline so, in essence, the increased income will not offset my decline in lifestyle.

15.31   a.   A-1 = −20, A-2 = −240, A-3* = 190 *Optimal

          b.   A-1* = 5.7, A-2 = 5.6, A-3 = 5.4 *Optimal

          c.   In this instance, the optimum act using payoffs is the worst choice using utils.

15.33 If they were regrets, there would have to be at least one zero reading for each event. This is due to the fact that the regrets are found by taking the maximum payoff, per event, then subtracting that value from every value in the row. There are no such readings in the table.

15.35 a.

	A	C
E-1	40,000	0
E-2	0	0
E-3	0	40,000

b. A = 28,000, C* = 4,000 *Optimal
c. The worst regret for each act is: A = 40,000*; C = 40,000*: *Optimal
d. Select C with 0 regrets.
e. The mean regrets are: A = 13,333.33*; C = 13,333.33*: *Optimal

15.37 The maximin technique is a nonprobabilistic technique, hence no change. The maximum likelihood would yield different results, one preferring A-2. The expected payoff approach would still prefer A-2 (A-1 = 5.2, A-2* = 356). *Optimal

15.39 A-1 = 16, A-2 = 28, A-3* = 13, A-4 = 37, A-5 = 36 *Optimal

15.41 I would first go by my national association to see if it had done a preliminary research to determine what the big chains would be expecting.

15.43 a. A-2 is inadmissible

b. A-1 = 10,800, A-3* = 12,500 *Optimal
c. EPPI = 12,800, EVPI = 300
d. With EVPI being small, both absolutely and relatively, it would not be worthwhile to pursue additional information. We should proceed with A-3.

15.45 a. There are no inadmissible acts.

b. A-1 = 4,100, A-2 = 4,600, A-3* = 5,000 *Optimal
c. EPPI = 10,000, EVPI = 5,000
EVPI is a relatively large percentage of the optimum choice using Bayes' rule. Additional information might be considered.
d. A-1 = 5,900, A-2 = 5,200, A-3* = 5,000 *Optimal
e. EVPI and the lowest weighted regret are synonyms.

15.47 a. Risk averter

b. A-1 = 6.2, A-2 = 4.0, A-3 = 8.9* *Optimal
c. In this instance, the optimal act is A-3.

15.49 Subjective answer.

Mini-case 15.1

a. To find the inadmissible acts, it is necessary to analyze them in combinations of two. Start with A-1 and A-2. If E-1 occurs, A-2 is superior; if it's E-2, A-2 is equal to A-1; and if E-3 happens, then A-2 is better than A-1. The rule is that one payoff must be greater than and the remaining payoffs must be greater than or equal to the others. When you compare two acts, see if both acts are mentioned. In the A-1/A-2 comparison, for the three events the responses were A-2, the same, and A-2. Since A-1 was not mentioned it is inadmissible and should be eliminated from any further analysis.

   The next comparison is between A-2 and A-3. For the three events, the best choice would be the same A-2, and the same. Since A-3 was never mentioned it is also inadmissible and should be eliminated as a choice. The next combination up for examination is A-2 and A-4. For the three events, the choices would be A2, A-4, A-4. Since both acts are mentioned, neither is inadmissible. For A-2/A-5 it's A-2, A-5, and A-5. Finally, the last combination remaining is A-4/A-5. The choices would be A-4, A-5, and A-5. Therefore, the answer to the question is that A-1 and A-3 are inadmissible.

b. To determine the maximum expected payoffs, it would be necessary to multiply the payoffs for each act by the respective probabilities, and sum the results. For A-2, the computations are $(.5 \times 500) + (.3 \times 100) + (.2 \times 700) = 420$. This essentially says that if you were to make $500, 50% of the time; make $100, 30% of the time, and make $700, 20% of the time your average weighted payoff would be $420. The computations for A-4 and A-5 are: A-4 = $(.5 \times 200) + (.3 \times 500) + (.2 \times 900) = 430$; and A-5 = $(.5 \times -300) + (.3 \times 700) + (.2 \times 1,000) = 260$.

Events	Prob.	A-2		A-4		A-5	
E-1	.5	500	250	200	100	(300)	(150)
E-2	.3	100	30	500	150	700	210
E-3	.2	700	140	900	180	1,000	200
	TOTALS		420		430		260

The answer to part b is 430 from A-4.

c. For the maximin, we select the lowest payoff for each act. For the three acts, it's A-2 = 100, A-4 = 200, and A-5 = (300). The best of these worst conditions is 200 and it's associated with A-4. If we produce A-4, we have a guaranteed minimum income of 200. Remember that probabilities play no part in a maximin analysis.

d. For the maximum likelihood choice, we only look at the event with the greatest probability of occurring. This would be E-1 with a 50% chance of happening. If E-1 did occur, we would have preferred to produce A-2 and made 500.

e. For the maximax analysis, the best or highest payoff is recorded for each act. In our analysis, A-1 = 700, A-2 = 900, a-3 = 1,000, and the best is A-3 = 1,000. This is an overly optimistic way of evaluating the real world. We have selected a payoff we believe only has a 20% chance of occurring. Maximax does not consider the probabilities in its decision criteria.

f. For the principal of insufficient information reason equal weights are assigned to the three events (1/3 each). Assigning equal weights is analogous to computing a straight arithmetic mean. Therefore, for the three acts it's, A-2 = $(500 + 100 + 700)/3 = 433.33$, A-4 = $(200 + 500 + 900)/3 = 533.33$, and A-5 = $(-300 + 700 + 1,000)/3 = 466.67$. The optimum is A-4 at 533.33.

g. In order to compute the minimum weighted regret, regrets must first be computed from the payoffs given. For each event, select the largest individual payoff (maximum value) and subtract that number from every act. For E-1 the highest payoff is 500; therefore, 500 is subtracted from 500, from 200, and from a minus 300. Remember the double minus converts to addition. Since we are seeking an absolute difference between two payoffs, it is not possible to obtain a negative regret. The smallest number possible is zero. There must be at least one zero for each act in the problem. Because we have three acts, we must have at least three zeros in the matrix.

Ev.	Max Value	A-2	A-4	A-5
E-1	500	$500 - 500 = 0$	$500 - 200 = 300$	$500 - -300 = 800$
E-2	700	$700 - 100 = 600$	$700 - 500 = 200$	$700 - 700 = 0$
E-3	1,000	$1000 - 700 = 300$	$1000 - 900 = 100$	$1000 - 1000 = 0$

After the regret table is made, a weighted average regret will be obtained by multiplying corresponding weights and regrets, and summing the results. The lowest weighted regret refers to A-4 and is 230. Please note that even though A4 has no zero regrets, and A-5 has two of them, A-4 is still the optimum choice.

Events	Prob.	A-2		A-4		A-5	
E-1	.5	0	0	300	150	800	400
E-2	.3	600	180	200	60	0	0
E-3	.2	300	60	100	20	0	0
		TOTALS	240		230		400

h. For the minimax payoff, the worst regret is selected for each act (the largest numerical value), then the best (minimal) value is selected from that group. The worst scenario for A-2 = 600, for A-4 = 300, and for A-5 = 800. The optimum of these values would be the 300 associated with A-4. Minimax means selecting the minimal value of the column (acts) maximums. Remember that probabilities do not enter into the analysis.

i. The EVPI can be obtained two ways. First, it's equal to the minimum weighted regret (A-4 = 230). Second, it can be obtained by subtracting the expected payoff with perfect information from the maximum expected payoff (A-4 = 430). To compute the expected payoff, find the highest payoff for each event (row) and compute the weighted average.

Events	Probability	A-2	A-4	A-5	Optimum	Weight
E-1 .5		500	200	(300)	500	250
E-2	0.3	100	500	700	700	210
E-3	0.2	700	900	1,000	1,000	200

Expected Payoff With Perfect Information = 660
EVPI = 660 - 430 = 230

Mini-case 15.2

Events	Probability	A-1	A-2	A-3
E-1	0.2	$3,750	$5,000	$6,500
E-2	0.5	5,050	5,800	6,700
E-3	0.3	5,700	6,200	6,800

A-1: $4,985 - $1,000 = $3,985*
A-2: $5,760 - $1,750 + $4,010
A-3: $6,690 - $2,500 = $4,190

Answers to Concept Checks

16.A   False. We first will consider if we want additional information, prior to making our main decision.

16.B   True.

16.C   False. They could equal any value including 1, >1, and <1

16.D   False. We prune at each act and compute a weighted average at each event.

Answers to Odd-Numbered Exercises

Exercises 16.1, 16.11, 16.21, 16.31

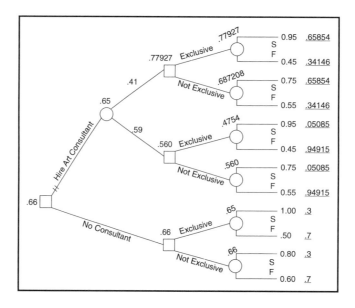

$$\begin{aligned}
\text{Pos S } .3 \bullet .9 &= .27 \quad .6585 = \Pr(S|Pos) = .27/.41 \\
\text{Pos F } .7 \bullet .2 &= .14 \quad .3415 = \Pr(F|Pos) = .14/.41 \\
\Sigma &= .41 \\
\text{Neg S } .3 \bullet .1 &= .03 \quad .0508 = \Pr(S|Neg) = .03/.59 \\
\text{Neg F } .7 \bullet .8 &= .56 \quad .9492 = \Pr(F|Neg) = .56/.59 \\
\Sigma &= .59
\end{aligned}$$

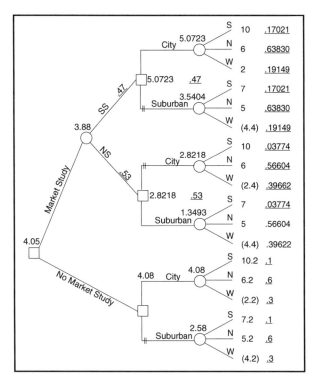

Exercises 16.3, 16.13, 16.23, 16.33

$$SS\ S\ .1\bullet.8 = .08 \quad .1702 = Pr(S|SS) = .08/.47$$
$$SS\ N\ .6\bullet.5 = .30 \quad .6383 = Pr(N|SS) = .30/.47$$
$$SS\ W\ .3\bullet.3 = .09 \quad .1915 = Pr(W|SS) = .09/.47$$
$$\Sigma = .47$$
$$NS\ S\ .1\bullet.2 = .02 \quad .0378 = Pr(S|NS) = .02/.53$$
$$NS\ N\ .6\bullet.5 = .30 \quad .5660 = Pr(N|NS) = .30/.53$$
$$NS\ W\ .3\bullet.7 = .21 \quad .3962 = Pr(W|NS) = .21/.53$$
$$\Sigma = .53$$

Exercises 16.5, 16.15, 16.25. 16.35

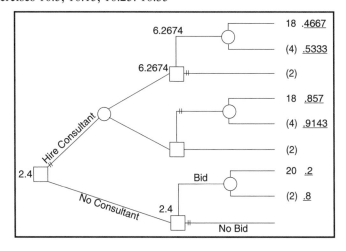

Fav S $.2 \bullet .7 = .14$ $.4667 = Pr(S|Fav) = .14/.30$
Fav F $.8 \bullet .2 = .16$ $.5333 = Pr(F|Fav) = .16/.30$
$\Sigma = .30$
Unf S $.2 \bullet .3 = .06$ $.0857 = Pr(S|Unf) = .06/.70$
Unf F $.8 \bullet .8 = .64$ $.9143 = Pr(F|Unf) = .64/.70$
$\Sigma = .70$

Exercises 16.7, 16.17, 16.27, 16.37

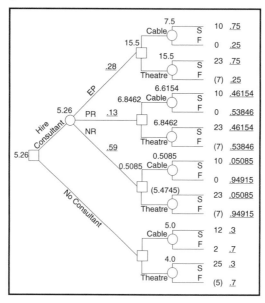

EP: S $.3 \bullet .7 = .21$ $.7500 = Pr \quad (S|ep) = .21/.28$
EP F $.7 \bullet .1 = .07$ $.2500 = Pr(F|EP) = .07/.28$
$\Sigma = .28$
PR S $.3 \bullet .2 = .06$ $.4615 = Pr(S|PR) = .06/.13$
PR F $.7 \bullet .1 = .07$ $.5385 = Pr(F|PR) = .07/.13$
$\Sigma = .13$
NR S $.3 \bullet .1 = .03$ $.0508 = Pr(S|NR) = .03/.59$
NR F $.7 \bullet .8 = .56$ $.9492 = Pr(F|NR) = .56/.59$
$\Sigma = .59$

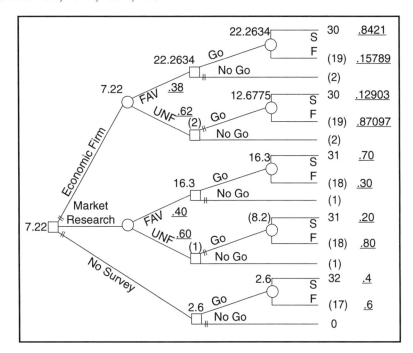

ECONOMETRIC FIRM

Fav S .4•.8 = .32   .8421 = Pr(S|Fav)

Fav F .6•.1 = .06   .1579 = Pr(F|Fav)

   Σ = .38

Unf S .4•.2 = 0.8   .1290 = Pr(S|Unf)

Unf F .6•.9 = .54   .8710 = Pr(F|Unf)

   Σ = .62

MARKET RESEARCH FIRM

Fav S .4•.7 = .28   .70 = Pr(S|Fav)

Fav F .6•.2 = .12   .30 = Pr(F|Fav)

Σ = .40

Unf S .4•.3 = .12   .20 = Pr(S|Unf)

Unf F .6•.8 = .48   .80 = Pr(F|Unf)

Σ = .60

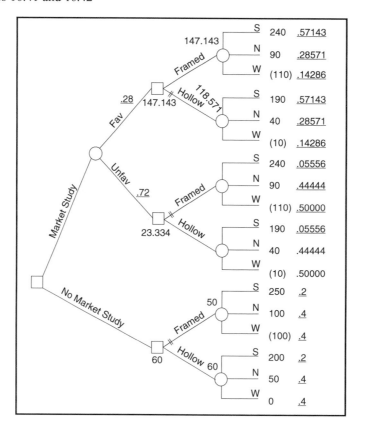

Fav S $.2 \bullet .8 = .16$ $.5715 = Pr(S|Fav) = .16/.28$
Fav M $.4 \bullet .2 = .08$ $.2857 = Pr(M|Fav) = .08/.28$
Fav W $.4 \bullet .1 = .04$ $.1428 = Pr(W|Fav) = .04/.28$
$\Sigma = .28$
Unf S $.2 \bullet .2 = .04$ $.0556 = Pr(S|Unf) = .04/.72$
Unf M $.4 \bullet .8 = .32$ $.4444 = Pr(M|Unf) = .32/.72$
Unf W $.4 \bullet .9 = .36$ $.5000 = Pr(W|Unf) = .36/.72$
$\Sigma = .72$

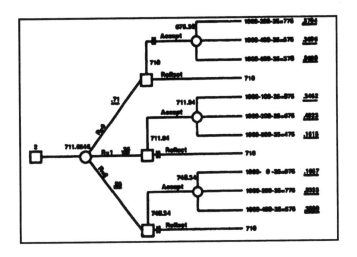

$$R = 0: p = .1 \qquad .5 \bullet .81 = .405 \qquad .5704 = .405/.710$$
$$R = 0: p = .2 \qquad .4 \bullet .64 = .256 \qquad .3606 = .256/.710$$
$$R = 0: p = .3 \qquad .1 \bullet .49 = .049 \qquad .0690 = .049/.710$$
$$\Sigma = .710$$
$$R = 1: p = .1 \qquad .5 \bullet .18 = .090 \qquad .3462 = .090/.260$$
$$R = 1: p = .2 \qquad .4 \bullet .32 = .128 \qquad .4923 = .128/.260$$
$$R = 1: p = .3 \qquad .1 \bullet .42 = .042 \qquad .1615 = .042/.260$$
$$\Sigma = .260$$
$$R = 2: p = .1 \qquad .5 \bullet .01 = .005 \qquad .1667 = .005/.030$$
$$R = 2: p = .2 \qquad .4 \bullet .04 = .016 \qquad .5333 = .016/.030$$
$$R = 2: p = .3 \qquad .1 \bullet .09 = .009 \qquad .3000 = .009/.030$$
$$\Sigma = .030$$

Exercise 16.45

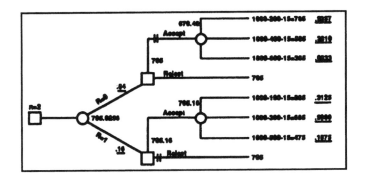

$$R = 0: p = .1 \qquad .5 \bullet .9 = .45 \qquad .5357 = .45/.84$$
$$R = 0: p = .2 \qquad .4 \bullet .8 = .32 \qquad .3810 = .32/.84$$
$$R = 0: p = .3 \qquad .1 \bullet .7 = .07 \qquad .0833 = .07/.84$$
$$\Sigma = .84$$
$$R = 1: p = .1 \qquad .5 \bullet .1 = .05 \qquad .3125 = .05/.16$$
$$R = 1: p = .2 \qquad .4 \bullet .2 = .08 \qquad .5000 = .08/.16$$
$$R = 1: p = .3 \qquad .1 \bullet .3 = .03 \qquad .1875 = .03/.16$$

Exercise 16.47

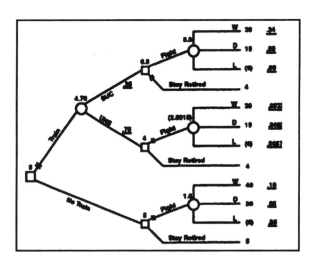

$$\text{Suc W } .10 \bullet .6 = .06 \qquad .2400 = \Pr(W|Suc) = .06/.25$$
$$\text{Suc D } .05 \bullet .4 = .02 \qquad .0800 = \Pr(D|Suc) = .02/.25$$
$$\text{Suc L } .85 \bullet .2 = .17 \qquad .6800 = \Pr(L|Suc) = .17/.25$$
$$\Sigma = .25$$
$$\text{Uns W } .10 \bullet .4 = .04 \qquad .0533 = \Pr(W|Uns) = .04/.75$$
$$\text{Uns D } .05 \bullet .6 = .03 \qquad .0400 = \Pr(D|Uns) = .03/.75$$
$$\text{Uns L } .85 \bullet .8 = .68 \qquad .9067 = \Pr(L|Uns) = .68/.75$$
$$\Sigma = .75$$

Exercise 16.49

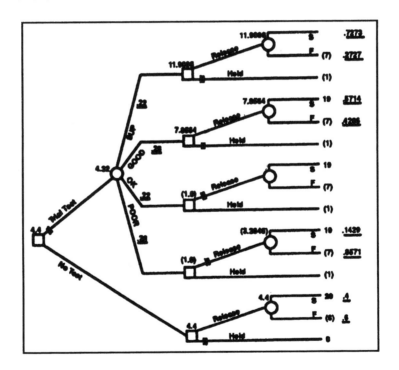

639

Sup S	$.4 \bullet .4 = .16$	$.7273 = \Pr(S	Sup) = .16/.22$
Sup F	$.6 \bullet .1 = .06$	$.2727 = \Pr(F	Sup) = .06/.22$
	$\Sigma = .22$	
Good S	$.4 \bullet .4 = .16$	$.5714 = \Pr(S	Good) = .16/.28$
Good F	$.6 \bullet .2 = .12$	$.4286 = \Pr(F	Good) = .12/.28$
	$\Sigma = .28$	
Ok S	$.4 \bullet .1 = .04$	$.2222 = \Pr(S	Ok) = .04/.22$
Ok F	$.6 \bullet .3 = .18$	$.7778 = \Pr(F	Ok) = .18/.22$
	$\Sigma = .22$	
Poor S	$.4 \bullet .1 = .04$	$.1429 = \Pr(S	Poor) = .04/.28$
Poor F	$.6 \bullet .4 = .24$	$.8571 = \Pr(F	Poor) = .24/.28$
	$\Sigma = .28$	

Answers to Mini-cases

Mini-case 16.1

Fav H	$.35 \bullet .90 = .315$	$.5575 = \Pr(H	Fav) = .315/.565$
Fav M	$.40 \bullet .50 = .200$	$.3540 = \Pr(M	Fav) = .200/.565$
Fav L	$.25 \bullet .20 = .050$	$.0885 = \Pr(L	Fav) = .050/.565$
	$\Sigma = .586$	
Unf H	$.35 \bullet .10 = .035$	$.0804 = \Pr(H	Unf) = .035/.435$
Unf M	$.40 \bullet .50 = .200$	$.4590 = \Pr(M	Unf) = .200/.435$
Unf L	$.25 \bullet .80 = .200$	$.4590 = \Pr(L	Unf) = .200/.435$
	$\Sigma = .435$	

Chapter 17   Solutions

 Answers to Concept Checks

17.A   False. Deming would probably say this was mass inspection.

17.B   True.

17.C   True.

17.D   True.

Answers to Odd-Numbered Exercises

17.1   Subjective answer.

17.3   Subjective answer.

17.5   The system is in control when there are no assignable causes, or when all of the variations in a system are random.

17.7   Ranges are very sensitive and volatile in large samples.

17.9 $X = 3.020$, LCL $= -47.45$, UCL $= 53.48$. System in control.

17.11 $S = 30.32$, LCL $= 0$, UCL $= 68.72$. System in control.

17.13

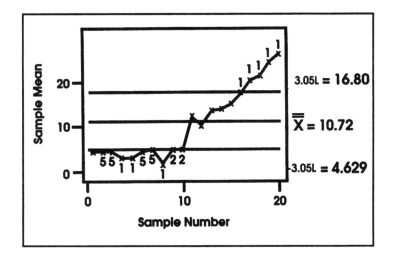

The means 17, 20, 20.667, 24, and 25.33 are above UCL. The system is not in control as an assignable cause seems to be influencing the data. Since we don't know what the data represents, we are unable to state if the change is something positive or negative.

17.15 $k = 24$, $n = 6$, $x = 71.321$, $R = 39.792$, UCL $= (2.004)(38.792) = 0$. UCL $= 39.792 = 3(14.847) = 84.333$; LCL $= 39.792 - 3(14.847) = 4.748$. Using formula 9.2c, samples #5, #9, and #19 are slightly outside the bounds and should be investigated. If we had used formula 9.2B, none are above UCL. $71.321 \pm (38.792)(.483)$; UCL $= 90.541$; LCL $= 52.101$. System in control.

17.17

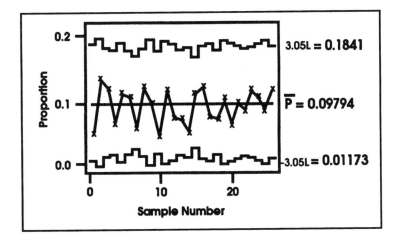

The system is in control.

17.19

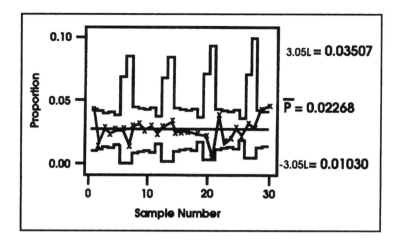

The system is not in control. Cases 1, 29, and 30 are above UCL. We are out of control. Case 21 is below LCL, which is good, but there is a very small sample size involved.

17.21 a. Inspection units.

b.

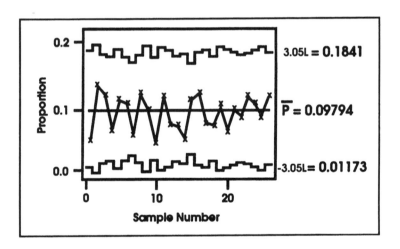

The system is out of control. On every 7th day, a problem develops which we need to investigate to find the assignable cause.

17.23 a. $R = 9.400$, LUL = 0, UCL = 24.19.

b. The system is in control.

17.25 $k = 24, n = 7$

36.125
UCL = (2.004)(36.125) = 72.395; LCL = (0)(52) = 0
The system is currently in control, but headed out of control. Too great a variation in speed will cause accidents and deaths.
59.625.
UCL = 59.625 = (36.125)(0.483) = 77.073; LCL = 59.625 − (36.125)(0.483) = 42.177.

The system is out of control. Speed kills. Corrective measures must be taken.

17.27 $p = 0.05774$, UCL $= 0.1402$, LCL $= 0$. The system is in control.

17.29

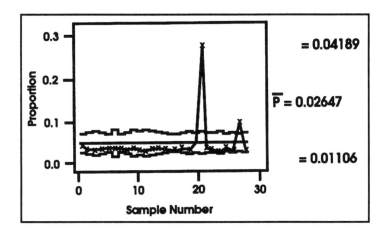

Weeks 20 and 26 are considerably above UCL. Week 23 is just below LCL. The system is out of control and must be corrected.

17.31   Individual project

Answers to Mini-cases

Mini-case 17.1

    a.   Because of multiple defects, the control chart.

    b. $625/40 = 15.625$

    c.   UCL $= 15.625 + 3 \div 15.625 = 27.484$
        LCL $= 15.625 - 3 \div 15.625 = 3.766$

    d.   Inspection units 21, 27, 35, 39 are above UCL. In addition, units 23, 28, 29, 34, 36, and 40 have more than 20 defects which did not exist in the old form. There may be a learning curve involved with the new form. It should be retested to see whether the defects continue to be this high. If they do, the system is out of control.

Mini-case 17.2

    A personal project. Sometimes all of us become out of control when facing daily pressures. It is important to recognize the loss of control and to initiate steps to bring ourselves back in control. This process sometimes requires professional help.

Appendix A– Statistical Tables

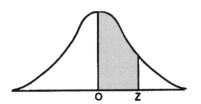

Table 1: **Areas Under the Normal Distribution**

z	.00	.01	02	.03	.04	.05	.06	.07	.08	.09
.0	.0000	.0040	.0080	.0120	.0160	.0199	.0239	.0279	.0319	.0359
.1	.0398	.0438	.0478	.0517	.0557	.0596	.0636	.0675	.0714	.0753
.2	.0793	.0832	.0871	.0910	.0948	.0987	.1026	.1064	.1103	.1141
.3	.1179	.1217	.1255	.1293	.1331	.1368	.1406	.1443	.1480	.1517
.4	.1554	.1591	.1628	.1664	.1770	.1736	.1772	.1808	.1844	.1879
.5	.1915	.1950	.1985	.2019	.2054	.2088	.2123	.2157	.2190	.2224
.6	.2257	.2291	.2324	.2357	.2389	.2422	.2454	.2486	.2517	.2549
.7	.2580	.2611	.2642	.2673	.2704	.2734	.2764	.2794	.2823	.2852
.8	.2881	.2910	.2939	.2967	.2995	.3023	.3051	.3078	.3106	.3133
.9	.3159	.3186	.3212	.3238	.3264	.3289	.3315	.3340	.3365	.3389
1.0	.3413	.3438	.3461	.3485	.3508	.3531	.3554	.3577	.3599	.3621
1.1	.3643	.3665	.3686	.3708	.3729	.3749	.3770	.3790	.3810	.3830
1.2	.3849	.3869	.3888	.3907	.3925	.3944	.3962	.3980	.3997	.4015
1.3	.4032	.4049	.4066	.4082	.4099	.4115	.4131	.4147	.4162	.4177
1.4	.4191	.4207	.4222	.4236	.4251	.4265	.4279	.4292	.4306	.4319
1.5	.4332	.4345	.4357	.4370	.4382	.4394	.4406	.4418	.4429	.4441
1.6	.4452	.4463	.4474	.4484	.4495	.4505	.4515	.4525	.4535	.4545
1.7	.4554	.4564	.4573	.4582	.4591	.4599	.4608	.4616	.4625	.4633
1.8	.4641	.4649	.4656	.4664	.4671	.4678	.4686	.4693	.4699	.4706
1.9	.4713	.4719	.4726	.4732	.4738	.4744	.4750	.4756	.4761	.4767
2.0	.4772	.4778	.4783	.4788	.4793	.4798	.4803	.4808	.4812	.4817
2.1	.4821	.4826	.4830	.4834	.4838	.4842	.4846	.4850	.4854	.4857
2.2	.4861	.4864	.4868	.4871	.4875	.4878	.4881	.4884	.4887	.4890
2.3	.4893	.4896	.4898	.4901	.4904	.4906	.4909	.4911	.4913	.4916
2.4	.4918	.4920	.4922	.4925	.4927	.4929	.4931	.4932	.4934	.4936
2.5	.4938	.4940	.4941	.4943	.4945	.4946	.4948	.4949	.4951	.4952
2.6	.4953	.4955	.4956	.4957	.4959	.4960	.4961	.4962	.4963	.4964
2.7	.4965	.4966	.4967	.4968	.4969	.4970	.4971	.4972	.4973	.4974

z	.00	.01	02	.03	.04	.05	.06	.07	.08	.09
2.8	.4974	.4975	.4976	.4977	.4977	.4978	.4979	.4979	.4980	.4981
2.9	.4981	.4982	.4982	.4983	.4984	.4984	.4985	.4985	.4986	.4986
3.0	.4987	.4987	.4987	.4988	.4988	.4989	.4989	.4989	.4990	.4990

Table 2:   Cumulative Values for the Binomial Probability Distribution

n	r	p = .01	p = .05	p = .10	p = .20	p = .30	p = .40	p = .50
1	0	0.9900	0.9500	0.9000	0.8000	0.7000	0.6000	0.5000
	1	1.0000	1.0000	1.0000	1.0000	1.0000	1.0000	1.0000
2	0	0.9801	0.9025	0.8100	0.6400	0.4900	0.3600	0.2500
	1	0.9999	0.9975	0.9900	0.9600	0.9100	0.8400	0.7500
	2	1.0000	1.0000	1.0000	1.0000	1.0000	1.0000	1.0000
3	0	0.9703	0.8574	0.7290	0.5120	0.3430	0.2160	0.1250
	1	0.9997	0.9927	0.9720	0.8960	0.7840	0.6480	0.5000
	2	1.0000	0.9999	0.9990	0.9920	0.9730	0.9360	0.8750
	3	1.0000	1.0000	1.0000	1.0000	1.0000	1.0000	1.0000
4	0	0.9606	0.8145	0.6561	0.4096	0.2401	0.1296	0.0625
	1	0.9994	0.9860	0.9477	0.8192	0.6517	0.4752	0.3125
	2	1.0000	0.9995	0.9963	0.9728	0.9163	0.8208	0.6875
	3	1.0000	1.0000	0.9999	0.9984	0.9919	0.9744	0.9375
	4	1.0000	1.0000	1.0000	1.0000	1.0000	1.0000	1.0000

n	r	p = .10	p = .20	p = .25	p = .30	p = .40	p = .50
5	0	.59049	.32768	.23730	.16807	.07776	.03125
	1	.91854	.73728	.63281	.52822	.33696	.18750
	2	.99144	.94208	.89648	.83692	.68256	.50000
	3	.99954	.99328	.98437	.96922	.91296	.81250
	4	.99999	.99968	.99902	.99757	.98976	.96875
	5	1.00000	1.00000	1.00000	1.00000	1.00000	1.00000
10	0	.34868	.10737	.05631	.02825	.00605	.00098
	1	.73610	.37581	.24403	.14931	.04636	.01074
	2	.92981	.67780	.52559	.38278	.16729	.05469
	3	.98720	.87913	.77588	.64961	.38228	.17187
	4	.99837	.96721	.92187	.84973	.63310	.37695
	5	.99985	.99363	.98027	.95265	.83376	.62305
	6	.99999	.99914	.99649	.98941	.94524	.82812
	7	1.00000	.99992	.99958	.99841	.98771	.94531
	8		1.00000	.99997	.99986	.99832	.98926
	9			1.00000	.99999	.99990	.99902
	10				1.00000	1.00000	1.00000

n	r	p = .10	p = .20	p = .25	p = .30	p = .40	p = .50
15	0	.20589	.03518	.01336	.00475	.00047	.00003
	1	.54904	.16713	.08018	.03527	.00517	.00049
	2	.81594	.39802	.23609	.12683	.02711	.00369
	3	.94444	.64816	.46129	.29687	.09050	.01758
	4	.98728	.83577	.68649	.51549	.21728	.05923
	5	.99775	.93895	.85163	.72162	.40322	.15088
	6	.99969	.98194	.94338	.86886	.60981	.30362
	7	.99997	.99576	.98270	.94999	.78690	.50000
	8	1.00000	.99921	.99581	.98476	.90495	.69638
	9		.99989	.99921	.99635	.96617	.84912
	10		.99999	.99988	.99933	.99065	.94077
	11		1.00000	.99999	.99991	.99807	.98242
	12			1.00000	.99999	.99972	.99931
	13				1.00000	.99997	.99951
	14					1.00000	.99997
	15						1.00000
20	0	.12158	.01153	.00317	.00080	.00004	.00000
	1	.39175	.06918	.02431	.00764	.00052	.00002
	2	.67693	.20608	.09126	.03548	.00361	.00020
	3	.86705	.41145	.22516	.10709	.01596	.00129
	4	.95683	.62965	.41484	.23751	.05095	.00591
	5	.98875	.80421	.61717	.41637	.12560	.02069
	6	.99761	.91331	.78578	.60801	.25001	.05766
	7	.99958	.96786	.89819	.77227	.41589	.13159
	8	.99994	.99002	.95907	.88667	.59560	.25172
	9	.99999	.99741	.98614	.95204	.75534	.41190
	10	1.00000	.99944	.99606	.98286	.87248	.58810
	11		.99990	.99906	.99486	.94347	.74828
	12		.99998	.99982	.99872	.97897	.86841
	13		1.00000	.99997	.99974	.99353	.94234
	14			1.00000	.99996	.99839	.97931
	15				.99999	.99968	.99409
	16				1.00000	.99995	.99971
	17					.99999	.99980
	18					1.00000	.99998
	19						1.00000
25	0	.07179	.00378	.00075	.00013	.00000	.00000
	1	.27121	.02739	.00702	.00157	.00005	.00000
	2	.53709	.09823	.03211	.00896	.00043	.00001
	3	.76359	.23399	.09621	.03324	.00237	.00008
	4	.90001	.42067	.21374	.09047	.00947	.00046
	5	.96660	.61669	.37828	.19349	.02936	.00204
	6	.99052	.78004	.56110	.34065	.07357	.00732
	7	.99774	.89088	.72651	.51185	.15355	.02164
	8	.99954	.85323	.85056	.67693	.27353	.05388
	9	.99992	.98267	.92867	.81056	.42462	.11476
	10	.99999	.99445	.97033	.90220	.58577	.21218

n	r	p = .10	p = .20	p = .25	p = .30	p = .40	p = .50
	11	1.00000	.99846	.98027	.95575	.73228	.34502
	12		.99963	.99663	.98253	.84623	.50000
	13		.99992	.99908	.99401	.92220	.65498
	14		.99999	.99979	.99822	.96561	.78782
	15		1.00000	.99996	.99955	.98683	.88524
	16			.99999	.99990	.99567	.94612
	17			1.00000	.99998	.99879	.97836
	18				1.00000	.99972	.99268
	19					.99995	.99796
	20					.99999	.99954
	21					1.00000	.99992
	22						.99999
	23						1.00000
50	0	.00515	.00001	.00000	.00000		
	1	.03379	.00019	.00001	.00000		
	2	.11173	.00129	.00009	.00000		
	3	.25029	.00566	.00050	.00003		
	4	.43120	.01850	.00211	.00017		
	5	.61612	.04803	.00705	.00072	.00000	
	6	.77023	.10340	.01939	.00249	.00001	
	7	.87785	.19041	.04526	.00726	.00006	
	8	.94213	.30733	.09160	.01825	.00023	
	9	.97546	.44374	.16368	.04023	.00076	.00000
	10	.99065	.58356	.26220	.07885	.00220	.00001
	11	.99678	.71067	.38162	.13904	.00569	.00005
	12	.99900	.81394	.51099	.22287	.01325	.00015
	13	.99971	.88941	.63704	.32788	.02799	.00047
	14	.99993	.93928	.74808	.44683	.05396	.00130
	15	.99998	.96920	.83692	.56918	.09550	.00330
	16	1.00000	.98556	.90169	.68388	.15609	.00767
	17		.99374	.94488	.78219	.23688	.01642
	18		.99749	.97127	.85944	.33561	.03245
	19		.99907	.98608	.91520	.44648	.05946
	20		.99968	.99374	.95224	.56103	.10132
	21		.99990	.99738	.97491	.67014	.16112
	22		.99997	.99898	.98772	.76602	.23994
	23		.99999	.99963	.99441	.84383	.33591
	24		1.00000	.99998	.99763	.90219	.44386
	25			.99996	.99907	.94266	.55614
	26			.99999	.99966	.96859	.66409
	27			1.00000	.99988	.98397	.76006
	28				.99996	.99238	.83888
	29				.99999	.99664	.89868
	30				1.00000	.99863	.94054
	31					.99948	.96755
	32					.99982	.98358
	33					.99994	.99233

n	r	p = .10	p = .20	p = .25	p = .30	p = .40	p = .50
	34					.99998	.99670
	35					1.00000	.99870
	36						.99953
	37						.99985
	38						.99995
	39						.99999
	40						1.00000
100	0	.00003					
	1	.00032					
	2	.00194					
	3	.00784					
	4	.02371	.00000				
	5	.05758	.00002				
	6	.11716	.00008				
	7	.20605	.00028	.00000			
	8	.32087	.00086	.00001			
	9	.45129	.00233	.00004			
	10	.58316	.00570	.00014	.00000		
	11	.70303	.01257	.00039	.00001		
	12	.80182	.02533	.00103	.00002		
	13	.87612	.04691	.00246	.00006		
	14	.92743	.08044	.00542	.00016		
	15	.96011	.12851	.01108	.00040		
	16	.97940	.19234	.02111	.00097		
	17	.98999	.27119	.03763	.00216		
	18	.99542	.36209	.06301	.00452	.00000	
	19	.99802	.46016	.09953	.00889	.00001	
	20	.99919	.55946	.14883	.01646	.00002	
	21	.99969	.65403	.21144	.02883	.00004	
	22	.99989	.73893	.28637	.04787	.00011	
	23	.99996	.81091	.37018	.07353	.00025	
	24	.99999	.86865	.46167	.11357	.00056	
	25	1.00000	.91252	.55347	.16313	.00119	
	26		.94417	.64174	.22440	.00240	
	27		.96585	.72238	.29637	.00460	.00000
	28		.97998	.79246	.37678	.00843	.00001
	29		.98875	.85046	.46234	.01478	.00002
	30		.99394	.89621	.54912	.02478	.00004
	31		.99687	.93065	.63311	.03985	.00009
	32		.99845	.95540	.71072	.06150	.00020
	33		.99926	.97241	.77926	.09125	.00044
	34		.99966	.98357	.83714	.13034	.00089
	35		.99985	.99059	.88392	.17947	.00176
	36		.99994	.99482	.92012	.23861	.00332
	37		.99998	.99725	.94695	.30681	.00602
	38		.99999	.99860	.96602	.38219	.01049
	39		1.00000	.99931	.97901	.46208	.01760

649

n	r	p = .10	p = .20	p = .25	p = .30	p = .40	p = .50
	40			.99968	.98750	.54329	.02844
	41			.99985	.99283	.62253	.04431
	42			.99994	.99603	.69674	.06661
	43			.99997	.99789	.76347	.09667
	44			.99999	.99891	.82110	.13563
	45			1.00000	.99946	.86891	.18410
	46				.99974	.90702	.24206
	47				.99988	.93621	.30865
	48				.99995	.95770	.38218
	49				.99998	.97290	.46021
	50				.99999	.98324	.53979
	51				1.00000	.98999	.61782
	52					.99424	.69135
	53					.99680	.79794
	54					.99829	.81590
	55					.99912	.86437
	56					.99956	.90333
	57					.99979	.93339
	58					.99990	.95569
	59					.99996	.97156
	60					.99998	.98240
	61					.99999	.98951
	62					1.00000	.99398
	63						.99668
	64						.99824
	65						.99911
	66						.99956
	67						.99980
	68						.99991
	69						.99996
	70						.99998
	71						.99999
	72						1.00000

Source: From Poisson's Binomial Exponential Limit by E. C. Molina (Van Nostrand, 1942).

650

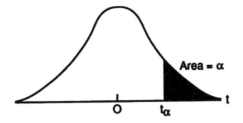

Area = α

t

O t_α

Table 3:   Student's t-Distribution

				PROBABILITIES FOR BOTH ONE- AND TWO-TAILED TESTS				
One Tail	.45	.35	.25	.15	.10	.05	.025	.01	.005
Two Tails	.90	.70	.50	.30	.20	.10	.05	.02	.01
Conf. Level	.10	.30	.50	.70	.80	.90	.95	.98	.99
df					Values of t				
1	.158	.510	1.000	1.963	3.078	6.314	12.706	31.821	63.657
2	.142	.445	.816	1.386	1.886	2.920	4.303	6.965	9.925
3	.137	.424	.765	1.250	1.638	2.353	3.182	4.541	5.841
4	.134	.414	.741	1.190	1.533	2.132	2.776	3.747	4.604
5	.132	.408	.727	1.156	1.476	2.015	2.571	3.365	4.032
6	.131	.404	.718	1.134	1.440	1.943	2.447	3.143	3.707
7	.130	.402	.711	1.119	1.415	1.895	2.365	2.998	3.499
8	.130	.399	.706	1.108	1.397	1.860	2.306	2.896	3.355
9	.129	.398	.703	1.100	1.383	1.833	2.262	2.821	3.250
10	.129	.397	.700	1.093	1.372	1.812	2.228	2.764	3.169
11	.129	.396	.697	1.088	1.363	1.796	2.201	2.718	3.106
12	.128	.395	.695	1.083	1.356	1.782	2.179	2.681	3.055
13	.128	.394	.694	1.079	1.350	1.771	2.160	2.650	3.012
14	.128	.393	.692	1.076	1.345	1.761	2.145	2.624	2.977
15	.128	.393	.691	1.074	1.341	1.753	2.131	2.602	2.947
16	.128	.392	.690	1.071	1.337	1.746	2.120	2.583	2.921
17	.128	.392	.689	1.069	1.333	1.740	2.110	2.567	2.898
18	.127	.392	.688	1.067	1.330	1.734	2.101	2.552	2.878
19	.127	.391	.688	1.066	1.328	1.729	2.093	2.539	2.861
20	.127	.391	.687	1.064	1.325	1.725	2.086	2.528	2.845
21	.127	.391	.686	1.063	1.323	1.721	2.080	2.518	2.831
22	.127	.390	.686	1.061	1.321	1.717	2.074	2.508	2.819
23	.127	.390	.685	1.060	1.319	1.714	2.069	2.500	2.807
24	.127	.390	.685	1.059	1.318	1.711	2.064	2.492	2.797
25	.127	.390	.684	1.058	1.316	1.708	2.060	2.485	2.787
26	.127	.390	.684	1.058	1.315	1.706	2.056	2.479	2.779
27	.127	.389	.684	1.057	1.314	1.703	2.052	2.473	2.771
28	.127	.389	.683	1.056	1.313	1.701	2.048	2.467	2.763
29	.127	.389	.683	1.055	1.311	1.699	2.045	2.462	2.756
30	.127	.389	.683	1.055	1.310	1.697	2.042	2.457	2.750
40	.126	.388	.681	1.050	1.303	1.684	2.021	2.423	2.704
60	.126	.387	.679	1.046	1.296	1.671	2.000	2.390	2.660
120	.126	.386	.677	1.041	1.289	1.658	1.980	2.358	2.617
α or z value	.126	.385	.674	1.036	1.282	1.645	1.960	2.326	2.576

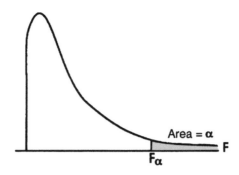

Table 4: Percentage Points of the F Distribution, $\alpha = .10$

		NUMERATOR DEGREES OF FREEDOM								
		1	*2*	*3*	*4*	*5*	*6*	*7*	*8*	*9*
D	1	39.86	49.50	53.59	55.83	57.24	58.20	58.91	59.44	59.86
E	2	8.53	9.00	9.16	9.24	9.29	9.33	9.35	9.37	9.38
N	3	5.54	5.46	5.39	5.34	5.31	5.28	5.27	5.25	5.24
O	4	4.54	4.32	4.19	4.11	4.05	4.01	3.98	3.95	3.94
M	5	4.06	3.78	3.62	3.52	3.45	3.40	3.37	3.34	3.32
I	6	3.78	3.46	3.29	3.18	3.11	3.05	3.01	2.98	2.96
N	7	3.59	3.26	3.07	2.96	2.88	2.83	2.78	2.75	2.72
A	8	3.46	3.11	2.92	2.81	2.73	2.67	2.62	2.59	2.56
T	9	3.36	3.01	2.81	2.69	2.61	2.55	2.51	2.47	2.44
O	10	3.29	2.92	2.73	2.61	2.52	2.46	2.41	2.38	2.35
R	11	3.23	2.86	2.66	2.54	2.45	2.39	2.34	2.30	2.27
	12	3.18	2.81	2.61	2.48	2.39	2.33	2.28	2.24	2.21
D	13	3.14	2.76	2.56	2.43	2.35	2.28	2.23	2.20	2.16
E	14	3.10	2.73	2.52	2.39	2.31	2.24	2.19	2.15	2.12
G	15	3.07	2.70	2.49	2.36	2.27	2.21	2.16	2.12	2.09
R	16	3.05	2.67	2.46	2.33	2.24	2.18	2.13	2.09	2.06
E	17	3.03	2.64	2.44	2.31	2.22	2.15	2.10	2.06	2.03
E	18	3.01	2.62	2.42	2.29	2.20	2.13	2.08	2.04	2.00
S	19	2.99	2.61	2.40	2.27	2.18	2.11	2.06	2.02	1.98
	20	2.97	2.59	2.38	2.25	2.16	2.09	2.04	2.00	1.96
O	21	2.96	2.57	2.36	2.23	2.14	2.08	2.02	1.98	1.95
F	22	2.95	2.56	2.35	2.22	2.13	2.06	2.01	1.97	1.93
	23	2.94	2.55	2.34	2.21	2.11	2.05	1.99	1.95	1.92
F	24	2.93	2.54	2.33	2.19	2.10	2.04	1.98	1.94	1.91
R	25	2.92	2.53	2.32	2.18	2.09	2.02	1.97	1.93	1.89
E	26	2.91	2.52	2.31	2.17	2.08	2.01	1.96	1.92	1.88
E	27	2.90	2.51	2.30	2.17	2.07	2.00	1.95	1.91	1.87
D	28	2.89	2.50	2.29	2.16	2.06	2.00	1.94	1.90	1.87
O	29	2.89	2.50	2.28	2.15	2.06	1.99	1.93	1.89	1.86
M	30	2.88	2.49	2.28	2.14	2.05	1.98	1.93	1.88	1.85
	40	2.84	2.44	2.23	2.09	2.00	1.93	1.87	1.83	1.79
	60	2.79	2.39	2.18	2.04	1.95	1.87	1.82	1.77	1.74
	120	2.75	2.35	2.13	1.99	1.90	1.82	1.77	1.72	1.68
	∞	2.71	2.30	2.08	1.94	1.85	1.77	1.72	1.67	1.63

652

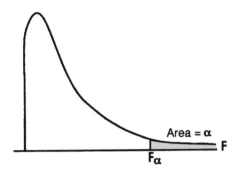

Area = α

F_α

F

		NUMERATOR DEGREES OF FREEDOM								
		10	*12*	*15*	*20*	*24*	*30*	*40*	*60*	*120*	∞
D	1	60.19	60.71	61.22	61.74	62.00	62.26	62.53	62.79	63.06	63.33
E	2	9.39	9.41	9.42	9.44	9.45	9.46	9.47	9.47	9.48	9.49
N	3	5.23	5.22	5.20	5.18	5.18	5.17	5.16	5.15	5.14	5.13
O	4	3.92	3.90	3.87	3.84	3.83	3.82	3.80	3.79	3.78	3.76
M	5	3.30	3.27	3.24	3.21	3.19	3.17	3.16	3.14	3.12	3.10
I	6	2.94	2.90	2.87	2.84	2.82	2.80	2.78	2.76	2.74	2.72
N	7	2.70	2.67	2.63	2.59	2.58	2.56	2.54	2.51	2.49	2.47
A	8	2.54	2.50	2.46	2.42	2.40	2.38	2.36	2.34	2.32	2.29
T	9	2.42	2.38	2.34	2.28	2.25	2.23	2.21	2.21	2.18	2.16
O	10	2.32	2.28	2.24	2.20	2.18	2.16	2.13	2.11	2.08	2.06
R	11	2.25	2.21	2.17	2.12	2.10	2.08	2.05	2.03	2.00	1.97
	12	2.19	2.15	2.10	2.06	2.04	2.01	1.99	1.96	1.93	1.90
D	13	2.14	2.10	2.05	2.01	1.98	1.96	1.93	1.90	1.88	1.85
E	14	2.10	2.05	2.01	1.96	1.94	1.91	1.89	1.86	1.83	1.80
G	15	2.06	2.02	1.97	1.92	1.90	1.87	1.85	1.82	1.79	1.76
R	16	2.03	1.99	1.94	1.89	1.87	1.84	1.81	1.78	1.75	1.72
E	17	2.00	1.96	1.91	1.86	1.84	1.81	1.78	1.75	1.72	1.69
E	18	1.98	1.93	1.89	1.84	1.81	1.78	1.75	1.72	1.69	1.66
S	19	1.96	1.91	1.86	1.81	1.79	1.76	1.73	1.70	1.67	1.63
	20	1.94	1.89	1.84	1.79	1.77	1.74	1.71	1.68	1.64	1.61
O	21	1.92	1.87	1.83	1.78	1.75	1.72	1.69	1.66	1.62	1.59
F	22	1.90	1.86	1.81	1.76	1.73	1.70	1.67	1.64	1.60	1.57
	23	1.89	1.84	1.80	1.74	1.72	1.69	1.66	1.62	1.59	1.55
F	24	1.88	1.83	1.78	1.73	1.70	1.67	1.64	1.61	1.57	1.53
R	25	1.87	1.82	1.77	1.72	1.69	1.66	1.63	1.59	1.56	1.52
E	26	1.86	1.81	1.76	1.71	1.68	1.65	1.61	1.58	1.54	1.50
E	27	1.85	1.80	1.75	1.70	1.67	1.64	1.60	1.57	1.53	1.49
D	28	1.84	1.79	1.74	1.69	1.66	1.63	1.59	1.56	1.52	1.48
O	29	1.83	1.78	1.73	1.68	1.65	1.62	1.58	1.55	1.51	1.47
M	30	1.82	1.77	1.72	1.67	1.64	1.61	1.57	1.54	1.50	1.46
	40	1.76	1.71	1.66	1.61	1.57	1.54	1.51	1.47	1.42	1.38
	60	1.71	1.66	1.60	1.54	1.51	1.48	1.44	1.40	1.35	1.29
	120	1.65	1.60	1.55	1.48	1.45	1.41	1.37	1.32	1.26	1.19
	∞	1.60	1.55	1.49	1.42	1.38	1.34	1.30	1.24	1.17	1.00

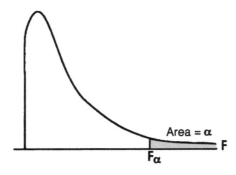

Area = α

F_α F

Table 4: Percentage Points of the F Distribution (Continued) $\alpha = .05$

NUMERATOR DEGREES OF FREEDOM

		1	2	3	4	5	6	7	8	9
D	1	161.4	199.5	215.7	224.6	230.2	234.0	236.8	238.9	240.5
E	2	18.51	19.00	19.16	19.25	19.30	19.33	19.35	19.37	19.38
N	3	10.13	9.55	9.28	9.12	9.01	8.94	8.89	8.85	8.81
O	4	7.71	6.94	6.59	6.39	6.26	6.16	6.09	6.04	6.00
M	5	6.61	5.79	5.41	5.19	5.05	4.95	4.88	4.82	4.77
I	6	5.99	5.14	4.76	4.53	4.39	4.28	4.21	4.15	4.10
N	7	5.59	4.74	4.35	4.12	3.97	3.87	3.79	3.73	3.68
A	8	5.32	4.46	4.07	3.84	3.69	3.58	3.50	3.44	3.39
T	9	5.12	4.26	3.86	3.63	3.48	3.37	3.29	3.23	3.18
O	10	4.96	4.10	3.71	3.48	3.33	3.22	3.14	3.07	3.02
R	11	4.84	3.98	3.59	3.36	3.20	3.09	3.01	2.95	2.90
	12	4.75	3.89	3.49	3.26	3.11	3.00	2.91	2.85	2.80
D	13	4.67	3.81	3.41	3.18	3.03	2.92	2.83	2.77	2.71
E	14	4.60	3.74	3.34	3.11	2.96	2.85	2.76	2.70	2.65
G	15	4.54	3.68	3.29	3.06	2.90	2.79	2.71	2.64	2.59
R	16	4.49	3.63	3.24	3.01	2.85	2.74	2.66	2.59	2.54
E	17	4.45	3.59	3.20	2.96	2.81	2.70	2.61	2.55	2.49
E	18	4.41	3.55	3.16	2.93	2.77	2.66	2.58	2.51	2.46
S	19	4.38	3.52	3.13	2.90	2.74	2.63	2.54	2.48	2.42
	20	4.35	3.49	3.10	2.87	2.71	2.60	2.51	2.45	2.39
O	21	4.32	3.47	3.07	2.84	2.68	2.57	2.49	2.42	2.37
F	22	4.30	3.44	3.05	2.82	2.66	2.55	2.46	2.40	2.34
	23	4.28	3.42	3.03	2.80	2.64	2.53	2.44	2.37	2.32
F	24	4.26	3.40	3.01	2.78	2.62	2.51	2.42	2.36	2.30
R	25	4.24	3.39	2.99	2.76	2.60	2.49	2.40	2.34	2.28
E	26	4.23	3.37	2.98	2.74	2.59	2.47	2.39	2.32	2.27
E	27	4.21	3.35	2.96	2.73	2.57	2.46	2.37	2.31	2.25
D	28	4.20	3.34	2.95	2.71	2.56	2.45	2.36	2.29	2.24
O	29	4.18	3.33	2.93	2.70	2.55	2.43	2.35	2.28	2.22
M	30	4.17	3.32	2.92	2.69	2.53	2.42	2.33	2.27	2.21
	40	4.08	3.23	2.84	2.61	2.45	2.34	2.25	2.18	2.12
	60	4.00	3.15	2.76	2.53	2.37	2.25	2.17	2.10	2.04
	120	3.92	3.07	2.68	2.45	2.29	2.17	2.09	2.02	1.96
	∞	3.84	3.00	2.60	2.37	2.21	2.10	2.01	1.94	1.88

Source From M. Merrington and C. M. Thompson, "Tables of Percentage Points of the Inverted Beta (F) = Distribution," *Biometrika*, 1943, 33, 78–88. Reproduced by permission of the *Biometrika* Trustees.

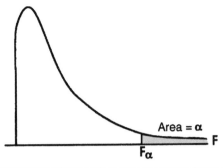

Area = α

F_α

F

NUMERATOR DEGREES OF FREEDOM

		10	12	15	20	24	30	40	60	120	∞
D	1	241.9	243.9	245.9	248.0	249.1	250.1	251.1	252.2	253.3	254.3
E	2	19.40	19.41	19.43	19.45	19.45	19.46	19.47	19.48	19.49	19.50
N	3	8.79	8.74	8.70	8.66	8.64	8.62	8.59	8.57	8.55	8.53
O	4	5.96	5.91	5.86	5.80	5.77	5.75	5.72	5.69	5.66	5.63
M	5	4.74	4.68	4.62	4.56	4.53	4.50	4.46	4.43	4.40	4.36
I	6	4.06	4.00	3.94	3.87	3.84	3.81	3.77	3.74	3.70	3.67
N	7	3.64	3.57	3.51	3.44	3.41	3.38	3.34	3.30	3.27	3.23
A	8	3.35	3.28	3.22	3.15	3.12	3.08	3.04	3.01	2.97	2.93
T	9	3.14	3.07	3.01	2.94	2.90	2.86	2.83	2.79	2.75	2.71
O	10	2.98	2.91	2.85	2.77	2.74	2.70	2.66	2.62	2.58	2.54
R	11	2.85	2.79	2.72	2.65	2.61	2.57	2.53	2.49	2.45	2.40
	12	2.75	2.69	2.62	2.54	2.51	2.47	2.43	2.38	2.34	2.30
D	13	2.67	2.60	2.53	2.46	2.42	2.38	2.34	2.30	2.25	2.21
E	14	2.60	2.53	2.46	2.39	2.35	2.31	2.27	2.22	2.18	2.13
G	15	2.54	2.48	2.40	2.33	2.29	2.25	2.20	2.16	2.11	2.07
R	16	2.49	2.42	2.35	2.28	2.24	2.19	2.15	2.11	2.06	2.01
E	17	2.45	2.38	2.31	2.23	2.19	2.15	2.10	2.06	2.01	1.96
E	18	2.41	2.34	2.27	2.19	2.15	2.11	2.06	2.02	1.97	1.92
S	19	2.38	2.31	2.23	2.16	2.11	2.07	2.03	1.98	1.93	1.88
	20	2.35	2.28	2.20	2.12	2.08	2.04	1.99	1.95	1.90	1.84
O	21	2.32	2.25	2.18	2.10	2.05	2.01	1.96	1.92	1.87	1.81
F	22	2.30	2.23	2.15	2.07	2.03	1.98	1.94	1.89	1.84	1.78
	23	2.27	2.20	2.13	2.05	2.01	1.96	1.91	1.86	1.81	1.76
F	24	2.25	2.18	2.11	2.03	1.98	1.94	1.89	1.84	1.79	1.73
R	25	2.24	2.16	2.09	2.01	1.96	1.92	1.87	1.82	1.77	1.71
E	26	2.22	2.15	2.07	1.99	1.95	1.90	1.85	1.80	1.75	1.69
E	27	2.20	2.13	2.06	1.97	1.93	1.88	1.84	1.79	1.73	1.67
D	28	2.19	2.12	2.04	1.96	1.91	1.87	1.82	1.77	1.71	1.65
O	29	2.18	2.10	2.03	1.94	1.90	1.85	1.81	1.75	1.70	1.64
M	30	2.16	2.09	2.01	1.93	1.89	1.84	1.79	1.74	1.68	1.62
	40	2.08	2.00	1.92	1.84	1.79	1.74	1.69	1.64	1.58	1.51
	60	1.99	1.92	1.84	1.75	1.70	1.65	1.59	1.53	1.47	1.39
	120	1.91	1.83	1.75	1.66	1.61	1.55	1.50	1.43	1.35	1.25
	∞	1.83	1.75	1.67	1.57	1.52	1.46	1.39	1.32	1.22	1.00

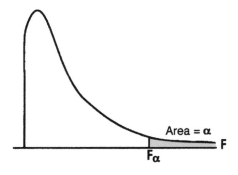

Table 4: Percentage Points of the F Distribution (Continued) $\alpha = .01$

NUMERATOR DEGREES OF FREEDOM

		1	2	3	4	5	6	7	8	9
D	1	4,052	4,999.5	5,403	5,625	5,764	5,859	5,928	5,982	6,022
E	2	98.50	99.00	99.17	99.25	99.30	99.33	99.36	99.37	99.39
N	3	34.12	30.82	29.46	28.71	28.24	27.91	27.67	27.49	27.35
O	4	21.20	18.00	16.69	15.98	15.52	15.21	14.98	14.80	14.66
M	5	16.26	13.27	12.06	11.39	10.97	10.67	10.46	10.29	10.16
I	6	13.75	10.92	9.78	9.15	8.75	8.47	8.26	8.10	7.98
N	7	12.25	9.55	8.45	7.85	7.46	7.19	6.99	6.84	6.72
A	8	11.26	8.65	7.59	7.01	6.63	6.37	6.18	6.03	5.91
T	9	10.56	8.02	6.99	6.42	6.06	5.80	5.61	5.47	5.35
O	10	10.04	7.56	6.55	5.99	5.64	5.39	5.20	5.06	4.94
R	11	9.65	7.21	6.22	5.67	5.32	5.07	4.89	4.74	4.63
	12	9.33	6.93	5.95	5.41	5.06	4.82	4.64	4.50	4.39
D	13	9.07	6.70	5.74	5.21	4.86	4.62	4.44	4.30	4.19
E	14	8.86	6.51	5.56	5.04	4.69	4.46	4.28	4.14	4.03
G	15	8.68	6.36	5.42	4.89	4.56	4.32	4.14	4.00	3.89
R	16	8.53	6.23	5.29	4.77	4.44	4.20	4.03	3.89	3.78
E	17	8.40	6.11	5.18	4.67	4.34	4.10	3.93	3.79	3.68
E	18	8.29	6.01	5.09	4.58	4.25	4.01	3.84	3.71	3.60
S	19	8.18	5.93	5.01	4.50	4.17	3.94	3.77	3.63	3.52
	20	8.10	5.85	4.94	4.43	4.10	3.87	3.70	3.56	3.46
O	21	8.02	5.78	4.87	4.37	4.04	3.81	3.64	3.51	3.40
F	22	7.95	5.72	4.82	4.31	3.99	3.76	3.59	3.45	3.35
	23	7.88	5.66	4.76	4.26	3.94	3.71	3.54	3.41	3.30
F	24	7.82	5.61	4.72	4.22	3.90	3.67	3.50	3.36	3.26
R	25	7.77	5.57	4.68	4.18	3.85	3.63	3.46	3.32	3.22
E	26	7.72	5.53	4.64	4.14	3.82	3.59	3.42	3.29	3.18
E	27	7.68	5.49	4.60	4.11	3.78	3.56	3.39	3.26	3.15
D	28	7.64	5.45	4.57	4.07	3.75	3.53	3.36	3.23	3.12
O	29	7.60	5.42	4.54	4.04	3.73	3.50	3.33	3.20	3.09
M	30	7.56	5.39	4.51	4.02	3.70	3.47	3.30	3.17	3.07
	40	7.31	5.18	4.31	3.83	3.51	3.29	3.12	2.99	2.89
	60	7.08	4.98	4.13	3.65	3.34	3.12	2.95	2.82	2.72
	120	6.85	4.79	3.95	3.48	3.17	2.96	2.79	2.66	2.56
	∞	6.63	4.61	3.78	3.32	3.02	2.80	2.64	2.51	2.41

Source: From M. Merrington and C. M. Thompson, "Tables of Percentage Points of the Inverted Beta (F) = Distribution," *Biometrika*, 1943, 33, 78–88. Reproduced by permission of the *Biometrika* Trustees.

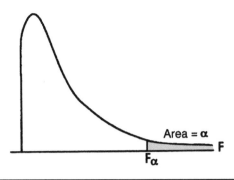

Area = α

$F_α$

F

		NUMERATOR DEGREES OF FREEDOM								
		10	*12*	*15*	*20*	*24*	*30*	*40*	*60*	*120*	*∞*
	1	6,056	6,106	6,157	6,209	6,235	6,261	6,287	6,313	6,339	6,366
D	2	99.40	99.42	99.43	99.45	99.46	99.47	99.47	99.48	99.49	99.50
E	3	27.23	27.05	26.87	26.69	26.60	26.50	26.41	26.32	26.22	26.13
N	4	14.55	14.37	14.20	14.02	13.93	13.84	13.75	13.65	13.56	13.46
O	5	10.05	9.89	9.72	9.55	9.47	9.38	9.29	9.20	9.11	9.02
M	6	7.87	7.72	7.56	7.40	7.31	7.23	7.14	7.06	6.97	6.88
I	7	6.62	6.47	6.31	6.16	6.07	5.99	5.91	5.82	5.74	5.65
N	8	5.81	5.67	5.52	5.36	5.28	5.20	5.12	5.03	4.95	4.86
A	9	5.26	5.11	4.96	4.81	4.73	4.65	4.57	4.45	4.40	4.31
T	10	4.85	4.71	4.56	4.41	4.33	4.25	4.17	4.08	4.00	3.91
O	11	4.54	4.40	4.25	4.10	4.02	3.94	3.86	3.78	3.69	3.60
R	12	4.30	4.16	4.01	3.86	3.78	3.70	3.62	3.54	3.45	3.36
	13	4.10	3.96	3.82	3.66	3.59	3.51	3.43	3.34	3.25	3.17
D	14	3.94	3.80	3.66	3.51	3.43	3.35	3.27	3.18	3.09	3.00
E	15	3.80	3.67	3.52	3.37	3.29	3.21	3.13	3.05	2.96	2.87
G	16	3.69	3.55	3.41	3.26	3.18	3.10	3.02	2.93	2.84	2.75
R	17	3.59	3.46	3.31	3.16	3.08	3.00	2.92	2.83	2.75	2.65
E	18	3.51	3.37	3.23	3.08	3.00	2.92	2.84	2.75	2.66	2.57
E	19	3.43	3.30	3.15	3.00	2.92	2.84	2.76	2.67	2.58	2.49
S	20	3.37	3.23	3.09	2.94	2.86	2.78	2.69	2.61	2.52	2.42
	21	3.31	3.17	3.03	2.88	2.80	2.72	2.64	2.55	2.46	2.36
O	22	3.26	3.12	2.98	2.83	2.75	2.67	2.58	2.50	2.40	2.31
F	23	3.21	3.07	2.93	2.78	2.70	2.62	2.54	2.45	2.35	2.26
	24	3.17	3.03	2.89	2.74	2.66	2.58	2.49	2.40	2.31	2.21
F	25	3.13	2.99	2.85	2.70	2.62	2.54	2.45	2.36	2.27	2.17
R	26	3.09	2.96	2.81	2.66	2.58	2.50	2.42	2.33	2.23	2.13
E	27	3.06	2.93	2.78	2.63	2.55	2.47	2.38	2.29	2.20	2.10
E	28	3.03	2.90	2.75	2.60	2.52	2.44	2.35	2.26	2.17	2.06
D	29	3.00	2.87	2.73	2.57	2.49	2.41	2.33	2.23	2.14	2.03
O	30	2.98	2.84	2.70	2.55	2.47	2.39	2.30	2.21	2.11	2.01
M	40	2.80	2.66	2.52	2.37	2.29	2.20	2.11	2.02	1.92	1.80
	60	2.63	2.50	2.35	2.20	2.12	2.03	1.94	1.84	1.73	1.60
	120	2.47	2.34	2.19	2.03	1.95	1.86	1.76	1.66	1.53	1.38
	∞	2.32	2.18	2.04	1.88	1.79	1.70	1.59	1.47	1.32	1.00

Table 5:   Critical Values for the Durbin–Watson d Statistic, $\alpha = .01$

n	k = 1 d_L	k = 1 d_U	k = 2 d_L	k = 2 d_U	k = 3 d_L	k = 3 d_U	k = 4 d_L	k = 4 d_U	k = 5 d_L	k = 5 d_U
15	.81	1.07	.70	1.25	.59	1.46	.49	1.70	.39	1.96
16	.84	1.09	.74	1.25	.63	1.44	.53	1.66	.44	1.90
17	.87	1.10	.77	1.25	.67	1.43	.57	1.63	.48	1.90
18	.90	1.12	.80	1.26	.71	1.42	.61	1.60	.52	1.80
19	.93	1.13	.83	1.26	.74	1.41	.65	1.58	.56	1.77
20	.95	1.15	.86	1.27	.77	1.41	.68	1.57	.60	1.74
21	.97	1.16	.89	1.27	.80	1.41	.72	1.55	.63	1.71
22	1.00	1.17	.91	1.28	.83	1.40	.75	1.54	.66	1.69
23	1.02	1.19	.94	1.29	.86	1.40	.77	1.53	.70	1.67
24	1.04	1.20	.96	1.30	.88	1.41	.80	1.53	.72	1.66
25	1.05	1.21	.98	1.30	.90	1.41	.83	1.52	.75	1.65
26	1.07	1.22	1.00	1.31	.93	1.41	.85	1.52	.78	1.64
27	1.09	1.23	1.02	1.32	.95	1.41	.88	1.51	.81	1.63
28	1.10	1.24	1.04	1.32	.97	1.41	.90	1.51	.83	1.62
29	1.12	1.25	1.05	1.33	.99	1.42	.92	1.51	.85	1.61
30	1.13	1.26	1.07	1.34	1.01	1.42	.94	1.51	.88	1.61
31	1.15	1.27	1.08	1.34	1.02	1.42	.96	1.51	.90	1.60
32	1.16	1.28	1.10	1.35	1.04	1.43	.98	1.51	.92	1.60
33	1.17	1.29	1.11	1.36	1.05	1.43	1.00	1.51	.94	1.59
34	1.18	1.30	1.13	1.36	1.07	1.43	1.01	1.51	.95	1.59
35	1.19	1.31	1.14	1.37	1.08	1.44	1.03	1.51	.97	1.59
36	1.21	1.32	1.15	1.38	1.10	1.44	1.04	1.51	.99	1.59
37	1.22	1.32	1.16	1.38	1.11	1.45	1.06	1.51	1.00	1.59
38	1.23	1.33	1.18	1.39	1.12	1.45	1.07	1.52	1.02	1.58
39	1.24	1.34	1.19	1.39	1.14	1.45	1.09	1.52	1.03	1.58
40	1.25	1.34	1.20	1.40	1.15	1.46	1.10	1.52	1.05	1.58
45	1.29	1.38	1.24	1.42	1.20	1.48	1.16	1.53	1.11	1.58
50	1.32	1.40	1.28	1.45	1.24	1.49	1.20	1.54	1.16	1.59
55	1.36	1.43	1.32	1.47	1.28	1.51	1.25	1.55	1.21	1.59
60	1.38	1.45	1.35	1.48	1.32	1.52	1.28	1.56	1.25	1.60
65	1.41	1.47	1.38	1.50	1.35	1.53	1.31	1.57	1.28	1.61
70	1.43	1.49	1.40	1.52	1.37	1.55	1.34	1.58	1.31	1.61
75	1.45	1.50	1.42	1.53	1.39	1.56	1.37	1.59	1.34	1.62
80	1.47	1.52	1.44	1.54	1.42	1.57	1.39	1.60	1.36	1.63
85	1.48	1.53	1.46	1.55	1.43	1.58	1.41	1.60	1.39	1.62
90	1.50	1.54	1.47	1.56	1.45	1.59	1.43	1.61	1.41	1.64
95	1.51	1.55	1.49	1.57	1.47	1.60	1.46	1.63	1.44	1.64
100	1.52	1.56	1.50	1.58	1.48	1.60	1.46	1.63	1.44	1.65

Source: From J. Durbin and G. S. Watson, "Testing for Serial Correlation in Least Square Regression, II." *Biometrika*, 1951, 30, 159–178. Reproduced by permission of *Biometrika* Trustees.

Table 5:   Critical Values for the Durbin–Watson d Statistic, $\alpha = .05$

	k = 1		k = 2		k = 3		k = 4		k = 5	
n	d_L	d_U	d_L	d_U	d_L	d_U	d_L	d_U	d_L	d_U
15	1.08	1.36	.95	1.54	.82	1.75	.69	1.97	.56	2.21
16	1.10	1.37	.98	1.54	.86	1.73	.74	1.93	.62	2.15
17	1.13	1.38	1.02	1.54	.90	1.71	.78	1.90	.67	2.10
18	1.16	1.39	1.05	1.53	.93	1.69	.82	1.87	.71	2.06
19	1.18	1.40	1.08	1.53	.97	1.68	.86	1.85	.75	2.02
20	1.20	1.41	1.10	1.54	1.00	1.68	.90	1.83	.79	1.99
21	1.22	1.42	1.13	1.54	1.03	1.67	.93	1.81	.83	1.96
22	1.24	1.43	1.15	1.54	1.05	1.66	.96	1.80	.86	1.94
23	1.26	1.44	1.17	1.54	1.08	1.66	.99	1.79	.90	1.92
24	1.27	1.45	1.19	1.55	1.10	1.66	1.01	1.78	.93	1.90
25	1.29	1.45	1.21	1.55	1.12	1.66	1.04	1.77	.95	1.89
26	1.30	1.46	1.22	1.55	1.14	1.65	1.06	1.76	.98	1.88
27	1.32	1.47	1.24	1.56	1.16	1.65	1.08	1.76	1.01	1.86
28	1.33	1.48	1.26	1.56	1.18	1.65	1.10	1.75	1.03	1.85
29	1.34	1.48	1.27	1.56	1.20	1.65	1.12	1.74	1.05	1.84
30	1.35	1.49	1.28	1.57	1.21	1.65	1.14	1.74	1.07	1.83
31	1.36	1.50	1.30	1.57	1.23	1.65	1.16	1.74	1.09	1.83
32	1.37	1.50	1.31	1.57	1.24	1.65	1.18	1.73	1.11	1.82
33	1.38	1.51	1.32	1.58	1.26	1.65	1.19	1.73	1.13	1.81
34	1.39	1.51	1.33	1.58	1.27	1.65	1.21	1.73	1.15	1.81
35	1.40	1.52	1.34	1.58	1.28	1.65	1.22	1.73	1.16	1.80
36	1.41	1.52	1.35	1.59	1.29	1.65	1.24	1.73	1.18	1.80
37	1.42	1.53	1.36	1.59	1.31	1.66	1.25	1.72	1.19	1.80
38	1.43	1.54	1.37	1.59	1.32	1.66	1.26	1.72	1.21	1.79
39	1.43	1.54	1.38	1.60	1.33	1.66	1.27	1.72	1.22	1.79
40	1.44	1.54	1.39	1.60	1.34	1.66	1.29	1.72	1.23	1.79
45	1.48	1.57	1.43	1.62	1.38	1.67	1.34	1.72	1.29	1.78
50	1.50	1.59	1.46	1.63	1.42	1.67	1.38	1.72	1.34	1.77
55	1.53	1.60	1.49	1.64	1.45	1.68	1.41	1.72	1.38	1.77
60	1.55	1.62	1.51	1.65	1.48	1.69	1.44	1.73	1.41	1.77
65	1.57	1.63	1.54	1.66	1.50	1.70	1.47	1.73	1.44	1.77
70	1.58	1.64	1.55	1.67	1.52	1.70	1.49	1.74	1.46	1.77
75	1.60	1.65	1.57	1.68	1.54	1.71	1.51	1.74	1.49	1.77
80	1.61	1.66	1.59	1.69	1.56	1.72	1.53	1.74	1.51	1.77
85	1.62	1.67	1.60	1.70	1.57	1.72	1.55	1.75	1.52	1.77
90	1.63	1.68	1.61	1.70	1.59	1.73	1.57	1.75	1.54	1.78
95	1.64	1.69	1.62	1.71	1.60	1.73	1.58	1.75	1.56	1.78
100	1.65	1.69	1.63	1.72	1.61	1.74	1.59	1.76	1.57	1.78

Source: From J. Durbin and G. S. Watson, "Testing for Serial Correlation in Least Square Regression, II." *Biometrika*, 1951, 30, 159–178. Reproduced by permission of *Biometrika* Trustees.

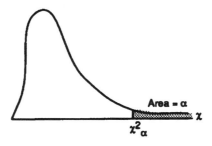

Area = α

χ^2_α

Table 6: Critical Value of Chi-Square

Degrees of Freedom	$\chi^2_{.100}$	$\chi^2_{.050}$	$\chi^2_{.025}$	$\chi^2_{.010}$	$\chi^2_{.005}$
1	2.70554	3.84146	5.02389	6.63490	7.87944
2	4.60517	5.99147	7.37776	9.21034	10.5966
3	6.25139	7.81473	9.34840	11.3449	12.8381
4	7.77944	9.48773	11.1433	13.2767	14.8602
5	9.23633	11.0705	12.8325	15.0863	16.7496
6	10.6446	12.5916	14.4494	16.8119	18.5476
7	12.0170	14.0671	16.0128	18.4753	20.2777
8	13.3616	15.5073	17.5346	20.0902	21.9550
9	14.6837	16.9190	19.0228	21.6660	23.5893
10	15.9871	18.3070	20.4831	23.2093	25.1882
11	17.2750	19.6751	21.9200	24.7250	26.7569
12	18.5494	21.0261	23.3367	26.2170	28.2995
13	19.8119	22.3621	24.7356	27.6883	29.8194
14	21.0642	23.6848	26.1190	29.1413	31.3193
15	22.3072	24.9958	27.4884	30.5779	32.8013
16	23.5418	26.2962	28.8454	31.9999	34.2672
17	24.7690	27.5871	30.1910	33.4087	35.7185
18	25.9894	28.8693	31.5264	34.8053	37.1564
19	27.2036	30.1435	32.8523	36.1908	38.5822
20	28.4120	31.4104	34.1696	37.5662	39.9968
21	29.6151	32.6705	35.4789	38.9321	41.4010
22	30.8133	33.9244	36.7807	40.2894	42.7956
23	32.0069	35.1725	38.0757	41.6384	44.1813
24	33.1963	36.4151	39.3641	42.9798	45.5585
25	34.3816	37.6525	40.6465	44.3141	46.9278
26	35.5631	38.8852	41.9232	45.6417	48.2899
27	36.7412	40.1133	43.1944	46.9630	49.6449
28	37.9159	41.3372	44.4607	48.2782	50.9933
29	39.0875	42.5569	45.7222	49.5879	52.3356
30	40.2560	43.7729	46.9792	50.8922	53.6720
40	51.8050	55.7585	59.3417	63.6907	66.7659
50	63.1671	67.5048	71.4202	76.1539	79.4900
60	74.3970	79.0819	83.2976	88.3794	91.9517
70	85.5271	90.5312	95.0231	100.425	104.215
80	96.5782	101.379	106.629	112.329	116.321
90	107.565	113.145	118.136	124.116	128.299
100	118.498	124.342	129.561	135.807	140.169

Source: From C. M. Thompson, "Tables of the Percentage Points of the χ^2 Distribution," *Biometrika*, 1941, 32, 188–189. Reproduced by permission of the *Biometrika* Trustees.

Index

663